ASIAN LAUGHTER

THE SINO-JAPANESE IDEOGRAPH MEANING LAUGHTER

An Anthology

ASIAN LAUGHTER

edited by
Leonard Feinberg

of Oriental Satire and Humor

New York • WEATHERHILL • *Tokyo*

This is one of the volumes assisted by the Asian Literature Program of the Asia Society, New York

First edition, 1971

Published by John Weatherhill, Inc., 149 Madison Avenue, New York 10016, with editorial offices at 7-6-13 Roppongi, Minato-ku, Tokyo 106, Japan. Printed in the Republic of Korea.

LCC Card No. 73-157272 ISBN 0-8348-0064-0

for Lilian

CONTENTS

China

Japan

Ceylon

Ceylon

EDITOR'S PREFACE

Although there have been collections of jokes and humorous anecdotes and short witty poems published in Asian countries, this is as far as I know the first anthology to offer in English a broad survey of Asian satire and humor. The countries included are China, Japan, and India, because they are the giants of the Orient, and Ceylon for personal reasons: a token of thanks for much gracious hospitality received during the year I spent as a Fulbright lecturer at the University of Ceylon, where this book was conceived.

For each country I give examples of humorous literature ranging from proverbs to novels, including short fiction, poetry, sketches, jokes and anecdotes, and, when possible, drama. The earliest items in the book go back to the fifth century before Christ; the most recent were published during the 1960's.

The proverbs—in which category I have also included a few aphorisms of known authorship—are scattered throughout the appropriate sections of the book because most readers are averse to solid pages of unrelated statements, no matter how witty. The Chinese proverbs have been translated by Herbert A. Giles, Lin Yutang, and others; the Japanese, by Rokuo Okada and several anonymous translators; the Indian, by Arthur W. Ryder (excerpts from the *Panchatantra*), N. K. Sethi, and B. Hale Wortham; the Ceylonese, by John M. Senaveratna.

Problems of consistency arise concerning the spelling and style of names of authors and translators, particularly in the case of Chinese and Japanese names. To avoid confusion, I have tried to standardize such names in the by-lines by using the more commonly accepted spellings and following these rules: Chinese names have the surname first; Japanese names, following the practice of most Japanese themselves when writing in English, have the surname first in the case of pre-1868 individuals and last in the case of modern individuals. Departures from these rules are the result of the known preferences of the individuals named. I have not, however, attempted to standardize names within the selections themselves but have simply followed the original texts.

In the by-lines, the general rule is to give first the name of the author and then that of the translator, separating the two by a slash mark. The original sources of the selections are included in the Bibliography, and permissions to use copyrighted material are listed in the Acknowledgments.

Unless otherwise indicated, footnotes to selections are by the original translators.

ACKNOWLEDGMENTS

Getting this anthology of Asian humor published proved to be a much more complicated project than I had expected, and the book would have been delayed even longer if the Asia Society, New York, had not provided administrative, financial, and psychological support. I am most grateful to Bonnie R. Crown, director of the Asian Literature Program, who showed immediate interest in the manuscript, found a publisher, and arranged the necessary details of publication.

The long and hard job of tracing copyright holders all over the world, and getting their permission to use material, was done by Barbara Cagan of the Asia Society. I want to thank her for her patience, diligence, and ingenuity in solving the many problems that arose.

Additional financial aid for the publication of this book was provided by the Iowa State University Research Foundation. The university gave me time for research through the Sciences and Humanities Research Institute and by granting me a sabbatical leave. Dr. George Christensen, Dean Chalmer Roy, Dr. Albert L. Walker, and Professor Daniel Griffen, Jr., were particularly helpful in arranging this assistance.

Among the many people who helped me at various stages were Dr. and Mrs. Roland McCormack, Professor and Mrs. John B. McClelland, Etsuko Tsuchia, Stuart Lawrence, Heng-Sheng Cheng, Linda Lucas, Professor Shinji Takuwa, Mrs. Romola Sinha, Mary Meixner, Edna Henry, Wayne DeVaul, and my daughter Ellen F. Reynolds. My wife's aid was, as always, of inestimable value.

Grateful acknowledgements are likewise due the following individuals, publishers, and agencies for having granted permission to include copyrighted materials in this book:

Atlas magazine, New York, for "China's Enemy Within," *Atlas,* February, 1967.

G. S. Sharat Chandra, for the poems "On the Way to Mount Kailash," "At the Pub," and "About Time."

Chatto & Windus, Ltd., London, for *The Prevalence of Witches,* by Aubrey Menen.

Constable Publishers, London, for *A Hundred and Seventy Chinese Poems,* translated by Arthur Waley.

Coward-McCann, Inc., New York, for *Chinese Wit and Humor,* edited by George Kao. Copyright 1946 for the United States by Coward-McCann, Inc. (I have been unable to locate the British Commonwealth copyright holder, Nancy Parker.)

Doubleday & Company, New York, for *Twentieth Century Chinese Poetry,* edited by Hsu Kai-yu. Copyright 1963 by Hsu Kai-yu.

Dover Publications, Inc., New York, for *Gems of Chinese Literature*, translated by Herbert A. Giles.

The Far East Book Company, Taipei, for *Six Hundred Chinese Proverbs*, edited by Chen Cheng-chi.

Foreign Languages Press, Peking, for *Chinese Fables and Anecdotes; The Day the New Director Came*, by Ho Chui, translated by Chung Wei-hsien, from *Saturday Afternoon at the Mill and Other One-Act Plays; Third Sister Liu*, translated by Yang Hsien-yi and Gladys Yang; *The Scholars*, by Wu Ching-tzu, translated by Yang Hsien-yi and Gladys Yang; *Yeh-Hsuan's Fables*, by Ho Yi; and *Soy Sauce and Prawns*, by Yuan Shui-p'ai, translated by Sidney Shapiro.

Mrs. S. Hatharasinghe, Mrs. S. Perera, and Mrs. S. Soza, for *Wiles and Ways of Women*, by John M. Senaveratna, and *Dictionary of Proverbs of the Sinhalese*, by John M. Senaveratna.

Hokuseido Press, Tokyo, for material from *Oriental Humour*, edited and translated by R. H. Blyth; *Senryu: Japanese Satirical Verses*, edited and translated by R. H. Blyth; and *Kappa*, by Ryunosuke Akutagawa, translated by Seiichi Shiojiri.

Indiana University Press, Bloomington, for paraphrased material from *Oral Tales of India*, by Stith Thompson and Jonas Bałys.

Japan Travel Bureau, Inc., Tokyo, for *Japanese Humour*, by R. H. Blyth, and *Japanese Proverbs and Proverbial Phrases*, by Rokuo Okada.

Michael Joseph, Ltd., London, for *I Am a Cat*, by Soseki Natsume, translated by Katsue Shibata and Motonari Kai.

Norbert Kaneko for *Old Japanese Humor*, published by Tokyo News Service, Ltd. Copyright 1959 by Norbert Kaneko.

Robert M. McBride Publishers, New York, for "A Fickle Widow," translated by A. K. Douglas. (I have been unable to locate Mr. McBride.)

Michigan State University Press, East Lansing, for *Swami and Friends and The Bachelor of Arts: Two Novels of Malgudi*, by R. K. Narayan.

William Morris Agency, New York, for *Dead Man in the Silver Market*, by Aubrey Menen, copyright 1953 by Aubrey Menen, and for *Grateful to Life and Death*, by R. K. Narayan, copyright 1953 by R. K. Narayan.

New Directions Publishing Corporation, New York, for *One Hundred Poems from the Japanese*, translated by Kenneth Rexroth, all rights reserved; *One Hundred Poems from the Chinese*, translated by Kenneth Rexroth, all rights reserved; and *The Life of an Amorous Women and Other Writings*, by Ihara Saikaku, translated by Ivan Morris, copyright 1963 by UNESCO.

Orient Publishing Company, Madras, for *Tenali Rama*, by A. S. P. Ayyar.

Oxford University Press, New York, for *The Floating World in Japanese Fiction*, by Howard Hibbett.

Peter Pauper Press, Mount Vernon, New York, for *Hindu Proverbs*, by N. K. Sethi.

Robert Payne, for *The White Pony: An Anthology of Chinese Poetry*, edited by Robert Payne. A Mentor Book published by the New American Library by arrangement with the John Day Company.

Laurence Pollinger, Ltd., London, for *The Life of an Amorous Woman*, by Ihara Saikaku, translated by Ivan Morris. Published by Chapman & Hall, Ltd. (proprietors: New Directions Publishing Corporation).

Random House–Alfred A. Knopf, Inc., for *Translations from the Chinese,* by Arthur Waley, copyright 1919 by Alfred A. Knopf, Inc., and renewed in 1947 by Arthur Waley; and *Wisdom of China and India,* by Lin Yutang, copyright 1942 by Random House, Inc.

Routledge & Kegan Paul, Ltd., London, for *Folk-Tales of Kashmir,* by J. H. Knowles. Published in 1893 by Kegan Paul, Trench, Trubner & Company.

Dr. Charles T. Ryder, Dr. William H. Ryder, Mrs. Viola Ryder Nicholson, and Annette Dunster Tolan, for *The Ten Princes,* by Dandin, translated by Arthur W. Ryder; and for *The Panchatantra,* translated by Arthur W. Ryder, copyright 1956 by Mary E. and Winifred Ryder and published by the University of Chicago Press, Chicago, 1964, all rights reserved. (I have been unable to locate Annette Dunster Tolan.)

Charles Scribner's Sons, Inc., New York, for *The Prevalence of Witches,* by Aubrey Menen.

Shankar's Weekly, New Delhi, for the poems "Head-Shrinking," by Leonora, and "New Year Resolution in India," by M. P. Bhaskaran.

Teachers' Publishing House, Madras, for *Indian After-Dinner Stories,* vols. I, II, and III, by A. S. P. Ayyar.

Charles E. Tuttle Publishing Company, Rutland, Vt., and Tokyo, for *The Ink-Smeared Lady and Other Kyogen,* translated by Shio Sakanishi; *This Scheming World,* by Ihara Saikaku, translated by Masanori Takatsuka and David C. Stubbs; *The Life of an Amorous Man,* by Ihara Saikaku, translated by Kengi Hamada; and *Shank's Mare,* by Jippensha Ikku, translated by Thomas Satchell.

University of California Press, Berkeley and Los Angeles, for *Flowers in the Mirror,* by Li Ju-chen, translated by Lin Tai-yi. Reprinted by permission of the Regents of the University of California.

University of Chicago Press, Chicago, for *Tales of Ancient India,* by J. A. B. Van Buitenen, and *The Panchatantra,* translated by Arthur W. Ryder, copyright 1956 by Mary E. and Winifred Ryder and published by the University of Chicago Press, 1964, all rights reserved.

J. Vijayatunga, for *Grass for My Feet,* published by Edward Arnold & Company, London.

Tarzie Vittachi, for "Let's Build Another Sigiriya? . . . Let's Not!" and "Tempus Definitely Fugits," published by Lake House, Colombo.

Wang Chi-chen, for *Ah Q and Others,* by Lusin. Published by the Columbia University Press, 1941, and the Greenwood Press, 1968.

ASIAN LAUGHTER

INTRODUCTION

Trying to understand another country merely by reading its literature results in limited knowledge even when the literature read is genuinely representative of the country's various facets. But to delete from the sampling as large and important an element of a nation's culture as its humor and satire is to create a hopelessly distorted image. This deletion has been performed so successfully that at the present time the educated layman in the United States is seldom aware of a single comic or satiric work in Oriental literature.

In recent years the publication of Asian literature in the United States has expanded, but the selection of material has been so circumscribed that the result approximates trying to teach an Asian about the United States by letting him read the Bible, Ralph Waldo Emerson, and Henry James. The bulk of Asian literature traditionally made available to American readers consisted of religious and philosophical writings and ancient classics. Only recently have anthologies begun to include realistic fiction and modern writing. This book tries to give Western readers a more balanced view of Asian people by presenting their humor and satire.

Generalizations about countries tend to become misleading oversimplifications. Among the myths current in the West are the notions that Indians are "mystic," Chinese are "practical," Japanese are "proper." Books about India, for example, traditionally portrayed its inhabitants as spiritually centered, concerned primarily with the future habitats of their souls. It is true that quasi-religious procedures are evident in the ordinary daily activities of many Indians, but it is revealing that no other Asian nation considers Indians "spiritual." The neighbors of India consider its citizens as traders no less materialistic than Chinese and Japanese. Indian satirists have exposed the ostentatious flaunting of wealth by maharajas in the past and the conspicuous consumption of India's middle class today. Judging from the ancient *Panchatantra* and the modern *Shankar's Weekly,* it is the poor who are likely to make a virtue of abstention, while those who can afford temporal pleasures enjoy them as much as secular Westerners.

Similarly, the popular concept of Chinese as hardheaded realists ignores the powerful strand of Taoism in the nation's culture. Japanese decorum has been shown by such satirists as Saikaku, Jippensha, Natsume, and Akutagawa to be surprisingly superficial and largely limited to behavior in public. And Ceylon's Buddhists, whose religion is based on a noble contempt for the transient rewards of a sensual world, exhibit an interest in wealth and carnal pleasures remarkably similar to that of Christians, Jews, Hindus, and Muslims. Lin Yutang observed that the Chinese venerate form while disregarding content; in varying degrees, this is true for all cultures, Western as well as Eastern. It is naïve to assume that the traditional religion or ethos of a country is necessarily a significant influence in the daily lives of its people.

But the temptation to generalize is irresistible, and R. H. Blyth offers at least the virtue of succinctness: "There are three world views and three only, the Buddhist, the Christian, and the Japanese. The Buddhist is that of supermundane calm, transcendental desirelessness; the Christian, of suffering into power; the Japanese, of unsought and inevitable interpenetration with nature. . . . The Japanese view is thus poetic and humorous, and though not so high as the Buddhist, or so deep as the Christian, is wider and embraces more than either." (*Oriental Humour,* p. 565)

Though less dramatic, it is probably more accurate to say that, although the major systems of Asian thought began as predominantly religious (or, as in China, ethical) orientations, every culture in the Orient worked out its own pragmatic adaptation to the needs of its people and the unique requirements of its institutions. Emphasizing the spiritual element of Asian people at the expense of their practicality may gratify the wistful longings of Occidentals, but no Western diplomat, businessman, or soldier dealing with Asians has any delusions about their spirituality.

Every country in the Orient has its own personality. Even if differences in culture and art did not demonstrate salient divergences, as they do, such traditional animosities as those between Thais and Burmese, Cambodians and Vietnamese, would offer convincing proof that each nation is conscious of its individuality and jealous of it. The Buddhism of Ceylon is quite different from the Buddhism of China, and the Khmer art of Cambodia is clearly distinguishable from both its Hindu and its Buddhist origins. Afghans are patently dissimilar to Ceylonese, and the culture of Tibet bears no resemblance to that of Indonesia.

Yet there are additional differentiations. Within each nation one can recognize distinct levels of aesthetic taste, not necessarily corresponding to economic status. In every Western country there is a similar stratification, and the readers of the *New Yorker* are outnumbered by *Mad* magazine aficionados. The subtle satire of Aubrey Menen is not appreciated by the Indian masses, and the intellectual humor of magazines founded by Lin Yutang failed to draw enough readers in China to survive. The intelligentsia of India appreciate *Punch,* and Ceylonese sophisticates like the *New Yorker*. But the cultural proletariat of one country often has more in common with the cultural proletariat of another country than it does with its own intelligentsia. The bourgeoisie shares the same tastes, regardless of national borders. In satire and humor this taste reveals a clear preference for the obvious and the physical, and a distaste for the subtle and the intellectual. American comic strips are popular all over Asia, but Thurber and E. B. White are read only by a few aesthetes scattered throughout the Orient. Critics may say that they are discussing a nation's humor, but it almost always proves to be only one selected part of that humor that they are discussing.

At its lowest level—slapstick, physical deformity or mental deficiency, embarrassment—humor seems to be pretty much the same in all cultures. In Buddhist Ceylon recently, at a theater showing alternating movies, a dozen people watched an excellent Indian movie on the life of the Buddha; after they left, every seat in the theater was filled with patrons eager to see *Ma and Pa Kettle*. Collectors of folklore have found variations of the same jokes in India and the Balkans, China and Finland. American movies featuring the Three Stooges have entertained large crowds in several Asian countries. This level, of obvious or physical incongruity, is the most popular form of humor everywhere. Nor is its appeal limited to innocuous entertainment. As recently as the 1950's, Ho Chi Minh sent an old Vietnamese songwriter into the villages, singing and teaching satiric verses that ridiculed the French.

Satire—entertaining criticism in artistic form—also appears in every country which has attained a minimum level of civilization, if only in the form of satiric proverbs, caustic jokes, and derisive folktales. In more sophisticated form, one country may consciously imitate the art of another, as medieval Japan adapted Chinese culture, and as Lin Yutang founded humor magazines in China modeled on *Punch* and the *New Yorker*.

In Asian countries humor and satire have usually been considered inferior forms of aesthetic expression. Chinese scholars who wrote satiric fictions published them under pseudonyms; most of the humor appeared in the arts of the common people—jokes and popular (as distinguished from classical) novels. In Japan also official court policy frowned on lighthearted and disparaging literature, so that again satiric expression was most prevalent below the aristocratic and scholarly classes. The same thing is apparent in India, whose upper classes encouraged epics and romantic dramas; the realistic stories and earthy folktales came from the common people. Asia never gave to its satiric geniuses the kind of official recognition that the West has accorded to Aristophanes, Cervantes, Molière, and Rabelais.

Generalizing about aesthetic forms is a risky business. We are often told that understatement is typical of English humor, and it is true that *Punch,* many English jokes, and sophisticated Englishmen do use understatement very effectively. But the most popular English humor remains the work of Dickens and Lewis Carroll, Fielding and the variety theater—and no one can accuse these writers of stressing understatement. French humor is supposed to be subtle and wry, intellectual humor—but France has given us Rabelais and Molière. We find the same condition in the Orient. Japanese satire is described by scholars as oblique and delicate, but the most popular comic novel in Japan is *Hizakurige,* which relies for its humorous and satiric effects on slapstick, caricature, scatology, grotesque details, sexual adventures, obscene insults, and practical jokes. Chinese humor is often called earthy and crude, but Chinese novels often work by indirection. And Indian humor, from the folktale to Narayan, exhibits considerably less than total preoccupation with spiritual concerns.

Several scholars have quoted with approval Judge Wu's remark "Whereas Westerners are seriously humorous, the Chinese are humorously serious." The statement is neatly balanced and has an element of truth in it; but by the time one has resolved the semantic ambiguities and qualified the epigram (Which Chinese? Which Westerners?) there isn't too much useful information left. R. H. Blyth says, "Japanese humor is more subtle," then gives examples of Japanese jokes and farces just as blunt and crude as those of other countries.

Nor is it safe to make casual assumptions about the purposes of satirists. Reform has been proclaimed, by themselves, as the purpose of many Western writers from Juvenal to Pope. And didacticism has been directly affirmed by the Indian *Panchatantra,* or alleged by Chinese satirists writing in a Confucianist culture, or implied by Saikaku's attack on the immorality of women. But Saikaku's contemporaries chose a flippantly amoral attitude and there are no moral lessons to be learned from the rascally protagonists of *Hizakurige*. *Golden Lotus* is more pornographic than satiric, and its appeal clearly does not depend on Confucian morality.

In the Orient as in the West, satire attempts to avoid the censor, both legal and societal (as in T'ang poems and *The Scholars*), and to express aggression (as in *Hizakurige*). Some Asian satire is realistic, as in the Japanese *Botchan,* the Chinese *Scholars,* and certain Indian tales and *The Little Clay Cart*. And some Asian satire makes use of fantasy, as in the Chinese *Monkey* and *Flowers in the Mirror,* the Japanese *Kappa* and *I Am a Cat,* and the writings of the Indian Narayan. Even twentieth-century Asian satire displays both the Juvenalian indignation of Lusin and the Horatian wit of Aubrey Menen.

In each Asian country, a special quality is evident in the flavor, the tone, the texture of its literature. But generalizations about these special qualities are almost always misleading; they are only partially true, or true only under specific conditions. The distinctions often consist of shifts in emphasis, nuances, subtle variations which cannot be accurately identified in summaries or formulae. The best way to get the flavor of a nation's satire is to read it.

More than any other form of literary expression, satire is likely to suffer when read by foreigners. Often it seems pointless or puzzling to the alien reader. Not until the local background has been explained, the private allusion identified, does he understand the satiric reference. But by that time much of the spontaneous delight in satire has vanished. Much of the satire which entertains its native audience is likely to perplex foreigners. The satiric journal *Shankar's Weekly* amuses thousands of Indian readers, but its jibes would not mean much to Americans.

In addition to the problem of content there remains the problem of style, and almost every translator of Asian satire apologizes for his failure to convey in English all that the piece did in the original language. Wang Chi-chen, for example, remarks that "Lusin offers special difficulties as the humor and effectiveness of his style depends so much upon the ironical twists and turns that he gives to classical allusions and contemporary slogans." The translator of *Kappa* says: "The beauty of Akutagawa's style can hardly be appreciated except in the language he used." Professor Aston says of *Hizakurige:* "It is hopeless by translation to give any idea of the copious flow of rollicking humor which pervades every page of this really wonderful book." And George Kao notes that "the salacious appeal and the play on words which account for much of China's laughing matter are both inadmissible in an anthology for the Western reader."

In spite of these handicaps, the difficulty of translation, unfamiliarity with local context, and the transience of contemporary allusion, a great deal of pleasure and insight can be gained by reading English translations of Asian humor and satire. The major objects of satire in Asian literature prove to be depressingly similar to those in the West. It may be that East is East and West is West, but the two meet effortlessly in choosing the victims for their satirists.

Hypocrisy provides the richest source of Western satire—and hypocrisy permeates the behavior of individuals in Asian literature and folklore. The procurers and sycophants in China's *Golden Lotus* make hypocrisy a way of life. In *I Am a Cat* a businessman smokes an imported brand of cigarettes which he cannot afford, admittedly to impress other Japanese businessmen. A medieval Japanese poem tells of the man who manages to find excuses for eating fish on forbidden days, and a modern senryu describes a servant being polite to a caller, unaware that he is addressing an insurance salesman. The Japanese high school described by Natsume in *Botchan* is full of sycophantic teachers currying favor with the principal; the same writer's *I Am a Cat* ridicules the fulsome expressions in letters soliciting funds. And in the seventeenth century Saikaku satirized homosexual priests, male concubines, and thieves who robbed fresh graves for female hair and nails.

If women feel that they have been unfairly treated by Western satirists, they had better avoid looking at what Asian writers—admittedly male—have said about them. The proverbs of every Oriental country fulminate against women. In India this trend is illustrated even in Buddhist legend; the Jataka stories include a number of virulent attacks on women and warnings about their deceitfulness, lust, and perverse preference for ugly hunchbacks as sexual partners. (Several queens in *The Arabian Nights* reveal a similar taste for slave paramours.) In *Kappa,* Akutagawa complains about the sexual aggressiveness of twentieth-century females. A century earlier another Japanese writer, Shikitei Samba, described maidservants as lazy, flirtatious, gossiping, and malicious. And an old Ceylonese proverb asks, "Why take a ladder to the gallows when you can go there easily with the help of a woman?" The Chinese opera *Butterfly Dream* satirizes the fickleness of woman, a theme also common to several tales of ancient India.

Religion—in the form of priests, monks, and nuns—has always provided a tempting target for satirists. The discrepancy between religion's aspirations and human imperfections appears in the Orient no less frequently than in the West. Dull sermons, nymphomanic nuns, sycophantic monks, lecherous priests, all have provided material for Asian scoffers. "With money you can move the Gods," says an ancient Chinese proverb. A character in the *Panchatantra* says that a sure way to get to hell is to become a priest. In a seventeenth-century sketch, the Japanese satirist Kiseki suggests that most Confucianists are unconscionable bores. His contemporary, Saikaku, describes a courtesan's service as a priest's mistress, living in a temple. Both Saikaku and Kiseki wrote parodies of Buddhist sermons. In *Hizakurige,* a priest sells pictures of the goddess Kannon which he claims will cure all ills; the head priest of a large temple entertains and flatters two rogues who he thinks have won a lottery; as soon as he discovers his mistake, he has them thrown out.

As in the West, most of the professions are subjected to satiric treatment and usually for the same reason: hypocritical behavior. "Rich doctors don't visit poor patients," says an old Chinese proverb. In *Hizakurige* there is a hilarious episode involving a young doctor who mistakes a male guest for a pregnant woman and gives him the jargon of the universal quack. Nor are the other professions immune, and bureaucrats are bitterly attacked in Liu T'ieh-yun's *Travels.* "Officials think they are masters of the people rather than servants," complains a character in a Japanese story. "Win your lawsuit and lose your money," says a Chinese proverb.

The miser gets a good deal of attention in Asian literature, and greed is ridiculed as often—and as ineffectually—as in Western satire. Saikaku wrote a funny sketch in *This Scheming World* about a terribly stingy man who resembles the stereotype Jack

Benny created. A medieval Chinese joke tells of a man who falls into the water. His little son calls for help but the drowning father cries, "If they will save me for three coins, all right, but not for more." Jippensha Ikku describes men from Kyoto so stingy that they go from person to person asking for a light, thus smoking other people's pipes.

Scholars are satirized for pedantry, use of jargon, impracticality, pretense of wisdom. In *The Travels of Lao Ts'an,* Liu T'ieh-yun warns readers to beware the tyranny of reason. The most sustained Chinese satire, *The Scholars,* ridicules the affectations, absurdities, and pretensions of supposedly learned men. Henpecked husbands provide a rich lode for humorists; and mothers-in-law are not universally loved, judging by this Tamil proverb: "It is said that six months after the death of the mother-in-law a tear came into the eye of the daughter-in-law." Vanity is satirized in the story of the dog who chose to starve to death in a Brahman's house rather than move to a well-fed lower-caste home.

Fools provide a universal source of humor—and offer proof that satire is based on social norms rather than moral criteria, for there is nothing immoral about being a fool. Even the assigning of fools to particular locales holds true for the Orient; in India, a sardar is traditionally a fool, as are the inhabitants of Gotham in England and Chelm in Poland. A Ceylonese woman, told by a beggar that he has just returned from heaven where he married the woman's daughter, gives him jewels to deliver to his wife. And Japanese fools are ridiculed in Kyogen, senryu, and prose fiction.

The most scathing satire, however, is reserved for the abomination of war, as in the poems of ancient China and the Swiftian fulminations of twentieth-century Lusin.

A great many Asian satires might have been written by a Western satirist; or, to view the matter from Asian eyes, many examples of Western satire might have been written in the East. The Japanese proverb "No standing in the world without stooping" reminds us of Jonathan Swift's remark, "Climbing is performed in the same posture with creeping." There are other resemblances to Swift. In the Chinese novel *Flowers in the Mirror,* the travelers visit a Country of Tall People and a Country of Little People; later they come to the Country of Intelligent People where mathematicians behave somewhat like the inhabitants of Gulliver's Lagado. In the twentieth-century Japanese satire *Kappa,* unemployed workers are eaten by wealthy citizens, providing tougher meat than Swift recommended in *A Modest Proposal.* And, like Gulliver, the narrator cannot stand the smell of men after his return from the land of the Kappas.

Flowers in the Mirror also includes a proposal of Rabelais—married monks and nuns turn out to be happier and better human beings than celibates. Rabelais' *Gargantua* has been compared to Wu Ch'eng-en's *Monkey.* The two writers were contemporaries, and "comic exuberance" is a dominant element of their books. Still another similarity of *Flowers in the Mirror,* this time to Voltaire's *Candide,* appears when the Chinese travelers visit a land where jewels are valueless and used for playthings. And the Asian proverb "Cultivate a ricefield rather than make verses" reminds one of the last sentence in *Candide.* Kiseki's attack on Japanese women in 1700 is similar in intensity to Juvenal's "Sixth Satire." Akutagawa's *Kappa,* like Butler's *Erewhon,* asks each unborn baby whether it really wants to enter this unpleasant world; babies who refuse are excused, in a rather harsh manner. *Kappa* anticipates *Catch-22* by providing in its penal code exoneration for criminals who are caught after the circumstances which motivated the crime change; the thief who stole for a son who subsequently died is immediately freed. And the device of looking at the world through the eyes of animals is used in the Indian *Panchatantra* and the Japanese novel *I Am a Cat,* among many others.

The familiar anecdotes of the West can be found again and again in Oriental folklore. We speak of "counting our chickens before they are hatched." A Chinese anecdote tells about two hunters who, seeing a goose, argue about the best way to cook it; by the time they resolve the argument, the goose has flown away. And the Ceylonese have a story about a man who dreamed about all the wealth he would eventually accumulate from the drumstick tree in his garden; he would put the wealth in storehouses, and since the tree blocked the path to the storehouses, he cut it down.

There is a well-known American anecdote about a violinist who, with a pianist friend, was watching the debut of Yehudi Menuhin. Midway through the performance he turned to his friend and said, "It's a very hot night." "It's not a hot night for pianists, Mischa," the friend replied. A Chinese story tells of the general who had been sitting in his stove-heated tent and drinking glass after glass of wine. Sweating profusely, he said to the guard on duty outside the tent, "The weather seems very warm for this season of the year." The guard replied, "The weather seems normal where I'm standing."

A cynical contrast to O. Henry's sentimentality is provided by the Japanese anecdote of the husband whose wife sold part of her hair to buy wine for him. Touched by her love, he fondled her hair and murmured, "But you still have another half bottle's worth." La Rochefoucauld wrote, "We all have enough courage to bear up under the troubles of others," matching the Japanese cliché "a fire across the river" (meaning: it is no concern of mine). And the French anecdote of the priest who put a silver crucifix into the dying moneylender's hand ("Very light, very light," muttered the dying man; "I can give no more than ten francs") resembles the Indian story of a miser on his deathbed who refused to take any medicine until assured that it was free.

Finally, Juvenal has counterparts in the Orient, in an ancient Chinese essay on flunkeyism which corresponds to the Roman writer's satire on parasites and in the caustic remarks in the *Panchatantra* on old age, women, and parvenus.

Since all humor depends, in varying degrees, on incongruity, those pieces of satire which use humor to aid their critical purpose must utilize the unexpected or inharmonious or incompatible. This is as true for Asian satire as for Western. Not all satire, of course, is funny; sometimes invective or ingenuity or grotesqueness serves instead of humor to make the criticism more striking, or more entertaining, than complaint alone could be. But most popular satire, in the East as well as the West, does use humor as the fundamental device to make its criticism palatable.

All of the popular techniques for achieving humor in the West have been used in the Orient. Exaggeration, particularly in the forms of caricature, invective, and *reductio ad absurdum;* understatement; epigrams using paradox, witty cynicism, and twisting of clichés; unexpected truth; unexpected logic; verbal irony; dramatic irony;

parody; disguise and deception; and appealing to the reader's superiority to the victims of small misfortunes and to the butts of insults. These basic devices for attaining humor are used in the East as extensively as in the West.

The most common humorous mechanism is exaggeration. The tall tale appears everywhere, in Indian folklore and American frontier tales, in Münchhausen and the Chinese *Scholars*. In a Japanese Kyogen, *The Seed of Hojo,* a man and his uncle compete in the telling of tall tales until the wily oldster finally wins. *Reductio ad absurdum,* an ingenious form of exaggeration used by Western satirists from Aristophanes to Swift, is illustrated in a Ceylonese tale. While thieves are robbing a house a wall collapses and kills one of them. The thieves complain about inferior construction and the king seeks a victim to punish. But the house owner, the mason, the plasterer, and a number of other people offer what seem to the king valid excuses, until only a thin goldsmith is left who is sentenced to be gored to death by the royal elephant. The goldsmith persuades the king that the elephant would break his tusk goring through so thin a man. So an innocent neighbor of the goldsmith, a fat Moorman, is killed instead.

Like the pun, parody is hard to appreciate outside the particular culture or in-group that is familiar with the original which is burlesqued. Aristophanes' contemporaries recognized the lines from Euripides and Aeschylus which he parodied in *The Frogs* and the religious customs which he travestied in *Lysistrata,* but modern viewers of those plays often miss the point. Since Westerners have little knowledge of Asian literature and traditions, Oriental parodies rarely provide satiric pleasure for them. But parody is a time-honored device in the East in sculpture and painting, in dance and folk theater, as well as in jokes, folklore, and literature. In the Ceylonese folk plays called *sokari* the actors burlesque politicians during the interludes between acts. Saikaku parodied an incident from *The Tale of Genji* in *The Life of an Amorous Man;* mimicked the Buddhist confessional tale in *The Life of an Amorous Woman;* and used the title *Twenty Examples of Unfilial Conduct,* aware of the popularity of a moralistic book called *Twenty-four Examples of Filial Conduct.* The Kyogen sometimes burlesqued popular Noh plays. And the most popular haiku have been parodied innumerable times.

The humor of unexpected logic is often used for satiric purposes. Defending concubinage in the nineteenth century, Ku Hung-wing reasoned: "You always see a teapot with four teacups, but you never find a teacup with four teapots." A character in *I Am a Cat* suggests that since suicide is the only sure way of avoiding trouble, courses in suicide should be offered in all schools.

In every culture there is an unwritten agreement not to express aloud certain unpleasant or embarrassing truths. When they are expressed, by a child or a naïf or a wit, we are pleased by the violation of a taboo, a small revolt against the restrictions of a hypocritical but powerful society. In Western satire Bernard Shaw, Oscar Wilde, and Lewis Carroll have been particularly successful with this device, incongruous because the truth is expressed at a moment when we expect the conventional lie. In a Ceylonese anecdote parents have married off their daughter to a poor man of high birth. When they come to visit her, she has nothing to offer them to eat, so she puts an empty frying pan on the fire and pretends to stir its contents. When the parents ask what she is doing, she says, "I am trying to fry the honor you got for me." One Chinese proverb says: "Great politeness usually means 'I want something.'" Another points out that while we often hear peddlers praise their products, we never hear them call out, "Bitter melon," or "Thin wine."

Apart from the pleasure derived from incongruity, a great deal of satiric humor clearly depends on the superiority the reader or viewer feels to the butt of the joke. Here, admittedly, cultural differences play a large part. South Pacific cannibals felt that the funniest sight in the world was a captive hopping up and down, screaming inside the pot as the water came to a boil. Shakespeare's contemporaries laughed at cripples and madmen. Civilized societies are presumably more fastidious and restrict the pleasures of superior laughter to small misfortunes, harmless embarrassments, and the like. But this too varies from class to class in every culture, and wars and dictatorships result in fast reversions to brutal humor. The twentieth century has provided enough examples of sadistic pleasure—in the West and the East—to suggest that the veneer of civilization is very thin and the potentialities for cruelty are ubiquitous. Many scholars think that almost all humor stems from the feeling of superiority, the satisfaction derived from the discomfiture of someone, under conditions that do not threaten the safety or comfort of the laugher.

Asian humor is loaded with small misfortunes. When Yaji gets caught between the beams of a temple and is subjected to all sorts of indignities before he is pulled out, the onlookers howl with laughter in *Hizakurige*. When a barber ties Kita's queue so tightly that Kita can't bend his head to eat, his friend Yaji is delighted. More fun is provided when Kita mistakenly climbs into an old woman's bed instead of her granddaughter's. In the Kyogen called *Family Quarrel* the son-in-law splashes water, then throws mud, on his father-in-law while the decorous Japanese audience screams with laughter. In another Kyogen a man steals a blind man's wife and leaves a monkey in her place. Still another blind man is tricked into carrying a traveler across the river.

The insult is generally assumed to be an unkind form of communication, but Asian humor revels in insults. Characters in *Hizakurige* are named Gaptooth, Snotface, Scratchy. A universal joke in its Chinese version depends for humor on the obscene names a father and son call each other. A postboy on the road to Kyoto tells other postboys that their wives are whores. At one of the stops on the Tokaido road two girls make a living by letting tourists throw coins at their faces while the girls play the samisen. A speaker in the *Panchatantra* remarks, somewhat ungallantly, that a poor man's hopes fall helpless on his bosom, "like the flabby breasts of widows." Natsume's precocious cat observes that his angry gestures are as incomprehensible to crows as symbolic poems are to laymen.

Outwitting people appeals to Asians as much as to Occidentals. The clever servant was a staple of Roman comedy, and the servant almost always outwits the master in the Kyogen. One of the most popular stories about the Ceylonese jester Andare tells of his collecting rewards in anticipation of his promise to move an enormous rock. When the time comes, he offers to carry the rock away—as soon as the owner puts it on his shoulders. The cookie-stealing Kita is robbed by a "blind" shampooer. In *Hizakurige* the conniving travelers are themselves gulled by an old man into paying a large restaurant bill and are tricked by watermen into paying to be carried across the deep part of the river; the watermen return over the safe, shallow part.

In spite of the assertion of scholars that practical jokes are rare in Japan, Japanese humor provides a great many examples of planned discomfiture. Natsume's books offer several instances: the schoolboys in *Botchan* play tricks on their teachers, and some of the teachers plan practical jokes on other teachers. In *I Am a Cat* a character orders a nonexistent dish in a restaurant, and a group of schoolboys send a fake love letter to a conceited girl. *Hizakurige* is full of practical jokes: Yaji gives his friend Kita a dumpling with a hot cinder attached and laughs heartily when Kita burns his mouth. A boy with a purse on a string keeps fooling passersby who try to pick it up. Yaji tricks Kita into stepping into a scalding bath. Kita tells a maid with whom Yaji has arranged an assignation that Yaji has a venereal disease, so the maid runs away. And there is a reference in the book to a man in Osaka still remembered for his practical jokes.

Nor are other Asian countries innocent of enjoying this particular form of embarrassing people. The Ceylonese jester Andare tells his wife and the queen that the other is deaf, then brings them together for a yelling conversation. And in his reminiscences about a Ceylonese village, Vijayatunga tells about the time pranksters "married" the village idiot to a man dressed up as a woman.

Irony appears in Asian literature sometimes in obvious form, sometimes by implication. In Akutagawa's *Rashomon* the irony stems from different people seeing the same event in very different ways. And Akutagawa implies that his madman in *Kappa* may be more sane than "normal" people. The selfish sons of an old Kashmiri begin treating him well as soon as they are tricked into thinking that he has acquired more wealth. In *Rickshaw Boy* an innocent servant is punished for the political activities of his employer. And the men who have manipulated the dismissal of a teacher in *Botchan* give a farewell banquet in his honor. The irony is perhaps most poignant in Chinese poems: a mistreated boy wants to write a letter to his dead parents; a laborer watches rich men pay more for bouquets of flowers than "the taxes of ten poor houses"; after forty years' imprisonment among Tartars, a Chinese escapes to his home province—but is there mistaken for a Tartar and imprisoned again. Perhaps the best-known example of dramatic irony in Chinese folklore is the story of the farmer whose runaway horse, undeserved dividend, and son's injury and escape from military service in each instance reverse the expected order of events.

Like Western satirists, Asians found a long time ago that the addition of certain kinds of details added interest to their narratives, among these the most common being grotesque material, scatological items, and sexual references. It is revealing that the fastidious Japanese enjoys the grotesque as much as the genteel Englishman does, probably for the same reason: release of repressions in a society which places excessive restrictions on spontaneity. In Japan's most popular comic novel, for example, an old woman lets her tears and running nose help fill the glasses of wine she is selling, to the disgust of her customers but presumably to the delight of the readers of *Hizakurige*. In *Kappa* the narrator unknowingly eats the flesh of the natives, then vomits. Natsume describes the revolting eating habits of children, including a baby's greedy mastication of food spat out by another child. And when Kita and Yaji unintentionally eat the ashes which a newly widowed man is bringing from the crematorium, we are reminded of the gruesome Little Willie jokes that delighted Victorian Englishmen. But in Chinese poetry the grotesque is devastating, not funny:

locusts lay their eggs in corpses and bits of slain soldiers' flesh festoon tree branches, brought there by feasting birds.

Unlike Swift, whose obsession with scatological details may have been pathological, most Asian writers handle such material with Rabelaisian gusto. Defecation, urination, breaking wind, all are presented in the Orient as subjects for hearty laughter rather than guilty sniggers. For Saikaku, breaking wind is the subject of humorous sketches in *The Life of an Amorous Man,* and there are a number of senryu with this theme. Defecating is an even more frequent subject. *Hizakurige* contains incidents involving a dung collector; a bunch of bullies threaten to make Yaji eat dung; and a good deal of slapstick is based on mishaps in privies. Urinating offers similar satisfactions. Cicadas relieve themselves on Natsume's cat, and a horse urinates on Jippensha's Yaji. One of the funniest scenes in *Hizakurige* involves Yaji's urinating in a bamboo pipe on the erroneous assumption that the other end of the pipe is closed; since this mistake occurs in a boat full of passengers, considerable commotion is created. On another occasion, in another boat, Yaji mistakes a teapot for a urinal; the passengers who later drink are somewhat discomfited.

References to sex please Asian readers as much as anyone else. In *Journey to the West* female monsters try to rape the monk Tripitaka; they've heard a rumor that his semen guarantees immortality. In the same book, the ladies of the court complain that the usurping king has been neglecting his bedroom duties. The rascals Yaji and Kita get a great deal of pleasure out of peeping at a honeymooning couple—until the wall collapses. A number of Indian folk tales are built around sexual mishaps, and the tricks used by harlots are explained in meticulous detail. Chinese humor frequently uses sexual details as an adjunct to narrative interest.

In mixing the comic and serious, the trivial and important, Asian satire follows a path chosen by Western satirists as well. W. G. Aston felt that the "great drawback to the fun of *Hizakurige* is that it is unrelieved by serious humor." But in the other great works of Asian satire there is likely to appear an intermingling of sentiment and cynicism, playfulness and discernment, superficiality and acuteness. In the *Panchatantra* we find moralizing and bawdiness, in Narayan's novels comedy and mysticism, in *Monkey* spiritual aspiration and slapstick, in Saikaku a juxtaposing of the sacrosanct and the commonplace in a manner similar to the *New Yorker's.* The best Asian satirists draw their material from ordinary human behavior, in which inconsistency is not unknown.

Like Western satirists, Asian writers mix not only incongruous materials but incongruous techniques. In twentieth-century Japan, Natsume varied in style from lyric to colloquial; two centuries earlier Saikaku, as Hibbett observes, "exploited poetic techniques in his prose rhythms and syntax, figures of speech and quick associational transitions." The *Panchatantra* mixes narrative, fable, prose, poetry, and proverbs.

Kenneth Burke shrewdly identifies proverbs as "strategies for living." They serve many purposes—consolation, inspiration, venting of aggression, rationalization. Western proverbs offer handy tags for opposing wishes: "Absence makes the heart grow fonder" and "Out of sight, out of mind," "Look before you leap" and "He who hesitates is lost." The Japanese match this with "A wife and a pot get better as they get older" and "A wife and floor mats are good when new and fresh." Asian proverbs satisfy the usual folk-needs, and Asian satiric proverbs reveal a materialism and cynicism which theoretically should not exist among people devoted to the teachings of the Buddha, Confucius, and the Brahmans.

The satiric proverbs and epigrams of the Orient are formed by devices similar to those of Western wits: changing a cliché slightly so that an incongruous effect is created; coining cynical definitions; stating pungently beliefs widely held but rarely expressed; and, sometimes, expressing an original idea in a memorable way.

Perhaps the most obvious characteristic of these pithy statements is their reliance on what some call unexpected truth, others cynicism. "It is the beautiful bird that is caged," say the Chinese. The Indian proverb "No one wants to hear unpleasant truth" is expressed in Ceylon as "The truthful man finds no room even in the tavern." The *Panchatantra* is full of cynical remarks about the power of money, and China has contributed a number of similar sentiments, including "Gold will influence Heaven itself." Among the following Chinese proverbs some might be considered cynical: "There are no filial children at the bedside of long-sick people." "More trees are upright than men." "The influence of good is all too little. The influence of bad is all too much." "Even if stone were changed to gold, the heart of man would not be satisfied."

Scholars have long recognized, sometimes acrimoniously, that proverbs attributed to one country originated in another. That India was the source of many Ceylonese proverbs is known, and the influence of China on Japanese culture is generally recognized, though not everyone will go as far as Herbert Giles in his insistence that not only Japanese proverbs but "all the high-class literature of Japan, its art, and its civilization, are essentially of Chinese origin." So many similar proverbs appear in different Asian cultures that provenance is not likely to be determined now.

The protagonists in Asian satire are likely to be unheroic characters or amiable rascals. In *Hizakurige,* for example, which Professor Aston calls "beyond question, the most humorous and entertaining book in the Japanese language," the two main characters, Yaji and Kita, "are cowardly, superstitious, and impudent. Lies . . . fall from their lips on the smallest provocation or in mere wantonness." Of the characters in *The Scholars,* Wu Tsu-hsiang says: "Wu Ching-tzu has a deep sympathy for all his characters and makes his readers feel that these degenerate scholars, ridiculous and despicable as they may be, are also much to be pitied." In his analysis of *Journey to the West,* C. T. Hsia writes, "Monkey and Pigsy are fully as memorable as . . . Don Quixote and Sancho Panza. . . . The Tripitaka of the novel . . . often appears as a deliberate caricature of a saintly monk. . . . Wu Ch'eng-en's supreme comic creation is Pigsy, who symbolizes the gross sensual life in the absence of religious striving and mythical ambition. He is doubly comic because as a reluctant pilgrim he has no calling whatever for the monastic life and because with all his monstrous size and strength he entertains no ambition beyond a huge meal and a good sleep with a woman in his arms. . . . In Pigsy, with all his unflattering physical and moral features, Wu Ch'eng-en has drawn the portrait of every common man who finds his fulfillment in his pursuit of respectable mundane goals." (*The Classic Chinese Novel,* chap. 4 *passim*)

Nor are the protagonists of Natsume's novels particularly admirable. The young naïf in *Botchan* is goodhearted but impetuous, stubborn, and gullible. Both the cat and his master in *I Am a Cat* exhibit most of the human and animal defects, although the cat is by all odds the more likable individual. The important characters in Asian satires turn out to be, like their counterparts in Western literature, rascals like Yaji and Kita, or cowards like Tripitaka, or uninhibited sensualists like Pigsy, or weaklings like the cat's master, or naïfs like Botchan, or the sympathetic innocents in Narayan's books. The characters in Asian satire will seem familiar to Western readers. We have met all of them before, under different names in another culture.

LEONARD FEINBERG

CHINA

ON CHINESE HUMOR

In spite of E. B. White's warning that humor should not be dissected, many scholars have tried to analyze not only humor in general but the comic spirit of different countries. Lin Yutang, like most other scholars, finds the source of Chinese humor in the nation's practicality: "Chinese philosophy, or Confucianism, is a philosophy of common sense and this common sense . . . is the basis of Chinese humor."[1] The large component of censure in that humor Lin Yutang accounts for in the following way: "The Chinese, I believe, are the world's greatest gossipers. The goal of gossiping is to prick the bubbles of the great of the world and re-establish a comfortable sense of equality in all mankind."

George Kao, however, attributes the comic spirit in Chinese life to Taoism rather than Confucianism. "For purposes of humor," Kao writes, "the Taoists have taken care of the Chinese gentleman in his off moments. Being resigned to nature, the Taoist can see man in his limitations; being the perennial outsider, he can afford to relax and laugh." Kao also suggests that "Chinese humor, to a greater degree than that of any other people, sees the ludicrous in the pathos of life. It is the result of a philosophical reaction to adversity coupled with innate optimism about the future." He observes that "what appears funniest to the Chinese is outside the realm of writing . . . and unfunny to the Westerner even if translated."

Chinese humor is often direct and earthy, sometimes crude and scatological. But it can also be poignant and delicate, subtle and sophisticated. The prevalence of salacious material in Chinese popular literature, and the casual attitude toward that material, can be better understood in the context of China's cultural orientation. Francis Hsu's explanation is helpful: "In situation-centered China, sex is controlled more by external barriers than by internal restraints. . . . The individual needs merely to refrain from sexual expression in inappropriate situations. . . . In the [Christian] approach, sex is a sin, regardless of circumstances. In the [Chinese] approach, sex is a natural urge of man, like eating, to which expression must be given in the right place and with the right parties."[2]

Perhaps the shrewdest observation Lin Yutang makes about the Chinese comic spirit is his suggestion that Chinese humor "consists in complying with outward form as such and the total disregard of the substance in actuality."[3] He adds: "Humor often

1. The quotations in this and the following paragraph are from Kao's *Chinese Wit and Humor,* pp. xxx, xxi, 3, xxi, xxvi.

2. Quoted in Gardner Murphy's *Asian Psychology* (New York, 1968), p. 170.

3. The quotations in this paragraph are from Lin Yutang's *My Country and My People,* pp. 67, 67, 71.

takes a tolerant view of vice and evil and instead of condemning them, laughs at them, and the Chinese have always been characterized by the capacity to tolerate evil. . . . A humorist is often a defeatist, and delights in recounting his own failures and embarrassments, and the Chinese are often sane, cool-minded defeatists." He concludes: "We really look upon life as a stage, and the kind of theatrical show we like best is always high comedy, whether that comedy be a new constitution, or a bill of rights, or an anti-opium bureau."

Most of this humor was limited to subliterary expression, or at best was considered beneath the dignity of educated gentlemen and upper-class persons. Lin Yutang explains the reason for this condition: "There is a peculiar twist which prevented the output of Chinese humorous literature from being as prolific as it should be. That is Confucian puritanism. Confucian decorum put a damper on light, humorous writing, as well as on all imaginative literature except poetry. Drama and the novel were despised as unworthy of a respectable scholar's occupation. . . . But humorous literature and jokes flourished in a joke-loving people in spite of Confucian puritanism and outside the sanctimonious territory of 'orthodox' literature."[1] All of the forms of Western satire appear in China, in some instances long before the West produced that kind of literature.

From Socrates to Koestler men have tried to explain the reason for laughter and have offered so many theories one begins to suspect that no single explanation accounts for all the varieties of laughter. All we can say is that humor almost always involves incongruity, that it usually appeals to a momentary feeling of superiority, and that it functions best in an atmosphere of security. Other theories of humor tend to fall under the rubrics of ambivalence, release from restraint, or avoidance of the censor.

Most jokes and humorous anecdotes use one or more of the following devices to achieve their effect: exaggeration (caricature, invective, *reductio ad absurdum*), understatement, disparaging comparison or contrast, verbal irony, dramatic irony, pun, parody, disguise, deception, unexpected logic, unexpected truth, small misfortunes, ignorance, unmasking, and witty insults.

Obviously, this anthology offers only a small, hopefully representative sampling of the satiric and humorous literature of a country with what Professor S. H. Chen calls "the oldest, almost intact cultural patrimony" in the world. Among the works omitted, some of which are Chinese classics and contain varying amounts of satire and humor, are *Journey to the West* (entitled *Monkey* in Arthur Waley's translation), *The Travels of Lao Ts'an* (a novel by Liu T'ieh-yun published in 1907), *The Golden Lotus* (perhaps the most popular Chinese novel ever written, described by its American publisher as the Chinese *Decameron*), *Dream of the Red Chamber* (by Tsao Hsueh-chin, eighteenth century), and the opera *The Butterfly Dream*, which satirizes woman's fickleness.

And what of the new China? In a recent interview with an Italian journalist Dr. Suh Tsung-hwa, the most famous neurologist in Communist China, concluded his analysis of the Chinese character with these words: "I find myself unable to explain to you what seems a paradox, because, as I said, I am Chinese. I understand China;

1. Quoted in Kao, *op. cit.*, p. xxi.

you do not. . . . We are able to understand you because European civilization is more explicit than implicit and . . . much younger than that of China. . . . I only want to say that you must not try to understand the mind of the Chinese, which is quite simple, sane, and almost infantile, but rather the heart of the Chinese, which is very complicated, has suffered much pain and is old, ancient."[1]

1. Goffredo Parise, "No Neurotics in China." *Atlas*, February, 1962, pp. 46–47.

JOKES

translated by R. H. Blyth, George Kao, and others

The Customer Is Always Right / In old Peiping restaurants, waiters are well known for their polite and efficient service. A visitor from the South one day dined at a famous Peiping inn and, midway through his meal, took notice of the ingratiating young fellow who hovered about and administered to his every wish. In a mood to make friends, the man started a conversation with his waiter.

"What's your name, young man?" he asked.

"Anything you say, sir," the waiter answered, all smiles.

"Well, I have two guesses. Your name is either Chang or Li."

"Both are correct, sir!" the waiter answered.

"How can both be correct?" the customer asked.

"Well, sir," the waiter explained, "I was born in the Chang family but adopted into the Li family. That's why both your guesses are correct."

Then the customer asked the waiter how old he was. And again the waiter answered, "Anything you say, sir!"

"I would say, you are either twenty-three or twenty-five."

"Both are correct, sir!"

"Well, now, how can both of my guesses be correct in this case?" the man protested.

"It's like this, sir. I am twenty-three years of age. But a fortuneteller told me that it is an unlucky age for me, so he changed it to twenty-five. That's why both your guesses are correct."

Finally the customer asked the waiter what month of the year he was born in. And once again the waiter bowed and said, "Anything you say, sir!"

"Maybe you were born in June, or maybe you were born in January."

"Both are correct, sir!" the waiter exclaimed, polite as ever.

"Come, come, certainly that can't be true!"

"Oh, yes!" said the waiter. "I was born in the month of June, but when I saw that it was so hot, I went right back and didn't appear again until January."

•

The Champion Miser / In a certain village there lived two misers, Old Chang and Old Wang, both famous for their stinginess. For a long time the villagers could not decide which one of the two was the greater miser, and a sort of rivalry developed between them in the art of penny-pinching.

When the Mid-Autumn Festival came around, on the fifth day of the fifth moon, and it was the custom to exchange seasonal gifts, Miser Chang thought he would take the occasion to assert his claim as the champion miser. He painted a fish on a piece of paper and instructed his son to present it to his friend, Mr. Wang, with his compliments.

The "fish" was accepted by Old Wang with a great show of appreciation. As Confucian etiquette calls for reciprocity, Old Wang prepared to send Chang a suitable gift in return. He called aside his son and gave instructions to do thus and so.

Toward the end of the day Little Wang returned from his mission. "Did you do as I told?" Old Wang asked. "Oh, yes!" replied his son. "When I saw Mr. Chang I bowed to him and said, 'In return for your very substantial gift my father asked me to present to you this moon cake,' and I used the fingers of my hands to form the shape of a round moon cake."

Instead of being pleased, Old Miser Wang was outraged by his son's conduct, and he gave the boy a slap on the face. "Who told you to be so extravagant?" he shouted, extending the fingers of one hand to show how it should have been done. "Half a cake would have been enough!"

•

Cook's Holiday / A cook was chopping meat in his own home. When nobody was looking, he hid a piece in his lap. His wife observed this and scolded him.

"Why did you do it?" she asked. "This is your own meat."

"Oh, I forgot," he said.

•

Appointment with Lord Chou / A teacher dozed off before his class. When he woke up he told a fib to his pupils to cover it up.

"I had an appointment with Lord Chou in dreamland," he said.

The next day one of his pupils followed his example and also went to sleep in class. The teacher waked him up with a stick, and said, "How dare you sleep in the class?"

The pupil said, "I, too, had an appointment with Lord Chou."

"Well, and what did Lord Chou say to you?" the teacher demanded.

"Lord Chou said, 'I didn't see your honorable teacher yesterday.' "

•

The Best Doctor in the World / The king of Hell sent one of his messengers to the world in search of the best doctor, with these instructions:

"When you see a doctor at whose door there are no avenging ghosts, then you will have found the best doctor in the world."

The messenger looked far and near, but there was not a doctor who had not a host of avenging ghosts gathered at his door. Finally, he came upon one where there was a lone ghost wandering in front of the door. The messenger said to himself, "That's a good enough doctor for me."

When he inquired he found that the doctor had hung up his shingle only the day before.

•

It's a Date / A man was miserly to the extreme and he never gave a party. One day one of his neighbors gave a party in his house. Someone saw it and asked his servant, "Is your master giving a party today?" The servant said, "If you expect my master to give a party you will have to wait until the next incarnation!" Hearing this, the master scolded the servant, saying, "Who told you to promise any dates?"

•

Cold Wine / A man who loved to drink found a jug of cold wine in his dream. He was about to warm it up and drink it when all of a sudden he awoke.

"I should have had it cold!" he said with profound regret.

•

Who's Crying? / A bride on the way to her wedding cried all the way in a most heartbreaking fashion. The sedan-chair carriers were so moved that they said, "Young lady, how about letting us carry you back home?"

"The crying's stopped now," replied the bride instantly.

•

Rice / A certain man had an affair with another man's wife. One day when they were making love to each other the husband returned, and the wife hurriedly hid her lover in a sack. The husband saw that the wife was a bit nervous and he began to look around and saw something moving in the sack.

"What is in that sack?" demanded the husband.

The wife couldn't find any ready answer.

"What is in that sack, I say?" demanded the husband again.

In his desperation, the lover in the bag shouted on behalf of the wife, "Rice!"

•

The Manly Way / A man was beaten by his wife and had to go and hide under the bed.

"You come out this minute!" the wife commanded.

"A man's a man," he answered. "When he says he won't come out, there's nothing you can do about it. He won't come out."

•

Wine for Breakfast / A man was so poor that he could have only the cheapest food, fermented rice cakes, for his breakfast. Every morning when he went out he would be slightly tipsy from the fermented rice.

One day a friend saw him and asked: "Have you been drinking this early?"

"No," he answered, "I just had some fermented rice cakes."

When he went home and told this to his wife, she said, "Why didn't you just say you had been drinking wine? It would sound much more elegant."

The next day when his friend asked the same question he told him he had been drinking wine.

"How did you drink it," his friend insisted on knowing, "hot or cold?"

"It's toasted," he answered.

The friend smiled and said, "It is only fermented rice again."

When his wife learned of this she blamed him once more and said, "How could you ever refer to wine as toasted? Next time you must say you drank it hot." The husband said, "Now I know."

The next time he saw the friend he volunteered the information without waiting to be asked.

"This time I drank hot wine," he said.

"How much did you have?" the friend asked.

"Two pieces," he said, extending two fingers.

•

Big Drum / Chang-three said, "We have a drum at home so big, when you beat it, it can be heard a hundred miles away."

Li-four said, "We have a cow in our home so big, when she takes a drink at the south bank of the river her head reaches out and touches the north bank."

Chang-three shook his head and exclaimed, "How could there be a cow of that size!"

Li-four said, "If there weren't cows of this size, where would you get the hide to make that drum?"

•

The Tutor's Son / A tutor, who was bragging about his son's cleverness as a book student, ended by suggesting that he might join in the lessons of his employer's son. This was readily agreed to; and the tutor, on his return home for the holidays, said to his son, "Next year I am going to take you with me for a course of study. I have praised you to my employer, whereas in reality you are a hopeless idiot and cannot read a single word." Then he wrote down three words—"coverlet," "rice," and "father"—and bade his son learn them carefully in order to bring them out when asked. Soon after their arrival, the employer examined the boy about a few words, of all of which he showed himself totally ignorant.

"He is nervous," said his father; "let me write a few words down, and you will see that he really knows something." The first word was "coverlet," which the boy failed to recognize. "Think of what is on the top of your bed," hinted his father. "Grass matting," replied his son. "What is this?" asked the father, writing down "rice." Again the boy failed, and again the father helped him with, "What is it you eat at home?" "Corn meal," replied his son. Finally the word "father" was written down, and once more the boy made no answer. This made the father angry, and he roared out, "Who is it sleeps with your mother?" To this the boy replied at once, "My uncle."

•

The Doctor's Wife / A doctor, who had doctored a man's son to death and was threatened with legal proceedings, agreed to hand over his own son for adoption. Later on, he managed to cause the death of a client's servant, and was obliged to give up the only servant he had. One night there came a knock at his door from a neighbor, who said: "My wife is having a baby. Please come and attend to her at once!"

"Ah, the blackguard!" cried the doctor to his wife. "I know what he wants this time—he wants you!."

•

Choosing a Career / A doctor, a girl, and a thief died and appeared before the Judge of Purgatory.

"And what did you do," said the Judge to the doctor, "to earn your living in the upper world?"

"Your servant," replied the doctor, "practiced as a physician, and was able to raise dying people to life again."

"You scoundrel!" roared the Judge. "You dared to interfere with my prerogative? Away with him, lictors, to the caldron of boiling oil."

Then, turning to the girl, the Judge bade her give an account of her doings.

"I made love to gentlemen," replied the girl, hastily adding, "but only to those who have no wives."

"You might do worse," said the Judge. "Take a further span of twelve years' life on earth."

The thief came next. He said, "I have been a bad man in robbing people and spending their money in extravagance, but I will now make some restitution."

"You have only done what other people do," remarked the Judge. "I give you ten more years of life."

"Oh, dear, oh, dear!" cried the doctor to the Judge. "If that is the way you administer justice, only let me go back to the upper world. I have a daughter and a son, and I shall know what professions to put them into."

•

All That Money Can't Buy / A Judge of Purgatory decided that a certain disembodied spirit should return to earth as a rich man.

"But I don't want to be a rich man," cried the spirit. "I only ask for a regular supply of food, with no worries, that I may burn pure incense and drink bitter tea, and thus pass through life."

The Judge replied: "Money I can provide, to any amount; but this peaceful, happy life you require is more than I can give."

•

Money Is Life / A farmer who had been planting eggplants, but could not make them grow, asked the advice of an old gardener.

"There is no difficulty about that," was the reply. "Under every plant bury a copper cash."

"How so?" inquired the farmer.

"With money," said the gardener, "there is life; without it, death."

•

A Foolish Bird / A guest at a dinner sat tight and showed no signs of leaving. At length the host called his visitor's attention to a bird on a tree and said, "As our last course has been served, wait till I cut down the tree, catch the bird, have it cooked, and tell the butler to bring up some wine. What do you say to that?"

"Well", replied the guest, "I expect that by the time the tree is down, the bird will have flown."

"No, no," said the host, "that is a foolish bird, and doesn't know when to go."

•

Sleepy Dog / A deaf man went to call at the house of a friend, whose watchdog, as soon as it caught sight of him, barked loud and long. He paid no attention to what he did not hear, but went in; and after the usual compliments had been exchanged, he said to his friend, "I imagine that the honorable dog which guards your palace did not get much sleep last night."

"How so?" asked the friend.

"Well," replied the deaf man, "from the moment it saw me, it did nothing but yawn."

Filial Piety / A father and son were chopping firewood together, when the father, who had the hatchet, accidentally wounded the son's fingers.

"You old pimp!" cried the son. "Are you blind?"

A grandson, who was standing by hearing his grandfather cursed like this, and feeling much hurt, turned to his father and said, "You son of a bitch! How dare you curse your own father?"

•

His Wife's Lover / A lady had a lover who lived next door. Hearing her husband come home, the lover jumped out of the window; but when the husband got in, the first thing he saw was a man's shoe. Cursing his wife roundly, he put the shoe under his pillow and went to sleep, saying, "Wait till tomorrow, when I will find out whose shoe this is and settle accounts with you."

The wife kept awake until he was sound asleep, and then gently drew out the shoe and placed one of her husband's own shoes in its place. In the early morning, the husband got up and began again to curse his wife; but he soon discovered that the shoe was his own. Repenting of his behavior, he said to his wife, "I was wrong in my suspicions of you. I must have been the man who jumped out of the window."

•

A Tea Connoisseur / A countryman went up to town to see a relative, who entertained him with some choice tea made with water from a famous spring.

"Delicious! Delicious!" cried out the countryman several times. "You, my old relative, are evidently a connoisseur."

"Is it the tea or the spring water," asked the host, "which takes your fancy?"

"I like it," replied the countryman, "because it's hot."

•

A Grass Rope / A man stole an ox, and was put in the cangue (large square wooden collar). A friend came along and asked him what crime he had committed to get this punishment. The thief said, "I was just walking along the street when I saw on the ground a grass rope. Thinking it was of no use, I made the mistake of picking it up and taking it home; and so I got into this trouble."

"But what is there wrong," asked the friend, "in thus picking up a grass rope?"

"Well," replied the thief, "there was something else tied to the rope."

"And what was that?" asked the friend; to which the thief replied, "A very small ox."

•

Three Precious Things / A man who was in the habit of telling tall tales said to his relatives that he had at home three precious things: an ox which could walk a thousand li a day, a cock which uttered a single crow at each watch of the night, and a dog which could read books.

"If you have all these wonderful objects," cried his relatives, "tomorrow we will pay you a visit and hope you will let us see them."

The man went home and told his wife that he had been lying, asking her how he was to make good.

"That will be all right," replied his wife; "I have a plan."

Next day, when the relatives arrived, she declared that her husband had gone off early in the morning to Peking.

"And when will he be back?" inquired the relatives.

"Oh, in seven or eight days," answered the wife. Then when they wanted to know how he could possibly do the journey in such a short time, she replied, "He is riding our ox."

"And have you got the wonderful cock which keeps the watches?" asked the relatives a moment before the cock crew, as it happened to be noon.

"There you are," said the wife. The relatives next wished to see the dog that could read books. "Well," replied the wife, "I will not deceive you. We are very badly off, and the the dog has taken a job as tutor."

•

Knowing One's Place / Once a rich man was traveling with his servant and felt hungry. They went into a restaurant to eat. When the bill was tendered, the rich man discovered that while he had eaten only a bowl of plain white rice, the servant had ordered himself a meat to go with it. The rich man paid, and the two left the restaurant and continued on their journey. The rich man became angrier and angrier, thinking about what had happened, and after a few steps he turned around and told his servant, who was following behind, "I am your master, not the horse (which goes into battle first to meet the enemy's arrows). Why are you walking behind me?"

The servant hurried to the front of his master, and they walked for a little while this way. Then the rich man said, "I am not your servant. Why are you walking in front of me?"

The servant backed up a few steps, and the two walked shoulder to shoulder for a while. Then the rich man said, "You and I are not equals. Why are you walking shoulder to shoulder with me?"

The servant said, "What shall I do then, if I am not to walk behind you, or ahead of you, or shoulder to shoulder with you?"

The rich man said angrily, "Well, to tell you the truth, you'd better pay me for that meat you ordered."

•

The Man Who Would Not Admit His Mistake / Hsueh Tao (Pre-15th cen.) / In the State of Chu lived a man who did not know where ginger grew. He thought it grew on trees.

Someone told him it grew in the ground.

He could not believe this was true, and said, "I will lay a bet with you with my donkey. Let us ask ten people; if they all say it grows in the ground, the donkey is yours!"

They asked ten men, who all said that it grew in the ground.

"Take the donkey!" said the man. "But, all the same, I know ginger grows on trees!"

•

Nothing to Do with Me / Hsueh Tao / A surgeon once boasted about his ability. A soldier, returning from battle with an arrow penetrating his leg, came to him for treatment.

The surgeon took a pair of sharp scissors and cut off the stem of the arrow close to the flesh, then asked for pay.

"But you haven't taken out the head of the arrow," complained the soldier.

"That's an internal matter. That's a physician's business, not mine," was the reply.

•

Abnormal Weather / Hsueh Tao / A general was drinking in the camp on a cold winter's night. Candles were lighted and coal was burning well in the stove. After a few bowlfuls of wine, beads of sweat appeared on his forehead.

"Extraordinary weather we're having this year!" said the general. "When it should be cold, it's warm."

His words were heard by his orderly, who was standing outside in the cold. Entering the tent, he knelt respectfully before the general and said, "The weather seems normal enough where your servant was standing, sir."

•

Honesty / Hsueh Tao / A corrupt official wanted to show that he was pure and honest. So, before assuming office, he took an oath in public, saying, "If my right hand accepts bribes, let it fester; if my left hand accepts bribes, let it fester, too."

After some time, a person offered him a hundred teals of silver as a bribe. He wanted to accept but feared that the oath might take effect.

To help him out of his quandary, the runner said, "Why not place the money in your Honour's sleeve so that it, and only it, will rot, if rot it must!"

The official thought it was a sound idea and accepted the money.

•

A Good Man Is Easy to Bully / Chao Nan-hsing (1550–1627) / In the temple by the roadside of a village there was a wooden image of a deity. A man passing by found a ditch across his path, so he pulled down the image and placed it over the ditch as a bridge. Another passerby saw the figure on the ground and, feeling sorry for it, restored it to its place. But the image took umbrage because he had offered no sacrifice to it, and placed a curse on him, causing him to suffer a bad headache.

The spirits of the kingdom of the underworld were nonplussed. "You let the one who trod on you go free, but punished the one who helped you up. Why?"

"You don't understand," said the deity. "It is so easy to bully a good man."

•

Drowning / Anon. (ca. 1500) / A man had fallen in the water and was drowning. His son called for someone to come and save him, but the father raised his head from the water and cried, "If they will save me for three coins, all right, but not for more."

•

Lighting a Candle to Find the Flint / Su Shih (1036–1101) / One night, Ai Tzu asked his pupil to strike a flint to light the lamp. For a long time nothing happened. So Ai Tzu urged him in a loud voice.

"It is so dark, how am I going to find the flint?" the pupil complained. Then he added, "All right, master, you light the candle and let us find it together."

•

Swallowing a Date Whole / Pai Ting (11th or 12th cen.) / A fool once heard someone say that pears were good for the teeth but harmful to the spleen, and that dates were good for the spleen but harmful to the teeth. After thinking about it for a while, he said, "From now on, when I eat a pear, I will only chew and not swallow it. And when I eat a date, I will swallow it whole."

A Scholar Buys a Donkey / Yen Chih-tui (531–91) / One day a learned scholar was buying a donkey in the market.

A deed had to be filled out recording the transaction.

The man who had sold the donkey watched the scholar writing sheet after sheet till three sheets were finished, but could not see the word "donkey." He urged the scholar to complete the deed.

"You only have to make it clear in the deed that the donkey has been paid for and liability assumed by each party. Why are you writing so much?" asked the seller.

"Don't be impatient, I'll soon come to the donkey," the scholar replied.

•

Flattery / Tu Pen-chun (Ming dynasty) / A rich man and a poor man were talking.

"I have a hundred ounces of gold," said the rich man. "If I give you twenty, will you flatter me?"

"It would not be fairly shared, so how could I flatter you?"

"Suppose I give you half, would you flatter me then?"

"We would be equal. I would not flatter you."

"And if I give you all the gold, how then?"

"If I had all the gold, I would have no need to flatter you."

•

The Tree Fork / Feng Meng-lung (Ming dynasty) / The people living on a certain mountain used tree forks for stool legs. A father sent his son to get one. The son took an axe and went. But at the end of the day he came back empty-handed.

When his father scolded him, he answered, "Of course there are plenty of tree forks there, but they all grow upwards."

•

I Want Your Finger / Feng Meng-lung / A poor man one day met an old friend who had become an immortal. After hearing his friend complain of his poverty, the immortal pointed his finger at a brick by the roadside, which immediately turned into a gold ingot. He presented it to his friend. When the man was not satisfied with this, he gave him a big gold lion. But the man was still not pleased.

"What more do you want?" the immortal asked.

"I want your finger," was the reply.

•

The Compassionate Man / Yueh Ke (12th or 13th cen.) / A compassionate man once caught a turtle. He wanted to make it into soup, but unwilling to be accused of taking life he boiled a panful of water and, placing a rod over the pan, said to the turtle, "If you can get across the pan on the rod, I will set you free."

The turtle knew what the man's intentions were. But he did not want to die. So, summoning up all his will, he walked on the rod across the pan.

"Well done," said the man. "Now please try it again."

•

Old Custom / Seng Wen-ying (10th cen.) / A newly appointed prefect was giving a grand banquet for the local gentry with many musicians to entertain the party. In the midst of the revelry, a singer sang, "Out with the old, in with the new; out with the evil star, in with the lucky star!"

The prefect was highly flattered.

"Who composed that?" he asked.

"It is an old custom in our town to sing this when a new prefect arrives. It is the only lyric I know," replied the singer.

•

Two Ways of Cooking the Goose / Liu Yuan-ching (15th cen.) / A man saw a wild goose flying in the sky. Fitting an arrow to his bow, he said, "If I can bring it down, we will stew it."

"No, it would be better to roast it," said his younger brother.

They argued for a while. Finally they went to a senior member of the clan, who settled the matter by suggesting a half-and-half treatment. But when they came out to look for the wild goose again, it was nowhere to be seen.

•

The Leaf of Invisibility / A poor man of Ch'u read in a book called *Huainantzu* that the praying-mantis, when it catches a cicada, hides itself behind a leaf that it holds up. He went to a tree and lo and behold, there was a mantis holding up a leaf, about to catch a cicada. He tried to take the leaf from it, but it slipped from his hand and fell to the ground below the tree. Unfortunately he couldn't distinguish it from the other leaves which had already fallen on the ground, so he gathered together a bagful of leaves and took them home. Picking them up one by one he said to his wife, "Can you see me?" to which she kept on saying, "Of course I can see you!" but he persisted so long, so many days, she was wearied to death, and at last said, "I can't see you." The man was overjoyed, and taking that leaf went out into the town, and right in front of everybody stole something from a shop, but a policeman arrested him at the very moment. When examined, he explained everything, and the judge, laughing heartily, pronounced him innocent, and set him free.

•

A Divorce / T'sochiu of Pingyuan went as a bride to the house of Motai. The bride had beauty, and womanly tact, and the two were on good terms. But when the first son was born and they went back to the wife's native village, the mother, Mrs. Ting, who was already rather old, came and greeted them, and when they got back home the bridegroom told the bride he would divorce her. On being asked the reason for this sudden change, he said, "I saw your mother yesterday; she's already decrepit and ill-favoured. When you get old you'll look the same. That's the reason, and no other."

•

Seasoning / A certain man was making some soup and tasting it with a ladle. The taste wasn't quite right, so he put some salt in the soup and tasted what remained in the ladle. "Still it's not salty enough!" he wondered, and put more salt in, but however much he tasted the soup in the ladle he found it no saltier, and put a whole pound of salt in with no apparent effect whatever.

•

Biting One's Own Nose / Two men quarrelled, and one said the other had bitten him on the nose. When they went before the magistrate the other man said the first had bitten his own nose. The magistrate said, "How could he have done that? The nose is in a high place and the mouth in a lower one!" "May it please your worship, but he stood on a table to do it."

•

A Looking Glass / A certain woman was not rich enough to have had or seen a mirror. One day her husband bought one and brought it back with him. Picking it up and looking in it she was thunderstruck, and cried to her mother, "My husband has brought another woman home." The mother peeped in the mirror and said, "Besides that, he's brought her mother too!"

•

Fools / Yen Ying, of the country of Ch'i, a man of small stature, took a message to the Emperor of Ch'u, and at that time the emperor asked him, "Have they no fine big man in Ch'i?" Yen Ying answered, "As for the country of Ch'i, they send foolish messengers to foolish princes." "Am I a fool then?" "I am a fool, so I have come to your Majesty."

•

Eloquence / The court of Chen once sent an envoy to the State of Sui, and this court, to find out how much learning and wisdom the envoy had, ordered Hou Pai to disguise himself in old clothes, and pretend to be a poor man in attendance on him. The envoy, taken in by his appearance, thought little of him, and talked to Hou Pai while reclining and farting at his ease. Hou Pai, though disgusted by this behavior, had to put up with it. The envoy, still lying there, asked carelessly, "Are horses in your country cheap or dear?" Hou Pai immediately replied, "There are several kinds of horses, and the price varies. A fine, well-trained horse that is smart and fleet of foot costs more than thirty kuan. If its action is pretty good, and it can be used as a riding horse, it will bring more than twenty kuan. If however the horse is untrained but stout of body and can be used as a packhorse, it costs four or five kuan. But, a horse of decrepit tail and cracked hooves, useful for nothing, which can only lie down and fart, costs nothing at all." The envoy was astonished, and asking his name, heard he was Hou Pai, and, most embarrassed, apologized.

•

Forgetting / Liu Chen of the Sui Dynasty, Governor of Loyang, was famous for his absent-mindedness. A man once committed a crime which required the punishment of the bastinade. Liu Chen, angry at the misdeeds of the prisoner, prepared the rod, and told him to strip himself. The criminal did so, but just when the punishment was about to be put into effect, Liu Chen was called away to see a visitor, with whom he talked for some time. It was a cold day, and the prisoner crept to a sunny place near the house, crouching there with his coat over him. A little later Liu Chen saw the visitor off, and on his way back noticed the criminal. "Who are you?" he said, "How dare you hunt for lice just outside my room!" The criminal ran away, but still Liu Chen was unaware of his mistake.

•

Dreams / Chang Liche of T'ang was a very erratic man. Once he suddenly woke up, got on his horse, and rode into the castle, where he met his superior, Tengyun. He bowed to him and said, "I hear you are going to condemn me to death." Tengyun replied, "Don't talk nonsense!" "But such and such an official said so." Yun became very angry, and had the official arrested and was going to have him thrashed with the cat-o'-nine-tails for the crime of setting officials at variance. But the official vehemently protested his innocence, whereupon Chang came and said, "Please let him go; it seems to have been something in my dream."

•

To Tell the Truth / Hsi Ang was very intimate with Wei Chih. One day they were talking about the rulers of T'ang, and Chih said, "Who was the most incompetent of them?" Hsi Ang said, without thinking, "It was Wei Anshih (the father of Chih)." Then, noticing what he had said he rushed off. On the way, he met Chi Wen who asked him why he was in such a hurry. "I was just talking about the most incompetent of the rulers of T'ang, and absent-mindedly said Wei Anshih when I really meant Chi So (the uncle of Wen)." Realising he had made another slip of the tongue he again rushed away, whipping his horse until he reached the residence of Fang Kuan, who kindly asked him what had happened, and he told him, concluding, "I really meant to say Fang Kuan."

Wife / Kuei was very much afraid of his wife, and even when the Emperor gave him two ladies-in-waiting as a reward for his services, he would not accept them. Tu Chenglun made fun of him on this account, but Kuei said, "I have three good reasons for being so afraid of my wife. First, when we married, she was as noble as a bodhisattva, and, as you know, we are all afraid of bodhisattvas. Then when she gave birth to a child, she was like a tiger with its cub. Who is not afraid of a tiger? And now, when she is old, her face is all wrinkles and she looks like a demon, and all men fear demons. So is it not natural that I should be afraid of my wife?"

•

Tears for the Unborn / Lu Wenli of the T'ang Dynasty was fond of study, and was good at writing, and was promoted to the position of an official of the Yanchou district. But he was born a little "off" in some ways. For example, a certain lower official brought a letter from another official, Chang Shih, in which it said, "This is to send a notice concerning choosing the day, sister having died." When he read, "sister having died," Wenli began to sob. The lower official waited until his weeping had subsided a little and then said, "This is about Chang Shih's sister!" After a while Wenli said, "I see: it was about Chang Shih's sister." "Yes, sir, that's right." "You know, I have no sister, so it seemed somehow odd."

•

An Unbearable Beard / Tsai Chunmo had a remarkable beard. One day, at an Imperial Party the Emperor said to him, "Your beard is truly wonderful; when you sleep do you put it under the coverlet, or outside?" He answered, "I'm sorry, I don't remember." When he got home and went to bed he thought of what the Emperor had asked, and tried both ways, inside and outside, but both seemed uncomfortable, and he could not sleep all night long.

•

O My Eyes! My Ears! / Wei Ming of the Southern T'ang was fond of versifying, often writing poems of several hundred characters, but none of them were much good. One day he visited Han Hsitsai, who told him to leave it on his desk, with the excuse that he was suffering from some eye disease. Ming said, "Then I will read it to you." "No, no!" said Han Hsitsai, "I have something wrong with my ears as well."

A Drunkard / The wife of Liu Ling was often annoyed by her husband's excessive drinking, and plotted with his concubine to kill him. She brewed a large cask of wine. Liu Ling asked for some of the wine every day, but she kept answering, "Wait till it's properly ripened, then you shall drink as much as you like!" When the wine was quite ripe she invited Liu Ling to drink, and together with his concubine pushed him down into the cask. They put the lid on, got something heavy onto it, and waited for him to be drowned in the wine. After three days there was still no sound in the cask, so they thought he must be dead. The wife took off the lid and looked in the cask—and there was no wine in it. There he sat, quite drunk, among the lees. After some time, Liu Ling managed to lift his head, and said to his wife, "Only a little while ago you said you would let me drink as much as I liked, but you just seem to want me to sit here doing nothing."

•

Can't Cut / A man called a tailor to his house and told him to cut some cloth. But the tailor only stared at it in silence, and did not even try to cut it. The man asked him what was the matter, and the tailor made answer, "If I make my suit out of this cloth there won't be enough for you, and if I make yours there won't be sufficient left for me, so I don't know what to do."

•

Frailty, Thy Name Is Man / One day a group of henpecked husbands gathered together to discuss how they could remove the fear they felt of their wives, and regain their husbandly dignity. However, someone, to scare them off, came and told them that their wives had got wind of their discussion and were about to march in on them. The frightened husbands scattered in all directions, but one man still remained there. The messenger, wishing to know who it was that had no fear of his wife, looked at him closely, and found that he had been scared to death.

•

Heads I Win, Tails You Lose / A certain man thought himself good at chess. One day he played three games with his opponent, and lost every game. Being asked by someone how many times he had played, he answered, "Three." "And what happened?" "I didn't win the first game, and my opponent didn't lose the second. I wanted to draw the third game, but he didn't agree. That's all."

•

Burglaric Scorn / A thief broke into the house of a poor man. He groped about in every corner of the house but could find nothing whatever to steal. He spat in contempt, and was just going off, when the poor man, still lying in bed, called out, "Please shut the door after you!" The thief said, with a sneer, "Let me assure you there is no need to!"

•

One Fool Makes Two / A carpenter made a gate, and by mistake put the bar outside. The owner of the house abused him, "You blind fool, you!" The carpenter retorted, "It's you who are blind!" The owner, taken aback, asked how that could be. "If you were not blind, you wouldn't have employed a carpenter like me!"

•

The Gate / A certain man with a long bamboo pole was trying to enter the gate of a castle-town. He held it broadside and could not make his way in; he held it straight up and couldn't get it in. He was at his wits' end. Another man nearby said to him, "There's a very wise man called Li Sanlao about ten miles away from here. Why don't you go and ask his advice?" Sanlao happened to come riding along and everybody was pleased to see him. However, he was seen to be sitting on the hindquarters of the donkey, and the man asked him why he did not sit in the middle of the donkey's back, as is customary. The wise old chap replied, "The ears which I use as a bridle are too long to sit in the middle."

•

Joint Sowing / There were two brothers who used to sow and labour in the same field together. When the rice was ripe, they talked over the question of how to divide the results of their labour. The elder brother suggested, "I'll take the upper part, and you the lower." This seemed unfair to the younger brother, but the elder soothed him, saying, "It's all right; next year you may take the upper, and I will have the lower." The next year the younger brother urged the elder to begin sowing. The elder agreed, and said, "But this year let's sow potato seed."

•

Borrowing Tea / A man wanted to treat a visitor to a cup of tea, so he sent someone next door to borrow some. Before he came back the hot water had boiled, so he added some cold water. This happened several times until the huge kettle was full of water. Still the tea had not come. The wife said to the husband, "We know this friend of ours pretty well; how about treating him to a bath?"

•

Ice / A foolish son-in-law visited the native place of his wife, and his father-in-law treated him to a feast. There were some pieces of ice in one of the dishes, and these tasted so delicious to him he wrapped one in a piece of paper when nobody was looking and slipped it into his pocket. When he got back home he told his wife that he had brought with him some specially nice thing for her to taste too. When he searched his pocket he found it had disappeared. Surprised, he cried out, "Good heavens, it pissed and ran away!"

•

A Long Face / A certain man had the saddle of his horse stolen. He saw someone with a long face, sunken in the middle, and recognising it as his saddle, seized it. The man said, "This is my face, don't make a fool of me!" But the other persisted and was taking him to court when a passerby stopped and asked what was happening. Hearing the reason he looked at the long-faced man carefully and then said, "I advise you to give him the money. In court, the case will go against you."

•

Wellside / A woman went to the court and sued a man. She said, "I went to the well to draw water, and this man came from behind and raped me." The judge asked, "Then why didn't you run away?" "I was afraid that if I stood up and went away it wouldn't be finished."

•

Shooting a Tiger / A man was seized and carried off by a tiger. His son ran after it and was going to shoot it when from the mouth of the tiger the father shouted, "Aim at the feet! Don't injure the fur!"

A Birthmark on a Certain Place / A physiognomist said, "If a woman has a mole on a certain place, she will give birth to a noble child." Hearing this a man was very glad and said, "If that is so, my sister-in-law will have a fine son." "How do you know your sister-in-law has that mark?" "My father told my wife, and she told me."

•

Not Feasting a Visitor / A visitor came from a distant place and stayed at a certain man's house. The yard was full of cocks and hens, but he said he had nothing to feast his guest with. The visitor took his sword and was going to kill his own horse for dinner. The man said, "But how can you go back, without a horse?" The visitor answered, "I was going to borrow one of your cocks and ride back on it."

•

Obstinacy / A father and son were both stubborn and unbending. One day the father had a visitor and sat drinking with him while his son went to the town to buy some meat. The son had bought the meat and was on his way back when he met a man as he was going out of one of the town gates. They would neither give way to the other and stood there a long time. At last the father came to see what was happening and said to the son, "You take the meat back and eat it. I will stand here for you."

•

A Shortsighted Man / There was a banquet in a certain house and two men were sitting there in the principal seat. One had no left eye, the other no right eye. A shortsighted man came into the chamber and looked around at the guests. He whispered to the man next to him, "Who is that broad-faced man in the chief seat?"

•

Inserting the Medicine / A certain woman had something wrong with her internally, and went to the doctor with her husband. Seeing that he was a fool, the doctor said, "I must put the medicine in personally." The husband stood looking down at them for some time, and then said, "If the medicine were not on it, I would be very jealous."

•

Never Inviting Guests / A certain miserly old chap had something that he wanted prayed for, so he called in a mountain priest and asked him to pray to some god. The priest prayed to some very far-off deity. The man asked why he chose such a distant god. "Those around here know you are stingy, and even if they are invited they won't come."

•

The Fartress / A maidservant happened to fart in front of her master, and he became angry, and was going to strike her, but, seeing her white hips, his anger suddenly abated, and he took his pleasure with her. The next day, when he was in his study, there was a knock at the door. It was the maid-servant. "What is it? What do you want?" "Please, sir, I farted again a little while ago."

•

Slow to Anger Others / A certain man was very slow in everything. One winter day he was sitting by the fire with some other people when he noticed that one of the men's skirts was burning. He said to him, "There is something I want to tell you, but I'm afraid; you get angry so quickly. But if I don't tell you, you will be angry; what shall I do, tell you or not?" The other said, "What on earth are you talking about?"

So he answered, "Your clothes are burning." The other patted his clothes hurriedly and exclaimed, with anger, "Why didn't you tell me before?" The man said, "I told you would be angry, and so you are."

•

Escorting a Priest / An official was taking to the court a priest who had committed some crime or other. This priest was a very clever man, and on the way he made the official drunk, shaved his head with his sword, bound him with the rope round himself, and ran off. Early the next morning the official woke up and looked for the priest, but he was nowhere to be seen. When he stroked his own head he found it was shaven, and the rope was round his neck. "Here is the priest," he said, "but where am I?"

•

Globe Fish / A married pair bought a swell-fish when it was the season. Talking it over, as it might be very poisonous, they kept pressing each other to eat it. At length the wife took up her chopsticks and said, with tears in her eyes, "Please look after the two children, and when they are of age, don't neglect to tell them on no account to eat globe fish."

•

The Doctor-Undertaker / A certain doctor had killed somebody's child and promised to take it home in his sleeve and bury it. So, to see that he should carry out his promise, the people of the house had the servant follow him. When he got to the middle of a bridge he took out the dead body of a child from his sleeve and threw it into the river. The servant was infuriated and said, "Why did you throw our child into the water?" "No, no!" cried the doctor, lifting up the other sleeve. "The child of your house is here all right."

•

Please Kick Me! / A wood-cutter, while carrying firewood, knocked against a doctor and begged his pardon. But the doctor was angry and clenched his fist to strike him. The woodcutter fell on his knees, and said, "I implore you to use your foot on me." A passerby commented, "Yes, indeed, if the doctor used his hands, it would be all over with him."

PROVERBS

Deal with the faults of others as gently as with your own.

A red-nosed man may be a teetotaler, but no one will think so.

With money you can move the gods; without it, you can't move a man.

More trees are upright than men.

Long visits bring short compliments.

Medicine cures the man who is fated not to die.

No image-maker worships the gods; he knows what they are made of.

We love our own compositions, but other men's wives.

The faults which a man condemns when out of office, he commits when in.

Everyone gives a shove to the tumbling wall.

A pretty woman entering a family has the ugly ones for her foes.

The Art of Swimming / A certain doctor had killed so many patients, their relatives rose up in arms and captured him, but he escaped during the night, dived into the river, and made his getaway. Reaching home he found his son reading *Mochue,* a book of medicine. He said hastily to him, "Don't be in such a hurry to study that book; what you need to do first is to learn to swim."

•

The Wrong Person Died / The mother of the wife of a certain man died, and he asked the master of a temple school to write a funeral address for him. The master looked up some old writings and copied out by mistake that for a wife and gave it to him. The man thought there was something wrong about it, and when he asked him, the other said, "This writing is printed in a book and there can be no mistake. Perhaps the person who died made a mistake, but that is not my responsibility."

•

Just a Joke / A man was married to a virago, and she died. In front of her coffin was hung a picture of her, which confronting, the widower clenched his fist and shook it at her. A gust of wind at that moment blowing, the picture moved a little, and the man, hurriedly unclenching his fist, quavered, "I was only joking!"

•

Relations / While an official was hearing a judgment somebody farted. "What's that sound? Arrest it and bring it here!" The lower official said, "Your Honor, it's something that can't be arrested." "What do you mean by saying a thing like that? Go and get it!" The lower official put some excreta in a paper and came with it. "The actual criminal got away, but here is his relation."

•

Helped by the Target / A warrior was almost defeated in the battle, when reinforcements suddenly appeared in the shape of a soldier spirit, and he gained a great victory. Bowing deeply, he asked what the god's name might be. "My name is Target." "When did I earn the favor of the target god?" "All your life you never once struck me with an arrow, and thus my gratitude is equally boundless."

•

Rice Bran / A poor man had a meal of bran and then went out for a walk. He met a rich friend on the way who invited him to a riverside teahouse. "This morning I had a good meal of dog-meat, and so I feel quite full, but I don't mind accepting a cup of wine," he said, and they went in. Unfortunately, when he had drunk the wine he vomited and brought up the bran. The other man was surprised. "You say you ate dog-meat; how is it that bran came out?" After staring at it for some time, he said, "I ate the dog-meat; but the dog must have eaten the bran."

•

Ill from Using Too Much Energy / A certain man drank too much and did it too much, and became ill. The doctor said, "The illness is due to your excesses. You must be continent from now on." His wife glared at the doctor, who hurriedly added, "I mean, about drinking." The man said, "I think the other does me more harm. That's what I must be careful about." His wife said, "How can you expect to get better if you don't listen to what the doctor says?"

Changing Horses / A man went out riding on a donkey, and happened to meet a man on a fine horse. He dismounted suddenly, bowed, and said, "Wouldn't you like to change your mount for mine?" The other said, "Why, are you a fool?" "No," said the man, "but I thought you might be."

•

Boasting of Wealth / A man was boasting of his possessions. "We have everything in our house." So saying, he bent two of his fingers, and continued, "The only things not in our house are the sun and moon." Just then a servant came up to him and said, "We have no firewood in the kitchen." The man crooked another finger, and said, "No sun, no moon, no firewood."

•

A Charm for Mosquitoes / People in ancient times believed it possible to keep away mosquitoes by means of a talisman. A man paid some money for a charm and brought it home. He stuck it on the wall, but the mosquitoes seemed to become even more numerous than before, so he went to the charm-seller and complained about it. The charm-seller said, "There must be something wrong with your house, so I will go to your home and investigate the matter." They went to the house together, and the charm-seller said, "No wonder you can't keep away the mosquitoes! You have no mosquito net. And the charm must be hung *inside* the mosquito net."

•

A Hasty Person / A very irritable and hot-tempered master was going to punish his servant for making some mistake or other, but couldn't find the cane for a moment. He became every moment more furious, so the servant said, "Just give me a slap on account."

•

The Gunnybag / A man went out with some money to buy rice. He lost the bag, and when he got home he said to his wife, "The market was so crowded, someone lost his bag." His wife said, "How about you?" "I couldn't help losing mine," he replied. His wife was upset and asked, "How about the money?" "Oh, that's all right. I tied it safely in the neck of the bag."

•

Goldfish Wine / A guest was given some very well-watered wine. After swallowing a cup he praised the cook highly. The host said, "You haven't eaten anything yet; how can you tell he's a good cook?" "It's not necessary to taste the rest of the food to know that, he knows how to flavour the hot water so delicately."

•

A Great Tub / A very boastful fellow once bragged, "In my province, at a certain temple there is a tub so big that a thousand people can all bathe in it together." Another man who heard what he said retorted,"That's nothing much! In my province we have something far more wonderful that would really astonish you!" When asked what it was, he replied, "In a certain temple there's a grove of bamboos. In less than three years the bamboo grows to a height of several hundred thousand feet. But it doesn't get in the way of it; it grows down again from the sky. Doesn't that surprise you?" The people listening didn't seem to believe the story he had told, so he added, "If there were no such tall bamboos, what would they use to bind the tub round with?"

Sawing Off a Cup / A certain man attended a party, held by a man who poured out only half a cup of wine each time. At last he said to the host, "Would you mind lending me a saw, if you have one?" The host asked him what he wanted with a saw. "There's no wine in the upper part of the cup, so it's better to cut off the top half and not leave it in its emptiness."

•

Next to Famous / There was once an old woman named Wang who was not only rich but vainglorious, and asked a Taoist scholar to write a valedictory poem to be put on her coffin. She paid him a lot to compose a fine one, so as to show it to the people of the village. The Taoist thought and thought, but could find nothing to praise about her, so he wrote: "The old woman Wang, who lives next door to the Director of the Imperial Bureau, Royal Tutor, and Censor of National Documents."

•

Once More / Disregarding decency, a countryman excreted in front of a Confucian temple. The principal was very indignant, and taking him to the provincial court, asked that he be punished. The magistrate asked, "Why did you insult the Sages?" "When I come to the city I always pass by the temple and suddenly I wanted to evacuate my bowels and I did so; I had no intention of insulting the Sages." "Well, do you want to be prosecuted, or will you pay a fine?" "I would rather pay a fine." "As a punishment for your outrage you must pay one tael of gold which must be weighed in this place." The countryman brought two taels of gold and said, "Please divide this into halves."' The magistrate said, "Bring it here." As it was gold, his expression softened, and he put it in his sleeve, saying, "This should not be divided. You are forgiven. Tomorrow morning go and excrete once more in front of the temple."

•

A Lovely Fist / A certain man went to Pekin, and when he came back he praised everything in Pekin. One day he was walking in the moonlight with his father, and met someone who said, "A fine moon tonight!" He answered, "What's good about this moon? You should see the moon in Pekin! It's far, far better." His father was angry and said, "The moon is the same everywhere. There's nothing specially good about the moon in Pekin!" and clenching his fist he gave him a box on the ears. In a lachrymose voice the son replied, "Your fist is nothing wonderful. You should feel the fists in Pekin!"

•

The Entrance Greeting / When a certain teacher set up his school, a pupil offered fifty shillings as an entrance fee, writing on his card, "I respectfully offer these fifty shillings, together with a hundred bows." The teacher returned the card, having written on it, "Make it a hundred shillings and fifty bows!"

•

Portrait Painting / A certain man who painted protraits never had a commission, so someone recommended him to make a portrait of himself and his wife and hang it up as an advertisement, and he did so. One day his father-in-law came, and said, looking at the portrait, "Who is that woman?" "It's your daughter." "Then why is she with that strange man?"

A Cloud Near the Sun / A near-sighted man was at a banquet, and opposite him sat a man with a bushy beard, eating a ripe persimmon. He stood up suddenly and said, "My house is rather far from here. I'm afraid I must be saying good-bye." The host said, "But the sun is still shining!" "Yes," said the guest, "but it's going to rain soon. Look at that dark cloud near the sun!"

•

A Side-Dish / Two sons asked their father what the side-dish would be for dinner. He answered, "We are told that the ancients quenched their thirst by gazing at a blossoming plum tree. Just have a look at the salted salmon hanging on the wall while eating a morsel. That will be the side-dish." The two sons did as they were told, but the younger one said suddenly, "Elder brother looked too long!" The father said, "That would make it too salty."

•

An Older and a Sadder Man / A merchant once invited a singing-girl and, asking her age, was told eighteen. Several years later, after suffering many losses, he went to the same girl, who did not remember him, and when he asked her age, she answered, "Seventeen." Again after several years he saw the same girl, and this time she said she was sixteen. The merchant burst into tears, and on her asking him the reason, he replied, "Your age is like my capital, getting gradually less and less. When I think of that, how can I not be sad?"

ANECDOTES

translated by Herbert A. Giles, Lin Yutang, and others

Bad Government / T'an Kung (4th cen. B.C.) / When Confucius was crossing the T'ai mountain, he overheard a woman weeping and wailing beside a grave. He thereupon sent one of his disciples to ask what was the matter. The latter addressed the woman, saying, "Some great sorrow must have come upon you that you give way to grief like this."

"Indeed it is so," she replied. "My father-in-law was killed here by a tiger; after that, my husband; and now my son has perished by the same death."

"But why, then," asked Confucius, "do you not go away?"

"The government is not harsh," answered the woman.

"There!" cried the Master, turning to his disciples, "remember that. Bad government is worse than a tiger."

•

The Elixir of Death / Anon. (3rd cen. B.C.) / A certain person having forwarded an elixir of immortality to the Prince of Ching, it was received as usual by the door-keeper. "Is this to be swallowed?" asked the chief warden of the palace.

"It is," replied the door-keeper. Thereupon, the chief warden took it and swallowed it.

At this, the prince was exceedingly wroth and ordered his immediate execution. But the chief warden sent a friend to plead for him, saying, "Your Highness's servant asked the door-keeper if the drug was to be swallowed; and as he replied in the affirmative, your servant accordingly swallowed it. The blame rests entirely with the doorkeeper. Besides, if the elixir of life is presented to your Highness, and because your servant swallows it, your Highness slays him, that elixir is clearly the elixir of death; and for your Highness thus to put to death an innocent official is simply for your Highness to be made the sport of men."

The prince spared his life.

•

Pragmatist / Mo-tzu (5th cen. B.C.) / Once, Confucius was in straits between Ts'ai and Ch'en, having only vegetable soup without even rice to eat. After ten days of this, Tse Lu cooked a pig for him. Confucius did not inquire whence the meat came, and ate. Tse Lu robbed someone of his garment and exchanged it for wine. Confucius did not inquire whence the wine came, and drank. But when Lord Ai received Confucius, Confucius would not sit on a mat that was not placed straight and would not eat meat that was not cut properly. Tse Lu went to him and asked: "Why the reverse to what you did on the borders of Ch'en and Ts'ai?" Confucius answered: "Come, let me tell you. Then, our goal was to keep alive. Now our goal is to behave righteously." When hunger-stricken he was not scrupulous about the means of keeping alive, and when satiated he acted hypocritically to appear refined. What foolery, perversion, villainy, and pretension can be greater than this!

•

Rationalizing / Lieh-tzu (3rd cen. B.C.) / There was a man who had lost money and thought that his neighbor's son had stolen it. He looked at him and it seemed that his gait was that of a thief, his expression was that of a thief, and all his gestures and movements were like those of a thief. Soon afterwards he found the money in a bamboo drain pipe. Again he looked at the neighbor's son and neither his movements nor gestures were those of a thief.

•

The Death of Chuang tzu's Wife / Chuang-tzu (4th cen.B.C.) / When Chuang Tzu's wife died, Hui Tzu went to condole. He found the widower sitting on the ground, singing, with his legs spread out at a right angle, and beating time on a bowl.

"To live with your wife," exclaimed Hui Tzu, "and see your eldest son grow to be a man, and then not to shed a tear over her corpse—this would be bad enough. But to drum on a bowl and sing; surely this is going too far."

"Not at all," replied Chuang Tzu. "When she died, I could not help being affected by her death. Soon, however, I remembered that she had already existed in a previous state before birth, without form, or even substance; that while in that unconditioned condition, substance was added to spirit; that this substance then assumed form; and that the next stage was birth. And now, by virtue of further change, she is dead, passing from one phase to another like the sequence of spring, summer, autumn, and winter. And while she is thus lying asleep in Eternity, for me to go about weeping and wailing would be to proclaim myself ignorant of these natural laws. Therefore I refrain."

•

Inference / Chuang-tzu / Chuang Tzu and Hui Tzu had strolled on to the bridge over the Hao, when the former observed, "See how the minnows are darting about! That is the pleasure of fishes."

"You not being yourself a fish," said Hui Tzu, "how can you possibly know in what the pleasure of fishes consists?"

"And you not being I," retorted Chuang Tzu, "how can you know that I do not know?"

"That I, not being you, do not know what you know," replied Hui Tzu, "is identical with my argument that you, not being a fish, cannot know in what the pleasure of fishes consists."

"Let us go back to the original question," said Chuang Tzu. "You ask me how I know in what consists the pleasure of fishes. Your very question shows that you knew I knew. I knew it from my own feelings on this bridge."

•

Independence / Chuang-tzu / Chuang Tzu was one day fishing, when the Prince of Ch'u sent two high officials to interview him, saying that his Highness would be glad of Chuang Tzu's assistance in the administration of his government. The latter quietly fished on, and without looking around replied, "I have heard that in the state of Chu there is a sacred tortoise, which has been dead three thousand years, and which the prince keeps packed up in a box on the altar in his ancestral shrine. Now do you think that tortoise would rather be dead and have its remains thus honored, or be alive and wagging its tail in the mud?"

The two officials answered that no doubt it would rather be alive and wagging its tail in the mud; whereupon Chuang Tzu cried out, "Begone! I too elect to remain wagging my tail in the mud."

•

The Old Man Who Lost a Horse / Lieh-tzu / An old man was living with his son at an abandoned fort on the top of a hill, and one day he lost a horse. The neighbors came to express their sympathy for this misfortune, and the old man asked, "How do you know this is bad luck?" A few days afterward, his horse returned with a number of wild horses, and his neighbors came again to congratulate him on this stroke of fortune, and the old man replied, "How do you know this is good luck?" With so many horses around, his son began to take to riding, and one day he broke his leg. Again the neighbors came around to express their sympathy, and the old man replied, "How do you know this is bad luck?" The next year, there was a war, and because the old man's son was crippled, he did not have to go to the front.

•

Burying Alive / T'an Kung / When Tzu-chu died, his wife and secretary took counsel together as to who should be interred with him. All was settled before the arrival of his brother, Tzu-k'ang; and then they informed him, saying, "The deceased requires someone to attend upon him in the nether world. We must ask you to go with his body into the grave."

"Burial of the living with the dead," replied Tzu-k'ang, "is not in accordance with established rites. Still, as you say someone is wanted to attend upon the deceased, who better fitted than his wife and secretary? If this contingency can be avoided altogether, I am willing; if not, then the duty will fall upon you two."

From that time forth the custom fell into desuetude.

•

Separation of Sexes / Meng-tzu (3rd cen. B.C.) / A philosopher asked Mencius, "That men and women, in giving and receiving, shall not touch hands—is such the rule of propriety?"

"It is," replied Mencius.

"But supposing," said the philosopher, "that a sister-in-law was drowning, should a man not give her his hand and pull her out?"

"A man," answered Mencius, "who could see his sister-in-law drown and not give her his hand, would be a wolfish brute. That men and women, in giving and receiving, do not touch hands, is a rule of propriety. But when a sister-in-law is drowning, to give her a hand and pull her out comes under the head of exceptions to the rule."

"Just now," retorted the philosopher, "the empire is drowning. Why do you not pull it out?"

"The drowning empire," replied Mencius, "must be saved by the eternal principles of Right; a drowning sister-in-law by the hand. Would you have me save the empire by my hand?"

Logic / Han-fei-tzu (d. 233 B.C.) / King Huan of Ch'i was drunk one day and lost his hat. For three days he shut himself up for shame, without giving an audience. Kuan Chung said to the king, "This is a disgrace for a ruler. Why don't you make amends by some generous act?" Accordingly, the king opened the granary and distributed grain to the poor for three days. The people praised the king for his generosity and said, "Why does not he lose his hat again?"

•

The Traveler / Liu Hsiang / An owl met a quail, and the quail asked, "Where are you going?" "I am going east," was the owl's reply. "May I ask why?" the quail asked. "The people of this village hate my screeching noise," replied the owl. "That is why I am going east." Then said the quail, "What you should do is to change that screeching noise. If you can't, you will be hated for it even if you go east."

•

A Sound Critic / Su Tung-p'o (1036–1101) / In Ssuch'uan there lived a retired scholar, named Tu. He was very fond of calligraphy and painting and possessed a large and valuable collection. Among the rest was a painting of oxen by Tai Sung, which he regarded as exceptionally precious and kept in an embroidered case on a jade-mounted roller. One day he put his treasures out to sun, and it chanced that a herdboy saw them. Clapping his hands and laughing loudly, the herdboy shouted out, "Look at the bulls fighting! Bulls trust to their horns, and keep their tails between their legs. But here they are fighting with their tails cocked up in the air. That's wrong!" Mr. Tu smiled and admitted the justice of the criticism. So truly does the old saying run: For ploughing, go to a ploughman; for weaving, to a servant-maid.

•

Outsides / Liu Chi (1311–75) / At Hangchow there lived a costermonger who understood how to keep oranges a whole year without letting them spoil. His fruit was always fresh-looking, firm as jade, and of a beautiful golden hue; but inside—dry as an old cocoon.

One day I asked him, saying, "Are your oranges for altar or sacrificial purposes, or for show at banquets? Or do you make this outside display merely to cheat the foolish, as cheat them, you most outrageously do?" "Sir," replied the orangeman, "I have carried on this trade now for many years. It is my source of livelihood. I sell: the world buys. And I have yet to learn that you are the only honest man about and that I am the only cheat. Perhaps it never struck you in this light. The baton-bearers of today, seated on their tiger skins, pose as the martial guardians of the state; but what are they compared with the captains of old? The broad-brimmed, long-robed ministers of today pose as pillars of the constitution; but have they the wisdom of our ancient counsellors? Evil doers arise and none can subdue them. The people are in misery, and none can relieve them. Clerks are corrupt, and none can restrain them. Laws decay, and none can renew them. Our officials eat the bread of the state and know no shame. They sit in lofty halls, ride fine steeds, drink themselves drunk with wine, and fatten on the richest fare. Which of them but puts on an awe-inspired look, a dignified mien?—all gold and gems without, but dry cocoons within. You pay, sir, no heed to these things, while you are very particular about my oranges."

I had no answer to make. I retired to ponder over this costermonger's wit, which reminded me forcibly of "The Wag." Was he really out of conceit with the age, or only quizzing me in defense of his fruit?

•

The Dream / Hsueh Tao / There was once a proctor who was very strict with his students. One day, a student committed a breach of discipline. Pulling a long face, the proctor sent for the offender, and sat himself in a chair to await his arrival. The student finally appeared, and, kneeling before the proctor, said, "I meant to come earlier. But the fact is I have just found a thousand ounces of gold and I've had a hard time deciding how to dispose of it."

The proctor melted a little when he heard about the gold. "Where did you find it?" he asked.

"Buried under the ground!"

"And what are you going to do with it?" asked the proctor again.

"I was a poor man, sir," answered the student. "I have talked it over with my wife and we agreed to put aside 500 ounces to buy land, 200 for a house, 100 to buy furniture, and another 100 to buy maidservants and pages. Then we'll use one-half of the last 100 to buy books, for from now on I must study hard, and the other half I will make as a small present to you for the pains you took in educating me."

"Ah! Is that so! I don't think I have done enough to deserve so precious a gift," said the proctor.

So saying, he ordered his cook to prepare a sumptuous dinner to which he invited the student. They had a happy time, talking and laughing and toasting each other's health. Just as they were getting tipsy, the proctor had a sudden thought.

"You came away in a hurry," he said. "Did you remember to lock the gold away in a cabinet before you came?"

The student rose to his feet. "Sir, I had just finished planning how to use the money when my wife rolled against me, and I opened my eyes to find the gold was gone. So what's the use of the cabinet?"

"So all this you've been talking about is only a dream?"

"Indeed, yes," answered the student.

The proctor was angry, but since he had been so hospitable to the student, it would have seemed churlish to lose his temper with him now, so he contented himself with saying, "I can see you keep me in mind even when you are dreaming. Surely you won't forget me when you really have the gold?"

And he urged him to more drinks before he let him go.

•

Catching Snakes / Liu Tsung-yuan (773–819) / In the wilds of Hu-kuang there is an extraordinary kind of snake, having a black body with white rings. Deadly fatal even to the grass and trees it may chance to touch, in man its bite is absolutely incurable. Yet if caught and prepared, when dry, in the form of cakes, the flesh of this snake will soothe excitement, heal leprous sores, remove sloughing flesh, and expel evil spirits. And so it came about that the Court physician, acting under Imperial orders, exacted from each family a return of two of these snakes every year; but as few persons were able to comply with the demand, it was subsequently made known that the return of snakes was to be considered in lieu of the usual taxes. Thereupon there ensued a general stampede among the people of those parts.

However, there was one man whose family had lived there for three generations; and from him I obtained the following information:—"My grandfather lost his life in snake-catching. So did my father. And during the twelve years that I have been engaged in the same way, death has several times come very near to me." He was deeply moved during this recital; but when I asked him if I should state his sad case to the authorities and apply for him to be allowed to pay taxes in the regular manner, he burst into tears and said, "Alas! sir, you would take away my means of livelihood altogether. The misery of this state is as nothing when compared with the misery of that. Formerly, under the ordinary conditions of life, we suffered greatly; but for the past three generations we have been settled in this district, now some sixty years since. During that period, my fellow-villagers have become more and more impoverished. Their substance has been devoured, and in beggary they have gone weeping and wailing away. Exposed to the inclemency of wind and rain, enduring heat and cold, they have fled from the cruel scourge, in most cases to die. Of those families which were here in my grandfather's time, there remains not more than one in ten; of those here in my father's time, not more than two or three; and of those still here in my own time, not more than four or five. They are all either dead or gone elsewhere; while we, the snake-catchers, alone survive. Harsh tyrants sweep down upon us, and throw everybody and everything, even to the brute beasts, into paroxysms of terror and disorder. But I—I get up in the morning and look into the jar where my snakes are kept; and if they are still there, I lie down at night in peace. At the appointed time, I take care that they are fit to be handed in; and when that is done, I retire to enjoy the produce of my farm and complete the allotted span of my existence. Only twice a year have I to risk my life: the rest is peaceful enough and not to be compared with the daily round of annoyance which falls to the share of my fellow villagers. And even though I were to die now in this employ, I should still have outlived almost all my contemporaries. Can I then complain?"

This story gave me food for much sad reflection. I had always doubted the saying of Confucius that "bad government is worse than a tiger," but now I felt its truth. Alas! Who would think that the tax-collector could be more venomous than a snake? I therefore record this for the information of those whom it may concern.

•

Sour Grapes / Ho Yi (b. 1914) / Many, many years ago, a wise slave whose name was Aesop told a story about a fox. The fox saw a grapevine in a certain place. Bunches of purple grapes hung on the vine. He wanted to eat some; but the grapes were not within his reach, because the vine was supported by a tall trellis. For a long time he tried in vain to reach the grapes. Unable to find a way to get a single grape he spat at them and said to himself: "These grapes are sour!" and walked away dejectedly. When he got home supper was already over. He had to go hungry that night. Aesop's story stops here.

What I'm going to tell you is about that same fox. To my knowledge, Aesop did not finish the story. If you want to know what happened, sit down and keep quiet. I'll tell you.

The fox lay awake on his bed, his belly clamouring for food. The more he thought about those grapes, the more annoyed and impatient he became. The next day, while the sun was still sleeping, he jumped out of his bed and rushed to the grapevine. A jackdaw was sitting on the vine, pecking away at the grapes. Envy burned in the fox's heart at this sight. He cried indignantly: "Fie upon you, you thief! How could you steal these grapes? Be off, you!"

The jackdaw was startled. He stopped eating his breakfast and looked down. The fierce look of the fox frightened him. He dared not answer back. So he spread his wings and flew away, chattering as he went.

The fox waited until the bird was gone. Then with a great effort he jumped, holding his front legs high up and fixing his eyes on the beautiful purple grapes. Saliva dribbled from his mouth. He longed to be able to reach that trellis, sit down at ease, and eat his fill, but he could not do it. There was a distance of about one foot between his front paws and the grapes, no matter how high he jumped or how much he stretched his legs. He was very hot and his hind legs were aching. He had no choice but to sit on the ground and rest.

A big monkey passed by. She saw the grapes and said to the fox with a smile: "You fool, why do you sit there so quietly and not try to eat some grapes? These are very good grapes indeed."

The fox answered: "I've already had some. They are sour, so sour that they set my teeth on edge!"

The monkey laughed: "Nonsense! How can such beautiful purple grapes be sour? Watch me eat them!" So saying, she climbed nimbly up the trellis, sat on it, picked the grapes and ate them. She chose a few green ones, threw them to the fox, and said: "Taste these."

The fox was angry, but he could do nothing. His mouth watered and he begged the monkey: "Please pick some purple ones for me."

The monkey sat on the trellis and continued her meal, paying no attention to the fox. Her appetite was so good that soon she had finished all the grapes. Then she slipped down and ran away.

The fox was furious. When the monkey was out of hearing he shouted loudly: "Wretch! Are you the only one privileged to enjoy these grapes? I'll see to it that you shan't enjoy them again!"

He got up and fetched a spade, intending to destroy the grapevine by breaking down the trellis, so that no one would be able to have grapes. But the posts were deeply rooted in the ground. After a long time he succeeded in digging up only one of them. The trellis did not collapse. He was still more angry, because all his labor had been of no use. So he dug around the vine instead. When he found the root, he hacked at it until it was broken. Then he heaved a sigh of relief, feeling as if he had avenged some wrong done to him, and said to himself:

"All right, let's see if they can eat grapes again!"

He went back, carrying the spade on his shoulder. When he reached home, supper was again over. He was hungry, so hungry that his head swam. He had not succeeded in eating a single grape nor had he had any food since early morning. But, strange to say, he felt contented, as contented as when he had had a good meal.

This selfish fox is still alive. I often meet him in the streets.

POETRY

It is in poetry that the most mature and sophisticated Chinese satire appears. Every gradation from Horatian elegance to Juvenalian denunciation can be found in the poems: ancient officials and modern ones are berated; social hypocrisy is slyly mocked; the barbarousness of war is exposed, sometimes with restraint and irony, sometimes with devastating bitterness. The political satire seems as applicable today as in the ninth century, and the image of human nature is as unsentimental as if the ancient Chinese poets had read Freud.

There are more poems here by Po Chü-i than anyone else because he not only wrote great poetry but considered it his mission to improve the world. Some of that reform he tried to achieve by positive suggestions, but often, instead, he resorted to attacks—varying in directness—on war, government, the wealthy, the exploiters of the poor, and hypocrites of all kinds.

Modern Communist satire is represented here primarily in the poems of Yuan Shui-p'ai.

A MALE LIGHT-OF-LOVE

Confucian ode / Herbert A. Giles

Away I must run;
There is work to be done,
Though I'm thinking today
Of the eldest Miss K.
In the mulberry-grove
I shall pour out my love;
For she's promised to meet me
And as lover to greet me—
The eldest Miss K.

Away I must run;
There is work to be done.
But today I shall be
With the eldest Miss E.
In the mulberry-grove
I shall pour out my love;

For she's promised to meet me
And as lover to greet me—
    The eldest Miss E.

Away I must run;
There is work to be done.
But today I shall sigh
For the eldest Miss Y.
In the mulberry-grove
I shall pour out my love;
For she's promised to meet me
And as lover to greet me—
    The eldest Miss Y.

AT BEST A CONTRADICTION

Confucian ode / Herbert A. Giles

A clever man will build a town,
A clever woman pull it down.
Though woman's wit is sometimes heard,
She's really an ill-omened bird;
Her long tongue's like a flight of stairs
Which leads to miserable cares.
It is not God who marks our lives,
The fault is rather with our wives.
Of all we cannot teach or train,
Women and eunuchs are our bane.

DESPERATE

Confucian ode / Herbert A. Giles

The ripe plums are falling,—
    One-third of them gone;
To my lovers I'm calling,
    " 'Tis time to come on! "

The ripe plums are dropping,—
    Two-thirds are away;
" 'Tis time to be popping!"
    To my lovers I say.

Down has dropt every plum;
    In baskets they lie.

What, will no lover come?
"Now or never!" say I.

TO A MAN

Confucian ode / Herbert A. Giles

You seemed a guileless youth enough,
Offering for silk your woven stuff;[1]
But silk was not required by you:
I was the silk you had in view.

ON COMES HER CHARIOT

(Satirizing the open shamelessness of a queen)

Anon. (pre-250 B.C.) / James Legge

On comes her chariot, fast and loud,
With screen of bamboos finely wove,
And leather bright, vermilion-hued;—
Ts'e's daughter hastes to lawless love.
To this from Loo the road is smooth and plain;
'Twas but last night she started with her train.

Her four black steeds are beautiful;
Soft are the reins the driver holds.
The road from Loo is smooth and plain;—
Ts'e's daughter's heart its joy unfolds.
Full of complacency is she; nor shame
Abashes her, nor fear of evil name.

Broad flow the waters of the Wan,
And crowds of travellers go by.
The road from Loo is smooth and plain;—
She looks around with careless eye.
That many see her gives her no concern;
Her thoughts to her licentious fancy turn.

On sweep the waters of the Wan;
More numerous are the travellers now.
The road from Loo is smooth and plain;—
Ts'e's daughter shows her brazen brow.

1. Pieces of stamped linen, used as a circulating medium before the introduction of the bank-note.

At ease and proud, she holds her onward way,
Careless of what all think of her display.

THE WOODMAN'S SONG

Anon. (Pre-250 B.C.) / James Legge

K'an-k'an upon the sandal trees
The woodman's strokes resound.
Then on the bank he lays the trunks
His axe brings to the ground;
The while the stream goes rippling by,
Its waters cool and clear.
You sow no seed; no harvest tasks
Your soft hands take in charge;
And yet each boasts three hundred farms,
And stores the produce large.
You never join the hunt's halloo,
Nor dare to share its toils;
Yet lo! Your wide courtyards are seen
Hung round with badgers' spoils.
That gentleman!
He does not eat the bread of idleness indeed!

K'an-k'an upon the sandal wood
The woodman's strokes resound,
Then by the river's side he lays
What fit for spokes is found;
The while the river onward flows,
Its waters clear and smooth.
You sow no seed; no harvest tasks
Your dainty fingers stain;
And yet each boasts three million sheaves;—
Whence gets he all that grain?
You never join the hunt's halloo,
Nor brave its ventures bold;
Yet lo! your wide courtyards display
Those boars of three years old.
That gentleman!
He does not eat the bread of idleness indeed!

K'an-k'an resound the woodman's strokes
Upon the sandal wood;
Then on the river's lip he lays
What for his wheels is good;

The while the river onward flows,
  Soft rippled by the wind.
You sow no seed; no harvest tasks
  Your soft hands undertake;
Yet grain each boasts, three hundred bins;—
  Who his that grain did make?
You never join the hunt's halloo;
  Your feeble courage fails;
Yet lo! your wide courtyards display
  Large strings of slaughtered quails.
That gentleman!
  He does not eat the bread of idleness indeed!

LARGE RATS

(The poet proposes to leave his country, Wei)

Anon. (Pre-250 B.C.) / James Legge

Large rats, large rats, let us entreat
That you our millet will not eat.
But the large rats we mean are you,
With whom three years we've had to do,
And all that time have never known
One look of kindness on us thrown.
We take our leave of Wei and you;
That happier land we long to view.
O happy land! O happy land!
There in our proper place we'll stand.

Large rats, large rats, let us entreat
You'll not devour our crops of wheat.
But the large rats we mean are you,
With whom three years we've had to do;
And all that time you never wrought
One kindly act to cheer our lot.
To you and Wei we bid farewell,
Soon in that happier State to dwell.
O happy State! O happy State!
There shall we learn to bless our fate.

Large rats, large rats, let us entreat
Our springing grain you will not eat.
But the large rats we mean are you,
With whom three years we've had to do.
From you there came not all that while

One word of comfort 'mid our toil.
We take our leave of you and Wei;
And to those happier coasts we flee.
O happy coasts, to you we wend!
There shall our groans and sorrows end.

THE NEW TOWER

(Satirizing the marriage of Duke Hsian and his queen, who had been contracted to marry his son)

Anon. / James Legge

The New Tower, fresh and bright, they show,
Where its vast volume rolls the Ho;—
For bride a palace rare.
To Wei she came, a mate to find;
She sought a husband young and kind,
But found this mis-shaped bear.

There stands the New Tower grand and high,
Where with still stream the Ho flows by;—
For bride a palace rare.
To Wei she came, a mate to find;
She sought a husband young and kind,
But found this mis-shaped bear.

As when the net for fish they set,
And lo a goose ensnared they get,
They stamp with sudden ire;
So might *she* stamp who came to wed
The genial son, and in his stead
Got but the humped-backed sire.

THE SMALL STARS[1]

Anon. (Pre-Confucian) / Robert Payne

The small stars are trembling,
Three or four in the east.
Reverently through the night we come.
In the early dawn we go from the prince's palace.

1. The poem describes the concubines of the prince who return to their quarters in the early morning. According to later practice, which may still have existed at the time of the Chou princes, the concubines were taken by eunuchs, wrapped in silks, through the courtyards, and then laid at the foot of the prince's bed, the silks being taken away from them. The complaint is against the wife of the prince, while the small stars are of course both the faint stars of dawn and the concubines themselves.

The small stars are trembling,
Orion and the Pleiades.
Reverently through the night we come
Covered in quilts and satins.
Our fates are not equal.

THE COCK CROWS

from "Book of Songs" (Pre-245 B.C.) / Robert Payne

The Lady: The cock has crowed.
The sun has risen.

The Lover: It is not yet cockcrow—
Only the buzzing of the bluebottles.

The Lady: The east is alight.
The sun is aflame.

The Lover: It is not the dawn—
Only the moon rising.

The Lady: The bluebottles must be drowsy.
It is sweet to lie by your side.

The Lover: Quick! Let me go from you.
Do not let me hate you.

THE FLOWERS OF THE BIGNONIA[1]

from "Book of Songs" / Robert Payne

The petals of the bignonia
Are deep yellow.
My heart is heavy.
Why should they wound me so?

The petals of the bignonia
Have deep green leaves.
If I had known what would come,
I would prefer not to have been born.

The ewes have swollen heads,
Three stars in the Fish trap—

1. A complaint against poverty disguised as a love song, and probably imitating some well-known love song of the time.

Though some men find food enough,
Few have enough to eat.

CHUNG TZU

Anon. (Pre-500 B.C.) / Robert Payne

I beg you, Chung Tzu,
Do not break into my house,
Do not force a way through the willows I planted.
It is not that I care for the willows,
Only I fear my father and mother.
I love you, Chung Tzu, dearly—
Oh, but I am afraid, really afraid
Of what my father and mother will say.

I beg you, Chung Tzu,
Do not leap through my wall,
Do not force a way through the mulberries I planted.
It is not that I care for the mulberries,
Only I fear my brothers.
I love you, Chung Tzu, dearly—
Oh, but I am afraid, really afraid
Of what my brothers will say.

I beg you, Chung Tzu,
Do not come through my garden,
Do not force a way through the sandalwood I have planted.
It is not that I care for the sandalwood,
I am afraid of people talking.
I love you, Chung Tzu, dearly,
Only I am afraid, really afraid
Of what they will say.

"AWAY WITH LEARNING!"

from "Tao Tes Ching" (4th. cen. B.C.?) / Robert Payne

Away with learning! Away with grieving!
Between *wei* and *o*
Where is the difference?
Between good and evil,
Where is the difference?
Must a man fear

What is feared by others?
Oh, pure idiocy!
All men are beaming with pleasure
As though feasting at the Great Sacrifice,
As though climbing the Spring Terrace:
I alone am silent, I have given no sign.
Like an infant who has not yet smiled,
Abandoned, like someone homeless.
All men have enough and to spare,
I alone seem to have nothing.
I am a man with the mind of an idiot,
A pure fool.
Everywhere men shine:
I alone am dark.
Everywhere men are gay:
I alone am disquieted.
Nervous as the sea,
Drifting, never ceasing.
Everywhere men have work.
I alone am stubborn, taking no part.
The chief difference lies in this:
I prize the breasts of the Mother.

THE ORPHAN

Anon. (1st cen. B.C.) / Arthur Waley

To be an orphan,
To be fated to be an orphan,
How bitter is this lot!
When my father and mother were alive
I used to ride in a carriage
With four fine horses.
But when they both died,
My brother and sister-in-law
Sent me out to be a merchant.
In the south I traveled to the "Nine Rivers"
And in the east as far as Ch'i and Lu.
At the end of the year when I came home
I dared not tell them what I had suffered—
Of the lice and vermin in my head,
Of the dust in my face and eyes.
My brother told me to get ready the dinner,
My sister-in-law told me to see after the horses.
I was always going up into the hall

And running down again to the parlour.
My tears fell like rain.
In the morning they sent me to draw water,
I didn't get back till night-fall.
My hands were all sore
And I had no shoes.
I walked the cold earth
Treading on thorns and brambles.
As I stopped to pull out the thorns,
How bitter my heart was!
My tears fell and fell
And I went on sobbing and sobbing.
In winter I have no great-coat;
Nor in summer, thin clothes.
It is no pleasure to be alive.
I had rather quickly leave the earth
And go beneath the Yellow Springs.[1]
The April winds blow
And the grass is growing green.
In the third month—silkworms and mulberries,
In the sixth month—the melon-harvest.
I went out with the melon-cart
And just as I was coming home
The melon-cart turned over.
The people who came to help me were few,
But the people who ate the melons were many,
All they left me was the stalks—
To take home as fast as I could.
My brother and sister-in-law were harsh,
They asked me all sorts of awful questions.
Why does everyone in the village hate me?
I want to write a letter and send it
To my mother and father under the earth,
And tell them I can't go on any longer
Living with my brother and sister-in-law.

THE DEW ON THE GARLIC-LEAF

(Sung at the burial of kings and princes)

Anon. (1st cen. B.C.?) / Arthur Waley

How swiftly it dries,
The dew on the garlic-leaf.

1. Hades.

The dew that dries so fast
Tomorrow will fall again.
But he whom we carry to the grave
Will never more return.

THE GRAVEYARD

(Sung at the burial of common men)

Anon. (1st cen. B.C.?) / Arthur Waley

What man's land is the graveyard?
It is the crowded home of ghosts—
Wise and foolish shoulder to shoulder.
The King of the Dead claims them all;
Man's fate knows no tarrying.

SATIRE ON PAYING CALLS IN AUGUST

Cheng Hsiao (ca. A.D. 250) / Arthur Waley

When I was young, throughout the hot season
There were no carriages driving about the roads,
People shut their doors and lay down in the cool:
Or if they went out, it was not to pay calls.
Nowadays—ill-bred, ignorant fellows,
When they feel the heat, make for a friend's house.
The unfortunate host, when he hears someone coming
Scowls and frowns, but can think of no escape.
"There's nothing for it but to rise and go to the door,"
And in his comfortable seat he groans and sighs.

The conversation does not end quickly:
Prattling and babbling, what a lot he says!
Only when one is almost dead with fatigue
He asks at last if one isn't finding him tiring.
(One's arm is almost in half with continual fanning:
The sweat is pouring down one's neck in streams.)
Do not say that this is a small matter:
I consider the practice a blot on our social life.
I therefore caution all wise men
That August visitors should not be admitted.

WOMAN

Fu Hsuan (d. 278) / Arthur Waley

How sad it is to be a woman!
Nothing on earth is held so cheap.
Boys stand leaning at the door
Like Gods fallen out of Heaven.
Their hearts brave the Four Oceans,
The wind and dust of a thousand miles.
No one is glad when a girl is born:
By *her* the family sets no store.
When she grows up, she hides in her room
Afraid to look a man in the face.
No one cries when she leaves her home—
Sudden as clouds when the rain stops.
She bows her head and composes her face,
Her teeth are pressed on her red lips:
She bows and kneels countless times.
She must humble herself even to the servants.
His love is distant as the stars in Heaven,
Yet the sunflower bends toward the sun.
Their hearts more sundered than water and fire—
A hundred evils are heaped upon her.
Her face will follow the years' changes:
Her lord will find new pleasures.
They that were once like substance and shadow
Are now as far as Hu from Ch'in.[1]
Yet Hu and Ch'in shall sooner meet
Than they whose parting is like Ts'an and Ch'en.[2]

DAY DREAMS

Tso Ssu (3rd cen.) / Arthur Waley

When I was young I played with a soft brush
And was passionately devoted to reading all sorts of books.
In prose I made Chia I my standard:
In verse I imitated Ssu-ma Hsiang-ju.
But then the arrows began singing at the frontier.
And a winged summons came flying to the City.
Although arms were not my profession,
I had once read Jang-chu's war-book.

1. Two lands. 2. Two stars.

I shouted aloud and my cries rent the air:
I felt as though Tung Wu were already annihilated.
The scholar's knife cuts best at its first use.
And my dreams hurried on to the completion of my plan.
I wanted at a stroke to clear the Yang-tze and Hsiang,
At a glance to quell the Tibetans and Hu.
When my task was done, I should not accept a barony,
But refusing with a bow, retire to a cottage in the country.

SIC TRANSIT

T'ao Ch'ien (365–427) / Herbert A. Giles

A tower a hundred feet erect
  Looks round upon the scene which girds;
'Tis here at eve the clouds collect,
  At dawn a trysting-place for birds.

Here hills and streams the observer hold,
  Or boundless prairie mocks the eyes:
Some famous warriors of old
  Made this their bloody battle-prize.

The centuries of time roll on,
  And I, a traveller, passing there,
Mark firs and cypresses all gone,
  And grave-mounds, high and low, laid bare.

The ruined tombs uncared-for stand—
  Where do their wandering spirits hide?—
Oh, glory makes us great and grand,
  And yet it has its seamy side.

BLAMING SONS

(An apology for his own drunkenness)

T'ao Ch'ien / Arthur Waley

White hair covers my temples,
I am wrinkled and seared beyond repair,
And though I have got five sons,
They all hate paper and brush.
A-shu is eighteen:
For laziness there is none like him.
A-hsüan does his best,

But really loathes the Fine Arts.
Yung-tuan is thirteen,
But does not know "six" from "seven."[1]
T'ung-tzu in his ninth year
Is only concerned with things to eat.
If Heaven treats me like this,
What can I do but fill my cup?

"A LONG TIME AGO"

T'ao Ch'ien / Arthur Waley

A long time ago
I went on a journey,
Right to the corner
Of the Eastern Ocean.
The road there
Was long and winding,
And stormy waves
Barred my path.
What made me
Go this way?
Hunger drove me
Into the World.
I tried hard
To fill my belly:
And even a little
Seemed a lot.
But this was clearly
A bad bargain,
So I went home
And lived in idleness.

FULL CIRCLE

Tao Yuan-ming (4th cen.) / R. H. Blyth

Long ago I heard the injunctions of my elders,
But stopped my ears, so disagreeable were they.
Now, after fifty years and more,
I suddenly find myself saying the very same thing.

1. Written in Chinese with two characters very easy to distinguish.

DRUNK AND SOBER

Tao Yuan-ming / Yang Yeh-tzu

A guest resides in me,
Our interests are not altogether the same.
One of us is drunk:
The other is always awake.
Awake and drunk—
We laugh at one another,
And we do not understand each other's world.
Proprieties and conventions—
Such folly to follow them in earnest.
Be proud, be unconcerned:
Then you will approach wisdom.
Listen, you drunken old man,
When day dies,
Light a candle.

PLUCKING THE RUSHES

(A boy and girl are sent to gather rushes for thatching)

Anon. (4th cen.) / Arthur Waley

Green rushes with red shoots,
Long leaves bending to the wind—
You and I in the same boat
Plucking rushes at the Five Lakes.
We started at dawn from the orchid-island:
We rested under the elms till noon.
You and I plucking rushes
Had not plucked a handful when night came!

BUSINESS MEN

Ch'en Tzu-ang (656–98) / Arthur Waley

Business men boast of their skill and cunning
But in philosophy they are like little children.
Bragging to each other of successful depredations
They neglect to consider the ultimate fate of the body.
What should they know of the Master of Dark Truth
Who saw the wide world in a jade cup,
By illumined conception got clear of Heaven and Earth:
On the chariot of Mutation entered the Gate of Immutability?

TO A KILLJOY

Wang Chi (584–644) / Herbert A. Giles

Indulgence in the flowing bowl
Impedes the culture of the soul;
And yet, when all around me swill,
Shall I alone be sober still?

TELL ME NOW

Wang Chi / Arthur Waley

"Tell me now, what should a man want
But to sit alone, sipping his cup of wine?"
I should like to have visitors come and discuss philosophy
And not to have the tax-collector coming to collect taxes:
My three sons married into good families
And my five daughters wedded to steady husbands.
Then I could jog through a happy five-score years
And, at the end, need no Paradise.

OUT OF OFFICE

Li Shih-chih (d. 747) / Herbert A. Giles

For my betters—my office resigned—I make way,
And seek with the wine-cup to shorten the day.
You ask for the friends who once thronged my hall:
Alas! with my place they have gone, one and all.

DRINKING ALONE UNDER MOONLIGHT

Li Po (701–62) / Tsang Bing-ching

Holding a jug of wine among the flowers,
And drinking alone, not a soul keeping me company,
I raise my cup and invite the moon to drink with me,
And together with my shadow we are three.
But the moon does not know the joy of drinking,
And my shadow only follows me about.
Nevertheless I shall have them as my companions,
For one should enjoy life at such a time.
The moon loiters as I sing my songs,
My shadow looks confused as I dance.

I drink with them when I am awake
And part with them when I am drunk.
Henceforward may we always be feasting,
And may we meet in the Cloudy River of Heaven.[1]

DRINKING ALONE IN MOONLIGHT

Li Po / Robert Payne

If Heaven had no love for wine,
There would be no Wine Star in Heaven;
If earth had no love for wine,
There would be no city called Wine Springs.
Since Heaven and Earth love wine
I can love wine without shaming Heaven.
They say that clear wine is a saint;
Thick wine follows the way of the sage.
I have drunk deep of saint and sage:
What need then to study the spirits and fairies?
With three cups I penetrate the Great Tao.
Take a whole jugful—I and the world are one.
Such things as I have dreamed in wine
Shall never be told to the sober.

AWAKING FROM DRUNKENNESS ON A SPRING DAY

Li Po / Robert Payne

Our life in the world is only a great dream.
Why should I toil my life away?
Let me be drunk all day,
Let me lie at the foot of the house gate.
When I wake up, I blink at the garden trees:
A lonely bird is singing amid the flowers.
I demand of the bird what season it is:
He answers: "The spring wind makes the mango bird sing."
Moved by his song, I sigh my heart away
And once more pour myself wine.
So I sing wildly till the bright moon shines.
The song over, all my senses are numb.

1. The Milky Way.

FIGHTING ON THE SOUTH FRONTIER

Li Po / Robert Payne

Last year we fought by the springs of San-kan River,
This year we fight on the Tsung-ho roads.
We have dipped our weapons in the waves of Chiao-chi Lake,
We have pastured our horses in the snows of the T'ien Mountains,
We have gone into battle ten thousand li away.
Our three armies are utterly exhausted.

The Huns think of slaughter as a kind of plowing.
From of old they have seen only white bones in the yellow sands.
Where the Ch'in emperors built walls against the barbarians,
The sons of Han burn beacon fires.
The beacons burn without ceasing.
There is no end to war!

On the field of battle men grapple each other and die,
The horses of the fallen utter lament to heaven,
Ravens and kites peck men's guts,
And flying away, hang them on the boughs of dead trees.
So men are smeared on the desert grass,
And the generals return empty-handed.
Know that weapons of war are utterly evil—
The virtuous man uses them only when he must.

SUPERSEDED[1]

Tu Fu (712–70) / Herbert A. Giles

Alas for the lonely plant that grows
beside the river bed,
While the mango-bird screams loud and long
from the tall tree overhead!
Full of the freshets of the spring,
the torrent rushes on;
The ferry-boat swings idly, for
the ferryman is gone.

1. A specimen of political allegory. The "lonely plant" refers to a virtuous statesman for whom the time is out of joint. The "mango-bird" is a worthless politician in power. The "ferry-boat" is our ship of state.

THE EMPTY PURSE

Tu Fu / Hsieh Wen-tung

The bitter pine cone may be eaten,
The mist on high gives nourishment.
The whole world takes to go-and-getting;
My way alone is difficult.
My oven is cold as the well at morning,
And the bed wants warmth from coverlets;
My purse, ashamed to be found empty,
Still keeps on hand a single coin.

QUATRAIN

Tu Fu / Hsieh Wen-tung

Before you praise spring's advent, note,
What capers the mad wind may cut:
To cast the flowers to the waves,
And overturn the fishing boat.

THE PRESSGANG

Tu Fu / Herbert A. Giles

There, where at eve I sought a bed,
A pressgang came, recruits to hunt;
Over the wall the goodman sped,
And left his wife to bear the brunt.

Ah me! the cruel serjeant's rage!
Ah me! how sadly she anon
Told all her story's mournful page,—
How three sons to the war had gone;

How one had sent a line to say
That two had been in battle slain:
He, from the fight had run away,
But they could ne'er come back again.

She swore 'twas all the family—
Except a grandson at the breast;
His mother too was there, but she
Was all in rags and tatters drest.

The crone with age was troubled sore,
But for herself she'd not think twice
To journey to the seat of war
And help to cook the soldiers' rice.

The night wore on and stopped her talk;
Then sobs upon my hearing fell...
At dawn when I set forth to walk,
Only the goodman cried Farewell!

WATCHING THE REAPERS

Po Chü-i (772–846) / Arthur Waley

Tillers of the soil have few idle months;
In the fifth month their toil is double-fold.
A south-wind visits the fields at night:
Suddenly the hill is covered with yellow corn.
Wives and daughters shoulder baskets of rice;
Youths and boys carry the flasks of wine.
Following after they bring a wage of meat
To the strong reapers toiling on the southern hill,
Whose feet are burned by the hot earth they tread,
Whose backs are scorched by flames of the shining sky.
Tired they toil, caring nothing for the heat,
Grudging the shortness of the long summer day.
A poor woman follows at the reapers' side
With an infant child carried close at her breast.
With her right hand she gleans the fallen grain;
On her left arm a broken basket hangs.
And I today . . . by virtue of what right
Have I never once tended field or tree?
My government-pay is three hundred tons;
At the year's end I have still grain in hand.
Thinking of this, secretly I grew ashamed;
And all day the thought lingered in my head.

PASSING T'IEN-MEN STREET IN CH'ANG-AN AND SEEING A DISTANT VIEW OF CHUNG-NAN MOUNTAIN

Po Chü-i / Arthur Waley

The snow has gone from Chung-nan;[1] spring is almost come.
Lovely in the distance its blue colors, against the brown of the streets.

1. Part of the great Nan Shan range, fifteen miles south of Ch'ang-an.

A thousand coaches, ten thousand horsemen pass down the Nine Roads;
Turns his head and looks at the mountains,—not one man!

GOLDEN BELLS

Po Chü-i / Arthur Waley

When I was almost forty
I had a daughter whose name was Golden Bells.
Now it is just a year since she was born;
She is learning to sit and cannot yet talk.
Ashamed,—to find that I have not a sage's heart:
I cannot resist vulgar thoughts and feelings.
Henceforward I am tied to things outside myself:
My only reward,—the pleasure I am getting now.
If I am spared the grief of her dying young,
Then I shall have the trouble of getting her married.
My plan for retiring and going back to the hills
Must now be postponed for fifteen years!

THE DRAGON OF THE BLACK POOL

(A satire)

Po Chü-i / Arthur Waley

Deep the waters of the Black Pool, colored like ink;
They say a Holy Dragon lives there, whom men have never seen.
Beside the Pool they have built a shrine; the authorities have established a ritual;
A dragon by itself remains a dragon, but men can make it a god.
Prosperity and disaster, rain and drought, plagues and pestilences—
By the village people were all regarded as the Sacred Dragon's doing.
They all made offerings of sucking-pig and poured libations of wine;
The morning prayers and evening gifts depended on a "medium's" advice.
When the dragon comes, ah!
The wind stirs and sighs.
Paper money thrown, ah!
Silk umbrellas waved.
When the dragon goes, ah!
The wind also—still.
Incense-fire dies, ah!
The cups and vessels are cold.[1]

1. Parody of a famous Han-dynasty hymn.

Meats lie stacked on the rocks of the Pool's shore;
Wine flows on the grass in front of the shrine.
I do not know, of all those offerings, how much the Dragon eats;
But the mice of the woods and the foxes of the hills are continually
drunk and sated.
Why are the foxes so lucky?
What have the sucking-pigs done,
That year by year they should be killed, merely to glut the foxes?
That the foxes are robbing the Sacred Dragon and eating His sucking-pig,
Beneath the nine-fold depths of His pool, does He know or not?

THE PEOPLE OF TAU-CHOU

Po Chu-i / Arthur Waley

In the land of Tao-chou
Many of the people are dwarfs;
The tallest of them never grow to more than three feet.
They were sold in the market as dwarf slaves and yearly sent to Court;
Described as "an offering of natural products from the land of Tao-chou".
A strange "offering of natural products"; I never heard of one yet
That parted men from those they loved, never to meet again!
Old men—weeping for their grandsons; mothers for their children!
One day—Yang Ch'eng came to govern the land;
He refused to send up dwarf slaves in spite of incessant mandates.
He replied to the Emperor "Your servant finds in the Six Canonical Books
'In offering products, one must offer what is there, and not what isn't there'.
On the waters and lands of Tao-chou, among all the things that live
I only find dwarfish *people;* no dwarfish *slaves*".
The Emperor's heart was deeply moved and he sealed and sent a scroll
"The yearly tribute of dwarfish slaves is henceforth annulled."
The people of Tao-chou,
Old ones and young ones, how great their joy!
Father with son and brother with brother henceforward kept together;
From that day for ever more they lived as free men.
The people of Tao-chou
Still enjoy this gift.
And even now when they speak of the Governor
Tears start to their eyes.
And lest their children and their children's children should forget the
Governor's name,
When boys are born the syllable "Yang" is often used in their forename.

THE GRAIN-TRIBUTE[1]

Po Chu-i / Arthur Waley

There came an officer knocking by night at my door—
In a loud voice demanding grain-tribute.
My house-servants dared not wait till morning
But brought candles and set them on the barn-floor.
Passed through the sieve, clean-washed as pearls,
A whole cart-load, thirty bushels of grain.
But still they cry that it is not paid in full:
With whips and curses they goad my servants and boys.
Once, in error, I entered public life;
I am inwardly ashamed that my talents were not sufficient.
In succession I occupied four official posts;
For doing nothing—ten years' salary!
Often have I heard that saying of ancient men
That "good and ill follow in an endless chain".
And today it ought to set my heart at rest
To return to others the corn in my great barn.

THE FLOWER MARKET

Po Chu-i / Arthur Waley

In the Royal City spring is almost over:
Tinkle, tinkle—the coaches and horsemen pass.
We tell each other "This is the peony season":
And follow with the crowd that goes to the Flower Market.
"Cheap and dear—no uniform price:
The cost of the plant depends on the number of blossoms.
For the fine flower—a hundred pieces of damask:
For the cheap flower—five bits of silk.
Above is spread an awning to protect them:
Around is woven a wattle-fence to screen them.
If you sprinkle water and cover the roots with mud,
When they are transplanted, they will not lose their beauty."
Each household thoughtlessly follows the custom,
Man by man, no one realizing.
There happened to be an old farm laborer who came by chance that way.
He bowed his head and sighed a deep sigh:
But this sigh nobody understood.

1. Written circa 812, showing one of the poet's periods of retirement. When the officials come to receive his grain-tribute, he remembers that he is only giving back what he had taken during his years of office. Salaries were paid partly in kind.

He was thinking, "A cluster of deep-red flowers
Would pay the taxes of ten poor houses."

THE PRISONER

Po Chu-i / Arthur Waley

Tartars led in chains,
Tartars led in chains!
Their ears pierced, their faces bruised—they are driven into the land of Ch'in.
The Son of Heaven took pity on them and would not have them slain.
He sent them away to the south-east, to the lands of Wu and Yueh.
A petty officer in a yellow coat took down their names and surnames.
They were led from the city of Ch'ang-an under escort of an armed guard.
Their bodies were covered with the wounds of arrows, their bones stood out from their cheeks.
They had grown so weak they could only march a single stage a day.
In the morning they must satisfy hunger and thirst with neither plate nor cup:
At night they must lie in their dirt and rags on beds that stank with filth.
Suddenly they came to the Yangtze River and remembered the waters of Chiao.[1]
With lowered hands and levelled voices they sobbed a muffled song.
Then one Tartar lifted up his voice and spoke to the other Tartars,
"*Your* sorrows are none at all compared with *my* sorrows."
Those that were with him in the same band asked to hear his tale:
As he tried to speak the words were choked by anger.
He told them "I was born and bred in the town of Liang-yuan.[2]
In the frontier wars of Ta-li[3] I fell into the Tartars' hands.
Since the days the Tartars took me alive forty years have passed:
They put me into a coat of skins tied with a belt of rope.
Only on the first of the first month might I wear my Chinese dress.
As I put on my coat and arranged my cap, how fast the tears flowed!
I made in my heart a secret vow I would find a way home:
I hid my plan from my Tartar wife and the children she had borne me in the land.
I thought to myself, 'It is well for me that my limbs are still strong',
And yet, being old, in my heart I feared I should never live to return.
The Tartar chieftains shoot so well that the birds are afraid to fly:
For the risk of their arrows I escaped alive and fled swiftly home.
Hiding all day and walking all night, I crossed the Great Desert.[4]
Where clouds are dark and the moon black and the sands eddy in the wind.
Frightened, I sheltered at the Green Grave,[5] where the frozen grasses are few:
Stealthily I crossed the Yellow River, at night, on the thin ice,

1. In Turkestsn. 2. North of Ch'ang-an. 3. The period Ta-li, 766-80. 4. The Gobi Desert.

5. The grave of Chao-chu, a Chinese girl who in 33 B.C. was "bestowed upon the Khan of the Hsiung-nu as a mark of Imperial regard" (Giles). Hers was the only grave in this desolate district on which grass would grow.

Suddenly I heard Han[1] drums and the sound of soldiers coming:
I went to meet them at the road-side, bowing to them as they came.
But the moving horsemen did not hear that I spoke the Han tongue:
Their Captain took me for a Tartar born and had me bound in chains.
They are sending me away to the south-east, to a low and swampy land:
No one now will take pity on me: resistance is all in vain.
Thinking of this, my voice chokes and I ask of Heaven above,
Was I spared from death only to spend the rest of my years in sorrow?
My native village of Liang-yuan I shall not see again:
My wife and children in the Tartars' land I have fruitlessly deserted.
When I fell among Tartars and was taken prisoner, I pined for the land of Han:
Now that I am back in the land of Han, they have turned me into a Tartar.
Had I but known what my fate would be, I would not have started home!
For the two lands, so wide apart, are alike in the sorrow they bring.
    Tartar prisoners in chains!
Of all the sorrows of all the prisoners mine is the hardest to bear!
Never in the world has so great a wrong befallen the lot of man,—
A Han heart and a Han tongue set in the body of a Turk."

THE CHANCELLOR'S GRAVEL-DRIVE

(A satire on the maltreatment of subordinates)

Po Chu-i / Arthur Waley

A Government-bull yoked to a Government-cart!
Moored by the bank of Ch'an River, a barge loaded with gravel.
A single load of gravel,
How many pounds it weighs!
Carrying at dawn, carrying at dusk, what is it all for?
They are carrying it towards the Five Gates,
To the West of the Main Road.
Under the shadow of green laurels they are making a gravel-drive.
For yesterday arrove, newly appointed,
The Assistant Chancellor of the Realm,
And was terribly afraid that the wet and mud
Would dirty his horse's hoofs.
The Chancellor's horse's hoofs
Stepped on the gravel and remained perfectly clean;
But the bull employed in dragging the cart
Was almost sweating blood.
The Assistant Chancellor's business
Is to "save men, govern the country
And harmonize Yin and Yang."[2]

1. *I.e.*, Chinese. 2. The negative and positive principles in nature.

Whether the bull's neck is sore
Need not trouble him at all.

THE TWO RED TOWERS

(A satire against clericalism)

Po Chü-i / Arthur Waley

The Two Red Towers
North and south rise facing each other.
I beg to ask, to whom do they belong?
To the two Princes of the period Cheng Yuan.[1]
The two Princes blew on their flutes and drew down fairies from the sky.
Who carried them off through the five Clouds, soaring away to Heaven.
Their halls and houses, that they could take with them,
Were turned into Temples planted in the Dust of the World.
In the tiring-rooms and dancers' towers all is silent and still;
Only the willows like dancers' arms, and the pond like a mirror.
When the flowers are falling at yellow twilight, when things are sad and hushed,
One does not hear songs and flutes, but only chimes and bells.
The Imperial Patent on the Temple doors is written in letters of gold;
For nuns' quarters and monks' cells ample space is allowed.
For green moss and bright moonlight—plenty of room provided;
In a hovel opposite is a sick man who has hardly room to lie down.
I remember once when at P'ing-yang they were building a great man's house
How it swallowed up the housing space of thousands of ordinary men.
The Immortals[2] are leaving us, two by two, and their houses are turned into Temples;
I begin to fear that the whole world will become a vast convent.

THE CHARCOAL-SELLER

(A satire against "Kommandatur")

Po Chü-i / Arthur Waley

An old charcoal-seller
Cutting wood and burning charcoal in the forest of the Southern Mountain.
His face, stained with dust and ashes, has turned to the color of smoke.
The hair on his temples is streaked with gray: his ten fingers are black.
The money he gets by selling charcoal, how far does it go?
It is just enough to clothe his limbs and put food in his mouth.
Although, alas, the coat on his back is a coat without lining,
He hopes for the coming of cold weather, to send up the price of coal!

1. 785–805. 2. Hsien Tsung's brothers?

Last night, outside the city,—a whole foot of snow;
At dawn he drives the charcoal wagon along the frozen ruts.
Oxen,—weary; man,—hungry; the sun, already high;
Outside the Gate, to the south of the Market, at last they stop in the mud.
Suddenly, a pair of prancing horsemen. Who can be coming?
A public official in a yellow coat and a boy in a white shirt.
In their hands they hold a written warrant: on their tongues—the words of an order;
They turn back the wagon and curse the oxen, leading them off to the north.
A whole wagon of charcoal,
More than a thousand pieces!
If officials choose to take it away, the woodman may not complain.
Half a piece of red silk and a single yard of damask,
The Courtiers have tied to the oxen's collar, as the price of a wagon of coal!

THE POLITICIAN

Po Chü-i / Arthur Waley

I was going to the City to sell the herbs I had plucked;
On the way I rested by some trees at the Blue Gate.
Along the road there came a horseman riding;
Whose face was pale with a strange look of dread.
Friends and relations, waiting to say good-bye,
Pressed at his side, but he did not dare to pause.
I, in wonder, asked the people about me
Who he was and what had happened to him.
They told me this was a Privy Councillor
Whose grave duties were like the pivot of State.
His food allowance was ten thousand cash;
Three times a day the Emperor came to his house.
Yesterday he was called to a meeting of Heroes:
Today he is banished to the country of Yai-chou.
So always, the counsellors of Kings;
Favor and ruin changed between dawn and dusk!
Green, green—the grass of the Eastern Suburb;
And amid the grass, a road that leads to the hills.
Resting in peace among the white clouds,
At last he has made a "coup" that cannot fail!

THE OLD MAN WITH THE BROKEN ARM

(A satire on militarism)

Po Chü-i / Arthur Waley

At Hsin-feng an old man—four-score and eight;
The hair on his head and the hair of his eyebrows—white as the new snow.

Leaning on the shoulders of his great-grandchildren, he walks in front of the Inn;
With his left arm he leans on their shoulders; his right arm is broken.
I asked the old man how many years had passed since he broke his arm;
I also asked the cause of the injury, how and why it happened?
The old man said he was born and reared in the District of Hsin-feng;
At the time of his birth—a wise reign; no wars or discords.
"Often I listened in the Pear-Tree Garden to the sound of flute and song;
Naught I knew of banner and lance; nothing of arrow or bow.
Then came the wars of T'ien-pao[1] and the great levy of men;
Of three men in each house,—one man was taken.
And those to whom the lot fell, where were they taken to?
Five months' journey, a thousand miles—away to Yun-nan.
We heard it said that in Yun-nan there flows the Lu River;
As the flowers fall from the pepper-trees, poisonous vapors rise.
When the great army waded across, the water seethed like a cauldron;
When barely ten had entered the water, two or three were dead.
To the north of my village, to the south of my village the sound of weeping and wailing,
Children parting from fathers and mothers; husbands parting from wives.
Everyone says that in expeditions against the Min tribes
Of a million men who are sent out, not one returns.
I, that am old, was then twenty-four;
My name and fore-name were written down in the rolls of the Board of War.
In the depth of the night not daring to let anyone know
I secretly took a huge stone and dashed it against my arm.
For drawing the bow and waving the banner now wholly unfit;
I knew henceforward I should not be sent to fight in Yun-nan.
Bones broken and sinews wounded could not fail to hurt;
I was ready enough to bear pain, if only I got back home.
My arm—broken ever since; it was sixty years ago.
One limb, although destroyed,—whole body safe!
But even now on winter nights when the wind and rain blow
From evening on till day's dawn I cannot sleep for pain.
Not sleeping for pain
Is a small thing to bear,
Compared with the joy of being alive when all the rest are dead.
For otherwise, years ago, at the ford of Lu River
My body would have died and my soul hovered by the bones that no one gathered.
A ghost, I'd have wandered in Yun-nan, always looking for home.
Over the graves of ten thousand soldiers, mournfully hovering."
So the old man spoke,
And I bid you listen to his words.
Have you not heard
That the Prime Minister of K'ai-yuan,[2] Sung K'ai-fu,

1. 742–55. 2. 713–42.

Did not reward frontier exploits, lest a spirit of aggression should prevail?
And have you not heard
That the Prime Minister of T'ien-Pao, Yang Kuo-chung[1]
Desiring to win imperial favor, started a frontier war?
But long before he could win the war, people had lost their temper;
Ask the man with the broken arm in the village of Hsin-feng!

THE RED COCKATOO

Po Chü-i / Arthur Waley

Sent as a present from Annam—
A red cockatoo.
Colored like the peach-tree blossom,
Speaking with the speech of men.
And they did to it what is always done
To the learned and eloquent.
They took a cage with stout bars
And shut it up inside.

THE BIG RUG

Po Chü-i / Arthur Waley

That so many of the poor should suffer from cold what can we do to prevent?
To bring warmth to a single body is not much use.
I wish I had a big rug ten thousand feet long,
Which at one time could cover up every inch of the City.

LAZY MAN'S SONG

Po Chü-i / Arthur Waley

I have got patronage, but am too lazy to use it;
I have got land, but am too lazy to farm it.
My house leaks; I am too lazy to mend it.
My clothes are torn; I am too lazy to darn them.
I have got wine, but am too lazy to drink;
So it's just the same as if my cellar were empty.
I have got a harp, but am too lazy to play;
So it's just the same as if it had no strings.
My wife tells me there is no more bread in the house;
I want to bake, but am too lazy to grind.

1. Cousin of the notorious mistress of Ming-huang, Yang Kuei-fei.

My friends and relatives write me long letters;
I should like to read them, but they're such a bother to open.
I have always been told that Chi Shu-yeh[1]
Passed his whole life in absolute idleness.
But he played the harp and sometimes transmuted metals,
So even *he* was not so lazy as I.

ON HIS BALDNESS

Po Chü-i, / Arthur Waley

At dawn I sighed to see my hairs fall;
At dusk I sighed to see my hairs fall.
For I dreaded the time when the last lock should go . . .
They are all gone and I do not mind at all!
I have done with that cumbrous washing and getting dry;
My tiresome comb forever is laid aside.
Best of all, when the weather is hot and wet,
To have no top-knot weighing down on one's head!
I put aside my dusty conical cap;
And loose my collar-fringe.
In a silver jar I have stored a cold stream;
On my bald pate I trickle a ladle-full.
Like one baptized with the Water of Buddha's Law,
I sit and receive this cool, cleansing joy.
Now I know why the priest who seeks Repose
Frees his heart by first shaving his head.

THINKING OF THE PAST

Po Chü-i / Arthur Waley

In an idle hour I thought of former days;
And former friends seemed to be standing in the room.
And then I wondered "Where are they now?"
Like fallen leaves they have tumbled to the Nether Springs.
Han Yü[2] swallowed his sulphur pills,
Yet a single illness carried him straight to the grave.
Yüan Chen smelted autumn stone[3]
But before he was old, his strength crumbled away.
Master Tu possessed the "Secret of Health":
All day long he fasted from meat and spice.
The Lord Ts'ui, trusting a strong drug,

1. Also known as Chi K'ang, a famous Quietist. 2. The famous poet, d. 824.
3. Carbamide crystals.

Through the whole winter wore his summer coat.
Yet some by illness and some by sudden death . . .
All vanished ere their middle years were passed.

Only I, who have never dieted myself
Have thus protracted a tedious span of age,
   I who in young days
Yielded lightly to every lust and greed;
Whose palate craved only for the richest meat
And knew nothing of bismuth or calomel.
When hunger came, I gulped steaming food;
When thirst came, I drank from the frozen stream,
With verse I served the spirits of my Five Guts;[1]
With wine I watered the three Vital Spots.
Day by day joining the broken clod
I have lived till now almost sound and whole.
There is no gap in my two rows of teeth;
Limbs and body still serve me well.
Already I have opened the seventh book of years;
Yet I eat my fill and sleep quietly;
I drink, while I may, the wine that lies in my cup,
And all else commit to Heaven's care.

THE PHILOSOPHERS

Po Chü-i / Arthur Waley

LAO-TZU

"Those who speak know nothing;
Those who know are silent."
These words, as I am told,
Were spoken by Lao-tzu.
If we are to believe that Lao-tzu
   Was himself *one who knew,*
How comes it that he wrote a book
   Of five thousand words?

CHUANG-TZU, THE MONIST

   Chuang-tzu levels all things
   And reduces them to the same Monad.
But I say that even in their sameness
Difference may be found.

1. Heart, liver, stomach, lungs, and kidneys.

Although in following the promptings of their nature
They display the same tendency,
Yet it seems to me that in some ways
A phoenix is superior to a reptile!

THE MIRROR

Po Chü-i / Arthur Waley

The brightness of a bronze mirror,
The whiteness of silken thread,
How can I prevent people knowing my age?
Surely you do not believe I have grown old?

HEAVY TAXES

Po Chü-i / Ching Ti

Yesterday I went to the yamen to pay my taxes,
And peeped through the storehouse gates.
The cloth and silk were piled as high as hills,
And gauzes and cotton mounted up like clouds.
They were fine tributes
To be offered to the sovereign,
But they were really the warmth stripped from my back
To buy them temporal favors,
That they might enter the golden royal house
And become dust throught the ages.

A BIRTH

Po Chü-i / Herbert A. Giles

At last, at fifty-eight I have a boy:
But sighs are mingled with my notes of joy.
We blame the single pearl the oyster grows;
Yet no one wants a quiverful of crows.

Late autumn sees the cassia's fruitful bough;
Spring winds the purple orchids stir—and now
I raise my glass and breathe my heart's desire—
Oh, be not such a fool as was thy sire!

"THE GAY LICENTIOUS CROWD"

Po Chü-i / Herbert A. Giles

With haughty mien they fill the ways,
And gorgeous gleam their saddletrees;
I ask, who are they? Someone says,
The Court officials these.

Scarlet-sashed ministers are there,
Red-tasselled generals in crowds;
Their minds are bent on sumptuous fare;
Their steeds pass by like clouds.

Wine of the rarest brands they take;
Rich meats are set before their eyes—
An orange from the Tung-t'ing lake,
And fish from Paradise.

Serenely full, their greed assuaged,
Half-drunken, and still happier then. . . .
That year a cruel famine raged,
And men were eating men.

A PROTEST IN THE SIXTH YEAR OF CH'IEN FU (A.D. 879)

Ts'ao Sung (ca. 900) / Arthur Waley

The hills and rivers of the lowland country
You have made your battle-ground.
How do you suppose the people who live there
Will procure "firewood and hay"?[1]
Do not let me hear you talking together
About titles and promotions;
For a single general's reputation
Is made out of ten thousand corpses.

ON HIGHWAYMEN

Li She (9th cen.) / Herbert A. Giles

The rainy mist sweeps gently
o'er the village by the stream,
When from the leafy forest glades

1. The necessaries of life.

the brigand daggers gleam. . . .
And yet there is no need to fear
or step from out their way,
For more than half the world consists
of bigger rogues than they.

SONG AT THE FRONTIER

Hsu Hun (9th cen.) / Robert Payne

All night they fought north of Hsiangkiang;
Half of our soldiers of Ch'in have not returned.
But when morning dawned, letters arrived from home,
The folks at home were sending them winter clothes.

NEXT DOOR

Mei Yao-ch'en (1002–60) / Kenneth Rexroth

My neighbors on the right
Have a young son who has just
Commenced to step out.
My neighbors on the left
Have a young daughter
Who is still a virgin.
In the heavy shadow
Under the gate it is very dark
After the sun has set.
Whose head is that, looking over the wall?

A WALK IN THE COUNTRY

Su Tung-p'o / Kenneth Rexroth

The spring wind raises fine dust from the road.
Everybody is out, enjoying the new leaves.
Strollers are drinking in the inns along the way.
Cart wheels roll over the young grass.
The whole town has gone to the suburbs.
Children scamper everywhere and shout to the skies.
Songs and drum beats scare the hills
And make the leaves tremble on the trees.
Picnic baskets and jugs litter the fields
And put the crows and kites to flight.

Who is that fellow who has gathered a crowd?
He says he is a Taoist monk.
He is selling charms to the passersby.
He shouts, waves his hands, rolls his eyes.
"If you raise silk, these will
Grow cocoons as big as pitchers.
If you raise stock, these will
Make the sheep as big as elks."
Nobody really believes him.
It is the spirit of spring in him they are buying.
As soon as he has enough money
He will go fill himself with wine
And fall down drunk,
Overcome by the magic of his own charms.

EPIGRAM

Su Tung-p'o / Kenneth Rexroth

I fish for minnows in the lake.
Just born, they have no fear of man.
And those who have learned,
Never come back to warn them.

ON THE BIRTH OF HIS SON

Su Tung-p'o / Arthur Waley

Families, when a child is born
Want it to be intelligent.
I, through intelligence,
Having wrecked my whole life,
Only hope the baby will prove
Ignorant and stupid.
Then he will crown a tranquil life
By becoming a Cabinet Minister.

THE OLD APOTHECARY

Lu Yu (1125–1209) / Pai Chwen-yu

He is as old as I,
Selling drugs to replace husbandry.

The coins he receives he gives to the wine seller,
And leaves not one for himself.

He accompanies old neighbors in singing,
And teaches the young when it is raining hard.
I would like to write his life,
But no one knows his name.

DRINKING

Hsin Ch'i-chi (1140–1207) / Ching Ti

Let me enjoy myself in drunkenness.
How can I spare a moment for my troubles?
Now I find there is not a single drop of truth
In all those books written by the ancients.

Last night I reeled against a pine tree.
I asked the tree how sober I was.
I thought the tree moved to offer me help;
Pushing against it, I said: "Go away!"

TO THE TUNE OF "THE UGLY SLAVE"

Hsin Ch'i-chi / Hsiung Ting

Young, I was unacquainted with sorrow,
Loving to climb the high places,
Loving to climb the high places,
Composing poems compelling myself to sorrow.

Now that I have dregged sorrow to the dregs,
I am loath to talk of it,
I am loath to talk of it.
I say instead "How nice is the cool autumn."

THE WILD FLOWER MAN

Lu Yu / Kenneth Rexroth

Do you know the old man who
Sells flowers by the South Gate?
He lives on flowers like a bee.
In the morning he sells mallows,

In the evening he has poppies.
His shanty roof lets in the
Blue sky. His rice bin is
Always empty. When he has
Made enough money from his
Flowers, he heads for a teahouse.
When his money is gone, he
Gathers some more flowers.
All the spring weather, while the
Flowers are in bloom, he is
In bloom, too. Every day he
Is drunk all day long. What does
He care if new laws are posted
At the Emperor's palace?
What does it matter to him
If the government is built
On sand? If you try to talk
To him, he won't answer but
Only give you a drunken
Smile from under his tousled hair.

THE LOCUST SWARM

Hsu Chao (ca. 1200) / Kenneth Rexroth

Locusts laid their eggs in the corpse
Of a soldier. When the worms were
Mature, they took wing. Their drone
Was ominous, their shells hard.
Anyone could tell they had hatched
From an unsatisfied anger.
They flew swiftly toward the North.
They hid the sky like a curtain.
When the wife of the soldier
Saw them, she turned pale, her breath
Failed her. She knew he was dead
In battle, his corpse lost in
The desert. That night she dreamed
She rode a white horse, so swift
It left no footprints, and came
To where he lay in the sand.
She looked at his face, eaten
By the locusts, and tears of
Blood filled her eyes. Ever after
She would not let her children

Injure any insect which
Might have fed on the dead. She
Would lift her face to the sky
And say, "O locusts, if you
Are seeking a place to winter
You can find shelter in my heart."

OMNES EODEM

Liu Chi / Herbert A. Giles

A centenarian 'mongst men
Is rare; and if one comes, what then?
The mightiest heroes of the past
Upon the hillside sleep at last.

APOLOGIA

Hsieh Chin (1369–1415) / Herbert A. Giles

In vain hands bent on sacrifice
or clasped in prayer we see;
The ways of God are not exactly
what those ways should be.
The swindler and the ruffian
lead pleasant lives enough,
While judgments overtake the good
and many a sharp rebuff.
The swaggering bully stalks along
as blithely as you please,
While those who never miss their prayers
are martyrs to disease.
And if great God Almighty fails
to keep the balance true,
What can we hope that paltry mortal
magistrates will do?

A BROKEN TRYST

Anon. (15th cen.) / Herbert A. Giles

"Meet me," said I, "at the rise of the moon."
The moon duly rose, but in vain did I wait;

For I live on the plain, where the moon rises soon,
And he among hills, where the moon rises late.

TO A BUDDHIST PRIEST

Ssu-K'ung Shan (16th cen.?) / Herbert A. Giles

Seeing the Way, a follower I would be;
How can I follow what I do not see?
The Way itself is unsubstantial air;
How can I follow that which is not there?
Those who to walk along the Way aspire,
Are seeking water-bubbles in a fire.
'Tis just like 'Punch and Judy' and its fun;
If the strings break, the little play is done.

ON A WINE-JAR IN AN OLD GRAVE

Hsu Wei (16th cen.) / Herbert A. Giles

My thoughts are with the owner, far away,
Who had a goblet, but who could not quaff;
A hare-shaped[1] piece of common yellow clay,
Sole friend for a millennium and a half.

But here beside him rests a legal deed[2]
For ground where now in winding-sheet he lies;
'Tis clear that long ere death his soul had freed
He had no lack of fortune's choice supplies—

Vessels of jade, all exquisitely wrought,
And silken robes with these upon a par—
By what spell were his dainty fingers taught
To raise to lips refined this earthen jar?

'Twixt quick and dead a grave-mound—a mere thing;
Yet joy and silence seem so far apart.
A living rat's more worth than a dead king;
A fact we'll all do well to lay to heart.

1. The hare is an auspicious animal. There is one in the moon, pounding drugs for the elixir of immortality.
2. The amount mentioned is 4,000,000 *cash,* whatever that might mean at such a remote date.

THE DIVINEST OF ALL THINGS

Chao I (1727–1814) / Herbert A. Giles

Man is indeed of heavenly birth,
Though seeming earthy of the earth;
The sky is but a denser pall
Of the thin air that covers all.
Just as this air, so is that sky;
Why call this low, and call that high?

The dewdrop sparkles in the cup—
Note how the eager flowers spring up;
Confine and crib them in a room,
They fade and find an early doom.
So 'tis that at our very feet
The earth and the empyrean meet.

The babe at birth points heavenward too,
Enveloped by the 'ternal blue;
As fishes in the water bide,
So heaven surrounds on every side;
Yet men sin on, because they say
Great God in heaven is far away.

AN AGNOSTIC

Anon. (18th cen.) / Herbert A. Giles

You ask me why I greet the priest
But not his God;
The God sits mute, the man at least
Returns my nod.

A SCOFFER

Yuan Mei (1715–97) / Herbert A. Giles

I've ever thought it passing odd
How all men reverence some God,
And wear their lives out for his sake
And bow their heads until they ache.
'Tis clear to me the Gods are made
Of the same stuff as wind or shade . . .

Ah, if they came to every caller,
I'd be the very loudest bawler!

THE SOUL OF SHANGHAI

Shao Hsun-mei (b. 1903?) / Hsu Kai-yu

I stand on top of a seven-storied building,
Above, there is the inaccessible sky;
Below, the cars, telephone wires, and the horse race track.

The front door of a theater, the back view of a prostitute;
Ah, these are the soul of a metropolis;
Ah, these are the soul of Shanghai.

Here one need not fear the rain or the sun:
Or the autumn and winter of death, or the spring of life:
How can any fiery summer be warmer than the lips?

Here there are true illusions, false sentiments;
Here there are unsleeping evenings, smiling lights;
Come, then, here is your burial ground.

AN IMPRESSION OF SHANGHAI

Kuo Mo-jo (b. 1892) / Hsu Kai-yu

I was shocked out of my dream!
Ah, the sorrow of disillusion!

Idle bodies,
Sensual and noisy flesh,
Men wearing long robes,
Women, short sleeves,
Everywhere I see skeletons,
And everywhere, coffins
Madly rushing,
Madly pushing.
Tears well up in my eyes,
And nausea, in my heart.

I was shocked out of my dream.
Ah, the sorrow of disillusion!

IRON VIRGIN

Kuo Mo-jo / Hsu Kai-yu

The Iron Virgin was found in Medieval Europe,
A really cruel torture was she.
Her inside was just a box with sharp nails,
But her outside showed the image of Holy Mary.

The Holy Lady was the door of the box,
From behind her breast a spike protruded.
The victim was put inside, and the door closed,
The long nail thus pierced the victim's chest.

In Manchuria the Japanese had a new invention,
Sharp nails were lined up on the inside of a barrel.
With the victim in it, and both ends sealed,
The barrel was left in the streets to be kicked around.

The torture had no kind looks of the Holy Lady,
But was equipped with such iron breasts as the Virgin's.
The Japanese, they say, just named it Nail Box,
Ah, they surely are good at imitation.

IN MEMORIAM: MY SON YUEH-CH'UN

Yu Ta-fu (1895–1945) / Hsu Kai-yu

How can his little soul enter our dream?
So many crossroads will require his guessing and hesitation.
For fear that someone might take advantage of him in the other world,
We bury him near the ancestral grave, and plant an ashplant for him.

THE LAUNDRY SONG

Wen Yi-tuo (d. 1946), ca. 1925 / Hsu Kai-yu

(One piece, two pieces, three pieces,)
Washing must be clean.
(Four pieces, five pieces, six pieces,)
Ironing must be smooth.

I can wash handkerchiefs wet with sad tears;
I can wash shirts soiled in sinful crimes.
The grease of greed, the dirt of desire . . .

And all the filthy things at your house,
Give them to me to wash, give them to me.

Brass stinks so; blood smells evil.
Dirty things you have to wash.
Once washed, they will again be soiled.
How can you, men of patience, ignore them!
Wash them (for the Americans), wash them!

You say the laundry business is too base.
Only Chinamen are willing to stoop so low?
It was your preacher who once told me:
Christ's father used to be a carpenter.
Do you believe it? Don't you believe it?

There isn't much you can do with soap and water.
Washing clothes truly can't compare with building warships.
I, too, say what great prospect lies in this—
Washing the others' sweat with your own blood and sweat?
(But) do you want to do it? Do you want it?

Year in year out a drop of homesick tears;
Midnight, in the depth of night, a laundry lamp . . .
Menial or not, you need not bother,
Just see what is not clean, what is not smooth,
And ask the Chinaman, ask the Chinaman.

I can wash handkerchiefs wet with sad tears,
I can wash shirts soiled in sinful crimes.
The grease of greed, the dirt of desire . . .
And all the filthy things at your house,
Give them to me—I'll wash them, give them to me!

THE DESK

Wen Yi-tuo / Hsu Kai-yu

At once all the inanimate things burst out singing:
Complaints from every part of the desk.
The ink case groans: "I am thirsty to death!"
The dictionary cries that the rain water is soaking its back.

The writing pad says its waist is aching with bending,
The fountain pen says the tobacco ash has clogged its mouth,

The ink brush says the match has burned its beard,
And the pencil says the toothbrush is weighing on its leg.

The incense pot grumbles: "The books are unreasonable—
Sooner or later they will throw me down!"
The steel-cased watch says its bones will rust with sleep.
"The wind is coming!" the writing paper fearfully laments aloud.

The inkstone claims it is meant to hold water:
"Why do I have to suffer cigar ash and stinking dirt?"
The desk says it is never cleaned more than once a year.
The inkpot proclaims: "I swilled you on a rainy day."

"Who the devil is the master of all of us?"
So all these inanimate objects burst out singing.
"If really we have to continue in this disorder,
It would be better if there were no existence at all."

The master bites his pipe and smiles blandly;
"The best thing to do is for all of you to remain where you are.
It is not my fault that you are all distressed.
The order of the universe is beyond my power."

EARLY SUMMER NIGHT

Wen Yi-tuo / Ho Yung

The setting sun leaves the poet to the dreary night,
And he reminds her: "Reveal all your secret treasuries."
The violet sky spills broken pearls,
He believes they should be strung together
As adornments upon the breasts of death.

Claws of cold undertow comb the withered hair of starved willows,
Wringing out their reflections from the pond in slivers of gold.
Halfway up the hill there is a fallen cypress, hunchbacked.
Her dark bony fists shake defiance at the sun.
The sleepless toads are overcome with weariness,
The village dogs bark in mournful, inquiring tones.
How can the nerves of thieves stand up to the strain?
A fire-swallowing, mist-spitting dragon climbs the iron stairway
With "War" engraved on the gray uniform, hoarsely shouting, sobbing.
The clapper of a great bell comforts the world,
Saying, "Sleep in peace," but who believes in the bell?
O God, knowing the pass the world has come to,
Are you not shuddering, O most benevolent God in the skies?

SERVES YOU RIGHT, BEGGAR

Hsu Chih-mo (1875–1931), ca. 1925 / Hsu Kai-yu

"Kindhearted ladies, charitable sirs,"
The northwest wind slashes his face like a sharp knife.
"Give me a little bit of your leftovers, just a little bit!"
A patch of dark shadow curls up near the gate.

"Have pity, my wealthy lord, I'm dying of hunger."
Inside the gate there are jade cups, warm fire and laughter.
"Have pity, my lord of good fortunes, I'm dying of cold."
Outside the gate the northwest wind chuckles,
"Serves you right, beggar!"

I am but a pile of black shadows, trembling,
Lying like a worm on the frontage road of humanity;
I wish only a bit of the warmth of sympathy
To shelter what's left of me, after repeated carving.
But this heavy gate stays tightly closed: Care who might?
In the street only the wind continues to ridicule,
"Beggar, serves you right!"

THE PAWNSHOP

Chu Hsiang (1904–33) / Hsu Kai-yu

Beauty runs a pawnshop,
Accepting only the hearts of men.
When the time comes for them to redeem their belongings,
She has already closed the door.

GET DRUNK

To Those Who Ever So Gently Sing

Ho Ch'i-fang (b. 1911) / Hsu Kai-yu

Get drunk, get drunk,
Those truly drunk are lucky
For paradise belongs to them.

If alcohol, books,
And lips that drip honey . . .
If none of these can cover up man's suffering,
If you proceed from being dead drunk to half sober

To fully awake finally,
Wouldn't you keep your hat cocked and
Your eyes half closed,
To act slightly intoxicated throughout your life?

The flies shivering in the cold wind
Flutter their wings before the paper window pane,
Dreaming of dead bodies,
Of watermelon rinds in high summer,
And of a dreamless void.

In the epilogue of my ridicule
I hear my own shame:
"You too are only buzzing and buzzing
Like a fly."

If I were a fly,
I'd await the sound of a fly swatter
Smashing on my head.

A DEAD SOLDIER ABANDONED ON THE ROADSIDE

Tu Yun-hsieh (b. ca. 1902) / Hsu Kai-yu

Give me a grave,
A grave like a black bun;
Even a flat one will do,
Like a small vegetable patch
Or a pile of manure.
Anything is fine, anything,
As long as there is a grave,
As long as I won't be exposed,
Like a pile of buffalo bones.
Because I'm afraid of dogs
I have always been afraid of dogs.
I'm ticklish, most ticklish,
That, my mother knew very well.
I was afraid of the dog's licking me,
It gave me goose-pimples.
And my eyes would turn red, about to cry.
I was afraid to see dogs fighting,
That noise was really too frightening,
Especially when they fought over a bone,
Their sharp white teeth were too frightening.
If one dog dragged a piece of flesh,

And another pulled a piece of bone,
With blood dripping in between them, like tears,
I would vomit and faint immediately.
I'm also afraid of the wilderness,
A wilderness with only wind and grass,
With wild animals foraging everywhere.
They are not afraid of blood,
All laugh so strangely,
Especially when they have drunk blood.
They gnaw on bones
With their even sharper teeth.
They are a greater threat than dogs.
I'm afraid of black birds,
As large as roosters,
They scare people from the treetops at night
And their beaks are so cleverly sharp . . .
I'm afraid, I'm afraid.
The wind has run away,
The fallen leaves have also run away,
So has the dust.
The trees are struggling, shaking their heads,
And are about to run away.
Ah, give me a grave,
Just any handful of dirt,
Any handful of dirt.

ON A CHILEAN CIGARETTE PACKAGE

Ai Ch'ing (b. 1910) / Hsu Kai-yu

A goddess of liberty,
Painted on a Chilean cigarette package,
Although she holds high a torch,
Only a black shadow of her is seen.

For a trademark, for advertising,
A bit of space is offered her.
You can buy it with small change
And after you are through, it vanishes in smoke . . .

The package is tossed on the roadside,
He steps on it, and you spit on it.
Whether it's a fact, or merely a symbol,
The goddess of liberty is but a pack of cigarettes.

THE ZERO DEGREE OF LIFE

A recent news headline: "Storm the day before yesterday, eight hundred children dead last night"

Tsang K'o-chia (b. ca. 1910), Shanghai, Feb. 6, 1947 / Hsu Kai-yu

Over eight hundred of them, once full of life,
In the "local news" column of the paper
Occupied only a tiny corner.
Nameless,
Ageless,
Homeless,
Even the way and the place where they froze to death
Received no description or explanation.
Such news items,
Glanced at under the people's eyes only a moment,
Were quickly passed over.
At most they earned several sighs.
What the papers like to print are:
A young girl ravished, a spider with a human head, a baby born with two bodies,
And a robber getting his loot or losing his life.
Your deaths
Are as unnoticed and unknown as your births.
You, such tender buds of man,
Before you could wait for the arrival of spring,
Hunger and cold
Have already nipped your life line in one snatch.
Where did you come from?
Under the whips of the landlords?
Or from the land of a barren village?
Did you come together with your parents,
Harboring a hope to seek life from within death,
To plunge into this largest metropolis of East Asia?

You were lost in the maze of towering buildings,
Your mouths watered at the scent of feasts.
The city's noise drowned your wailing,
Here every conscience is rusty.
Your look of dirtiness
Made dignitaries and noble ladies dodge.
Your trembling bodies and voices
Begged curses and nasty stares rather than sympathy.
The great Shanghai is immense
And warm,
And bright,
And rich.

But you,
Assailed by cold and hunger,
Retreated in defeat to the dark corners,
With empty stomachs, and chattering teeth . . .
Northwest winds roared all night long,
And snow churned.
Your bodies
Like so many thermometers,
Dropped little by little
Until they reached the zero degree of life.

You died,
All eight-hundred-odd of you, as if by previous agreement,
Clutching the same despair,
Passing out of this world in the same night.
I know, you were unwilling to die;
You tried to resist,
But from a stretch of pale imagination
You could grab
No weapons.
One by one the naked bodies,
And one by one the naked hearts,
Were rapidly knocked down
By the coldness of the world of man.
In a society where man eats man,
You have always
Existed only from hour to hour.
Wherever you dropped,
That was it!
I hate those philanthropists,
Who, after your death, picked up your bodies here and there.
Let your bodies
Stay forever
On those three feet of land.
Let those scientists who invented central heating
Look at you once
As they pass by.
Block the rich magnates' private cars,
Let them spit once or twice.
Let the fashionable ladies step on you,
And scream.
Let those corpses bleed, and rot,
Sending their stench to mix
In the breathing of the great Shanghai.

THE PORTRAIT OF A CHINESE SOLDIER (extracts)

Wang Ya-p'ing (b. ca. 1910) / Hsu Kai-yu

PAWNING AN ARM

Fine rain sprinkled ceaselessly outside the window,
The blades of grass drooped.
He threw open his blanket
"What happened to my arm?" he shouted in anger.
And he struggled with pain to get up.
The nurse tried to hum a lullaby,
And even to tell him the fairy tale of the "White-robed Goddess."
His sad eyes
Held back wrathful tears.
With his left arm he pounded on the bamboo cot
Making it repeat his insistent demand.
The nurse brought to him his amputated arm
Soaked in chemical solution.
He seized it and laughed wildly,
"My sweetheart, so many devils have you killed,
Today I am going to pawn you!"
Deliriously he pushed away the nurse,
Jumped over the fence of the hospital,
And, like a jail breaker fleeing his pursuer,
Darted into a pawnshop.
"I want to pawn this arm, for five dollars!"
Tung! The arm was tossed on the counter.
The shopkeeper scurried away in fright
The chemical solution was splashed all over the window.
"Our shop only permits redemption, no more pawning,"
The proprietor explained nervously.
"Damn it, this arm is more precious than anything you name.
It's worth a thousand gold pieces
Or ten thousand suits of clothes.
Stupid dog, listen,
I haven't been paid for three whole damn months,
You and the whole lot like you just wine and dine,
And don't give a damn about the country and the war."
The proprietor lit a cigarette,
Trying to force a smile on his face.
He angrily grabbed the arm,
Darted back into the main street,
Still laughing deliriously
He threw the arm at the pedestrians.

Fine rain kept falling from the sky,
And the sky was so gloomy.

A DISABLED SHADOW

The back view of a disabled soldier,
Minus his right arm,
A sleeve dangling at the side,
Drew startled looks everywhere.
He went to the street from the hospital
And from the street he went to the countryside
And again returned to the city,
Bearing his bitter hatred in silence.
Liu Te-ch'eng: In the history of the war against Japan
There is his glorious name.
The Red Cross sewn on his gray cotton-padded military jacket
Symbolized the grandeur of the man.
He walked forward, his chin up,
And laughed, in reminiscence of that struggle in blood and fire.
Yes, three months' toying with life and death,
Although one of his four limbs was gone
His robust life was spared.
Often on his face there protruded blue veins,
Anger locked his eyebrows
As he gazed at the rushing waves of the Ch'ien-t'ang River
That rolled and surged in a tide of blood.
The lush red fields on both banks
Were trampled under the enemy's iron hoofs.
Red clouds embraced the setting sun,
That retired slowly behind the blue hills.
He hated bitterly—when would victory be finally won!
The night wind blew on his wound
A sharp attack of pain, a shiver,
The feeling of loss prickled his heart.
No! If the country is gone, where is home?
Listen, the intense gunfire in the distance.
Battle cries in the dream . . .
Bayonets thrust at the dwarf enemies.
And when he woke up, the cool light of a sinking moon
Was kissing his thin blankets.
"Why didn't you let me die in the front line?"
Often he angrily shouted
And from his left and right heavily wounded comrades
Groaned sadly and in low voice, time and time again.
A morning breeze brought along the next dawn.

Guns and cannons howled on earth.
Our troops tough as steel
Marched toward a holy war.
From the supreme commander to the small shopkeeper
Banded together in an iron Great Wall
From the Ch'ang-pai Mountain to the mouth of the Pearl River.
The War of Resistance, a stupendous tidal wave of blood.
Four hundred and fifty million new sons and daughters
Struggled up from a blood bath, and shouted.
A new history of China
Must be revised according to a design sketched in blood.
Armless, legless,
So many shadows of the disabled,
Were the heroes who did the sketching.
Today a batch of them were carried back from the front,
Tomorrow perhaps there will be more.
On our immense territory
Thousands of shadows of the disabled moved about,
Into the bloody fire of a people's struggle
They cast a heroic sacrifice
To buy the dawn of freedom and liberation.

CAN'T KILL HIM (extracts)

The Reminiscences of a Fifty-seven-year-old Peasant Who Has Changed His Lot

Chang Chih-min (b. ca. 1918) / Hsu Kai-yu

Part I. Fiety-Seven Years Passed in Hell

MY NAME IS "CAN'T KILL HIM"

My Mother said: "You and Lai-hsi were born on the same day,
But Lai-hsi's family was a rich family."

For the rich family a new baby is a great joy!
The poor cannot afford feeding another boy.

His family bought wine and weighed in flour,
But Lai-hsi's family was a rich family.

For the rich family a new baby is a great joy!
The poor cannot afford feeding another boy.

His family bought wine and weighed in flour,
My mother lost her eyesight shortly after she delivered me.

To be born with lots of money is always lucky,
So they called him "Fortune comes" to a good family.

Fully six months had passed after I came,
No one had yet given me a name.

"What shall we call our child?" asked Mother;
Father said, "Call him 'Can't Kill Him'; the King of Hades must have made a mistake."

STRANGLE MY SISTER

Mother gave birth to a little sister
There was not even rice gruel to feed her.

My sister was strangled to death,
So Mother could work for others as a nurse.

Father would give me to the Li family,
Mother said: "Before you take my son away, first take me."

That was hard for him, for I was his only son;
His tears fell like pearls from a broken string.

All my blue veins showed, I was so thin;
Deep as wine cups my eyes sank in.

One day I saw Lai-hsi in the street, white steamed bread in his hand,
He called me to stop me, "Hi! Can't Kill Him!

"You crawl on the ground like a dog;
I'll give you a piece of bread; you snap at it with your mouth."

I crawled on the ground, hunger had killed my pride;
Right in my chest, he gave me a kick.

"Why don't you slap yourself when you are dying for food;
When did you last eat things so good!"

SELL MY MOTHER

Two pecks of rice we owed Lai-hsi;
Hard as we tried but we could not repay his family.

On New Year's Eve, we had nothing to eat.
Lai-hsi's father came; he was burning mad.

"I came to collect, not to beg, today.
Sell your wife, if you can't repay."

He forced us on the spot to sell Mother for money,
And at midnight he brought over a black donkey.

Mother saw it, she clawed her own face;
Blood streamed down her cheeks.

Father knocked his head against the wall:
I hung on the donkey's tail, and wouldn't let go at all.

"Mother, Mother, you mustn't go, you see,
If you go, who's to take care of me?"

PART II. I'VE COME BACK TO LIFE

SPEAK-BITTERNESS

A thunder rocked heaven;
Along came the Communist Party.

Under a big tree, Lai-hsi and his father were hung;
One whip flew up as another came down.

"You drove my whole family to ruin;
You forced my father to death and my mother to marry again.

"You, heartless wolf who sought only the death of the poor,
Even for cash you wouldn't sell your grain to us hungry folks.

"I've tended your sheep for over three years;
You figured again and again and said I still owed you more.

"You've beat me in the past, now I'll beat you;
Even after eating your flesh I still won't be through!"

YEN HSI-SHAN'S TAX AGENT

Liu Chia (b. ca. 1918), Western Front, Nov. 20, 1945 / Hsu Kai-yu

Yen Hsi-shan's tax agent
Came to the village.

Immediately he got hold of the village chief,
"In three days the rice levy must all be in.
If one grain is missing
We'll use your head to make up the balance."

He rode away as soon as he finished speaking.
Behind his horse
A rope led a cow and two sheep.
The villagers peeped from behind their doors,
Tears glistened in their eyes.

The village chief struck his gong
The villagers' hearts sank.
They went home,
Searched every basket and every urn;
Even the rice already in the kettle was taken, dripping,
And household articles were sold for rice to be given to the military governor.

The Japanese
And Governor Yen,
Six and half-a-dozen, they were the same.

The tax man came again.
His horse was chewing corn at the stable,
He himself sat half-drunk in the big house.
Before the village headquarters
Gathered a huge crowd in tatters.
They watched their food hauled on the scales;
Their hearts, like rocks, plunged.

He who scampered over the wall in flight
Was roped back,
And those hiding in haystacks,
Or sick in bed,
All were dragged out.
The tax man's whip was raised higher and higher,
The rope on the villagers was drawn tighter and tighter.
Lockers, beddings, clothes, pots and pans...
Everything was carried away.

From down the road came a woman running.
She rushed forward, her hair flying.
Pushing the crowd aside,
She threw down a sack:
"This is the tax grain, ah!

To be handed in to Governor Yen. If not enough...
Take me to the Governor."

The village chief was stunned.
Opening the sack he poured out the contents.
Everyone fell back, horrified— Good Heavens!
There were two children's heads, still dripping blood.
One head with a pigtail
Was the woman's child,
The three-year-old, Little Silver.
"Murder, Murder!"
The crowed scattered.
The woman turned around:
"I am the murderer.
I killed them with my own hands
To pay my tax to the Governor."

The tax man smiled.
Coldly he urged the village chief
"Hurry up!"
Those remaining stood motionless.
The northern wind was whistling in higher notes.

HEADLINE MUSIC[1]

Yuan Shui-p'ai (b. ca. 1908), Chungking, Dec. 14, 1944 / Hsu Kai-yu

Seven days and seven nights eating, sleeping, defecating on the top of a freight car
From 100 to 300 swept up at the entrance to the tunnel[2]
Big fire, Big fire, Big fire
Bodies, Bodies, Bodies
    The suggestive pictures on the walls
    Musclemen pushing their way forward
    Leg, Leg, Leg
    Curve, Curve, Curve
A pair of eyes protruding from the flames
And the flames shooting out from the eyes
City follows city, the rail line
From village to village, narrow trails and cavalries
    Infinite joy, when the moon is again full

1. These are almost all film ads, headlines of all sorts, and certain commonly used expressions in news dispatches, thrown together. I can think of no appropriate title, so I call it "Headline Music." —YUAN SHUI P'AI

2. Refers to the tragedy that occurred in the early summer of 1941 when hundreds of people were suffocated or trampled to death in the air-raid tunnel system in Chungking as the result of a panic and poor ventilation facilities.

Lots of people lose their hats in the thumping crowd
If the air raid siren sounds, full technicolor
First prize is definitely here, hurry up and get rich

Tense, Tense, Tense
Bullish, Bullish, Bullish
Four thousand million dollars tumble in the gold market
Change, No change, Don't discuss national affairs
Every tune grand, elegant, and elevating
Every scene full of exquisite music and dance
Sing in honor of schoolmates joining the army
Dance for benefit of the refugees
A queue tens of miles long, spending the night in the cold wind
Peerless art on creamy artificial ice, spring color in the palace of the moon
Every word is blood and grief, moving the audience to tears
They carried and supported their old and young, we were deeply touched
Domestically produced great film, a tragedy with costumes in the latest fashion
The plot touchingly sad, tender, tense
Ladies, old and young, are respectfully advised to bring more handkerchiefs
Skylight, Skylight, Skylight. . . .

INSCRIPTION ON A KLIM CAN

Yuan Shui-p'ai, Jan. 18, 1946 / Hsu Kai-yu

In the year A.D. *3000, a tin can was discovered in the ruin of a big seaport near the Yangtze River delta. Upon examination by distinguished archaeologists, it was identified as a precious antique dating back to the "People's Era." On the can were twenty-four lines of inscriptions as follows:*

Klim powdered milk
Inexpensive supply.
Chinese children's lives
On it rely.

Drink foreign milk
Recognize an alien parent,
How fortunate indeed
Are the children at present.

If the mother has no milk,
A dry nurse comes to the house.
There is no need
To trouble Chinese cows.

Simple and clear:
Everything needed daily
Is an imported item
From a foreign country.

Why develop industries?
That's too much ado.
Just open up your mouth
Let cakes come to you.

Living at others' mercy,
Be flexible, one's told.
This treasure must be kept
For generations to behold.

STRANGE TALES, DOMESTIC VINTAGE

Yuan Shui-p'ai, Oct. 11, 1946 / Hsu Kai-yu

Trucks smash trains,
Skulls knock rifle butts.
Pandas ride on airplanes
Bandits are promoted to generals.
Ladies escort Mr. John[1]
Masters swap flies.
Land and sea forces join
To smash up a dance joint.
Hard to take inventory in liberated areas,
Get a copy from Tokyo.
Chennault is a foreign name
But Charlie has become a compatriot.
Let's welcome more garrison troops
So they can hit the Chinese.
Abolish the rickshas
The unemployed can join the army.
The moon is better abroad,
But civil war is our specialty.
The fat ones play mahjong,
The thin ones are stakes.
Prostitute roundup in the city,
Pressgang for men in the country.
Hats fly over the sky,
Tails follow everyone.[2]
Democracy is Communism
Progressive is anti-revolution.

1. It was considered chic in those days to go out with members of the foreign colony.

2. Accusing someone of Communist affiliation was called "giving someone a red hat to wear," and "tailing" referred to spying.

Use gasoline to fight fire,
This is called "problem of face."
The victors are weeping sadly,
The vanquished chuckle with pride.
Traitors try traitors,
People kill people.
A mass of air of harmony
Ping pang ping pang ping.

"VERY INTERESTING" DEATH[1]

Yuan Shui-p'ai, May 14, 1949 / Hsu Kai-yu

At a "very interesting" gathering,
The ladies and gentlemen brought up a "very interesting" question.
The gentleman had a Chinese name,
The lady, however, bore a name of alien origin.

Question: "Firecrackers are expressions of joy,
Why then are they used at funerals in China?"
Answer: "Because life is so hard for the Chinese, and to them
Death means a happy nirvana."

Capital! Capital! Very, "very interesting!"
The Chinese regard death as happy liberation.
Absolutely correct! Absoutely correct! Otherwise why while living in this paradise,
Do they still hang themselves, or jump off a tall building, or plunge into the sea, or
 take poison?

For example: A peddler "possessed by the devil" fell off a tall building, his head
 cracked wide open,
But to him, that could be only a "pleasant relief."
Or take the girl "teaching Cantonese" at a hotel, who "died on the spot,"
Naturally, "I died happily" must have been her belief.

So, why must you say that their deaths were "self-inflicted"?
If you say that they were "inflicted by others," wouldn't it earn someone merit?
Aid in someone's death—aid in someone's pursuit of happiness.
Why do you waste effort to absolve yourselves? The world should thank you for it.

1. The author's note to this poem gives the detailed background of a special conference billed as "very interesting" by the intellectual and social elite in Hong Kong, including both Chinese and British. The subject was a comparative study of the Chinese and Western ways of life. The conversation in the poem is a part of what transpired at the conference. The reference to the deaths of a peddler and of a young girl, whose body was found half-naked on the sidewalk below a hotel, was based on two tragedies that rocked Hong Kong earlier that year.

Gentlemen, ladies, why don't you keep your dreams?
Ladies, gentlemen, why don't you keep your muddled heads?
Today you are looking down from the clouds, "very interestingly."
Tomorrow, don't tumble down and plunge directly in an outhouse.

OLD MOTHER BLINDS HER OWN SON

Yuan Shui-p'ai / Hsu Kai-yu

January 7, 1947, dispatch from Tan-yang, released in the Wen-hui Daily *of Shanghai: "A farmer of the Mei-chia Village was drafted. His mother stabbed his eyes when he was not looking. He lost his sight instantly."*

It's snowing hard,
The river froze.
We finished the nation's war, but now we fight our own people.
Conscription could not reach rich men,
It only reached after my son, over twenty years old.

I entreated heaven, heaven did not respond;
I pleaded with the earth, the earth had no power.
I begged other people, but no one sympathized.
I cried my eyes dry, dreading the arrival of dawn
For at dawn my son was to report to the army camp.

While my son was asleep,
And the neighborhood lay in total silence.
"Ah, my son,
Don't blame your mother for being too cruel,
Don't blame your mother for being too cruel."

I took needles.
Two steel needles,
And plunged them into my son's eyes.
He screamed and blood spurted out.
"Ah, my son, they don't take a blind man in the army."

SOY SAUCE AND PRAWNS

Yuan Shui-p'ai / Sidney Shapiro

News item, May, 1959: "The United States has prohibited transshipment of a cargo of Chinese canned prawns and sauce destined for Canada."

Neither canned prawns nor soy sauce
May America's borders cross;

Canadians, amazed, confused,
Are irritated and amused.

Soy sauce endangers security,
The reason's there for all to see,
So deeply red it's purple nearly
—Criminal nature proven clearly.

And as to Chinese big prawns canned,
They obviously must be banned;
In armor cased from tail to head,
When boiled they turn a fiery red.

An iron curtain America blinds,
Hysteria grips the White House minds;
"Strategic goods"—what if they're edible?
Such idiocy is scarcely credible.

MUSEUMS—LONDON, NEW YORK, AND POINTS WEST

Yuan Shui-p'ai / Sidney Shapiro

Rooms full of loot
From the east, from the west.
Carved Buddhist hands
By stone horse-heads rest;
Jewels and porcelain
—Yuan Ming Yuan,
Ancient skull fragments
—The Peking Man.
Great art from Paris,
Mummies Egyptian,
Embroidery, murals,
That beggar description;
What if your own country
Is culturally drab?
Just reach into others
And what you like—grab.

UNIVERSAL SHOUT

Yuan Shui-p'ai, Oct., 1961 / Sidney Shapiro

Little fleas
Bite on sight,

Yankees everywhere,
Day and night.

When they go south,
The south has trouble;
When they go north,
North gets it double;
When east they go,
Flying jeeps;
When west they go,
Snoops and creeps,
Yes, snoops and creeps
And agents and spies,
Some of them wearing
The "Peace Corps" disguise.

Do the Yanks think your land a charming place?
Flash! They make it their military base.
Is it your scenery that enchants them and enthrals?
They plaster it with bars and rock'n roll halls.

When science becomes their main attraction,
Science brings plague and putrefaction;
Is it literati the Yanks embrace?
They gulp down their souls, not leaving a trace.

Is it the Muse the Yanks adore?
They treat her like a two-bit whore.
Is it precious Buddhist idols a Yankee venerates?
He hacks off their heads and ships them home in crates.

"Get out, Yankees! Yanks, get out!"
—The world's most universal shout.

DRAMA

Two plays are included in this section: The Day the New Director Came, *written in Communist China in the 1950's, and* Third Sister Liu, *adapted for Communist audiences from an old folk play. The women in both plays are built up as heroines, earnest and courageous allies of the masses. As in most popular drama elsewhere in the world, the characterization is elementary and the plotting simple.*

The Day the New Director Came

Ho Chiu (20th cen.) / Chung Wei-hsien

CHARACTERS (in order of appearance):

Lao Li, the messenger at the General Administration Office of a certain bureau, aged fifty
Liu Shan-chi, a man in his forties, chief of the General Administration Office
Tai Wei, general clerk in the General Administration Office
Chu Ling, in her twenties, from the Construction Section Office
Comrade Chung, an office worker
Chang Yun-tung, in the neighborhood of fifty, the new director of the bureau

TIME: A morning in late spring

PLACE: The director's office in a certain bureau

SETTING: Center, back, a double frosted glass door opens onto a corridor. On the corridor side of the door, seen backwards from the audience, is "Private, Director of Bureau," in black paint. Left, there is a door which opens into the General Administration Office. Right, windows. The director's office is furnished with an executive desk, a swivel chair, a filing cabinet, and a round conference table and chairs. On the desk, stationery, a desk telephone, a small desk clock and a bell push.

When the curtain rises, the door into the corridor is shut. The door to the General Administration Office is open. Lao Li is sitting at the round table poring over a book, marking passages as he reads, his dust pan and broom beside him on the floor. The sky seen through the window is overcast; it looks like rain.

A volley of knocks is heard at the glass door. Lao Li puts his books down and hurries to open it. Liu Shan-chi, a bulging portfolio under his arm, rushes in.

LIU SHAN-CHI *(throwing the portfolio on the desk, gives a quick look at the door on the left and then says to Lao Li)*: Nobody here yet?

LAO LI *(baffled)*: Who should be here?

LIU *(again looking left through the door)*: Where's everybody? Hasn't Comrade Tai come yet?

LAO LI *(looking at the clock)*: Why, chief, there's an hour still before office hours begin.

LIU: Office hours! What d'you mean, office hours!

You people talk as though you're paid by the hour! The new director'll be coming this afternoon and there you are, waiting around for office hours! *(Picks up the book from the table.)* Whose is this?

LAO LI: Mine.

LIU *(patronizingly)*: Studying the General Line,[1] eh?

LAO LI: Yes.

LIU *(throws the book down)*: Messengers like you would do better, as far as the General Line goes, to put your minds to keeping the office clean and seeing to taking round the tea. *(Points at the dust pan lying on the floor.)* Look at that! The way you throw your dust pan and broom about is not according to the General Line, I can tell you. May I ask when you're going to clear up?

(Lao Li quietly picks up his dust pan and broom and starts to go.)

LIU: Hey, you, hold on a minute!

(Lao Li halts.)

LIU: Have you got the director's new office ready yet?

LAO LI: Yes.

LIU: Have the curtains and covers come?

LAO LI: Yes.

LIU: Have you put them up?

LAO LI: Yes.

LIU: I'll have a look later. That's all.

(Exit Lao Li, left, with his dust pan and broom.)

LIU *(sits down, wipes his perspiring forehead, picks up the telephone and dials a number)*: Hello! That the Chien Hsin Furniture Company? I want to speak to your manager. . . . *(Gruffly.)* Never mind who's calling. Just tell him to come to the phone. *(Impatiently presses the bell. When nobody comes, he calls, left.)* Lao Li! Lao Li!

(Lao Li enters hurriedly.)

LIU: Go and fetch Comrade Tai.

1. General principles of the policy to be adopted for building socialism in China, put forward by the Communist Party and adopted by the government after nationwide discussion.

LAO LI: Very well. *(Walks to the left door.)*

LIU: Wait!

(Lao Li stops.)

LIU *(The receiver is buzzing. He quickly speaks into the phone):* Hello! This is Liu Shan-chi speaking. *(Motions Lao Li away.)* You may go.

(Exit Lao Li, left.)

LIU: Hello! About the sofas we bought yesterday. Why haven't they been delivered yet? . . . What's that? No, nothing doing! They've got to be delivered before nine . . . before nine, I say, and not a minute later. *(He slams the receiver down, and then picks it up and dials again.)* Hello! Who's that? Oh, it's you, Lao Lu! I say, you know that spring bed we bought for our director yesterday? I want it delivered right away.

(There are loud voices off, left.)

LIU *(unable to hear the voice in the telephone, puts his hand over the mouthpiece and shouts loudly, left):* Who's making all that noise there?

(Tai Wei puts his head around the door, left.)

TAI WEI *(timidly):* It's me, chief. . . .
LIU: What the hell are you shouting about? Can't you see I'm trying to telephone?
TAI WEI: Comrade Chu of the Construction Section . . .
LIU: It would be! Tell her she'll have to wait.
TAI WEI: All right. *(His head disappears.)*
LIU *(on the phone again):* Hello! Hello! Hello, hello! *(No answer.)* Damn it! *(Slams down the receiver.)*

(The quarrelsome voices have not been stilled outside. Liu Shan-chi presses the bell petulantly. Tai Wei enters.)

LIU: What's all the argument about?
TAI WEI: It's those Construction Section people. . . .

(Chu Ling enters on Tai Wei's heels.)

CHU LING: Comrade Liu, just look at the sky! I'm sure it's going to rain today. And you know we can't leave that cement outside any longer.
LIU: *(assuming a considerate air, with an effort):* Comrade Chu, I thought you'd covered up that cement with oiled cloth?
CHU: I've got some, that's true, but seven or eight bags got soaked the day before yesterday when it rained, for all that.
LIU: Well, there simply isn't any storage space for it, so what do you expect me to do about it?
CHU: I know the storage is a problem, but something's got to be done about it just the same. That cement's government property, you know, and we can't just stand by and see it wasted, can we?

LIU: I've studied the General Line too, thank you! That doesn't alter the fact that we've got no storage place. That's where the difficulty lies.

CHU: I thought difficulties are meant to be overcome, aren't they?

LIU *(looking trapped)*: All right, all right. I'll try to overcome them—I promise. *(Looks at his watch.)* It's nearly time to start work; I'll talk it over then and see what can be done.

CHU: You people observe working hours pretty strictly, don't you?

LIU: Well, that's in conformity with the General Line, isn't it? It calls for increased production, but says nothing about overtime.

CHU: I'm afraid the rain won't keep to office hours! If that cement gets damaged, it'll be your office that's held responsible.

LIU: All right, all right! We'll take full responsibility. Only give me a little time, please. *(Looks at his watch again.)* Half an hour, and it'll be fixed. How's that?

CHU: All right, then. I'll be back in half an hour. *(Exit, left.)*

LIU: H'mmm! That Construction Section ought to be called the problem-making department. They've just no consideration for others.

TAI WEI: They're all the same there. Look at them! She herself came over five times yesterday, fussing away. She wouldn't listen to a thing I said. All she could see was her 300 bags of cement. She never gave a thought to our headaches.

LIU: When she comes back, just tell her that nothing can be done for the moment. And mind you don't let her get hold of me, whatever happens.

TAI WEI: You know she was demanding that downstairs room back, just then?

LIU: What the hell! I had that room emptied for the new director. Can't she see it has been newly done up?

TAI WEI: I told her that, but she said it was a waste of money. She said she couldn't see why we had to spend money on a new office for the director when there was this one already.

LIU: You can just tell her that this one's too small. It's not suitable for a director. And anyway, my office has got to handle all manner of business. We're overworked actually. We can't carry on without a decent office for ourselves, in fact.

TAI WEI: Well, she went on to speak her mind about us and said that it was only because we wanted a bigger office for our section that there was nowhere for the cement to go.

LIU: Nag, nag, nag! Always criticizing! (*Changes the subject, pointing at the lettering on the center door.*) Why hasn't that been changed yet?

TAI WEI: I'll get it done right away. Very simple. It only means changing "Director of Bureau" to "Chief of Section."

LIU: But I want another line underneath, "General Administration Office."

TAI WEI: Very well.

(Lao Li enters, left, with a wooden sign, saying: Private, Director of Bureau.)

LAO LI: Chief, here's the new sign.

LI *(takes over the sign and examines the writing)*: H'mmm! Sung dynasty style, eh! Not bad! Not bad at all! *(Hands it to Tai Wei.)* Have it hung right away.

TAI WEI *(takes it)*: Very well. *(To Lao Li, pointing to the glass door.)* Lao Li, scratch off "Director of Bureau" there, will you? I'll send someone over to do the painting.

LAO LI: Right you are.

(Tai Wei and Liu Shan-chi exeunt, left.)

LAO LI *(muttering)*: I must say he's got a lot of energy, that chief of ours. He's even got to see to hanging up signs! *(As he talks, he starts to scratch the words off the glass door with an old knife.)*

(Enter Comrade Chung from left.)

CHUNG: Lao Li, where is your section chief?
LAO LI: He went downstairs.
CHUNG: Can you find him for me?
LAO LI: The office isn't open yet, Comrade Chung. Is there something special you want to see him about?
CHUNG: Yes. You know how the roof of our hostel leaks. I want to know whether the General Administration Office is going to do anything about it or not.
LAO LI: Of course we are. But Comrade Chung, our section chief . . .
CHUNG: Your section chief knows too well how not to do things. All he ever does is talk about "the budget" or the "bureau rules." Now, when he comes in, will you be sure to tell him this: We've found a man to do the roof ourselves. He'll be coming in a minute. What we want is for your office to see him, and settle the price. If your chief refuses to pay for it, we'll share the expenses among ourselves.
LAO LI: Who is this man? What's his name?
CHUNG: He's the manager of the Hsiang Tai Construction Company. Rather a tall fellow. His name's Chang.
LAO LI: All right, then. When he comes, I'll take him to see the section chief.
CHUNG: Thanks very much. *(Exit, center door.)*
LAO LI *(shaking his head with a sigh)*: What's the use? The whole department is so busy with this new director coming that we don't know whether we're on our heads or our heels. How shall we find the time to bother about a thing like a leaking roof?

(He resumes his work on the door with his knife. There is a short pause. Then a knock on the door is heard. Lao Li stops his work and opens the door. Enter Chang Yun-tung.)

CHANG YUN-TUNG: Excuse me, is this the director's office?
LAO LI: Well . . . *(Looking at the words on the glass.)* It was, but now it is the chief of the General Administration Office.
CHANG: Where's your section chief then?
LAO LI *(taking a good look at the visitor)*: Why? Do you want to see him?
CHANG: Yes.
LAO LI: Your name, please?
CHANG: My name's Chang.
LAO LI: Oh, yes! Manager Chang.
CHANG *(puzzled)*: Manager Chang?
LAO LI: Yes, I know about you. Comrade Chung's just this moment told me. *(In an earnest voice.)* I really ought to tell you it's not a good moment, Manager Chang. Why butt your head against the wall? Our new director's coming to take

over this afternoon, and our section chief's madly busy getting his new office ready. He's got his hands full. He'll never give the time to talk to you about house repairs.

CHANG *(more and more puzzled):* House repairs?

LAO LI: Yes, of course. In the first place, you see, there's no doubt that our hostel building *is* a bit ancient, and on top of that, the storm we had last week smashed a lot of tiles. So now, every time it rains, there's a proper lake indoors! But what can we do about it? The office for the new director needs whitewashing, and new furnishings and new flooring, not to mention sofas and a spring bed. That'll cost us over 400 yuan alone. How much does that leave for house repairs this month, I ask you!

CHANG: Yes, but if your roof leaks so badly, it's got to be done somehow.

LAO LI: Of course it should. We've had such a lot of rain recently, and whenever it comes down half the workers simply stop and go over there to get the leaking-pans out. If it happens to rain during the night, well, nobody gets any sleep. The result is that they've practically declared war on the General Administration Office! But our chief is the kind who sticks to his rules and keeps a tight hold on the purse-strings, and all he'll do is to tell everyone they'll have to put up with it until next month.

CHANG: Whereabouts is the hostel? Can you let me have a look at it?

LAO LI: You can easily find it yourself. Downstairs and turn right. You can't miss it. Come to think of it, Manager Chang, it wouldn't be a bad idea if you went there now just to take a look, and make an estimate. It'll have to be done next month anyway, and then we can give you the contract.

CHANG *(nodding, with a faint smile):* Thank you. That'll be fine. *(Exit, center door.)*

(The sky outside is getting darker. Now and again there's a distant roll of thunder.)

LAO LI *(looks out at the window with a sigh):* There's going to be another shower. I'd better close these windows now, so the floor doesn't get wet again. *(He shuts all the windows, and then picks up the knife and goes back to his scratching.)*

(Chu Ling and Liu Shan-chi enter, left, arguing with each other.)

LIU: You win, you win, my dear Comrade Chu. But you promised to give me half an hour, and here you've hardly turned your back before you come bothering me again. If everyone behaved this way, how d'you think I'd be able to get any work done at all?

CHU: What ever do you mean, bothering you?— Bothering! What a word to use! I'm here on proper business, mine and yours.

LIU: I'll take you at your word on that, comrade! If it's business, let's go about it in a business-like way. So let me remind you, Comrade Chu, that it's not our office hours yet.

CHU: Oh, pooh! You can see for yourself how it's getting darker and darker, and you must have heard the thunder just now!

LIU: I know, I know, I heard it. But you must also admit we provided you with oiled cloth, didn't we?

CHU: Of course, I know you did, but the stuff you gave us was perished. It's not waterproof any longer.

LIU *(vexed):* You do nothing but make demands all the time! What are you really after?

CHU: That room downstairs.

LIU: What room?

CHU: The one where the cement used to be stored.

LIU: My dear girl, that room's the new office for the Director of the Bureau. Do you mean to say that you want to use the director's office for storing cement in?

CHU: Not all of it. Half would do us very nicely, if you really can't find a vacant place for us anywhere else.

LIU: Let you have half of it?

CHU: That would do, I reckon. Three hundred bags of cement, you see. . . . I think half the room would do.

LIU: I see! Half the room for your cement and the other half for the director's office. Sweet and simple, isn't it?

CHU: Don't you really think you ought to do something about that cement? It's very important to us, you know.

LIU: Now, which is more important, some cement belonging to the Construction Section, or the office for the director? Anyhow, the director's coming this afternoon. D'you think I'd let anyone mess his office up? Not on your life!

(There is another roll of thunder.)

CHU *(agitated):* D'you hear that? More thunder! It'll rain any minute! You must do something, for goodness' sake!

LIU *(calmly):* Comrade, you've studied the General Line, haven't you? There's the economy drive to think of, isn't there? After all, you keep on forgetting that we've managed to supply you with that oiled cloth. That's already something, in view of the need for economy, I can tell you.

CHU: Yes, but what about the cement? You simply don't . . . *(A loud peal of thunder.)* See? The rain will start any minute!

(Chang Yun-tung enters, center.)

CHANG *(to Lao Li):* Comrade, where's your section chief? I must see him.

LAO LI *(in a tight corner:)* Manager Chang, you . . . you had better not . . .

LIU *(ill-humored):* What is it now?

LAO LI: Eh . . . h'mmm! Pardon me, Manager Chang, this gentleman *is* our section chief.

LIU *(to Lao Li):* Who's this?

LAO LI: It's Manager Chang, the contractor for the roof. Comrade Chung sent him over.

CHANG: I beg your pardon, I am . . .

LIU *(interrupting him):* Which roof needs repairing?

LAO LI: The roof of the staff's hostel. It lets in water all over.

CHANG: That's a fact. I've just had a good look at it.

LIU: Well, I'll be damned! Just for a few drops of rain, they kick up such a commotion. They don't seem to understand that we'd never get our work done if we didn't keep to the rules. If everyone can go and get a roofing contractor in every time they think something wants repairing, where ever should I be?

CHANG: I think it's very possible that they haven't kept to your rules. But who's really responsible for that?

LIU: Look here, you run along and talk to whoever it was who got you here. *(Looks at his watch. To Lao Li.)* There's half an hour before it's time to start. I'm going to have a bit of shut-eye and I don't want you to let anyone disturb me. *(He puts his portfolio under his arm and makes ready to leave.)*

(Chu Ling immediately bars the way.)

CHU: I'm not going to let you get away like that! Those 300 bags of cement simply mustn't be left out in the rain again.

LIU: What do you propose to do about it, then?

CHU: I want to use that downstairs room. Look here, Comrade Liu, the new director isn't coming till the afternoon, is he? We've got until then. You could easily let us use it for the time being. Directly it stops raining we'll shift it again.

LIU: You've got a nerve! You see for yourself, comrade, that room's just been whitewashed and the floor's been waxed. By the time you've had your cement in and out, d'you think the room would ever get cleaned up again?

CHU: Oh, you always have good reasons for not doing anything. Talking never gets anywhere with you. I can tell you, Comrade Liu, that I am going right down to get someone to give me a hand with moving that cement. If we do mess the room up, and if it upsets the new director, I'll take the consequences. *(She starts to go off, left.)*

LIU *(jauntily)*: Sorry, Comrade Chu, but you'll find the door locked. *(He fishes a key out of his pocket, tosses it nonchalantly, and then gives it to Lao Li.)* Here, it'll be in your charge. When the sofas come, see that they're put in the office. *(He turns away, pauses, and speaks again to Lao Li.)* No one is allowed to open the door without my direct permission! D'you understand? *(Sweeping everybody with a glance, he goes off, left.)*

CHU *(vehemently)*: Look at that! Just look at that! I don't know what goes on in his head, I'm sure! *(She is so angry that she can say no more and she sits down to get a breath.)*

LAO LI *(with a sympathetic sigh)*: He's got a heart of cement.

CHANG *(to Chu Ling)*: Comrade, are those bags piled up downstairs the cement you've been talking about?

CHU: Yes. But if it gets wet it won't be cement any more. What good are a few sheets of oiled cloth?

CHANG: Why does it have to be stored outside?

CHU: It used to be stored in that empty room downstairs. Then, with the change of director, the chief of the General Administration Office said we were to move it out, so that he could have the room redecorated for the director's office. He promised that something would be done about the cement, but we never thought that this something would turn out to be a couple of sheets of oiled cloth!

CHANG: What was the matter with this office? Why change it?

CHU: This one's too small, it seems. After all, it *is* for the director. It should be grander, I suppose.

CHANG: Grander! Do you think that's the real reason?

CHU: What do you think?

CHANG: I think it's pure nonsense!

CHU: I couldn't agree more! Pure, unadulterated nonsense! All he cares about is how his own office looks—government property doesn't matter! What would you call such a director?

CHANG *(grinning)*: I should say he was a bad one, if he's really like that.

(Another roll of thunder, this time loud and near.)

CHU: Oh! The rain's going to start!

LAO LI *(looks out the window)*: That's right; here it comes!

(Chu Ling runs over to the window, opens it and puts her hand out, then shuts the window hastily.)

CHU: It's started! My, poor cement'll be soaked. *(Rushes to the door, left.)*

LAO LI: What are you going to do, Comrade Chu?

CHU: I'm going over to my office to see if there's anyone there who can help.

LAO LI: Well! If your office could think of a way out, you could have saved yourself all your trips here.

CHU *(in a quandary)*: Oh, what can we do? *(She pauses a moment, and then an idea comes to her.)* I've got it! I can get the bed quilts! *(She starts to run off.)*

LAO LI: Then, Comrade Chu, how many quilts would you need? You'd need all the bed quilts we have, and then no one will be able to sleep! Come on, let's move that cement. I've got the key.

CHU: Oho! Move it! Into the new director's office?

LAO LI: It's the only place there is, isn't it? Let's move it there, for the time being, anyway.

CHU: What about you? Won't you get into trouble with your boss?

LAO LI: Never mind about him. I may be only the messenger, but I've studied the General Line myself, and *I've* got things clear now. Come on! I'll be fully responsible.

CHANG *(to Lao Li)*: Comrade, you are doing the right thing.

CHU *(shaking hands with Lao Li excitedly)*: Good for you, Lao Li!

LAO LI: All right, but let's go. There's no time to waste.

(Chu Ling and Lao Li are just going when Chu Ling stops.)

CHU: Oh, I forgot! There'll be no one to give us a hand! With this rain everyone'll be over in the hostel putting pans under the leaks! Where on earth can we get help?

CHANG: Don't worry, come on. We'll all come.

CHU: But three of us won't be enough! There are 300 bags of the stuff! It'll take us all day. The moment it comes down really hard, it'll all be done for, for all our worrying.

CHANG: Then go and tell everyone to come over immediately to salvage the cement. Tell them the new director says so.

CHU: The new director says so? I oughtn't to say that, ought I?

CHANG: Go and try. I'm sure they'll believe you.

CHU: But you . . . you really mean I should fool them?

CHANG: You won't be fooling them. I am . . .

CHU *(with a start)*: What? Are you . . . ?

LAO LI: Do you mean to say you're . . .

CHANG *(smiling)*: Yes, I'm the new director of your bureau.

(Chu Ling and Lao Li are both dumbfounded).

CHU: Well! . . . The new director! *(She is so overcome with excitement that she doesn't know what to say.)* Come on, Lao Li, let's go and shift that cement!

CHANG: That's the stuff! I'll be along immediately. You two go ahead and get everyone together.

CHU: Of course, of course! *(She pulls Lao Li out through the center door jubilantly.)*

(Chang Yun-tung scribbles down a note, using the pen and paper on the desk, and follows them. The stage is empty for a few moments. Vivid flashes of lightning can be seen through the window. The noise of rain gradually grows louder. Liu Shan-chi and Tai Wei enter, left.)

LIU: No, I said nothing of the kind. Get on the phone and tell them to send them over immediately.

TAI WEI: Very well. *(Takes up the receiver.)*

(Liu Shan-chi sits down at the round table, smoking.)

TAI WEI *(speaking on the phone)*: Hello! Is that the Chien Hsin Furniture Company? I want to speak to your manager. . . . Oh, good morning, manager. Our section chief told me to get on to you to see whether you've sent the sofas we bought. . . . Not yet? Why not? . . . You've got to wait until the rain stops? *(Puts his hand over the mouthpiece and speaks to Liu Shan-chi.)* He says he'll send them as soon as it stops raining.

LIU: Nonsense! Ask him if he is a meteorologist, or something, who knows when the rain's going to stop.

TAI WEI *(speaking into the phone)*: Hello! My chief wants me to ask you if you are a meteorologist, and know when the rain will stop . . . no? Well, then, you'd better do something. . . .

LIU: I'll give him half an hour to deliver them in. . . .

TAI WEI: What's that? Oh, I see. *(Puts his hand over the mouthpiece and speaks to Liu Shan-chi.)* He says as soon as he can have them packed in oiled cloth, he'll send them over.

LIU: Nothing doing! Oiled cloth's no good! *(Grabs the receiver from Tai Wei, and speaks himself.)* Hello! Let me ask you just one question: Have you studied the General Line or not? Those sofas have been bought by the government; they're state property. We've got to take good care of them. . . . Nonsense! That won't do! What are you thinking of! Oiled cloth is no good. You'll have to get a van. . . . What's that? Transport charges? You must charge us? All right, all right! But mind you send them over at once? *(Hangs up the phone.)* Can't see an inch beyond their own interests, these business people. He even tries to make a bit on the transport.

(Chang Yun-tung enters, center, soaked through, mopping his face with a handkerchief.)

LIU: So you're still here. It's no use you hanging around, I'll tell you; we're not interested in house repairs.

CHANG: Why not? That dormitory leaks like a sieve. Why don't you repair it?

LIU: I like that! Surely it's up to us to decide whether it needs repairing or not, isn't it? I fail to see that it's any of your business.

CHANG: Why don't you go and look at it yourself? Have you any idea what state that hostel's in? Pails, basins, spittoons—everything is mobilized. What's more, you have to keep shifting the things around from one corner to the other. All your workers' quilts are drenched. Don't you worry about things like that?

LIU: Now look here! It's not your business to read me a lecture: I should have known better than to waste any courtesy on commercial people like you. The movement against the Five Corruptions is hardly over, and yet here you are, worming your way right into our bureau. I wondered what you were up to here!

(While this exchange is going on, Tai Wei discovers the note on the desk. He reads it, jumps, and hastens to hand it to Liu Shan-chi.)

TAI WEI: Chief, our director . . .

LIU *(takes the slip, but doesn't look at it)*: Incidentally, I must warn you our new director thoroughly detests the likes of you. If you are wise you'll get out before you're kicked out. Otherwise, if you run into him, you won't be treated with the consideration I've shown you.

TAI WEI *(pointing to the slip in Liu Shan-chi's hand)*: But. . . but the new director has come. . . .

LIU *(still has no ear for Tai Wei)*: That reminds me, when the director comes, I certainly shan't forget to report all this to him. See if I don't tell him how much trouble the people here make for me, sending over a private contractor here.

CHANG: Trouble for *you?* When it rains, your people have to leave their offices and go over to the hostel to put out the pans to catch the drips! Do you realize the loss that causes? Not to mention the conditions in the hostel itself, with everything damp, and getting mildewed! Don't you realize that'll affect their health? Why do you always have to stick to your budget and rules so rigidly and always insist upon doing nothing "until next month"?

LIU *(in a rage)*: Damn you! Do you realize where you are? This is an office, a government office! I forbid you to brawl here. *(To Tai Wei.)* Throw him out!

TAI WEI *(trying to push Chang Yun-tung out)*: You'd better leave, Manager Chang, you'd better leave. You might as well give up hope of getting any business from us. It won't do you any good to exasperate him! Think of the old saying, "Go out to get wool, and come home shorn."

CHANG *(protesting aloud)*: Let me tell you something, Comrade Liu. When you hear yourself criticized, remain cool and think things over. It'll do you good.

LIU *(stamping his feet)*: Get out! Get out, I say!

TAI WEI: Now, now, please. *(Pushing Chang Yun-tung out, center, back.)*

LIU: Preposterous! This is simply preposterous!

TAI WEI *(turns back and says urgently)*: Chief, the new director's here already.

LIU: What! Here?

TAI WEI *(pointing at the slip in Liu Shan-chi's hand)*: Look at that! He's left a note for you.

LIU *(hurriedly unfolds the note and reads it aloud)*: "To the Chief of the General Administration Office: Please assign the director's office quarters downstairs to the Construction Section, so that it may be used to store the cement in as before. Also have the roof of the staff hostel repaired within two days. Chang Yun-tung." . . . Impossible! When did this note come?

TAI WEI: That's what I've been wondering myself.

LIU *(turns to the door, left)*: Lao Li! Lao Li! . . . Blast the idiot! Where the hell does he get to when he's needed?

(Chu Ling enters, center, back, carrying a jacket and trousers.)

CHU: Comrade Liu, where's Director Chang?

LIU: Director Chang?

CHU: Yes! He told me just now that I should find him here.

LIU: What? Then why haven't I seen him?

CHU: Haven't you? I'd better go and look for him, I suppose. *(Turns to go.)*

LIU *(barring the way)*: Look here, Comrade Chu, do you know the new director?

CHU: I met him just now. Why?

LIU *(hesitantly)*: Nothing, I was just wondering.

CHU: What about?

LIU: You see, he left this note. *(Handing the slip to Chu Ling.)*

CHU *(takes the slip and reads it)*: That's right. He was rather displeased with the cement being left outside.

LIU: Oh, was he? Did he say anything else?

CHU *(bluntly)*: He was very much dissatisfied with you. He said that you were careless of public property, and that you didn't bother about how your comrades had to live. Even when you knew their rooms leaked, you didn't mind, he said.

LIU: But doesn't he realize that it's because of the rules there's no money left this month? It's simply got to be postponed till next month.

CHU: Well, the new director asked how it was then that you could have an office whitewashed, and a new floor laid. There was room for that in the plan, I suppose! He also wondered how it was that there was plenty of money for sofas and new furnishings!

LIU: What! He even knew I had bought sofas?

CHU: Of course he knew, and he was furious about it, too. He said that things like that shouldn't be charged to the office account, and that you ought to pay for them yourself, and take them home.

LIU: What? Me pay for them? But that's three months' salary!

CHU: Well, if you can afford a sofa set here, won't it look more like a section chief's office? *(She goes out, center, back, still carrying the clothes.)*

LIU *(holding his head)*: I'll be damned! Here's a nice fix! . . . *(To Tai Wei.)* Go and get that contractor back immediately.

(Tai Wei hurries out, center, back.)

LIU *(paces up and down nervously. Suddenly he walks to the telephone and dials):* Hello! Is that the Chien Hsin Furniture Company? I want to speak to your manager. . . . Hello, this is Liu Shan-chi. . . . No, no, I am not rushing you. On the contrary, I am thinking of cancelling that sofa order. . . . What's that? Already on the way? Then call it back at once. . . . What's that? You can't? The truck's already gone quite a while? In that case, order it back when it gets here. . . . Now, look here, we are old friends, aren't we? You must help me out. . . . Certainly, certainly! We'll pay for the transport. *(Hangs up the phone and dials again.)* Hello! Who's that? Oh, Lao Lu! I say, you know that spring bed I bought? I want to cancel it. Our new director is not used to sleeping in a bed with a spring mattress—you know how it is. . . . What's that? It's on its way? Hello! Hello! *(The line is dead.)* Damn it! *(Slams down the receiver, and then presses the bell in a temper.)* Lao Li! Lao Li! *(Strides to the left door.)* Damn it! Not a soul there!

(Tai Wei pushes open the front door, and with a great show of politeness, ushers Chang Yun-tung in.)

TAI WEI: After you, Manager Chang. Please come in and have a chat with us.

(Chang Yun-tung enters.)

LIU: Please sit down. *(Holds out a packet of cigarettes.)* Will you smoke?
CHANG *(grinning):* No, thanks. I don't smoke.
LIU: Pardon me, I am so forgetful. Your name is . . .
TAI WEI *(interrupting him):* Chang, Manager Chang.
LIU: Yes, of course. Manager Chang.
CHANG: No, I am . . .
LIU *(hastens to apologize):* We had a slight misunderstanding before, I'm afraid. I hope you didn't mind. *(To Tai Wei.)* You go and keep a sharp lookout at the front gate. When either the bed or the sofas arrives, tell whoever brings them to take them straight back.
TAI WEI: Return them, you mean?
LIU: Yes, return them—the whole lot.
TAI WEI: But . . .
LIU: But what?
TAI WEI: But the charge for the truck and delivery service . . .
LIU: Pay them anything they want, but see that you don't accept delivery.

(Tai Wei hurries, left.)

LIU: Manager Chang, I am a blunt, outspoken man. I hope you will excuse me for what happened a little while ago.
CHANG: Comrade, I did not come here to see to house repairs. I . . .
LIU: I understand perfectly. You didn't come of your own accord. They sent you here. It really makes no difference one way or the other. You shall have the business anyway. It won't be much of a contract, but you'll be able to make something out of it.

CHANG: But I . . .

LIU *(hastens to clarify his proposition):* Don't worry! I am an understanding person. Name your price, and we'll pay. The only thing is, it'll be a rush work. It's got to be finished today. Well, it doesn't have to be an awfully solid job, if you know what I mean.

CHANG: You mean you'll pay any price, and I can get away with a sloppy job?

LIU *(handing him the note):* Well, see this? That's the way our new director wants it. Repairs to be done in two days, it says. Well, they are orders from above, and orders are orders.

CHANG: I see!

LIU: There's one more thing I'd like you to do to oblige me: if the new director happens to speak to you about it, tell him that I asked you to make an estimate some time ago, and that you only started today because you'd been busy.

CHANG: Why?

LIU *(heaving a sigh):* For one thing, there are too many people around who like to indulge in foolish talk. The director is new—a complete stranger here. It's quite possible that a piece of gossip or back-biting will reach his ears and give him a wrong impression.

CHANG: I see!

LIU: Actually I have nothing to be afraid of. The director and I are old friends. He knows how I do my work.

CHANG: Oh! You and the new director are old friends, you say?

LIU: That's right! Really old friends. We fought together as guerrillas, worked in the land reform movement together . . . together always. . . . *(By now he has adopted a painfully sentimental tone.)* But I haven't seen him for years. He must be getting very old now. *(Sighs.)* He's the nicest fellow except for a strange quirk—he has a strong aversion to private contractors. I advise you, therefore, to keep your distance if you should see him. It'll save you from getting into trouble.

(Lao Li and Chu Ling enter, left.)

LAO LI *(to Chu Ling):* See? I *told* you he was here.

PROVERBS

One man spreads a false report and a hundred report it as truth.

Gold is tested by fire; man, by gold.

The influence of good is all too little; the influence of bad is all too much.

For every man that Heaven creates, Earth provides a grave.

A man who has a beautiful soul always has some beautiful things to say, but a man who says beautiful things does not necessarily have a beautiful soul.—CONFUCIUS

When a country is in order, it is a shame to be a poor and common man. When a country is in chaos, it is a shame to be rich and an official.—CONFUCIUS

When someone said, "What do you think of repaying evil with kindness?" Confucius replied, "Then what are you going to repay kindness with? Repay kindness with kindness, but repay evil with justice."

LIU *(to Lao Li)*: You have been completely invisible all this time. Where the devil have you been?

LAO LI: I went down to give a hand with the cement.

LIU: Give a hand with the cement? What d'you mean?

LAO LI: We've moved it into the director's office.

LIU: What! Who told you to do it?

LAO LI: The new director. Director Chang told us to. He helped, too.

LIU: Oh! The new director's downstairs? Come on, Lao Li, I must go down and meet him. Hurry up! *(Grabs his portfolio from the desk, ready to leave.)*

CHU: Comrade Liu, whatever's the matter with you? The director's sitting right here with you. Why d'you think you've got to look for him?

LIU *(stupefied)*: The new director? *(Pointing at Chang Yun-tung.)* Him? Is that . . . *(His voice fails him.)*

LAO LI: Yes, he is the man you are looking for. That's the new director, Chang Yun-tung.

LIU *(nervously)*: I see, I see! So he is . . . *(To Chang Yun-tung.)* Director! Director Chang! I . . . I am Liu . . . Liu Shan-chi of the General Administration Office.

CHANG: H'mmm, it is certainly a privilege to have met you.

LIU: You are flattering me, director. *(To Lao Li.)* Lao Li, what are you waiting for? Go and bring some tea!

CHANG: Don't bother, Lao Li. You have worked hard enough with the cement. You must be very tired. You'd better go and have a rest.

LIU: Quite right. Go and rest yourself, Lao Li.

(Exit Lao Li, left.)

CHU: Pardon me, director, but you must be careful not to catch cold. You'd better change your clothes.

CHANG: I am quite all right, Comrade Chu. I've got used to it. I was going around like this quite often, when Comrade Liu and I were fighting in the guerrilla forces.

CHU: So you two used to fight together in guerrilla forces?

CHANG: Didn't we, Comrade Liu?

LIU *(extremely embarrassed)*: Yes, but I . . . I . . . eh . . .

CHANG: Now, Comrade Chu, how about the cement? Did you get it all moved?

CHU: Yes, all of it.

CHANG: How many bags got wet?

CHU: None.

CHANG: You got dozens of people to help you just like that. You did a very good job.

CHU: Thanks to you, though. All I had to say was that the new director himself was moving cement for our section, aren't you going to help, and everybody came at once.

CHANG: Why did you say *I* was moving the cement for *your* section? Aren't I part of the Construction Section? I think I've got a share in the cement, too.

CHU: Of course, you're quite right. The cement is government property, and every citizen has a share in it.

LIU: Quite right. Comrade Chu has studied the General Line and has readily acquired a lot of civic sense. The cement is government property. It is clear that everybody has a part in it.

CHU *(dryly)*: H'mmm, but you certainly didn't play much part in any of those 300 bags! You yourself didn't seem to want to, either.

LIU *(most uneasy)*: Comrade Chu, you . . . you are a little too . . . too . . .

CHU: Too what? Too critical? Not a bit! Your mind's full up of arrant nonsense from the old days. You knew very well the hostel roof leaked but you never bothered. You also knew that the cement would get wet if it rained, but that meant nothing to you. All you care about is sucking up to your superiors. You've spent the whole of the last few days furnishing the director's office with hangings and curtains and sofas. All you thought about was promotion.

CHANG: I am used to sitting on hard benches, you know, *(turning to Liu Shan-chi)* and now you deliberately want to spoil me.

LIU: Well . . . eh, well . . . but that was because . . . eh . . . because the General Administration Office budget could spare a little this month.

CHANG: Then why didn't you have the hostel roof repaired as being more important?

LIU: I did mean to. As a matter of fact, I, er, got an estimate . . .

CHANG: It's only because the contractor had been otherwise engaged that the repairing has been postponed again and again until today, I suppose?

LIU *(embarrassed)*: Not exactly. What I said to you a short while ago was due to a slight misunderstanding. I hope you don't mind.

CHANG: Slight misunderstandings! If they were slight I wouldn't mind, but I've seen too much to call them slight.

LIU: Of course, of course.

(Lao Li enters, center, back.)

LAO LI: Chief, the spring bed's come. Where do you want it put?

LIU *(confused)*: The spring bed? . . . Oh, yes! Where is Comrade Tai? Doesn't he know about it?

LAO LI: Comrade Tai is at the front gate, apparently waiting for someone. He's not seen the spring bed because they brought it to the back gate.

LIU: Oh! Very well, then. . . . Tell them to deliver it to my house.

LAO LI *(pointing at the invoice in his hand)*: Then, this bill . . .

LIU: Tell. . . eh . . . tell my wife to pay.

(Lao Li turns to go.)

LIU *(calls him back)*: Wait! Wait! Tell Comrade Tai to come immediately.

(Exit Lao Li from the front door.)

LIU *(hastens to explain to Chang Yun-tung)*: The bed . . . eh . . . my wife wanted this bed. She's rather spoilt, I'm afraid!

(Tai Wei sneaks in, left.)

TAI WEI *(whispering)*: Chief!

LIU *(quickly draws him aside to speak to him in a low voice)*: Keep a good lookout at the back door. The sofas will come any minute.

TAI WEI: At the back gate?

LIU: Yes! The back.

TAI WEI: But the front gate . . .

LIU *(pressingly)*: Back gate, back gate. They are using the back gate.

(Tai Wei scurries off. Lao Li enters, center, back.)

LAO LI: Chief!

LIU: What is it?

LAO LI: The sofas have come.

LIU *(embarrassed)*: Sofas?

LAO LI: Yes, there's a big one and two small ones.

LIU: Oh, yes! But, then, why didn't Comrade Tai . . . ?

LAO LI: You told him to wait at the back gate, and they've just brought the sofas to the front.

LIU *(extremely uneasy)*: I see, I see! Very well, then.

LAO LI: Shall I bring them up here?

LIU: No! Let me see . . . let me see . . .

CHU: It seems to me that the best place your section chief can have them delivered to is his home. His wife's spoilt, he says. She'll like those sofas, I'm sure.

LIU: No, no, not that! As a matter of fact, Comrade Director, I had already arranged for the store to take them back.

LAO LI *(presenting Liu Shan-chi with a bill)*: What about the delivery charges . . . ?

LIU *(grabs the bill from Lao Li)*: All right, all right, give it to me, I'll pay it. Director, please excuse me. I am just going to have a look. I'll be back in a minute.

CHANG: Certainly.

(Exit Liu Shan-chi, flustered, through center, back.)

CHANG: Comrade Li, you showed a high sense of duty today in salvaging government property. You did a good job and did it courageously. On behalf of all of us here in the Bureau, I want to tell you that we appreciate it. *(Goes to shake hands warmly with Lao Li.)*

LAO LI *(rather abashed)*: But . . . but I was only doing my duty. . . . Director, are you starting work today?

CHANG: Well, yes! I've already started, I should think!

LAO LI: But what about your office?

CHANG: This office will do perfectly well.

LAO LI: Then I'll just move Chief Liu's things back where they were.

CHANG: I don't think it's urgent. I rather feel that Comrade Liu will have to be assigned to a more suitable job.

CHU: You mean you're going to . . .

CHANG: I shall have to. It's only my duty to the people, and to him as well.

LAO LI *(takes out the key)*: Director, this key . . .

CHANG: Let the Construction Section keep it. But that room is quite big and sunny, and it's just been done up. We shouldn't really keep it for storing cement in. Wouldn't it make better quarters than they've got at present for some of our staff? It can't be worse than they've got now, anyway! We'll repair the roof of the hostel at once, and turn some of it over temporarily, at least, to the Construction Section. Comrade Chu, would that arrangement suit you?

CHU: Suit me? You bet! It's a wonderful idea!

CHANG *(jokingly)*: Don't go flattering me too soon. It's early days yet. I hope you'll have no cause to call me names again in future.

CHU *(quite embarrassed)*: Director, please forgive me . . . I didn't mean you.

CHANG: It doesn't matter really. If you do find me making mistakes in the future, I shall expect you to call me even worse names!

LAO LI *(looking out of the window)*: The rain's stopped.

(Chang Yun-tung and Chu Ling walk to the window. Sunlight, streaming through the window, lights up their smiling faces.)

CHANG: Yes, the rain's over, and the sun's shining again.

CHU: Let's open the windows. It's stuffy in here.

LAO LI: That's a good idea. Let's open the windows and have a change of air.

(Lao Li and Chu Ling throw all the windows open.)

CHANG: That's right. Open all the windows and let out this stagnant, filthy air.

(The three of them facing the morning sun take a deep breath of fresh air.)

The curtain falls slowly.

Third Sister Liu (extracts)

1960 version of a folk opera / Yang Hsien-yi and Gladys Yang

SCENE IV

AN OFFER OF MARRIAGE IS REFUSED

PLACE: In front of the inner curtain.

(Enter the Go-between Mrs. Wang, carrying the Landlord's gifts.)

GO-BETWEEN *(singing)*:

I have glib lips, a ready tongue,
Those who want to marry come to me;
I can trick a fox into dancing,
Or a peacock into mating with a turtle dove.

I am Mrs. Wang the go-between. I neither till nor sow but make my living by arranging matches. Yesterday Mr. Mo ordered me to call on Third Sister Liu with an offer of marriage.

(Singing.) The Liu family's girl is known to all,
She is saucy and has a quick tongue;
No common roadside flower is she,
But hot pepper high on the hill.

(Reflectively.) Hmm. I, Mrs. Wang the go-between, am pretty smart too. I'll use my ready tongue to have a try, if only for the sake of his silver.

(Singing.) My eyes are black, silver is white;
I care for nobody, but for money alone;
Just let me get my hands on silver,
And away with conscience and right! *(Exit.)*

(The inner curtain rises.)

TIME: Immediately after.

PLACE: The yard in front of Liu Erh's house with two papaya trees, a melon trellis and a bamboo fence.

GO-BETWEEN: I've come to congratulate you both, dear.
SISTER: Why should you congratulate us, Mrs. Wang?
GO-BETWEEN: Dear, clever as you are, how can you be so dense now?
You're a champion singer and pretty as a flower. Your name is known far and near on every side. *(Receiving no encouragement, she dares not speak outright.)* You're in luck, dearies! Mr. . . . Mr. Mo of our village . . .
SISTER: Mr. Mo has ten thousand *mou* of land.
GO-BETWEEN: That's right, that's right!
SISTER: Mr. Mo has ten thousand strings of cash.
GO-BETWEEN: Just so, just so!
SISTER: His family eats all the delicacies of hill and sea.
GO-BETWEEN: That's right, that's right!
SISTER: They all dress in brocade and silk.
GO-BETWEEN: Just so, just so!
(Singing.) He has not only ten thousand strings of cash—
SISTER *(singing)*: But nine wives and concubines too!
GO-BETWEEN *(singing)*: All his nine wives are childless.
SISTER *(singing)*: May all tigers and wolves die out!
GO-BETWEEN *(singing)*: His steward has come to me time and again.
SISTER *(singing)*: If you want to make a match, I'll help you.
GO-BETWEEN: My dear, dear girl, how intelligent you are!
SISTER: In whom is Mr. Mo interested now?
GO-BETWEEN: Well . . .
(Singing.) First she must have charm.
SISTER *(singing)*: Secondly, a ready tongue.
GO-BETWEEN *(singing)*: Thirdly, a name known far and near.
SISTER *(singing)*: Fourthly, talent and beauty to match.
GO-BETWEEN: Such a woman . . .
SISTER: Such a paragon is not hard to find.
GO-BETWEEN: You could say she is as far as the distant horizon, or as near as . . .
SISTER: Someone right before your eyes! *(Pointing to the Go-between.)*
(Singing.) You surely have the most charm,
Gadding about mincing and swinging your hips.

You surely have the readiest tongue,
Like a mad dog that yelps at the sun.
Your fame has surely travelled far,
Your name is mud throughout the land.
Your talent and beauty match his,
With your yellow teeth, bleary eyes and smarmy tongue.
You and the landlord will make a pair,
Like a wild hog matched with an ape.
We shall burn incense to thank heaven and earth,
When this hag is packed out of the way.

GO-BETWEEN: For shame, Third Sister Liu! Don't take this the wrong way.

(Enter Liu Erh with his hoe, followed by Hsiao-niu and several other young people.)

SISTER *(singing)*:

A good basket will never hold rubbish,
A good woman will never be a go-between;
Today, up against Third Sister Liu,
You're grilled like a potato over the flames.

LIU ERH: What's the matter, sister?

GO-BETWEEN: Liu Erh, Mr. Mo has taken a fancy to your sister. With the best will in the world I came to arrange a match. . . .

SISTER *(declaiming)*:
There are ninety-nine roads before you!
Get out quickly, go-between!

GO-BETWEEN *(declaiming)*:
The landlord is waiting for your golden words;
I shall not leave until the match is made.

SISTER *(declaiming)*:
I have seen wolves and tigers in the mountains,
Why should I be afraid of a bitch like you?

LIU ERH *(returning the gifts to the Go-between)*: Mrs. Wang, there is an old proverb: A bamboo door should face a bamboo door, a wooden gate should face a wooden gate. We dare not accept such an honor.

YOUNG MEN: Be off now, quickly!

HSIAO-NIU *(singing)*:

Stubborn old mule,
Trot away with your pack on your back.
I have a way with wicked mules—
Not whipping their rump but their legs!

(The others laugh.)

GO-BETWEEN: Very well. The pair of you don't know what's good for you. . . . Just wait. . . . Just wait. . . .

(Enter the Steward, who steps on the Go-between's foot.)

GO-BETWEEN: Ouch! What headless ghost . . . *(Looking up to see the Steward, she puts on a smiling face.)*

(The Steward turns to greet Mo Hai-jen, entering with his servants.)

STEWARD: Liu Erh, Mr. Mo has come in person to see you and your sister.

GO-BETWEEN: Third Sister, Mr. Mo has come in person. Tell him whatever you have in mind.

LIU ERH: Mr. Mo! I'm sorry we haven't even a chair here.

LANDLORD *(with affected solicitude)*: Have you recovered from your illness, Liu Erh? I have been so busy that I haven't helped you as I'd have liked. In future, though . . .

STEWARD: In future, leaning on the big Mo family tree, you need fear neither wind nor rain.

SISTER *(singing)*:

> The landlords elsewhere have tried to kill me,
> But the landlord here wants me to live;
> I have always seen stoves cook rice,
> Today it seems the rice is cooking the stove!

(The young people roar with laughter.)

LIU ERH: Please don't take offence, sir. My young sister is too wilful and we can't. . .

LANDLORD: On the contrary, your third sister is most intelligent. I shall be very happy if she will be my companion.

LIU ERH: Ours is a poor, unlucky family. We really cannot aspire to such an honor.

STEWARD: That's no way to reply to such condescension, Liu Erh. Don't forget that it's Mr. Mo's land you're tilling, it's his rice you're eating. If you offend him he'll take the land away. . . .

SISTER *(singing)*:

> Let him take the land if he wants,
> I'd sooner starve to death than bow my head;
> Many folk with no land at all
> Make a living by cutting wood.

STEWARD: Let's put our cards on the table, Liu Erh. Do you agree or not?

LIU ERH: Mr. Mo had better choose someone more suitable.

LANDLORD: If you won't agree, all right. Steward. . . .

STEWARD *(producing his abacus and ledger)*: Last year you borrowed silver to cure your illness, Liu Erh. The loan with compound interest comes to fifteen taels and thirty-seven cents.

LANDLORD: You must pay it back at once!

STEWARD: Pay it back at once!

LIU ERH: But . . .

LANDLORD: But . . . but what? You haven't the money, is that it? Take Liu Erh to the yamen to be punished.

SISTER: Wait! What is my brother's crime?

STEWARD: His crime? You're the offender. Singing insulting songs . . .

LANDLORD: Hold your tongue, man. If she agrees to this match, he won't have to give back the land, repay the debt or be sent to the yamen for punishment.

SISTER *(singing)*:

What sort of match is this,
What kind of marriage?
It's plain you wish us evil.
I can see at one glance
The drugs you have in your gourd.

(The villagers start whispering together.)

LANDLORD: The idea! How dare you say I wish you evil?

SISTER *(singing)*:

To seize the hill he claimed it for his ancestral graves;
In his hate for me he has proposed this marriage.
There are door gods pasted outside but devils within;[1]
This is clearly because he is afraid of my songs.

(The villagers begin to understand.)

LANDLORD: Indeed! You think I am afraid of your songs?

STEWARD: How could Mr. Mo be afraid of her songs, good folk? What a ridiculous idea!

SISTER: Very well, then.

(Singing.) My character is odd,
I love singing but not money;
If you are not afraid of my songs,
There must be a singing match before we wed.
If anyone can outsing me,
I'll come to you without the bridal chair.

LANDLORD: You want a singing match, eh?

SISTER: Our Chuang custom is to have a singing match before a marriage.

STEWARD AND GO-BETWEEN: We can't agree to this, sir!

LANDLORD: If I find someone who can outsing you, you'll marry me?

SISTER: You'll find someone? *(She thinks.)* What if he fails?

LANDLORD: Why . . . I'll say no more of marriage.

SISTER: And stop trying to seize the tea plantation on the Western Hill!

LANDLORD: As for that . . .

CROWD: Don't you dare agree?

LANDLORD: All right, I agree.

SISTER: You mean it?

LANDLORD: Certainly.

SISTER: You won't go back on your word?

LANDLORD: How can a man of honor like me go back on his word?

CROWD: Very well. We're witnesses.

LANDLORD: Let's go.

1. It was the custom at New Year to paste pictures of gods on the doors to drive away evil spirits. Here she means that the landlord pretends to be kind but has a sinister purpose.

(The Landlord and his followers leave.)

HSIAO-NIU: Third Sister, I'll beat the drum at the singing match to encourage you.

LAN-FEN: And I'll bring all the singers in the village.

CROWD: That's the idea!

(Curtain)

SCENE V

THE SINGING CONTEST

TIME: Some days after the last scene.

PLACE: In front of the inner curtain.

(The Steward and four servants carrying cases of song books pass by. Enter three scholars, Tao, Li and Lo.)

(The crowd roars with laughter.)

LANDLORD: Please start the contest quickly, gentlemen. If you win, I shall reward you well.

FISHERMAN: Now the singing will begin.

LANDLORD: Who will start?

TAO: Let me start. *(He sings.)*

Chih-hu-yeh-cheh-yi-yen-tsai[1]
There's no wisdom but in the classics.
Who created heaven and earth?
Who mended the vault of heaven?

SISTER *(singing)*:

All you can mouth is yi-yen-tsai,
Chih-hu-yeh-cheh, you mangy pedant!
Pan Ku it was who made heaven and earth
And Nu Kua[2] who mended heaven.

LI *(singing)*:

Here is a riddle for you to solve;
What lies long buried in the ground,
Springs forth to astonish heaven and earth?
Who doesn't know the great height I attain?

SISTER *(singing)*:

You are the bamboo-shoot in the hills,
Thick-skinned and sharp of tongue
But empty and hollow inside,
Dug up to sell for filthy lucre.[3]

1. An untranslatable list of auxiliary particles used in classical writing. Their excessive use was the hallmark of a pedant.

2. According to Chinese mythology a battle was fought between Chu Jung and the giant Kung Kung. The giant in his rage at being defeated knocked his head against the mountain which propped up the vault of heaven. Then heaven cracked open and the earth sagged southeastward. The goddess Nu Kua mended heaven with colored stones.

3. Bamboo-shoots are sold as delicacies.

LO (*singing*):

Stop boasting of your wit;
Divide three hundred dogs into four;
Each part an odd number, three large and one small—
Let's see what you make of that!

SISTER (*singing*):

Ninety-nine dogs go out hunting,
Ninety-nine dogs tend the sheep,
Ninety-nine dogs guard the house,
Leaving three . . .

THE SCHOLARS: Well! What of them?

SISTER (*singing*): . . . dogs as scurvy scholars.

(The crowd roars with laughter.)

TAO (*singing*):

Tell me, if you are sharp.
How many nails a big boat has?
How many grains a bushel?
How many catties does the rocky mountain weigh?

SISTER (*singing*):

I can tell you this:
You count the boats, not the nails;
Your reckon grain by weight not by number,
And if you'll bring me the mountain, I'll weigh it for you.

(The three scholars hastily look through their song books.)

LI (*singing*):

What is round above and square below?

TAO (*singing*):

What is round below and square above?

LO (*singing*):

What is round within and square without?

ALL THREE (*singing*):

What is round without and square within?

SISTER (*singing*):

A crate is round above and square below,
Chopsticks are round below and square above;
Braziers are round within and square without,
Copper coins are round without and square within.

(The scholars, much dismayed, do not know how to go on. They search hastily through their volumes.)

LO: This one, this one!

TAO: No good, no good. She can answer that.

LANDLORD: Hurry up!

(The scholars have nothing to sing. The crowd laughs.)

LAN-FEN *(singing while the others join in):*

In singing, there must be no pause;
In drinking, the wine pot must stay filled;
Since you dared to come to this contest
Why don't you answer with a song?

(Enter the Go-between and the servants.)

GO-BETWEEN: The sedan-chair is late, the sedan-chair is late! Now let the bride get in quickly.

(Music for the wedding approaches. The crowd laughs.)

LANDLORD *(embarrassed):* Keep away for the moment, keep away for the moment!

(The Go-between goes back followed by four servants.)

LANDLORD *(seeing that things are going badly):* These three gentlemen have travelled a long distance today and are tired after the journey. Let us stop the contest for the present and resume it some other day.

HSIAO-NIU *(singing while the others join in):*

We are half way through the contest,
How can you leave before the outcome's known?
If you stop half way, you must admit defeat;
If you won't admit defeat, you must sing on.

LANDLORD: Very well. Go on singing.

TAO *(singing):*

Don't be so arrogant,
Peddling learning before Confucius!
Can a sparrow compare with a phoenix?
Can a peasant compare with a scholar?

SISTER *(singing):*

Ridiculous!
You are wielding a big sword before Lord Kuan.[1]
If we grew no crops,
You would soon starve to death.

LO *(singing):*

Gross impertinence!
This comes of never reading the sages' books;
Without reading the "Four Books"[2] you know no manners,
I advise you to start with "The beginning of man."[3]

SISTER *(singing):*

You pedants can only eat and read without understanding the meaning;

1. A famous general of ancient times who wielded a big sword. This simile, like the earlier one about Confucius, means that someone who has not mastered a subject should not show off before experts.

2. The *Four Books* are Confucian classics—*The Confucian Analects, Mencius, The Great Learning,* and *The Doctrine of the Mean.*

3. The first words in an old Chinese primer. The quotation implies starting from the beginning.

The more you read, the sillier you grow;
Far better farm with us,
Helping to plough the fields and sow the crops.

LI *(singing):*

Are you out of your mind
That you dare abuse scholars?
If you anger the sage Confucius,
That will be the end of all learning.

SISTER *(singing):*

You will make me die of laughing
With your claim that scholars know most.
Tell me: when do you sow wheat?
When do you sow peanuts?

(The scholars are at a loss.)

LAN-FEN: Answer the question, quick!

TAO *(making a bold guess, sings):*

You must have lost your senses
To ask about such trifles;
In the third month you sow wheat,
In the middle of the eighth month peanuts.

(The crowd laughs.)

GRANDMA *(singing):*

The very idea!
Who sows peanuts in the eighth month?
If you sow wheat in the third month,
You won't even have dung to eat.

SISTER *(singing):*

All you scholars can do is eat white rice,
You have never muddied your hands and feet;
If we gave you a plot of land,
How would you harrow? How would you plough?

(The scholars urge each other to answer. Tao and Li push Lo forward.)

LO *(singing):*

Here is my reply:
Boundless my family estate,
And I have turned my hand to ploughing;
I walk in front and the ox plods behind.

(The villagers laugh as if they will never stop. The Landlord is too angry to speak.)

LI: Let's not talk about ploughing and tilling the land. Suppose we talk . . . er. . . of astronomy or geography.

SISTER *(singing):*

Talk of earth if you please,

Talk of heaven if you choose.
What makes wind and rain in the sky?
What makes hills and streams on earth?

TAO *(craftily)*: Who said we'd talk of heaven and earth? Let's discuss what's right before your eyes.

SISTER *(singing)*:

We'll speak of what's before our eyes;
How many hairs has your eyebrow?
How thick is the skin of your face?
How heavy the bridge of your nose?

(The scholars are dumbfounded, unable to answer. The crowd roars with laughter.)

SISTER *(singing while the crowd joins in)*:

The peach blossom is blown down by the wind,
The plum is battered down by rain,
The worthless gong is broken by a staff—
How can fallen blossoms and a cracked gong sing?

LANDLORD: Answer her quickly!

LO *(singing)*:

Yours is a hard life farming,
Barefoot the whole year round;
You had better marry Landlord Mo,
To have gold and silver and live in a fine mansion.

SISTER *(singing)*:

I am not afraid of hardships,
If you hanker after gold and mansions,
Why not persuade your own sister
To become Mo's concubine?

STEWARD *(singing)*:

The Mo family is rich and powerful,

PROVERBS

The bamboo stick makes a good child.

Only the highest and the lowest characters don't change.—CONFUCIUS

It is easy to govern a kingdom, but difficult to rule one's family.

Other people's harvests are always the best harvests, but one's own children are always the best children.

There are no filial children at the bedside of long-sick people.

If there is no food for one day, a father's love grows cold; if there is no food for three days, a wife's love grows cold.

Even brothers keep careful accounts.

Every family cooking-pot has one black spot.

Master easy, servant slack.

Spring is as changeable as a stepmother's face.

Curse not your wife in the evening, or you will have to sleep alone.

Nine out of ten matchmakers are liars.

You can't clap with one hand.

Eggs must not quarrel with stones.

With pages and maids in rows.

GO-BETWEEN *(singing):*

If you marry into the Mo family,
You'll be carried wherever you go.

SISTER *(singing):*

Don't boast of the landlord's wealth;
His heart is more venomous than any snake;
He washes his hands in a pond and the fish die;
He passes verdant hills and the trees wither.

LANDLORD: How dare you!

TAO: This is slander!

SISTER *(singing on):*

High the mountain, low the valley,
Third Sister loves to sing against injustice.
Let me ask these learned scholars:
Why are there so few rich men, so many poor?

TAO *(singing):*

The poor are many, being not a few.

LI *(singing):*

The rich are few, not being many.

LO *(singing):*

Not a few is not many, many is not few.

LANDLORD *(singing):*

Stop hedging and answer quickly!

(The three scholars search frantically through their song books.)

CROWD *(singing):*

If you can't sing, come with us;
Help carry umbrellas and shoes;
If you can't do even that,
Jump off the cliff for shame!

THE SCHOLARS: We'll take our leave. *(They withdraw, thoroughly crestfallen.)*

FISHERMAN *(singing):*

Go home!
Go home and scrape your rice pans clean;
Eat a dozen bowls at one go,
Or you'll lie awake all night.

(The crowd laughs loudly.)

LANDLORD *(declaiming):*

What use are all your songs?
How can they compare with my wealth?
By spending three hundred taels of gold
I can put an end to your singing.

SISTER *(singing):*

I know your family's wealth,

You grab whatever you see.
You rob men of their grain, their land,
Their houses, horses, mules. . . .
You'd move your family graves to seize a hill;
You kidnap girls to be your concubines;
But my voice is one thing you can't seize,
And with that I shall sing my songs.

(The crowd joins in the last four lines.)

LANDLORD: Is this a revolt?

FISHERMAN: Aha, Landlord Mo, say what you like, you've been worsted in this contest.

CROWD *(singing)*:

We laugh at your raving, we laugh at your rage,
It's no use building a bridge of rush;
When you pour tung oil on flames they burn higher;
When you draw water in a basket, you get nothing.

(Exit the Landlord bursting with fury. The villagers sing in their triumph and dance for joy.)

(Curtain)

SCENE VII

THE ORDER IS DEFIED

(Enter the Steward with a servant.)

STEWARD: "I catch the ball and and hang it at my breast, every thread tugs at my heart." Good, that's a good song! If you must sing, fellow countrymen, just sing songs like that. Don't learn those queer, vicious songs that Third Sister Liu sings.

FISHERMAN: What are queer, vicious songs, steward?

STEWARD: All those songs that abuse the landlord, defy the law of the land and offend the gods are queer and vicious.

FISHERMAN: Why, steward, you've made me more confused that ever. Let me sing you a song and you tell me whether it's a good one or a bad one.

(Singing.) What is roomy and square?
What couple sits there?
What kind of creatures trot to and fro?
What devours whole tons of grain?

LAN-FEN AND TUNG-MEI *(singing)*:

The pigsty is roomy and square.
The landlord and his wife . . .

FISHERMAN *(interrupting them to sing)*:

The hog and the sow sit there,

LAN-FEN AND TUNG-MEI:

They trot to and fro to grab food,
And devour whole tons of grain from countless homes.

FISHERMAN: How about it, steward!

STEWARD: It's all right when you sing about pigs.

(The crowd laughs.)

FISHERMAN *(singing)*:

Who was born with big ears?
Who wears a white and black gown?
What makes his belly so fat?
When does he go on all fours with back in the air?

GRANDMA *(singing)*:

The landlord was born with big ears,
He wears a white and black gown;
It's his good fortune that makes his belly so fat;
At court, he goes on all fours with back in the air.

STEWARD: That is quite a good song praising our master's good fortune and prosperity.

(The crowd roars with laughter.)

SERVANT: Why, steward, it's a pig that has big ears, a fat belly and its back in the air.

(The crowd laughs.)

STEWARD *(growing angry)*: The insolence! How dare you . . .

FISHERMAN: Don't be angry, steward. Here's a pleasanter song.

(Singing.) Whose heart is more venomous than any viper?
Who sits dangling his legs till the crops are ripe?
What person is a parasite among men?
Let whoever's sharp answer quickly!

LAN-FEN AND TUNG-MEI *(singing)*:

The landlord's heart is more venomous than a viper,
The landlord sits dangling his legs till the crops are ripe;
He eats and idles, a parasite among men;
A thousand familes keep him in idleness.

STEWARD: Ah, now that is Third Sister Liu's song.

LAN-FEN: Since I've learned it, it's become mine.

CROWD: We've all learned it, so it's our song.

STEWARD: This is a subversive song. You mustn't let Third Sister Liu stir up discontent.

YA-MU AND YA-HSIANG *(singing)*:

The world today is full of strange things,
Horses grow horns and buffaloes lay eggs;
When injustice rankles, men will sing
Without being stirred up by others.

STEWARD: Don't let Third Sister Liu take you in, fellow countrymen. Singing subversive songs can cost you your heads. It's for your own good that Mr. Mo forbids you to sing such songs.

FISHERMAN *(singing)*:

> Seems the world today has turned topsy-turvy,
> The wild cat comes to greet the hens at New Year;
> The dragon's horns have sprouted on the pig's head,
> The elephant's tusks have grown on the dog's jaw.

STEWARD *(seizing the fisherman)*: You old devil! Pretending to be a half-wit—you can't take me in! It was you who brought Third Sister Liu here in your boat.

(Enter the Landlord with four servants.)

LANDLORD: Stop! *(He looks for Third Sister in the crowd.)*

STEWARD: Third Sister Liu isn't here yet, sir.

(Enter Third Sister, Hsiao-niu and Liu Erh to quickly mingle with the crowd.)

LANDLORD: Listen, folk! Third Sister Liu has gathered crowds to teach them rebellious songs. Now the magistrate has issued an order forbidding the singing of folk songs. Since she is a stranger, young and foolish, out of the goodness of my heart I put in a word for her to the magistrate. But from now on she must mend her ways and sing no more folk songs.

SISTER *(singing)*:

> When the magistrate goes out the gong is sounded;
> When the monk goes out he chants Amida Buddha!
> When the emperor holds court, men cry All Hail!
> Work in the fields is hard and peasants must sing.

LANDLORD: So you are here, Third Sister Liu.

SISTER: I heard that the magistrate had ordered my arrest and punishment, but that you had put in a word for me. I've come specially to thank you.

LANDLORD: If you admit your mistake here publicly and sing no more folk songs, Third Sister, I'll not only see to it that you're not punished but reward you handsomely too.

SISTER: I am so young and foolish, Mr. Mo, that I don't know where I've gone wrong and what my crime is.

LANDLORD: You have gathered crowds to sing.

SISTER: What's meant by a "crowd"?

LANDLORD: Two people are company, three make a crowd.

SISTER: If someone gathers a crowd to sing, what should the punishment be?

LANDLORD: First offenders will be beaten, more serious cases will be put in jail.

SISTER: How about the ringleader?

LANDLORD: Decapitation!

SISTER: Fellow countrymen, do you all remember my singing contest with Mo Hai-jen?

CROWD: We do!

SISTER: He invited the three scholars Tao, Li and Lo. No more and no less—just three. So, Mo Hai-jen, as the ringleader who assembled a crowd, it seems you'll have to lose your head.

(The excited crowd shouts approval.)

LANDLORD *(with a grin):* Third Sister Liu, do you see this?

(His servant unrolls the magistrate's prohibition.)

STEWARD: Here is the magistrate's order forbidding singing.

(Declaiming.) These rustics defy the enlightenment of the government.
They are singing subversive songs to incite people;
So for the public good
The magistrate forbids all singing henceforward!

SISTER *(singing):*

Big stars in heaven rule over lesser stars,
Lions on earth rule over unicorns,
The emperor rules over high officials,
But who dare to rule over singers?

(The crowd joins in the last two lines.)

Fellow countrymen, let us go and sing.

LANDLORD: Don't you dare!

CROWD: Let's go and start singing.

SISTER: Come on, let's go and sing.

LANDLORD: How dare you!

SISTER *(singing):*

Life is sad without songs. *(Exit.)*

CROWD *(singing):*

Unless a road is trodden the grass grows rank;
Unless a sword is sharpened it grows rusty;
Unless a man stands straight his back grows bent.

(The Steward and the servants run after Third Sister.)

LANDLORD: Fellow countrymen and neighbors. . . .

CROWD *(singing):*

Our songs are like the water from Dragon Spring
Which flows through the hills and woods;
If any man tries to stem its flow,
It will burst its bank and flood the land.

LANDLORD: Since His Honor the Magistrate has forbidden singing, I think it would be wise for you not to sing.

(Third Sister emerges from the crowd with an umbrella.)

SISTER *(singing while the crowd joins in the chorus):*

What a fool!
What a fool the magistrate is to forbid singing!
The louder you gong and drum, the greater the din;
The more you prohibit songs, the more there will be!

(The Steward returns during the singing and reports: "Sir, Third Sister has disappeared." The Landlord tells him: "That's her with the umbrella." The Steward pursues the girl with the umbrella.)

SISTER *(Singing while the crowd joins in the chorus):*

Flowers on the hilltop make the valley fragrant,
Water beneath the bridge makes it cool above;
When injustice rankles in the heart,
Songs like flames of fire burst forth.

LANDLORD: I forbid you to sing!

SISTER *(comes out singing from the crowd, which joins in the chorus):*

We sing songs to work better in the fields,
Singing wastes neither time nor money;
This is neither stealing nor robbing;
When all the people sing we are stronger than Heaven!

(The crowd surrounds a girl while singing the last two lines. The landlord seizes her from the crowd, mistaking her for Third Sister.)

LANDLORD: Ha, Third Sister Liu!

(Enter the Steward bringing a girl with an umbrella.)

STEWARD: Sir, this isn't Third Sister Liu!

(The Landlord sees that neither girl is Third Sister, but both are wearing the same dress as hers. He pushes them furiously aside. Third Sister comes out singing from another group.)

SISTER *(singing while the crowd joins in):*

I sing my songs while you make your arrests;
Here's another song for you:
You can never seal the lips of the poor,
You can never stop their singing. *(Exit.)*

HSIAO-NIU *(singing while the crowd joins in):*

When you cut the cedar its root survives,
When you burn the banana its heart lives on;
When you cut a man's head and it rolls on the ground—
Even then it will go on singing!

LANDLORD: I forbid you to sing!

(Songs burst out on every side.)

CROWD *(singing):*

In a downpour the sky is hidden,
When rivers rise no boat can be seen;
All about are songs and Third Sister has gone—
The old fox is chasing his tail around.

(The landlord is nearly choking with anger.)

LAN-FEN AND TUNG-MEI *(singing):*

May he die of rage!
In rage the crab scuttles around;
Loud sound the songs from every side,
May the old turtle burst with rage!

LANDLORD: So you miserable little beggars dare to insult me too with your songs!

SISTER *(suddenly appearing on a rock under the banian tree to sing):*

The cockerel has a flaunting tail,
The poor of each generation love to sing;
They sing till heaven and earth spin round,
And the rich and the officials can do nothing!

LANDLORD: How dare you ignore the government and violate its order?

SISTER *(singing):*

Few the rich, many the poor;
We will seize the grey dragon,[1] what is there to fear?
We pull out the dragon's scales for tiles,
We cut off the dragon's head for a pedestal;
Our strength is infinite, our wisdom boundless—
And we dare to fight the dragon king himself!

(Hsiao-niu aims his arrow at the magistrate's order and shoots it down.)

CROWD *(singing):*

Few the rich, many the poor;
We will seize the grey dragon, what is there to fear?
We pull out the dragon's scales for tiles,
We cut off the dragon's head for a pedestal;
Our strength is infinite, our wisdom boundless—
And we dare to fight the dragon king himself!

(Trembling, the Landlord picks up the order.)

LANDLORD: Here, men! Arrest Third Sister Liu!

(Enter servants armed with daggers. The crowd will not let them approach Third Sister, who runs off through the crowd.)

SISTER *(singing):*

I am not afraid though hills crumble and the earth splits;
I am not afraid though the whole world is flooded;
My songs are echoed far and wide;
Why should I be afraid of a murderous landlord?

LANDLORD: Here! Arrest her!

HSIAO-NIU: Take care, Mo Hai-jen! *(He shoots off the Landlord's hat.)*

(The crowd cheers. The terrified landlord runs away with his servants. The inner curtain goes down.)

CROWD *(singing before the inner curtain):*

We sing folk songs;

1. This refers to the reactionaries.

One sings and ten thousand join in;
We sing till the poor laugh for joy,
Till the landlord trembles with fear.

FISHERMAN: Liu Erh, I don't think that old dog Mo Hai-jen will stop at this.

LIU ERH: I agree, I'm afraid the magistrate may send troops. . . .

STRANGER: Third Sister, we beg of you to leave here at once. Come to us.

LAN-FEN: Why to you?

STRANGER: To teach us songs.

(All the other strangers ask Third Sister to go and teach them her songs.)

LIU ERH: Go then, sister, with Hsiao-niu. Go everywhere and sing wherever you go to kindle the hearts of all the poor.

SISTER AND HSIAO-NIU: What will you do, brother?

LIU ERH: Don't worry, just go. I can shoulder the responsibility here, however big.

CROWD: That's right. We'll be behind you!

LAN-FEN: Sister, we shall always sing the songs you've taught us.

CROWD *(singing)*:

We shall sing of all the injustice in the world,
We shall sing of all that is in the hearts of the poor;
We shall sing till one stalk of rice grows nine ears,
Till after the dark night the sun shines red.

EPILOGUE

THE SONGS ARE SPREAD

(The inner curtain rises to reveal a radiant morning sky and golden waves tumbling in the great river.)

CROWD *(singing)*:

We see Third Sister off to the great river,
Riding the wind, braving the waves, she will spread her songs;
The rich will tremble at the sound,
The poor, hearing her songs, will laugh aloud.

(Amid the singing, Third Sister and Hsiao-niu board the Old Fisherman's little boat.)

SISTER *(singing)*:

Riding the wind, braving the waves, I go to teach my songs;
Hills of sword, seas of fire are a smooth slope to me;
All the poor in the world are united as one;
When one sings, ten thousand join in.

CROWD *(singing)*:

When one sings, ten thousand join in;
We sing till golden waves tumble in the river;
The river flows on without end,
For a thousand generations there will be singing.

(Curtain)

SHORT STORIES

A Fickle Widow

Anon. / A. K. Douglas

In Chinese stories such as this, designed to be recited aloud in teahouses and market-places, certain motifs tended to recur. The faithlessness of women was a frequent subject, not surprising in view of the fact that almost all the writers and storytellers were male. Another fashionable theme was the activities of ghosts, tales involving supernatural elements having a long history in China. Both of these elements, the disloyal wife and the supernatural character, appear in this anonymous story of medieval China, written in the fifteenth century or earlier.

At a distance from the capital, and in the peaceful retirement of the country there dwelt many centuries ago a philosopher named Chwang, who led a pleasurable existence in the society of his third wife, and in the study of the doctrines of his great master, Lao-tze. Like many philosophers, Chwang had not been fortunate in his early married life. His first wife died young; his second he found it necessary to divorce, on account of misconduct; but in the companionship of Lady T'ien he enjoyed a degree of happiness which had previously been denied him. Being a philosopher, however, he found it essential to his peace that he should occasionally exchange his domestic surroundings for the hillsides and mountain solitudes. On one such expedition he came unexpectedly on a newly made grave at the side of which was seated a young woman dressed in mourning, who was gently fanning the new mound. So strange a circumstance was evidently one into which a philosopher should inquire. He therefore approached the lady, and in gentle accents said, "May I ask what you are doing?"

"Well," replied the lady, "the fact is that this grave contains my husband. And, stupid man, just before he died he made me promise that I would not marry again until the soil above his grave should be dry. I watched it for some days, but it got dry so very slowly that I am fanning it to hasten the process." So saying she looked up into Chwang's face with so frank and engaging a glance that the philosopher at once decided to enlist himself in her service.

"Your wrists are not strong enough for such work," he said. "Let me relieve you at it."

"By all means," replied the lady briskly. "Here is the fan, and I shall owe you an everlasting debt of gratitude if you will fan it dry as quickly as possible."

Without more ado, Chwang set to work, and by exercise of his magical powers he extracted every drop of moisture from the grave with a few waves of the fan. The lady was delighted with his success, and with the sunniest smile said, "How can I thank you sufficiently for your kindness! As a small mark of my gratitude, let me present you with this embroidered fan which I had in reserve; and as a token of my esteem, I really must ask you to accept one of my silver hairpins." With these words she presented the philosopher with the fan, and drawing out one of her ornamented hairpins, she offered it for his acceptance. The philosopher took the fan, but possibly having the fear of Lady T'ien before his eyes, he declined the pin. The incident made him thoughtful, and as he seated himself again in his thatched hall, he sighed deeply.

"Why are you sighing?" inquired the Lady T'ien, who happened to enter at that moment, "and where does the fan come from which you hold in your hand?"

Thus invited, Chwang related all that had passed at the tomb. As he proceeded with the tale, Lady T'ien's countenance fell, and when he had concluded she broke forth indignantly, inveighing against the young widow, who she vowed was a disgrace to her sex. So soon as she had exhausted her vituperations, Chwang quietly repeated the proverb, "Knowing men's faces is not like knowing their hearts."

Interpreting this use of the saying as implying some doubts as to the value of her protestations, Lady T'ien exclaimed:

"How dare you condemn all women as though they were all formed in the same mold with this shameless widow? I wonder you are not afraid of calling down a judgment on yourself for such an injustice to me, and others like me."

"What need is there of all this violence?" rejoined her husband. "Now, tell me, if I were to die, would you, possessed as you are of youth and beauty, be content to remain a widow for five, or even three years?"

"A faithful minister does not serve two princes, and a virtuous woman never thinks of a second husband," sententiously replied the lady. "If fate were to decree that you should die, it would not be a question of three years or of five years, for never, so long as life lasted, would I dream of a second marriage."

"It is hard to say, it is hard to say," replied Chwang.

"Do you think," rejoined his wife, "that women are like men, destitute of virtue and devoid of justice? When one wife is dead you look out for another, you divorce this one and take that one; but we women are for one saddle to one horse. Why do you say these things to annoy me?"

With these words she seized the fan and tore it to shreds.

"Calm yourself," said her husband; "I only hope, if occasion offers, you will act up to your protestations."

Not many days after this Chwang fell dangerously ill, and as the symptoms increased in severity, he thus addressed his wife:

"I feel that my end is approaching, and that it is time I should bid you farewell. How unfortunate that you destroyed that fan the other day! You would have found it useful for drying my tomb."

"Pray, my husband, do not at such a moment suggest suspicions of me. Have I not studied the 'Book of Rites,' and have I not learned from it to follow one husband, and one only? If you doubt my sincerity, I will die in your presence to prove to you that what I say, I say in all faithfulness."

"I desire no more," replied Chwang; and then, as weakness overcame him, he added faintly, "I die. My eyes grow dim."

With these words he sank back motionless and breathless.

Having assured herself that her husband was dead, the Lady T'ien broke out into loud lamentations, and embraced the corpse again and again. For days and nights she wept and fasted, and constantly dwelt in her thoughts on the virtues and wisdom of the deceased. As was customary, on the death of so learned a man as Chwang, the neighbors all came to offer their condolences and to volunteer their assistance. Just as the last of those had retired, there arrived at the door a young and elegant scholar, whose face was like a picture and whose lips looked as though they had been smeared with vermilion. He was dressed in a violet silk robe, and wore a black cap, an embroidered girdle, and scarlet shoes. His servant announced that he was a prince of the Kingdom of Tsoo, and he himself added by way of explanation:

"Some years ago I communicated to Chwang my desire to become his disciple. In furtherance of this purpose I came hither, and now, to my inexpressible regret, I find on my arrival that my master is dead."

To evince his respectful sorrow, the Prince at once exchanged his colored clothing for mourning garments, and prostrating himself before the coffin, struck his forehead four times on the ground, and sobbed forth, "Oh, learned Chwang, I am indeed unfortunate in not having been permitted to receive your instructions face to face. But to show my regard and affection for your memory, I will here remain and mourn for you a hundred days."

With these words he prostrated himself again four times, while he watered the earth with his tears. When more composed, he begged to be allowed to pay his respects to Lady T'ien, who, however, thrice declined to see him, and only at last consented when it was pointed out to her that, according to the most recondite authorities, the wives of deceased instructors should not refuse to see their husbands' disciples.

After then receiving the Prince's compliments with downcast eyes, the Lady T'ien ventured just to cast one glace at her guest, and was so struck by his beauty and the grace of his figure, that a sentiment of more than interest suffused her heart. She begged him to take up his abode in her house, and when dinner was prepared, she blended her sighs with his. As a token of her esteem, so soon as the repast was ended, she brought him the copies of "The Classic of Nan-hwa," and the "Sutra of Reason and of Virtue," which her husband had been in the habit of using, and presented them to the Prince. He, on his part, in fulfillment of his desire of mourning for his master, daily knelt and lamented by the side of the coffin, and thither also the Lady T'ien repaired to breathe her sighs. These constant meetings provoked short conversations, and the glances, which on these occasions were exchanged between them, gradually betook less of condolence and more of affection, as time went on. It was plain that already the Prince was half enamored, while the lady was deeply in love. Being desirous of learning some particulars about her engaging guest, she one evening summoned his servant to her apartment, and having plied him with wine, inquired from him whether his master was married.

"My master," replied the servant, "has never yet been married."

"What qualities does he look for in the fortunate woman he will choose for his wife?" inquired the lady.

"My master says," replied the servant, who had taken quite as much wine as was good for him, "that if he could obtain a renowned beauty like yourself, madam, his heart's desire would be fulfilled."

"Did he really say so? Are you sure you are telling me the truth?" eagerly asked the lady.

"Is it likely that an old man like me would tell a lie?" replied the servant.

"If it be so, will you then act as a go-between, and arrange a match between us?"

"My master has already spoken to me of the matter, and would desire the alliance above all things, if it were not for the respect due from a disciple to a deceased master, and for the animadversions to which such a marriage would give rise."

"But as a matter of fact," said the Lady T'ien, "the Prince was never my husband's disciple; and as to our neighbors about here, they are too few and insignificant to make their animadversions worth a thought."

The objections having thus been overcome, the servant undertook to negotiate with his master, and promised to bring word of the result at any hour of the day or night at which he might have anything to communicate.

So soon as the man was gone, the Lady T'ien gave way to excited impatience. She went backwards and forwards to the chamber of death, that she might pass the door to the Prince's room, and even listened at his window, hoping to hear him discussing with his servant the proposed alliance. All, however, was still until she approached the coffin, when she heard an unmistakable sound of hard breathing. Shocked and terrified, she exclaimed, "Can it be possible that the dead has come to life again!"

A light, however, relieved her apprehensions by discovering the form of the Prince's servant lying in a drunken sleep on a couch by the corpse. At any other time such disrespect to the deceased would have drawn from her a torrent of angry rebukes, but on this occasion she thought it best to say nothing, and on the next morning, she accosted the defaulter without any reference to his escapade of the night before. To her eager inquiries the servant answered that his master was satisfied on the points she had combated on the preceding evening, but that there were still three unpropitious circumstances which made him hesitate.

"What are they?" asked the lady.

"First," answered the man, "my master says that the presence of the coffin in the saloon makes it difficult to conduct marriage festivities in accordance with usage; secondly, that the illustrious Chwang having so deeply loved his wife, and that affection having been so tenderly returned by her in recognition of his great qualities, he fears that a second husband would probably not be held entitled to a like share of affection; and thirdly, that not having brought his luggage, he has neither the money nor the clothes necessary to play the part of a bridegroom."

"These circumstances need form no obstacle to our marriage," replied the lady. "As to the first objection, I can easily have the coffin removed into a shed at the back of the house; then as to the second, though my husband was a great Taoist authority, he was not by any means a very moral man. After his first wife's death he married a second, whom he divorced, and just before his own decease, he flirted outrageously with a widow whom he found fanning her husband's grave on the hill yonder. Why, then, should your master, young, handsome, and a prince, doubt the quality of my affection? Then as to the third objection, your master need not trouble himself about the expenses connected with our marriage; I will provide them. At this moment I have twenty taels of silver in my room, and these I will readily give to him to provide himself clothes withal. Go back, then, and tell the Prince what I say, and remind him that there is no time like the present, and that there could be no more felicitous evening for our marriage than that of today."

Carrying the twenty taels of silver in his hand, the servant returned to his master, and presently brought back word to the lady that the Prince was convinced by her arguments, and ready for the ceremony.

On receipt of this joyful news, Lady T'ien exchanged her mourning for wedding garments, painted her cheeks, reddened her lips, and ordered some villagers to carry Chwang's coffin into a hut at the back of the house, and to prepare for the wedding. She herself arranged the lights and candles in the hall, and when the time arrived stood ready to receive the Prince, who presently entered, wearing the insignia of his official rank, and dressed in a gaily embroidered tunic. Bright as a polished gem and a gold setting, the two stood beneath the nuptial torch, radiant with beauty and love. At the conclusion of the ceremony, with every demonstration of affection, the Prince led his bride by the hand into the nuptial chamber. Suddenly, as they were about to retire to rest, the Prince was seized with violent convulsions. His face became distorted, his eyebrows stood on end, and he fell to the ground, beating his breast with his hands.

The Lady T'ien, frantic with grief, embraced him, rubbed his chest, and when these remedies failed to revive him, called in his old servant.

"Has your master ever had any fits like this before?" she hurriedly inquired.

"Often," replied the man, "and no medicine ever alleviates his sufferings; in fact, there is only one thing that does."

"Oh, what is that? asked the lady.

"The brains of a man, boiled in wine," answered the servant. "In Tsoo, when he has these attacks, the King, his father, beheads a malefactor and takes his brains to form the decoction; but how is it possible here to obtain such a remedy?"

"Will the brains of a man who has died a natural death do?" asked the lady.

"Yes, if forty-nine days have not elapsed since the death."

"My former husband's would do then. He has only been dead twenty days. Nothing will be easier than to open the coffin and take them out."

PROVERBS

When the blind lead the blind, both will fall into the water.

Win your lawsuit and lose your money.

Don't climb a tree to look for fish.

When you have tea and wine, you have many friends.

It is difficult to win a friend in a year; it is easy to offend one in an hour.

If good luck comes, who doesn't? If good luck does not come, who does?

The tongue is like a sharp knife; it kills without drawing blood.

Great politeness usually means "I want something."

Don't ask a guest if you should kill a chicken.

Though annoyed to death, do not file a lawsuit.

Money will open a blind man's eyes and will make a priest sell his prayer books.

"But would you be willing to do it?"

"I and the Prince are now husband and wife. A wife with her body serves her husband, and should I refuse to do this for him out of regard for a corpse, which is fast becoming dust?"

So saying, she told the servant to look after his master, and seizing a hatchet, went straight to the hut to which the corpse had been removed. Having arranged the light conveniently, she tucked up her sleeves, clenched her teeth, and with both hands brought down the hatchet on the coffin-lid. Blow after blow fell upon the wood, and at the thirty-first stroke the plank yielded, and the head of the coffin was forced open. Panting with her exertions, she cast a glance on the corpse preparatory to her further grim office, when, to her inexpressible horror, Chwang sighed twice, opened his eyes, and sat up. With a piercing shriek she shrank backwards, and dropped the hatchet from her palsied hands.

"My dear wife," said the philosopher, "help me to rise."

Afraid to do anything else but obey, she assisted him out of the coffin and offered him support, while he led the way, lamp in hand, to her chamber. Remembering the sight that would there meet his eyes, the wretched woman trembled as they approached the door. What was her relief, however, to find that the Prince and his servant had disappeared. Taking advantage of this circumstance, she assumed every woman's wile, and in softest accents, said, "Ever since your death you have been in my thoughts day and night. Just now, hearing a noise in your coffin, and remembering how, in the tales of old, souls are said to return to their bodies, the hope occurred to me that it might be so in your case, and I took a hatchet to open your coffin. Thank Heaven and Earth my felicity is complete; you are once more by my side."

"Many thanks, madame," said Chwang, "for your deep consideration. But may I ask why you are dressed in such gay clothing."

"When I went to open your coffin, I had, as I say, a secret presentiment of my good fortune, and I dared not receive you back to life in mourning attire."

"Oh," replied her husband, "but there is one other circumstance which I should like to have explained. Why was not my coffin placed in the saloon, but tossed into a ruined barn?"

To this question Lady T'ien's woman's wit failed to supply an answer. Chwang looked at the cups and wine which formed the relics of the marriage feast, but made no other remark thereon, except to tell his wife to warm him some wine. This she did, employing all her most engaging wiles to win a smile from her husband; but he steadily rejected her advances, and presently, pointing with his finger over his shoulder, he said, "Look at those two men behind you."

She turned with an instinctive knowledge that she would see the Prince and his servant in the courtyard, and so she did. Horrified at the sight, she turned her eyes towards her husband, but he was not there. Again looking towards the courtyard she found that the Prince and his servant had now disappeared, and that Chwang was once more at her side. Perceiving then the true state of the case, that the Prince and his servant were but Chwang's other self, which he by his magical power was able to project into separate existences, she saw that all attempts at concealment were vain; and taking her girdle from her waist, she tied it to a beam and hung herself on the spot.

So soon as life was extinct Chwang put his frail wife into the coffin from which he had lately emerged, and setting fire to his house, burnt it with its contents to ashes. The only things saved from the flames were the "Sutra of Reason and of Virtue," and "The Classic of Nan-hwa," which were found by some neighbors, and carefully treasured.

As to Chwang, it is said that he set out as on a journey towards the West. What his ultimate destination was is not known, but one thing is certain, and that is, that he remained a widower for the rest of his life.

Our Story of Ah Q (extracts)

Lusin (1881–1936) / Wang Chi-chen

By the time Lusin died in 1936 he had become, says Lin Yutang, "God to the leftist writers of China." Perhaps the most vitriolic satirist of pre-Maoist China, he was strongly influenced by Western ideas (in his essays he refers casually to Nietzsche, Schopenhauer, Ibsen, Thomas Huxley, Marx, Lunacharsky, and others) and advocated the total rejection of traditional Chinese culture. Revolution was what he demanded, but Western critics suspect that he would have remained a vituperative critic under orthodox Marxism as well. In "The Diary of a Madman," Lusin depicted the entire history of China as a continuous period of man eating man.

Of his most famous story, Wang Chi-chen, writing in the introduction to his translation of Lusin's stories (p. xx), says: " 'Our Story of Ah Q' will stand out . . . as the most important single contribution to Chinese literature since the literary revolution, for in this story Lusin succeeded in translating his diagnosis of China's fundamental weakness. . . . Ah Q is the personification of two of the most despicable traits in human nature: the tendency to rationalize things to our own supposed advantage and the cowardly habit of turning upon those weaker than ourselves after we have been abused by those stronger than ourselves." In modern China, Wang adds, such expressions as "That's Ah-Q logic" and "He is the perfect image of Ah Q" have become part of everyday speech.

The fact is that I do not know the surname of Ah Q. At one time it appeared to have been Chao, but by the following day it had become a matter of uncertainty. This was at the time when the gong-beating messengers brought news that the son of His Honor Chao had passed his examination. Ah Q had just drunk two cups of wine and was feeling effusive. He announced excitedly that it was a great honor for him because he and His Honor Chao were kinsmen and that he, Ah Q, was, come to think of it, three generations higher than the new licentiate in the family tree. This made a great impression on some of the bystanders. But the next day the village constable summoned Ah Q to His Honor's house. At the sight of Ah Q, His Honor turned red with fury and thundered:

"Ah Q, you knave! Did you say that I am a kinsman of yours?"

Ah Q was silent.

This infuriated His Honor still more; he advanced a few steps, saying, "How dare you blab such nonsense. How could I have a kinsman like you? Is your surname Chao?"

Ah Q did not open his mouth; he considered a retreat. His Honor jumped up and slapped him in the face.

"How could your name be Chao? You!"

Ah Q did not try to argue that his name was really Chao; he simply backed out with the constable, nursing his left cheek. Outside, the constable gave him a lecture and accepted two hundred *cash* from him for wine money. All those who heard about this incident agreed that Ah Q had invited the thrashing by his own impudence, that his surname was probably not Chao, and that even if it had been, he should not have been so presumptuous as to talk the way he did.

Not only were Ah Q's name and origin unknown, but his "life and deeds" were likewise clothed in obscurity. The villagers of Wei were interested in Ah Q only when they needed an extra laborer, only as an object of jibes and practical jokes; no one paid any attention to his life and deeds. Ah Q himself did not throw any light on the subject. When engaged in quarrels he would sometimes allude to the past, saying, "We used to be much better off than you! Who do you think you are?"

Having no home, Ah Q lived in the village temple and worked for people by the day, harvesting wheat, husking rice, punting boats. When his work lasted for a period of time he stayed at his employer's house. So he was remembered only when extra hands were needed; but this was mere labor, not life and deeds. During the slack season, Ah Q himself was completely forgotten, to say nothing of his life and deeds. Once an old man praised him, saying, "What a hard worker Ah Q is!" At that moment Ah Q, stripped to the waist, was standing idle, doing nothing at all. Others were not sure whether the old man was sincere or sarcastic, but Ah Q, not being so precise, was greatly pleased.

Ah Q was very proud and held all the inhabitants of Wei in contempt, even to the extent of sneering at the two students. Now a student might one day pass his examination and become a licentiate. The reason Their Honors Chao and Chien were so esteemed by the villagers was that, besides their wealth, they were fathers of students. But in spirit Ah Q had no special regard for them. "My son would be much better than they," he would assure himself. The few trips that he had undertaken to the city naturally contributed to his pride, though he had no use for city folks either. For instance, to himself and the people of Wei a bench three feet long and three inches wide across the top was a *ch'ang-teng,* yet the city people called it *t'iao-teng.*[1] This was absurd and laughable, he thought. In frying fish, people in Wei used pieces of green onions half an inch in length, but in the city they cut the onion up in fine shreds. This too was absurd and laughable. But what ignorant country louts were the villagers of Wei! They had never seen how fish was fried in the city!

Once much better off, a man of wide experience, hard working—Ah Q would have been a perfect man but for some slight physical flaws. The most humiliating of these were some scars on his head from sores he had had he knew not when. Although these were his own scars Ah Q did not seem to be proud of them, for he avoided the use of the word sores and all its homophones. Later by extension he avoided the words

1. "Long bench" and "a strip of a bench" respectively.

shiny and bright, and still later even candle and lamp were taboo. Whenever these taboos were violated, intentionally or otherwise, Ah Q would become red in the face and would either curse or fight according to whether the offender was slow of words or weak of limb. For some reason or other Ah Q always came out the loser. He gradually changed his tactics and contented himself with an angry glare.

But the idlers of Wei only became more relentless after he adopted this new policy. As soon as they saw him, they would exclaim as though surprised, "Hey! how bright it has become all of a sudden!"

Ah Q glared.

"No wonder! We have a safety lamp hereabouts," someone else would remark, unimpressed by his glare.

"You haven't got it, anyway." This retort, which he finally hit upon, gave him some comfort, as though his scars were no longer shiny evidences of a bygone affliction but something quite extraordinary, something to be envied.

As the idlers still would not let him alone, a fight usually followed. Ah Q inevitably lost and ended up by being held by the queue while his head was thumped noisily against the wall. This was of course only an outward defeat. After his adversary had gone with the laurels of victory, Ah Q would say to himself, "I have been beaten by my son. What a world we live in today!" and he too would go off satisfied and spiritually victorious.

At first he thought thus only to himself; later he got into the habit of saying it aloud. This method of securing spiritual victory became generally known, so that an idler, holding him by his queue, would say to him:

"Now Ah Q, this is not a case of a son beating his father, but a man beating a beast!"

Protecting his hair with his hands, Ah Q would plead:

"You are beating a worm. I am nothing but a worm. How is that? Now let me go!"

Even after this humiliating admission the idler would not let his victim go without first banging his head half a dozen times against something convenient. Surely Ah Q cannot claim a victory this time, the victor would think as he went away in triumph. But in less than ten seconds Ah Q would also go away in triumph, for he felt that surely he was the most self-deprecatory of men, and is not a superlative—the first or the most of anything—a distinction to be achieved and envied? Is not a *chuang-yuan* only the first in the ranks of the successful candidates in the triennial examinations? "So what are you, after all?"

After conquering his enemies by such ingenious means as these, Ah Q would go to the tavern, drink a few cups of wine, jest and quarrel a bit, and return, after scoring more victories, to the temple and would fall asleep with a light heart. If he happened to have any money, he would join the crowd of gamblers squatted around in a circle, his face streaming with sweat and his voice heard above everyone else.

"Four hundred *cash* on the Black Dragon!"

"Hey! Here goes!" the dealer would shout as he uncovered the board, his face also streaming with sweat. "Here goes Heaven's Gate and Ah Q's money. . . . No one seems to like Human Harmony."

"A hundred on Human Harmony! No, a hundred and fifty!"

Gradually Ah Q's money would find its way into the pockets of other perspiring gamblers. Obliged to withdraw from the inner circle, he would watch from the fringe, shouting and perspiring for the active participants. He could never tear himself away until the party broke up, when he would return to the temple with reluctant steps. The next day he would go to work with swollen eyes.

But "who knows that it is not a blessing for the Tartar to have lost his horse?" The only occasion on which Ah Q did win, he came near to tasting defeat. It happened during the village festival. There was as usual an open air theater and there were several gambling concessions near the stage. The gongs and drums sounded very faint in Ah Q's ears, as though miles away; he could hear only the barking of the dealer. He won and won, his coppers turning into dimes, dimes into silver dollars, silver dollars growing into a big pile. He was happy and excited.

"Two dollars on Heaven's Gate!" he shouted.

Suddenly a fight broke out, no one knew who against whom or why. When the commotion subsided and Ah Q crawled to his feet, the gambling concessions and the gamblers had all disappeared. He felt aches here and there, indicating that he must have received a few blows and kicks. People stared at him wonderingly. He went back to the temple with an air of preoccupation and after recovering his wits realized that he no longer had his pile of silver dollars. As most of the gamblers were from other villages, there was nothing that he could do.

A pile of bright, white silver dollars—and his at that—had all disappeared. He could not find any lasting satisfaction in saying to himself that his sons had robbed him, or in calling himself a worm. For the first time he felt something akin to the humiliation of defeat.

But again he turned defeat into victory. He raised his right hand and gave himself two good slaps in the face. This restored his humor, as if one Ah Q had struck another Ah Q, and, after a while, as if Ah Q had struck someone else—although it was his own face that tingled with pain. And so he lay down to sleep as a victor, as pleased with himself as ever.

And he soon fell asleep.

Although Ah Q's list of victories was long and impressive, it was not until he was slapped by His Honor Chao that he became famous.

After paying the constable two hundred *cash* he went to his room in the temple and lay down with indignation in his heart. Then he thought, "What a world this is getting to be, a son striking his father." At the thought that His Honor Chao with all his power and prestige was now his son, Ah Q became quite pleased with himself. He got up and went to the tavern singing "The Little Widow at Her Husband's Grave" and feeling quite proud of His Honor Chao now that the latter had become his own son.

The strange thing was that people actually seemed to respect him more. Ah Q liked to think that it was because of the new status that he had conferred upon himself, but this was not the case. If Ah Seven should have a fight with Ah Eight or Li Four with Chang Three, the incident would pass unnoticed in Wei; in order to merit gossip the incident must be in some way connected with a personage such as His Honor Chao. Then by virtue of the fame of the chastizer the chastized would become famous, too. The victim's position was, in other words, analogous to that of the Great Offerings in the Confucian Temple, offerings which, though domestic beasts like other pigs and sheep, become sacred after the Sage has put his chopsticks to them. There was never any question that the fault lay with Ah Q. Wherefore? Because His Honor Chao could not be wrong. Then why was it that people respected him more than formerly? This is a little difficult to explain. Perhaps they were afraid that, even though he was slapped for it, there might be after all something to Ah Q's claim of kinship, and they felt it was better to be on the safe side.

Thus Ah Q basked in this reflected glory for many years.

One spring day as he was walking drunkenly on the street he espied Wang the Beard sitting against a wall in the sun, hunting for fleas in the coat that he had taken off. Ah Q felt an infectious itch. Now Wang was not only bearded but also mangy. Everyone called him Mangy Beard Wang, but Ah Q dropped off the word mangy as it reminded him of his bygone affliction. He held the Beard in great contempt, feeling that the mange was nothing unusual, not like a swarthy, unsightly beard. Ah Q sat down beside him. If it had been someone else Ah Q might have hesitated, but he was not afraid of the Beard. In fact, he was conferring an honor upon the latter by sitting down beside him.

Ah Q also took off his ragged coat and searched it hopefully, but, either because it had been recently washed or because of his lack of thoroughness he caught only three or four fleas after a long search. In the meantime the Beard caught one after another, putting them in his mouth and crushing them with a crisp sound between his teeth.

Ah Q felt only disappointment at first, but this feeling soon gave way to indignation. How humiliating that such a worthless fellow as the Beard should have caught so many while he so few! He wished to vindicate himself by finding a big one but after a great deal of trouble he succeeded in finding only a medium-sized one. He put it into his mouth and bit it with determination, but he did not make as much noise as the Beard.

His scars grew red. Throwing his coat on the ground he said, spitting with disgust, "The damned worm!"

"Whom are you cursing, scabby cur?" the Beard said raising his eyes contemptuously.

If the challenge had come from one of the idlers in whose hands he had suffered ignominious defeat, Ah Q, in spite of the distinction that he had recently won and the pride that he took in it, might have been more cautious about taking it up. But he did not feel any need for caution on this occasion; he felt very brave. How dare the hairy face talk to him like that?

"Whoever cares to take it," he said, standing up, his arms akimbo.

"Are your bones itching?" said the Beard, standing up and putting on his coat.

Ah Q thought that the Beard was going to run, so he rushed forward and struck with his fist. But the Beard caught hold of it and gave it a jerk. As Ah Q fell forward, the Beard had him by the queue and was about to bang his head against the wall.

"A gentleman argues with his tongue rather than his fists," Ah Q remonstrated.

The Beard did not seem to care whether he was a gentleman or not. Paying no heed to the remonstrance, he banged Ah Q's head against the wall five times, then gave him a push that sent him sprawling six feet away.

In Ah Q's memory this must have been the greatest humiliation of his life. Heretofore the Beard had been the butt of his scorn, never had he been the object of the Beard's jeers, much less his blows. Could it be true, as rumored on the street, that the Emperor had abolished the examinations, and no longer wanted any licentiates and graduates, so that the Chaos' prestige had been impaired and their kinsman might be treated with impudence?

As Ah Q stood and pondered on this inexplicable event, the eldest son of His Honor Chien, one of Ah Q's foes and abominations, approached from the distance. Young Chien had first gone to the city and entered one of those "foreign" schools and then he had for some reason gone to Japan. Half a year later he came back a different man: his legs had become straight and his queue was gone. His mother cried often and his wife tried to throw herself in the well no less than three times. Later his mother explained that Chien's queue had been cut off by some wicked people after they had made him drunk. "He was to have been appointed a big mandarin," she explained, "but now he must wait until his hair grows again."

Ah Q did not believe the explanations, insisted upon calling Chien a fake foreigner and a traitor, and would curse him under his breath whenever he saw him. What Ah Q hated most was the man's false queue, for surely one could not be said to be a man at all with a false queue, and his wife could not be a virtuous woman since she did not try the well a fourth time.

The fake foreigner drew near.

"Baldhead! Donkey!" Ah Q muttered aloud as his passion and his desire for revenge got the better of him.

The baldhead unexpectedly rushed at him with a yellow varnished stick—which Ah Q called the funeral stick—and instantly Ah Q realized that he was going to receive a thrashing. He tightened his muscles and hunched up his shoulders and waited. He heard a whack and realized that he must have gotten a blow on the head.

"I was speaking of him," Ah Q protested, indicating a boy nearby.

Whack! Whack! Whack!

In Ah Q's memory this must have been the second greatest humiliation of his life. Fortunately the whack-whack seemed to give him a measure of relief, as though ending some suspense for him. Furthermore, forgetfulness, a treasured trait which he had inherited from his ancestors, came to his aid, and enabled him to regain his complacency by the time he reached the tavern.

Just then a little nun from the convent went by. Ah Q had never let her pass without hurling an insult at her, even when he was quite himself. Now all the resentment that he had felt for his recent defeats and indignities turned against the hapless nun.

"I have been wondering why I have been so unlucky all day, so it's because of you!" he thought.

He went up to her and spat in disgust. The nun walked on without paying the slightest attention to him. Ah Q approached her, thrust out his hand and stroked her cleanshaven head, saying with an idiotic grin, "Baldhead! Hurry home. The monk is waiting for you."

"What has possessed you that you dare to touch me!" the nun said hurrying on, her face flushed.

People in the tavern laughed. Encouraged by the general appreciation, Ah Q pinched her cheek, saying, "Since the monk can touch you, why not I?"

The tavern laughed again. Ah Q became more pleased with himself and gave the nun another pinch for the benefit of the onlookers.

This encounter drove out the memory of Wang the Beard and of the fake foreigner, and avenged all his adversities of the day. He felt more lighthearted than the whack-whack had made him, so lighthearted that he positively floated on air.

"May Ah Q never have any offspring," sounded the pitiful voice of the nun as she hurried off.

"Ha! Ha! Ha!" laughed Ah Q triumphantly.

"Ha! Ha! Ha!" echoed the tavern. . . .

Another reason why Ah Q had returned to Wei was because he had become dissatisfied with city people's ways. The first complaint he had against them was an old one: they called a bench *t'iao teng* instead of *ch'ang teng* and used shredded onion instead of big sections of it in frying fish. The second complaint he had was the mincing gait of city women, which he had noticed on his last visit and which he found very offensive to his taste. There were, however, things to be said for city folks. For instance in Wei they played only a game of dominoes of thirty-two pieces; the only exception was the fake foreigner, who could play mah-jong: but in the city even the little turtles working in the brothels could play mah-jong well. The fake foreigner might be very proud of himself, but when matched against a small turtle in his teens, he would fare no better than would a little demon in the hands of the King of Hell. The listeners were duly impressed by these pronouncements.

"And have any of you seen a decapitation?" Ah Q suddenly asked. "*Hai,* a grand sight it is to watch the beheading of the revolutionaries. *Hai,* a grand sight, really a grand sight!" He shook his head appreciatively and sputtered saliva in Chao the watchman's face. In the awed silence that followed, Ah Q looked around and suddenly raised his right hand and struck Wang the Beard on the back of his neck as the latter craned forward in his eagerness not to miss anything, and said, "Zip! like this." . . .

NOVELS

The Scholars (extracts)

Wu Ching-tzu (1701–54) / Yang Hsien-yi and Gladys Yang

Considered by many scholars the first Chinese novel that is a social satire, The Scholars *elicited from the nineteenth-century critic Hsin Yuan-tui the following remark: "You are warned not to read this novel; for once you have read it, you will feel you are meeting its characters all the time in real life."*[1] *There are more than fifty major characters in this long book, sharply delineated and realistically presented.*

The Scholars *differs from most Western novels in its lack of continuity. A character is introduced, his fortunes are followed for a chapter or two, then another character is discussed, then another, with rare or no subsequent reference to the persons described earlier in the book. By the end of the book we are dealing with altogether different individuals in different locales.* The Scholars *is really a collection of tales, tenuously connected to create the illusion of a novel.*

But this is not important. The recreation of the milieu is so convincing, the details are so realistic, the sights and smells and sounds are so vivid, that the reader becomes enchanted with the succession of characters and finishes the book feeling that he has lived for weeks in old China. This is realistic satire at its best, never strained beyond the point of credibility, yet using all the devices of exaggeration and distortion by selecting details to create the critical effects the author desires. Although the main object of satire is the system of scholarship, whereby passing a series of stupid, rigidly prescribed examinations became the basic method of advancing in the civil service and attaining wealth, status, and a rich wife, by the time Wu is finished he has attacked hypocrisy, bureaucracy, corruption, wealth, and popular superstitions. In the yamen of the official and in the shanty of the laborer, the exploitation of the poor and the affectations of the sycophant are unforgettably depicted.

When Chou Chin fell senseless to the ground, his friends were greatly taken aback, thinking he must be ill.

"I suppose this place has been shut up so long that the air is bad," said the guild head. "That must be why he has collapsed."

"I'll hold him up," said Chin to the guild head, "while you go and get some hot water from the workmen over there to bring him to."

When the guild head brought back the water, three or four of the others raised Chou Chin up and poured water down his throat till he gave a gurgle and spat out some

1. Quoted by Wu Tsu-hsiang in his editor's foreword to *The Scholars,* p. 10.

phlegm. "That's better," they said, and helped him to his feet. But when Chou Chin saw the desk he beat his head against it again. Only, instead of falling unconscious, this time he burst into loud sobbing. Not all their entreaties could stop him.

"Are you out of your mind?" demanded Chin. "We came to the examination school to enjoy a bit of sightseeing. Nobody has died in your family. Why take on like this?" But Chou Chin paid no attention. He just leaned his head against the desk and went on crying. After crying in the first room, he rushed over to cry in the second and then the third, rolling over and over on the floor till all his friends felt sorry for him. Seeing the state he was in, Chin and the guild head tried to lift him up, one on each side; but he refused to budge. He cried and cried, until he spat blood. Then all the others lent a hand to carry him out and set him down in a teahouse in front of the examination school. They urged him to drink a bowl of tea. But he just went on sniffing and blinking away his tears, looking quite broken-hearted.

"What's your trouble, Mr. Chou?" asked one of them. "What made you cry so bitterly in there?"

"I don't think you realize, gentlemen," said Chin, "that my brother-in-law is not really a merchant. He has studied hard for scores of years, but never even passed the prefectural examination. That's why the sight of the provincial examination school today upset him."

Touched on the raw like this, Chou Chin let himself go and sobbed even more noisily.

"It seems to me you're the one to blame, Old Chin," said another merchant. "If Mr. Chou is a scholar, why did you bring him on such business?"

"Because he was so hard up," said Chin. "He had lost his job as a teacher; there was no other way out for him."

"Judging by your brother-in-law's appearance," said another, "he must be a very learned man. It's because nobody recognizes his worth that he feels so wronged."

"He's learned all right," said Chin, "but he's been unlucky."

"Anybody who buys the rank of scholar of the Imperial College can go in for the examination," said the man who had just spoken. "Since Mr. Chou is so learned, why not buy him a rank so that he can take the examination? If he passes, that will make up for his unhappiness today."

"I agree with you," rejoined Chin. "But where's the money to come from?"

By now Chou Chin had stopped crying.

"That's not difficult," said the same merchant. "We're all friends here. Let's raise some money between us and lend it to Mr. Chou, so that he can go in for the examination. If he passes and becomes an official, a few taels of silver will mean nothing to him—he can easily repay us. Even if he doesn't pay us back, we merchants always fritter away a few taels one way or another, and this is in a good cause. What do you all say?"

The others responded heartily:

"A friend in need is a friend indeed!"

"A man who knows what is the right thing to do, but doesn't do it, is a coward!"

"Of course we'll help. We only wonder if Mr. Chou will condescend to accept."

"If you do this," cried Chou Chin, "I shall look on you as my foster-parents.

Even if I become a mule or a horse in my next life, I shall repay your kindness." Then he knelt down and kowtowed to them all, and they bowed to him in return. Chin thanked them too. They drank a few more bowls of tea, and Chou Chin no longer cried, but talked and laughed with the others until it was time to return to the guild.

The next day, sure enough, the four merchants raised two hundred taels of silver between them. This they gave to Chin, who promised to be responsible for any expenses over and above that sum. Chou Chin thanked them again; and the guild head prepared a feast for the merchants on Chou Chin's behalf. Meantime Chin had taken the silver to the provincial treasury. As luck would have it, it was just the time for the preliminary test for the provincial examination. Chou Chin took the test and came first of all the candidates from the Imperial College. On the eighth of the eighth month he went to the examination school for the provincial examination, and the sight of the place where he had cried made him unexpectedly happy. As the proverb says, "Joy puts heart into a man." Thus he wrote seven excellent examination papers, then went back to the guild, for Chin and the others had not yet completed their purchases. When the results were published, Chou Chin had passed with distinction, and all the merchants were delighted.

They went back together to Wenshang County, where Chou Chin paid his respects to the magistrate and the local examiner, and officials sent in their cards and called to congratulate him. Local people who were no relations of his claimed relationship, and perfect strangers claimed acquaintanceship. This kept him busy for over a month. When Shen Hsiang-fu heard the news, he got the villagers in Hsueh Market to contribute to buy four chickens, fifty eggs and some rice balls, then went to the county seat to congratulate Chou Chin, who kept him to a feast. Mr. Hsun, it goes without saying, came to pay his respects too.

Soon it was time to go to the examination in the capital. Chou Chin's travelling expenses and clothes were provided by Chin. He passed the metropolitan examination too; and after the palace examination he was given an official post. In three years he rose to the rank of censor and was appointed commissioner of education for Kwangtung Province.

Now, though Chou Chin engaged several secretaries, he thought, "I had bad luck myself so long; now that I'm in office I mean to read all the papers carefully. I mustn't leave everything to my secretaries, and suppress real talent." Having come to this decision, he went to Canton to take up his post. The day after his arrival he burnt incense, posted up placards, and held two examinations.

The third examination was for candidates from Nanhai and Panyu counties. Commissioner Chou sat in the hall and watched the candidates crowding in. There were young and old, handsome and homely, smart and shabby men among them. The last candidate to enter was thin and sallow, had a grizzled beard and was wearing an old felt hat. Kwangtung has a warm climate; still, this was the twelfth month, and yet this candidate had on a linen gown only, so he was shivering with cold as he took his paper and went to his cell. Chou Chin made a mental note of this before sealing up their doors. During the first interval, from his seat at the head of the hall he watched this candidate in the linen gown come up to hand in his paper. The man's clothes were so threadbare that a few more holes had appeared since he went into the cell. Commissioner Chou looked at his own garments—his magnificent crimson robe and gilt belt—then he referred to the register of names, and asked, "You are Fan Chin, aren't you?"

Kneeling, Fan Chin answered, "Yes, Your Excellency."

"How old are you this year?"

"I gave my age as thirty. Actually, I am fifty-four."

"How many times have you taken the examination?"

"I first went in for it when I was twenty, and I have taken it over twenty times since then."

"How is it you have never passed?"

"My essays are too poor," replied Fan Chin, "so none of the honorable examiners will pass me."

"That may not be the only reason," said Commissioner Chou. "Leave your paper here, and I will read it through carefully."

Fan Chin kowtowed and left.

It was still early, and no other candidates were coming to hand in their papers, so Commissioner Chou picked up Fan Chin's essay and read it through. But he was disappointed. "Whatever is the fellow driving at in this essay?" he wondered. "I see now why he never passed." He put it aside. However, when no other candidates appeared, he thought, "I might as well have another look at Fan Chin's paper. If he shows the least talent, I'll pass him to reward his perseverance." He read it through again, and this time felt there was something in it. He was just going to read it through once more, when another candidate came up to hand in his paper.

This man knelt down, and said, "Sir, I beg for an oral test."

"I have your paper here," said Commissioner Chou kindly. "What need is there for an oral test?"

"I can compose poems in all the ancient styles. I beg you to set a subject to test me."

The commissioner frowned and said, "Since the emperor attaches importance to essays, why should you bring up the poems of the Han and T'ang dynasties? A candidate like you should devote all his energy to writing compositions, instead of wasting time on heterodox studies. I have come here at the imperial command to examine essays, not to discuss miscellaneous literary forms with you. This devotion to superficial things means that your real work must be neglected. No doubt your essay is

PROVERBS

Money hides a thousand deformities.

With money you are a dragon; without it you are a worm.

Better a live beggar than a dead king.

Our pleasures are shallow; our sorrows are deep.

A man does not live a hundred years, yet he worries enough for a thousand.

There are only two good men—one dead, the other unborn.

You may change the clothes; you cannot change the man.

As long as you do not ask them to help, all men are good-natured.

He who rides in the palanquin is a man; he who carries the palanquin is also a man.

Even if stone were changed to gold, the heart of man would not be satisfied.

An official never flogs the bearer of gifts.

nothing but flashy talk, not worth the reading. Attendants! Drive him out!" At the word of command, attendants ran in from both sides to seize the candidate and push him outside the gate.

But although Commissioner Chou had had this man driven out, he still read his paper. This candidate was called Wei Hao-ku, and he wrote in a tolerably clear and straightforward style. "I will pass him lowest on the list," Chou Chin decided. And, taking up his brush, he made a mark at the end of the paper as a reminder.

Then he read Fan Chin's paper again. This time he gave a gasp of amazement. "Even I failed to understand this paper the first two times I read it!" he exclaimed. "But, after reading it for the third time, I realize it is the most wonderful essay in the world—every word a pearl. This shows how often bad examiners must have suppressed real genius." Hastily taking up his brush, he carefully drew three circles on Fan Chin's paper, marking it as first. He then picked up Wei Hao-ku's paper again, and marked it as twentieth. After this he collected all the other essays and took them away with him.

Soon the results were published, and Fan Chin's name was first on the list. When he went in to see the commissioner, Chou Chin commended him warmly. And when the last successful candidate—Wei Hao-ku—went in, Commissioner Chou gave him some encouragement and advised him to work hard and stop studying miscellaneous works. Then, to the sound of drums and trumpets, the successful condidates left.

The next day, Commissioner Chou set off for the capital. Fan Chin alone escorted him for ten miles of the way, doing reverence before his chair. Then the commissioner called him to his side. "First-class honors go to the mature," he said. "Your essay showed real maturity, and you are certain to do well in the provincial examination too. After I have made my report to the authorities, I will wait for you in the capital."

Fan Chin kowtowed again in thanks, then stood to one side of the road as the examiner's chair was carried swiftly off. Only when the banners had passed out of sight behind the next hill did he turn back to his lodgings to settle his bill. His home was about fifteen miles from the city, and he had to travel all night to reach it. He bowed to his mother, who lived with him in a thatched cottage with a thatched shed outside, his mother occupying the front room and his wife the back one. His wife was the daughter of Butcher Hu of the market.

Fan Chin's mother and wife were delighted by his success. They were preparing a meal when his father-in-law arrived, bringing pork sausages and a bottle of wine. Fan Chin greeted him, and they sat down together.

"Since I had the bad luck to marry my daughter to a scarecrow like you," said Butcher Hu, "Heaven knows how much you have cost me. Now I must have done some good deed to make you pass the examination. I've brought this wine to celebrate."

Fan Chin assented meekly, and called his wife to cook the sausages and warm the wine. He and his father-in-law sat in the thatched shed, while his mother and wife prepared food in the kitchen.

"Now that you have become a gentleman," went on Butcher Hu, "you must do things in proper style. Of course, men in my profession are decent, high-class people; and I am your elder too—you mustn't put on any airs before me. But these peasants round here, dung-carriers and the like, are low people. If you greet them and treat them as equals, that will be a breach of etiquette and will make me lose face too. You're such an easy-going, good-for-nothing fellow, I'm telling you this for your own good, so that you won't make a laughing-stock of yourself."

"Your advice is quite right, father," replied Fan Chin.

"Let your mother eat with us too," went on Butcher Hu. "She has only vegetables usually—it's a shame! Let my daughter join us too. She can't have tasted lard more than two or three times since she married you a dozen years ago, poor thing!"

So Fan Chin's mother and wife sat down to share the meal with them. They ate until sunset, by which time Butcher Hu was tipsy. Mother and son thanked him profusely; then, throwing his jacket over his shoulders, the butcher staggered home bloated. The next day Fan Chin had to call on relatives and friends.

Wei Hao-ku invited him to meet some other fellow candidates, and since it was the year for the provincial examination they held a number of literary meetings. Soon it was the end of the sixth month. Fan Chin's fellow candidates asked him to go with them to the provincial capital for the examination, but he had no money for the journey. He went to ask his father-in-law to help.

Butcher Hu spat in his face, and poured out a torrent of abuse. "Don't be a fool!" he roared. "Just passing one examination has turned your head completely—you're like a toad trying to swallow a swan! And I hear that you scraped through not because of your essay, but because the examiner pitied you for being so old. Now, like a fool, you want to pass the higher examination and become an official. But do you know who those officials are? They are all stars in heaven! Look at the Chang family in the city. All those officials have pots of money, dignified faces and big ears. But your mouth sticks out and you've a chin like an ape's. You should piss on the ground and look at your face in the puddle! You look like a monkey, yet you want to become an official. Come off it! Next year I shall find a teaching job for you with one of my friends so that you can make a few taels of silver to support that old, never-dying mother of yours and your wife—and it's high time you did! Yet you ask me for travelling expenses! I kill just one pig a day, and only make ten cents per pig. If I give you all my silver to play ducks and drakes with, my family will have to live on air." The butcher went on cursing at full blast, till Fan Chin's head spun.

When he got home again, he thought to himself, "Commissioner Chou said that I showed maturity. And, from ancient times till now, who ever passed the first examination without going in for the second? I shan't rest easy till I've taken it." So he asked his fellow candidates to help him, and went to the city, without telling his father-in-law, to take the examination. When the examination was over he returned home, only to find that his family had had no food for two days. And Butcher Hu cursed him again.

The day the results came out there was nothing to eat in the house, and Fan Chin's mother told him, "Take that hen of mine to the market and sell it; then buy a few measures of rice to make gruel. I'm faint with hunger."

Fan Chin tucked the hen under his arm and hurried out.

He had only been gone an hour or so, when gongs sounded and three horsemen galloped up. They alighted, tethered their horses to the shed, and called out: "Where is the honorable Mr. Fan? We have come to congratulate him on passing the provincial examination."

Not knowing what had happened, Fan Chin's mother had hidden herself in the house for fear. But when she heard that he had passed, she plucked up courage to poke her head out and say, "Please come in and sit down. My son has gone out."

"So this is the old lady," said the heralds. And they pressed forward to demand a tip.

In the midst of this excitement two more batches of horsemen arrived. Some squeezed inside while the other packed themselves into the shed, where they had to sit on the ground. Neighbors gathered round, too, to watch; and the flustered old lady asked one of them to go to look for her son. The neighbor ran to the market place, but Fan Chin was nowhere to be seen. Only when he reached the east end of the market did he discover the scholar, clutching the hen tightly against his chest and holding a sales sign in one hand. Fan Chin was pacing slowly along, looking right and left for a customer.

"Go home quickly, Mr. Fan!" cried the neighbor. "Congratulations! You have passed the provincial examination. Your house is full of heralds."

Thinking this fellow was making fun of him, Fan Chin pretended not to hear, and walked forward with lowered head. Seeing that he paid no attention, the neighbor went up to him and tried to grab the hen.

"Why are you taking my hen?" protested Fan Chin. "You don't want to buy it."

"You have passed," insisted the neighbor. "They want you to go home to send off the heralds."

"Good neighbor," said Fan Chin, "we have no rice left at home, so I have to sell this hen. It's a matter of life and death. This is not time for jokes! Do go away, so as not to spoil my chance of a sale."

When the neighbor saw that Fan Chin did not believe him, he seized the hen, threw it to the ground, and dragged the scholar back by main force to his home.

The heralds cried, "Good! The newly honored one is back." They pressed forward to congratulate him. But Fan Chin brushed past them into the house to look at the official announcement, already hung up, which read: "This is to announce that the master of your honorable mansion, Fan Chin, has passed the provincial examination in Kwangtung, coming seventh in the list. May better news follow in rapid succession!"

Fan Chin feasted his eyes on this announcement, and, after reading it through once to himself, read it once more aloud. Clapping his hands, he laughed and exclaimed, "Ha! Good! I have passed." Then, stepping back, he fell down in a dead faint. His mother hastily poured some boiled water between his lips, whereupon he recovered consciousness and struggled to his feet. Clapping his hands again, he let out a peal of laughter and shouted, "Aha! I've passed! I've passed!" Laughing wildly he ran outside, giving the heralds and the neighbors the fright of their lives. Not far from the front door he slipped and fell into a pond. When he clambered out, his hair was dishevelled, his hands muddied and his whole body dripping with slime. But nobody could stop him. Still clapping his hands and laughing, he headed straight for the market.

They all looked at each other in consternation, and said, "The new honor has sent him off his head!"

His mother wailed, "Aren't we out of luck! Why should passing an examination do this to him? Now he's mad, goodness knows when he'll get better."

"He was all right this morning when he went out," said his wife. "What could have brought on this attack? What *shall* we do?"

The neighbors consoled them. "Don't be upset," they said. "We will send a couple of men to keep an eye on Mr. Fan. And we'll all bring wine and eggs and rice for these heralds. Then we can discuss what's to be done."

The neighbors brought eggs or wine, lugged along sacks of rice or carried over chickens. Fan Chin's wife wailed as she prepared the food in the kitchen. Then she took it to the shed, neighbors brought tables and stools, and they asked the heralds to sit down to a meal while they discussed what to do.

"I have an idea," said one of the heralds. "But I don't know whether it will work or not."

"What idea?" they asked.

"There must be someone the honorable Mr. Fan usually stands in awe of," said the herald. "He's only been thrown off his balance because sudden joy made him choke on his phlegm. If you can get someone he's afraid of to slap him in the face and say, "It's all a joke. You haven't passed any examination!"—then the fright will make him cough up his phlegm, and he'll come to his senses again."

They all clapped their hands and said, "That's a fine idea. Mr. Fan is more afraid of Butcher Hu than of anyone else. Let's hurry up and fetch him. He's probably still in the market, and hasn't yet heard the news."

"If he were selling meat in the market, he would have heard the news by now," said a neighbor. "He went out at dawn to the east market to fetch pigs, and he can't have come back yet. Someone had better go quickly to find him."

One of the neighbors hurried off in search of the butcher, and presently met him on the road, followed by an assistant who was carrying seven or eight catties of meat and four or five strings of cash. Butcher Hu was coming to offer his congratulations. Fan Chin's mother, crying bitterly, told him what had happened.

"How could he be so unlucky!" exclaimed the butcher. They were calling for him outside, so he gave the meat and the money to his daughter, and went out. The heralds put their plan before him, but Butcher Hu demurred.

"He may be my son-in-law," he said, "but he's an official now—one of the stars in heaven. How can you hit one of the stars in heaven? I've heard that whoever hits the stars in heaven will be carried away by the King of Hell, given a hundred strokes with an iron rod, and shut up in the eighteenth hell, never to become a human being again. I daren't do a thing like that."

"Mr. Hu!" cried a sarcastic neighbor. "You make your living by killing pigs. Every day the blade goes in white and comes out red. After all the blood you've shed, the King of Hell must have marked you down for several thousand strokes by iron rods, so what does it matter if he adds a hundred more? Quite likely he will have used up all his iron rods before getting round to beating you for this, anyway. Or maybe, if you cure your son-in-law, the King of Hell may consider that as a good deed, and promote you from the eighteenth hell to the seventeenth."

"This is no time for joking," protested one of the heralds. "This is the only way to handle it, Mr. Hu. There's nothing else for it, so please don't make difficulties."

Butcher Hu had to give in. Two bowls of wine bolstered up his courage, making him lose his scruples and start his usual rampaging. Rolling up his greasy sleeves, he strode off toward the market, followed by small groups of neighbors.

Fan Chin's mother ran out and called after him, "Just frighten him a little! Mind you don't hurt him!"

"Of course," the neighbors reassured her. "That goes without saying."

When they reached the market, they found Fan Chin standing in the doorway of a temple. His hair was tousled, his face streaked with mud, and one of his shoes had come off. But he was still clapping his hands and crowing, "Aha! I've passed! I've passed!"

Butcher Hu bore down on him like an avenging fury, roaring, "You blasted idiot! What have you passed?" and fetched him a blow. The bystanders and neighbors could hardly suppress their laughter. But although Butcher Hu had screwed up his courage to strike once, he was still afraid at heart, and his hand was trembling too much to strike a second time. The one blow, however, had been enough to knock Fan Chin out.

The neighbors pressed round to rub Fan Chin's chest and massage his back, until presently he gave a sigh and came to. His eyes were clear and his madness had passed! They helped him up and borrowed a bench from Apothecary Chen, a hunchback who lived hard by the temple, so that Fan Chin might sit down.

Butcher Hu, who was standing a little way off, felt his hand begin to ache; when he raised his palm, he found to his dismay that he could not bend it. "It's true, then, that you mustn't strike the stars in heaven," he thought. "Now Buddha is punishing me!" The more he thought about it, the worse his hand hurt, and he asked the apothecary to give him some ointment for it.

Meanwhile Fan Chin was looking round and asking, "How do I come to be sitting here? My mind has been in a whirl, as if in a dream."

The neighbors said, "Congratulations, sir, on having passed the examination! A short time ago, in your happiness, you brought up some phlegm; but just now you spat out several mouthfuls and recovered. Please go home quickly to send away the heralds."

"That's right," said Fan Chin. "And I seem to remember coming seventh in the list." As he was speaking, he fastened up his hair and asked the apothecary for a basin of water to wash his face, while one of the neighbors found his shoe and helped him put it on.

The sight of his father-in-law made Fan Chin afraid that he was in for another cursing. But Butcher Hu stepped forward and said, "Worthy son-in-law, I would never have presumed to slap you just now if not for your mother. She sent me to help you."

"That was what I call a friendly slap," said one of the neighbors. "Wait till Mr. Fan finishes washing his face. I bet he can easily wash off half a basin of lard!"

"Mr. Hu!" said another. "This hand of yours will be too good to kill pigs any more."

"No indeed," replied the butcher. "Why should I go on killing pigs? My worthy son-in-law will be able to support me in style for the rest of my life. I always said that this worthy son-in-law of mine was very learned and handsome, and that not one of those Chang and Chou family officials in the city looked so much the fine gentleman. I have always been a good judge of character, I don't mind telling you. My daughter stayed at home till she was more than thirty, although many rich families wanted to marry her to their sons; but I saw signs of good fortune in her face, and knew that she would end up by marrying an official. You see today how right I was." He gave a great guffaw, and they all started to laugh.

When Fan Chin had washed and drunk the tea brought him by the apothecary, they all started back, Fan Chin in front, Butcher Hu and the neighbors behind. The butcher, noticing that the seat of his son-in-law's gown was crumpled, kept bending forward all the way home to tug out the creases for him.

When they reached Fan Chin's house, Butcher Hu shouted: "The master is back!" The old lady came out to greet them, and was overjoyed to find her son no longer mad. The heralds, she told them, had already been sent off with the money that Butcher Hu had brought. Fan Chin bowed to his mother and thanked his father-in-law, making Butcher Hu so embarrassed that he muttered, "That bit of money was nothing."

After thanking the neighbors too, Fan Chin was just going to sit down when a smart-looking retainer hurried in, holding a big red card, and announced, "Mr. Chang has come to pay his respects to the newly successful Mr. Fan."

By this time the sedanchair was already at the door. Butcher Hu dived into his daughter's room and dared not come out, while the neighbors scattered in all directions. Fan Chin went out to welcome the visitor, who was one of the local gentry, and Mr. Chang alighted from the chair and came in. He was wearing an official's gauze cap, sunflower-colored gown, gilt belt and black shoes. He was a provincial graduate, and had served as a magistrate in his time. His name was Chang Chin-chai. He and Fan Chin made way for each other ceremoniously, and once inside the house bowed to each other as equals and sat down in the places of guest and host. Mr. Chang began the conversation.

"Sir," he said, "although we live in the same district, I have never been able to call on you."

"I have long respected you," replied Fan Chin, "but have never had the chance to pay you a visit."

"Just now I saw the list of successful candidates. Your patron, Mr. Tang, was a pupil of my grandfather; so I feel very close to you."

"I did not deserve to pass, I am afraid," said Fan Chin. "But I am delighted to be the pupil of one of your family."

After a glance round the room, Mr. Chang remarked, "Sir, you are certainly frugal." He took from his servant a packet of silver, and stated, "I have brought nothing to show my respect except these fifty taels of silver, which I beg you to accept. Your honorable home is not good enough for you, and it will not be very convenient when you have many callers. I have an empty house on the main street by the east gate, which has three courtyards with three rooms in each. Although it is not big, it is quite clean. Allow me to present it to you. When you move there, I can profit by your instruction more easily."

Fan Chin declined many times, but Mr. Chang pressed him. "With all we have in common, we should be like brothers," he said. "But if you refuse, you are treating me like a stranger." Then Fan Chin accepted the silver and expressed his thanks. After some more conversation they bowed and parted. Not until the visitor was in his chair did Butcher Hu dare to emerge.

Fan Chin gave the silver to his wife. When she opened it, and they saw the white ingots with their fine markings. he asked Butcher Hu to come in and gave him two ingots, saying, "Just now I troubled you for five thousand coppers. Please accept these six taels of silver."

Butcher Hu gripped the silver tight, but thrust out his clenched fist, saying, "You keep this. I gave you that money to congratulate you, so how can I take it back?"

"I have some more silver here," said Fan Chin. "When it is spent, I will ask you for more."

Butcher Hu immediately drew back his fist, stuffed the silver into his pocket and said, "All right. Now that you are on good terms with that Mr. Chang, you needn't be afraid of going short. His family has more silver than the emperor, and they are my best customers. Every year, even if they have no particular occasions to celebrate, they still buy four or five thousand catties of meat. Silver is nothing to him."

Then he turned to his daughter and said, "Your rascally brother didn't want me to bring that money this morning. I told him, 'Now my honorable son-in-law is not the man he was. There will be lots of people sending him presents of money. I am only afraid he may refuse my gift.' Wasn't I right? Now I shall take this silver home and curse that dirty scoundrel." After a thousand thanks he made off, his head thrust forward and a broad grin on his face.

True enough, many people came to Fan Chin after that and made him presents of land and shops; while some poor couples came to serve him in return for his protection. In two or three months he had manservants and maidservants, to say nothing of money and rice. When Mr. Chang came again to urge him, he moved into the new house; and for three days he entertained guests with feasts and operas. On the morning of the fourth day, after Fan Chin's mother had got up and had breakfast, she went to the rooms in the back courtyard. There she found Fan Chin's wife with a silver pin in her hair. Although this was the middle of the tenth month, it was still warm and she was wearing a sky-blue silk tunic and a green silk skirt. She was supervising the maids and they washed bowls, cups, plates and chopsticks.

"You must be very careful," the old lady warned them. "These things don't belong to us, so don't break them."

"How can you say they don't belong to you, madam?" they asked. "They are all yours."

"No, no, these aren't ours," she protested with a smile.

"Oh yes, they are," the maids cried. "Not only these things, but all of us servants and this house belong to you."

When the old lady heard this, she picked up the fine porcelain and the cups and chopsticks inlaid with silver, and examined them carefully one by one. Then she went into a fit of laughter. "All mine!" she crowed. Screaming with laughter she fell backwards, choked, and lost consciousness.

But to know what became of the old lady, you must read the next chapter. . . .

For three days Mr. Yen hovered between life and death, too weak to speak. On the evening of the third day an oil lamp was lit on his table, and the room was crowded with relatives. They could hear the beginning of the death-rattle in his throat; but he refused to die. He took his hand from beneath the quilt and stretched out two fingers.

The eldest nephew stepped up to the bed and asked, "Do you mean that there are two relatives who haven't come, uncle?"

Yen shook his head.

The second nephew stepped forward and asked, "Do you mean there are still two lots of silver you haven't told us about, uncle?"

Yen stared hard at him, shook his head even more vehemently, and held out his fingers more earnestly than ever.

The wet-nurse, who was carrying his son, put in, "The master must be thinking of the two uncles who aren't here."

But when he heard this, he closed his eyes and shook his head. Only his fingers did not move.

Then the new wife hastily stepped forward, dabbing at her eyes. "They are wide of the mark," she said. "I'm the only one who knows what you mean. You're worried because there are two wicks in the lamp—that's a waste of oil. If I take out one wick, it will be all right."

Suiting her actions to her words, she removed one wick. All eyes were fixed on Mr. Yen, who nodded his head, let fall his hand, and breathed his last. Then all the family, great and small, began to wail and prepare for the funeral, placing the coffin in the central hall of the third courtyard. . . .

When several days had passed, Senior Licentiate Yen ordered Lai-fu and Ssu Tou to hire two boats manned by boatmen from Kaoyao County to take them home, promising the boatmen twelve taels of silver to be paid on arrival. One boat was for the bride and bridegroom, the other for the senior licentiate. They chose an auspicious day and took leave of their relatives. One pair of golden and another pair of white placards and four spears, all emblems of the yamen, had been borrowed from the former Chao County magistrate and placed on deck, and musicians were hired to pipe them to the boat. The overawed boatmen did their best to please these important passengers, and the journey passed without incident.

The last day of the trip, when they were less than ten miles from Kaoyao, Senior Licentiate Yen suddenly had a spell of faintness. He retched and vomited, while Lai-fu and Ssu Tou took his arms to prevent him from falling.

"I feel ill, I feel ill," he groaned. "Put me down, Ssu Tou, and boil some water."

He flopped down groaning and whimpering, while Ssu Tou and the boatmen hastily boiled water and took it to his cabin. Then the senior licentiate unlocked a case, took out a dozen small walnut wafers, ate a few of them, rubbed his stomach, and immediately felt better. He left a few wafers by the tiller, as if he had no further use for them. The steersman, who happened to have a sweet tooth, went on steering with his left hand while with his right he carried wafer after wafer to his mouth. Yen, however, pretended not to see what he was doing.

Presently their boats moored at Kaoyao wharf. Senior Licentiate Yen told Lai-fu to hire sedan-chairs and escort the young couple home first, while he called dockers to put all their luggage ashore. When the boatmen and dockers came to ask for tips, Yen went back to his cabin and made a show of looking round for something.

"Where has my medicine gone?" he asked Ssu Tou.

"What medicine?"

"That medicine I was eating just now. I put it by the tiller."

"Do you mean those walnut wafers you left by the tiller?" asked the steersman. "I thought you didn't want them, so I finished them up."

"Walnut wafers, indeed!" exclaimed Yen. "Do you know what those wafers were made of?"

"Just melon seeds, walnuts, sugar and flour, I suppose."

"You dog!" roared Yen. "Because I have these fits of dizziness, I spent several hundred taels of silver to buy this medicine. Mr. Chang of the provincial capital bought the ginseng in it for me when he was an official in Shangtang, and Mr. Chou bought the gentian when he was magistrate in Szechuan. You had no business touching it, you scoundrel! Walnut wafers, indeed! Nearly a hundred taels' worth of medicine have disappeared down your throat! And what am I to take next time I have an attack? You've played me a dirty trick, you dog!"

He ordered Ssu Tou to open his portfolio, so that he could write a note to send this scoundrel to Magistrate Tang's yamen for a good beating.

With a scared, conciliatory smile the steersman said, "It tasted very sweet. I didn't know it was medicine. I thought it was walnut wafers."

"You still call it walnut wafers!" the senior licentiate bellowed. "Call it walnut wafers again and I'll box your ears!" He had already written the note and now handed it to Ssu Tou who started to hurry ashore. The dockers helped the boatmen to stop him. Both lots of boatmen were scared stiff.

"He was wrong, Your Honor," they said. "He shouldn't have eaten your medicine. But he's a poor man. Even if he sells everything he has, he won't be able to pay you anything like a hundred taels of silver. And if he's sent to court he'll be ruined. Please be generous, sir, and overlook it."

But Senior Licentiate Yen only flew into a worse rage.

Some of the dockers came aboard and said to the boatmen, "You brought this on yourselves. If you hadn't asked the gentleman for tips, he would have gone to his sedan-chair. But once you stopped him, he found out about his medicine. Since you know you're in the wrong, why don't you kowtow and ask Senior Licentiate Yen's pardon? Do you expect him to pay you if you don't make good his loss?"

Then they all forced the steersman to kowtow.

Yen softened a little, and said, "Very well. Since you've all pleaded for him, and I am busy with my son's wedding, I shall deal with this scoundrel later. He needn't think he can get away." After more curses he swaggered to his sedan-chair, followed by the servants and luggage. He left the boatmen gaping—for he had gone off without paying for the trip. . . .

The gate-keeper ushered the stranger into the hall, after which the two brothers came out to greet him and invited him to sit down.

"Your fame, which resounds like thunder, has long since reached my ears," said the stranger. "But hitherto I have had no opportunity of making your acquaintance."

"May we ask your honorable name?" said Lou Feng.

"Chen Ho-fu, at your service. I reside in the capital, but recently I accompanied Mr. Lu to your honorable district, so at last I am fortunate enough to meet you. I observe that Mr. Lou Feng's ears are whiter than his face—a sure sign that his fame will spread throughout the world; while the refulgence of Mr. Lou Chan's nose indicates that he will shortly receive news of official promotion."

"You are no doubt an adept at fortune-telling, sir," they said.

"I have a smattering of knowledge concerning the hexagrams, astrology, fortune-telling, medicine, surgery, yoga and chemistry, besides knowing how to consult the oracles," said Chen Ho-fu. "When I resided in the capital I was constantly invited by the ministers of all the great ministries and by the gentlemen of the literary yamens. And whenever I foretold promotion, it invariably came to pass. To tell you the truth, gentlemen, I always speak straight out, never keeping anything back or indulging in flattery. That is why great personages have always favored me.". . .

These ceremonies at an end, the music stopped and Chu Hsien-fu left his table to greet his father-in-law, his two uncles and the two go-betweens, after which he returned to his place and sat down again. Players came in next, kowtowed to the feasters, then clashed their cymbals and beat their drums as they danced the "Dance of Official Promotion." After that, they performed "The Fairy Brings a Boy," and "Golden Seal."

Now it had been raining heavily for two days and, although the rain had stopped, the ground was still wet; so the players in their new boots had to make a detour as they entered from the courtyard. After the first three items an actor with a list of plays from which to choose went up to Chu's table and knelt down. A servant, who had just brought in the first bowl of boiled birds'-nests, told the actor to stand up. He did so, but just as he was presenting the list of plays—bang!—something dropped from the ceiling straight into the bowl, knocking it over and splashing the scalding soup into his face and over the table. It was a rat which had slipped from the rafters! The hot soup gave it such a fright that it knocked over the bowl as it scuttled for safety, jumping on the bridegroom's knee and smearing his red silk official gown with grease. All present were aghast. They hastily removed the dish, wiped the table clean and brought the bridegroom another gown into which to change.

When they had finished several cups of wine and two courses, it was time to serve soup. Now the cook was a countryman who was standing in hobnailed shoes in the courtyard enjoying the plays as he held the tray with six bowls of soup. The servant had taken four of his bowls away, and there were still two left. But at the sight of an actor singing and posturing as a singsong girl, the cook was so carried away that he forgot all else, thought all the soup had been served and let the tray down to pour off any slops. The two bowls were smashed and all the soup spilt. Losing his head, the cook bent down to mop up the soup, but two dogs got there before him and started licking it up. Furious, the cook kicked with all his might at the dogs. In his haste, however, he missed the dogs and one of his hobnailed shoes flew off ten feet into the air.

Now Chen Ho-fu happened to be sitting at the first table on the left, where two plates of food had been served: one plate of pork dumplings, the other of dumplings stuffed with goose fat and sugar. These dumplings were steaming hot and there was another bowl of soup before him. He was just raising his chopsticks to his mouth when something black hurtled from behind the table to smash the two plates of sweetmeats. And as Chen Ho-fu jumped up in fright, he caught the bowl of soup with his sleeve and overturned it, so that it slopped all over the table. Everybody present was taken aback.

Mr. Lu was extremely put out, knowing this was most inauspicious; but he could not very well say anything. Instead, he called his steward and cursed him under his breath. . . .

"I know most of the military arts," announced Iron-armed Chang. "I can fight with eighteen different weapons on foot and eighteen different weapons on horse-back. I can use the whip, the mace, the axe, the hammer, the sword, the spear, the sabre and the halberd. In fact, I may be said to have mastered all these. But I am unlucky in my temperament, for whenever I see injustice done I must draw my sword to avenge the injured. I cannot resist fighting with the strongest in the empire; and whenever I have money, I give it to the poor. Thus I have ended up without a home, and that is how I come to be in your honorable district." . . .

It was towards the end of the month and the moon had not yet risen. The two brothers sat up talking by candlelight until nearly midnight, when they heard a thud on the roof and a blood-stained man dropped down from the eaves carrying a leather bag. By the light of the candle they recognized Iron-armed Chang.

The two brothers were very startled.

"What brings you, friend, to our inner chamber in the middle of the night?" they asked. "And what have you in that leather bag?"

"Please be seated, gentlemen," said Iron-armed Chang, "and let me explain. During my life I have had one benefactor and one enemy. I have hated my enemy for ten years without having an opportunity to kill him; but today my chance came and I have his head here. Inside this bag is a bloody human head! But my benefactor is some distance away, and I need five hundred taels to repay him for his kindness. Once this debt of honor is paid, my heart will be at rest and I can devote the rest of my life to you who have treated me so well. Believing that only you two gentlemen could help me—for no others are so understanding—I made bold to call on you tonight. But if you are unwilling to help, then I must go far away and never see you again."

Taking up the leather bag he started off.

"Don't do anything rash, friend!" cried the brothers, now thoroughly frightened. "Five hundred taels is a trifle—but what about this bag?"

"That's easy," replied Iron-armed Chang with a laugh. "I can remove all traces by means of certain arts that I know. But that will have to wait for the moment. If you will give me the five hundred taels, I shall come back in four hours, take out the object in the leather bag and apply a magic powder to it, so that it changes instantly to water and not a hair remains. You gentlemen might prepare a feast and invite guests to watch me."

Tremendously impressed, the two brothers hurried inside to fetch him five hundred taels. Then Iron-armed Chang put the bag down on the steps, stowed the silver about his person, thanked them and vaulted on the eaves. All they heard was a clatter on the tiles, as he vanished like lightning. The night was very still and the moon had just risen to shed its rays on the leather bag on the steps with its bloody human head.

But to know what happened to the head, you must read the chapter which follows.

The Lou brothers had given five hundred taels to Iron-armed Chang so that he might repay his benefactor, and he had left a leather bag containing a human head in their house. Although as members of the prime minister's house they could never get into serious trouble, the presence of a head dripping with blood on the steps of their inner chamber caused them a little uneasiness.

"A gallant like Iron-armed Chang can be counted on not to fail us," said Lou Chan to his brother. "So we must on no account act like the common herd. Let us prepare a feast and invite all our closest friends to wait for him to come and open this bag. It's not every day that you can see a head changed to water. Why not give a Human Head Party?"

Lou Feng agreed with him. As soon as it was light he gave orders for a feast to be prepared to which they invited Niu Pu-yi, Chen Ho-fu and Chu Hsien-fu, in addition, of course, to the three guests staying in their house. They described the occasion as a small drinking party, without disclosing the real reason for the feast, intending to take all their guests by surprise when Iron-armed Chang arrived and gave his display.

All the guests assembled and talked of this and that for six or seven hours; but Iron-armed Chang did not come. By midday there was still no sign of him.

These two incidents left the Lou brothers rather discouraged. They ordered the gate-keeper, if strangers called, to say that they had returned to the capital. And henceforward they remained behind closed doors, devoting themselves to household affairs. . . .

Chu Hsien-fu went home and told his wife: "Tomorrow Mr. Ma Chun-shang, an expert on the examination essays, is coming to call on me. We must ask him to dinner."

Very pleased, she immediately set about making preparations.

The next day Ma Chun-shang changed into a loose gown, wrote a visiting card, and called at Chu Hsien-fu's home. Chu ushered him in.

"We are not like ordinary friends, but have long been acquainted in spirit," said Chu. "Now that you have honored me with a visit I hope you will favor us with your company while we prepared a simple meal. You must excuse our lack of ceremony."

Ma Chun-shang was delighted.

Then Chu Hsien-fu asked: "What is the chief criterion you employ in selecting essays?"

"The reasoning," replied Ma Chun-shang. "No matter how styles change, the reasoning remains the same. During the reigns of Hung Wu and Yung Lo we find one style, and during the reigns of Cheng Hua and Hung Chih another; but careful investigation shows that the reasoning remains the same. Generally speaking, it is bad enough to write essays which read like commentaries, but worse to imitate the style of odes and elegies. For essays which read like commentaries will simply lack the literary flavor, whereas those which sound poetic will not resemble the words of ancient sages. Of the two, therefore, the poetic type is worse."

"You have been speaking of *writing* essays. May I ask how one should *comment* upon essays?"

"The same principle applies: you must not look for what is poetical. I often read the old masters' annotations, and when they are in flowery language they remind us of odes or elegies, and the content is likely to have a bad influence on later scholars. How right the ancients were when they said: 'In writing an essay the mind should remain as clear as the human eye.' It must hold no dust, not even of jade or gold. So when I comment upon essays I try to use the language of Chu Hsi, often sitting up half the night to write one note. And because I write nothing carelessly, students who have read one of my commentaries may think out the principles for a dozen essays. When my selection is ready I will send it to you for your criticism."

As they were speaking a simple meal was carried in: boiled duck, boiled chicken, fish and a big bowl of tender, braised pork. Mr. Ma's appetite was enormous.

"You and I are like old friends now," he said as he raised his chopsticks, "so I won't stand on ceremony. I propose that we leave this fish and concentrate on the pork."

Falling to, he ate four bowls of rice and finished the whole bowl of meat. When the mistress knew this, she sent out another bowl; but he finished this too, soup and all. Then the table was carried out, tea was brought in and they began talking.

"Gifted as you are and coming from an illustrious family," said Ma Chun-shang, "you should have passed the examinations long ago. How is it that you are still in retirement?"

"Since my father died early I was brought up by my grandfather and occupied with family business: I had no time to study for the civil service."

"That was a mistake. Right from ancient times all the best men have gone in for the civil service. Confucius, for instance, lived during the Spring and Autumn Period when men were selected as officials on the strength of their activities and sayings. That is why Confucius said: 'Make few false statements and do little you may regret, then all will be well.' That was the civil service of Confucius' time.

"By the time of the Warring States, the art of rhetoric had become the road to officialdom: that is why Mencius travelled through Chi and Liang delivering orations to the princes. That was the civil service of Mencius' time.

PROVERBS

Those who have free seats at the play hiss first.

Even the ten fingers are not of equal length.

The friendship of officials is as thin as papers.

A clever doctor never treats himself.

The doctor who rides in a chair will not visit the house of the poor.

To open a shop is easy; the hard thing is keeping it open.

A melon-seller never cries, "Bitter melons," nor a wine-seller, "Thin wine."

Planning is in the power of man; executing is in the hands of Heaven.

When times are easy we do not burn incense, but when trouble comes we embrace the feet of the Buddha.

"By the Han Dynasty, the examination system was designed to select men for their ability, goodness and justice; and thus men like Kung-sun Hung and Tung Chung-shu were appointed to office. That was the civil service of the Han Dynasty.

"By the Tang Dynasty, scholars were chosen for their ability to write poetry. Even if a man could talk like Confucius or Mencius, that would not get him a post; so all the Tang scholars learned to write poems. That was the civil serivce of the Tang Dynasty.

"By the Sung Dynasty, it was even better: all the officials had to be philosophers. That was why the Cheng brothers and Chu Hsi propagated neo-Confucianism. That was the civil service of the Sung Dynasty.

"Nowadays, however, we use essays to select scholars, and this is the best criterion of all. Even Confucius, if he were alive today, would be studying essays and preparing for the examinations instead of saying, 'Make few false statements and do little you may regret.' Why? Because that kind of talk would get him nowhere: nobody would give him an official position. No, the old sage would find it impossible to realize his ideal." . . .

Just then a man passed the door, called out a greeting and moved on. The runner noticed that this fellow looked thoughtful; so he told Huan-cheng to wait while he tiptoed after the other.

"He's beaten me up, but there are no wounds," he heard him mutter. "So I can't take the case to court. And if I wound myself the magistrate will easily find it out."

Then the runner quietly picked up a brick, charged forward like an avenging fury and hit the other man's head with the brick so that the blood gushed out.

The man stumbled.

"Hey! What are you doing?" he demanded.

"You were complaining that you had no wound. Isn't this a wound? And you couldn't have made it yourself either. I don't think the magistrate will be able to tell how it was done. Go ahead and lodge your complaint!"

The man thanked the runner from the bottom of his heart, then smeared his face with blood and went to lay his suit before the magistrate. To Huan-cheng, standing in the doorway of the tea-shop, this was another object lesson in finesse. . . .

Ma Chun-shang was just kneeling to learn his fortune when someone addressed him from behind, and he turned to see a man who looked like an immortal. Ma immediately bowed.

"I was not aware of your arrival," he said. "So I failed to greet you, sir. Since I have never had the honor of meeting you, may I ask how you knew that my name is Ma?"

"Is there anyone who does not know you? Now that you have met me, there is no need to ask your fortune. You had better come with me to my humble house."

"Where is your distinguished abode?"

"It is very near."

Taking Ma Chun-shang's hand, this stranger led him out of the temple to a wide flat road on which there was not a single stone, and in next to no time they had reached the temple of Wu Tzu-hsu.

Ma was surprised.

"This is a much shorter way!" he thought. "I must have taken the wrong road before. Unless, of course, he has some miraculous means of shortening the distance."

Soon they reached the gate of the temple.

"This is my humble home," said the stranger. "Please come in." . . .

"Making money is not difficult. You may have to wait a little, though, before amassing a real fortune. What would you say to making a little money as a start?"

Hung Kan-hsien appeared to be pondering for a moment.

"Well, I will give you something to try out in your lodgings," he said. "If it proves satisfactory, come and ask me for more. And if this experiment fails, we can think of something else."

He went into his inner chamber, opened a package beside his bed and took out several pieces of charcoal which he gave to Ma, saying: "Take these to your lodgings and light a brazier; then heat these above the flames in some container and see what happens. Come and tell me the result."

Ma Chun-shang took the charcoal, said goodbye to Mr. Hung and returned to his lodgings. That evening he lit a brazier, placed some of the charcoal in a pot over it and, after the fire had crackled for some time, emptied the pot to find that the charcoal had turned into an ingot of silver! Overjoyed, he immediately heated six or seven pots more, obtaining from them six or seven more ingots. Then, uncertain whether this was real silver or not, he went to bed.

The next morning he went out early to have his ingots examined by the money-changers; and when they assured him that the silver was genuine he changed a part of it for several thousand coppers which he took back to his lodging. When he had put the money away, he hurried to Hung Kan-hsien's house to thank him.

Mr. Hung came out to meet him.

"How did it go last night?" he asked.

"It was miraculous!" exclaimed Ma.

He described what had happened and how much silver he had obtained.

"That's nothing," said Hung Kan-hsien. "I have some more here. You had better take it and try again." He produced another package which contained three or four times as much as the first, entertained Ma to another meal, then saw him off.

Ma Chun-shang's brazier was kept busy for the next six or seven days producing silver, until he had used up all the charcoal; and he found when he weighed the silver that he had eighty or ninety taels' worth. Hardly able to contain himself for joy, he wrapped up the money and put it away.

One day Hung Kan-hsien sent a messenger to invite Ma to his house.

"You are from Chuchow and I am from Taichow," he said. "Coming from neighboring districts, we can consider ourselves as fellow countrymen. I am expecting a guest today, and I would like to introduce you to him as my cousin; for that will give you the opportunity you want. This is a chance you must on no account miss."

"May I ask the name of your distinguished guest?"

"He is the third son of the former minister Hu, and his name is Hu Chen. The minister left a fortune to his sons, but this gentleman is so fond of money that he thinks he can never have enough and he wants to learn my method of producing silver. He is willing to spend thousands of taels for the equipment; but we need an intermediary. Now Mr. Hu has heard of your great name; and since you are selecting essays in Literary Expanse Bookshop and have a fixed address, he can trust you. In another seven weeks, after we meet today and settle this matter, I shall produce the philosopher's stone which can turn any metal to gold. That will be worth millions. But since I don't need so much money myself, I mean to bid farewell to this world and return to the mountain, leaving part of the philosopher's stone to you. Then you will want for nothing."

After the wonders he had seen Hung Kan-hsien perform, Ma had implicit faith in him. So they waited together for Mr. Hu.

Presently Mr. Hu arrived, greeted Mr. Hung, looked at Ma and asked: "May I know this gentleman's honorable name?"

"This is my cousin, Ma Chun-shang of Chuchow," said Hung Kan-hsien. "You see his name in all the bookshop advertisements for essays."

Mr Hu greeted Ma with respect and they sat down together. When Mr. Hu cast his eyes round the room and noticed Mr. Hung's saintly appearance, the luxurious furniture and the four attendants presenting tea one after the other, and when he considered that Ma Chun-shang the editor was Mr. Hung's cousin, any misgivings he had had left him. He sat there in high good humor until it was time to leave.

The next day Hung Kan-hsien and Ma Chun-shang went by sedan-chair to return the visit. Ma presented Mr. Hu with a new selection of essays, after which Mr. Hu entertained them for some time; and soon after their return home a servant arrived from the Hu family with invitations for them both to a feast by the lake the following day.

"My master salutes you, gentlemen," said the servant. "The feast will be in the garden by Imperial Script Pavilion at the West Lake, and he hopes you will go there early tomorrow."

Mr. Hung accepted the invitations.

The next day they went by sedan-chair to the pavilion, found the gate of the garden wide open and Mr. Hu there to welcome them. Two tables had been spread and an opera was performed, and thus the day passed very pleasantly. Ma remembered how he had come here all alone and watched other people feasting, while today, by a happy coincidence, he was a guest here himself. The wine, food and sweetmeats were of the best, and he made an excellent meal.

Mr. Hu arranged to invite them to his home again in a few days to sign a contract which Ma would witness. He also promised to have a laboratory prepared in his garden and declared that he would make an initial payment of ten thousand taels so that Mr. Hung could buy the necessary equipment and take up his quarters in the laboratory. This matter decided, in the evening, the feast ended and Ma went back by sedan-chair to the bookshop.

When four days passed without any word from Hung Kan-hsien, Ma decided to call on him. But as soon as he went in, he found the four attendants in confusion and learned that Mr. Hung was seriously ill. In fact, the doctors declared that his pulse was so weak that further treatment was useless. Greatly shocked, Ma hurried upstairs to see the sick man; but he found him at his last gasp, unable to lift his head. Since

Ma was a kind-hearted man, he stayed by his sick friend's side all night. Two days later, however, Hung Kan-hsien breathed his last.

The four attendants were at their wits' end; for when they searched the house for valuables, they found only four or five silk gowns which might be worth a few taels. There was nothing else; all the cases were empty. And now it appeared that these four men were not servants. One of them was Hung Kan-hsien's son, two were nephews, and one was his son-in-law. When Ma heard this he was appalled. But since there was no money to buy a coffin and he was a good man, he hurried to his lodgings to fetch ten taels of silver for the funeral expenses. Then while the son wailed beside the corpse and the nephews went out to buy a coffin, the son-in-law, who had nothing to do, took Ma to a neightboring tea-house to chat.

"Your father-in-law was an immortal who had lived more than three hundred years," said Ma. "What made him die all of a sudden?"

"Three hundred years? Nonsense!" retorted the son-in-law. "The old man was only sixty-six this year. He was an old villain, a regular swindler. However much money he made, he always threw it away. That's why he's ended like this. To tell you the truth, sir, we were merchants before; but we gave up our business to help him bamboozle people. Now that he's gone, we shall have to beg our way home. All of us are in a bad way."

"By his bed the old gentleman had a number of packages of charcoal which would turn into silver if you heated them above a brazier."

"That wasn't charcoal! It was silver coated with charcoal! As soon as it was burnt, the silver reappeared. That was a trick to fool people; but when the silver was used up, that was the end of it."

"But there's another thing," persisted Ma. "If he wasn't a saint, how did he know that my name was Ma when he met me for the first time in Saint Ting's Temple?"

"He had you there again. When he came out of the Rocky Grotto that day after a seance, he saw you reading in the bookshop; and when the shopkeeper asked you your name, you told him you were the Mr. Ma who had edited that volume of essays. My father-in-law overheard you: that's how he knew. There aren't any saints in the world!"

Only then did Ma realize that the old man had made up to him in order to deceive Mr. Hu, and it was pure luck that Mr. Hu had not been swindled. . . .

"If you take my advice," said Ma during the meal, "after you reach home you should consider passing the official examinations as the most important way of pleasing your parents. There is no other way for men to achieve fame. That fortune-telling is a low profession goes without saying; but even teaching and secretarial work are not proper careers. If, however, you are brilliant enough to pass the examinations, you immediately reflect credit upon your whole family. That is why the *Book of Filial Piety* tells us that to reflect credit on your family and to spread your fame shows the greatest piety. At the same time, of course, you do very well for yourself. As the proverb says: There are golden mansions in study; there are bushels of rice and beautiful women. And what is study today if not our *paku* compositions? So when you go back to look after your parents, you must consider study for the examinations of prime importance. Even if your business does badly and you cannot give your father and mother all they want, that need not worry you. Writing compositions is the main thing. For when your father lies ill in bed with nothing to eat and hears you declaiming compositions, no doubt about it but his heart will rejoice, his sadness will disappear and his pain will pass away. This is what Tseng Tzu meant when he spoke of pleasing the parents. And if you are not lucky enough to pass all the examinations, you will at least be able to become a stipendiary which will enable you to be a tutor and apply for titles for your parents. I am old and good-for-nothing, but you are young and brilliant. You must listen to me so that later, when you become an official, we may meet again." . . .

"Mr. Huang was born in the same year and same month, on the same day and at the very same hour as Dr. Chao!"

"Yes, that *is* extraordinary!"

"But there's something more extraordinary to follow. Dr. Chao is fifty-nine this year and has two sons and four grandsons, while his wife has grown old with him; but he is still an ordinary citizen. Mr. Huang has passed the metropolitan examination and is a magistrate; but he lost his wife when he was thirty, and he has neither sons nor daughters."

"That is *really* extraordinary!" cried Chih Chien-feng. "They were born under the same stars, yet their fortunes have been totally different—they have nothing at all in common! This shows that astrology and horoscopy are unreliable." . . .

As they were speaking, noodles were served; and when they had eaten, Mr. Wei and Mr. Sui began to speak of the *paku* essays.

"Editing nowadays is going to the dogs," declared Mr. Wei.

"Very true," agreed Mr. Sui. "We ought to have edited a few essays from the last examination as models of criticism."

Mr. Wei cast a searching glance round.

"There were no essays in the last examination!" he stated.

"Excuse me, sir," Kuang Chao-hen could not help saying, "there are printed selections of the essays of the last examination everywhere. Why do you say there were no essays?"

"May I ask this gentleman's name?" said Mr. Wei.

"This is Mr. Kuang of Yuehching County," Ching told him.

"When I say there there are no essays," announced Mr. Wei, "I mean that none of them came up to standard."

"Surely," demurred Kuang Chao-jen, "if the candidates passed, their essays must have been up to standard. What other criterion is there?"

"My friend," said Mr. Wei, "you obviously do not understand. Essays express the teachings of the sages, and they must be written according to definite rules, unlike other frivolous forms of literature which you may write as you please. Thus from an essay you should be able to see not only the writer's rank and fortune, but also whether the empire is passing through a period of prosperity or decline. The Hung Wu and Yung Lo periods had one set of rules; the Cheng Huan and Hung Chih periods had another. Each reign has its particular rules which have been handed down from one group of scholars to another, forming an orthodox tradition. Now some of the candidates who pass the examinations may have written according to the rules, while others pass thanks to luck; but only those essays selected and annotated by us are assured of immortality. If we find no essays worth selecting from a certain examination, we say that there were no essays."

"We are not afraid of not passing the examinations, friend," put in Mr. Sui. "Our one fear is lest our three essays should not stand up to criticism *after* we have passed; for that would prove that we merely passed by chance, which would be something to be ashamed of all our lives." He turned to ask Mr. Wei: "Have you seen the selection of essays made recently by that fellow Ma Chun-shang?"

"Precisely! That kind of man is ruining the editing business. He has been staying in Prefect Chu's home at Chiahsing, where they talk of nothing but heterodox studies; and although I understand he has a flair for frivolous writing, he has not the faintest conception of the rules of essays. The result is that he creates extraordinary confusion, and even good essays are spoilt by his abominable commentaries! Whenever I see students reading his selections, I tell them to delete his notes." . . .

Presently they reached Flower Bay, where they urged Mr. Hu to go ashore to borrow the garden for their feast. When Mr. Hu tried to so do, however, the door was shut in his face. And although he blustered, the caretaker paid no attention.

Ching took the man aside and asked him the reason.

"Everybody knows what a skinflint Mr. Hu is!" said the caretaker. "How many feasts does he give here each year that I should put myself out for him? Last year he borrowed this place for two tables of guests, but didn't give a single tip! And when he left he didn't get anyone to clean the place up; instead he insisted that there must be two pecks of rice left over and ordered his servant to carry them back. I'm not going to wait upon gentlemen like that!"

There was nothing for it but to borrow a monk's quarters at Yu Chien's Temple, where the monk brewed tea for them. Mr. Hu, who had all their money, asked Ching Lan-chiang to go with him to do the shopping, and Kuang Chao-jen volunteered to accompany them. They went first to a shop selling ducks, where Mr. Hu stabbed the ducks' breasts with his earpick to see how fat they were, then asked Mr. Ching to bargain for the plumpest bird. Since there was a large party, they also bought several catties of meat, two chickens, a fish and some vegetables, which they ordered the servant who had come with them to carry back first.

Next they decided to buy some meat dumplings for a snack, and went into a shop where they found thirty dumplings. These dumplings were three coppers each, but Mr. Hu refused to give more than two coppers and started quarrelling with the shop people. Finally Ching Lan-chiang succeeded in making peace, and instead of dumplings they bought noodles which Ching carried. They went on to purchase dried bamboo shoots, salted eggs, fried chestnuts, melon seeds and other sundries to go with the wine; and these Kuang Chao-jen helped to carry.

When they had taken everything to the temple and given it to the monk to prepare, Chih Chien-feng asked: "Why didn't you get the cook to do this, Mr. Hu, instead of going to such trouble yourself?"

Mr. Hu looked surprised.

"That would have cost more," he said. He then weighed out a piece of silver and ordered his man to buy rice. . . .

Presently a man called to ask Pan's advice; and when he went out he saw that it was Wang Number Six, who kept a gambling house.

"I haven't seen you for a long time, Number Six," said Pan. "What do you want me for?"

"Would you mind stepping outside with me?" asked Wang.

Pan followed him to a quiet tea-house.

"There's a chance of making money, sir," Wang told him. "So I came straight to you."

"What is it?"

"Yesterday the police from Chientang County yamen caught some louts in Mao Family Fair raping a maid called Lotus, who has run away from a family in Yuehching County. The police caught this gang right in the act and reported them to the magistrate, who gave them each a few dozen strokes before letting them go; and he has sent this Lotus back to Yuehching. Now there's a rich man here named Hu, who's taken a fancy to this girl and asked me if we can't find some way to get hold of her. He's willing to fork a few hundred taels for her. Do you think it can be done?"

"Who was put in charge of her?"

"Huang Chiu."

"Has he gone himself?"

"No, he sent two of his men."

"When did they leave?"

"Yesterday."

"Does Huang Chiu know about this Mr. Hu?"

"Of course he does. He wants to make some money too; but he doesn't know how to."

"That is easy," said Pan. "Bring Huang Chiu here and we'll talk it over."

Wang Number Six assented and went off.

Pan Number Three was sitting there alone, sipping tea, when another man burst in. "Mr. Pan!" he cried. "I've been looking for you everywhere! So you were here all the time drinking tea!"

"What do you want?"

"About ten miles outside the city lives a man called Shih Men-ching, who decided to sell his younger brother's widow to a man called Huang Chiang-fu. In fact, he pocketed the money; but his sister-in-law refused to marry again. He consulted a go-between and they decided to have her kidnapped; but the go-between said: 'I don't know your sister-in-law; you'll have to tell me how to recognize her.' 'She goes out every morning to collect firewood behind the house,' said Shih. 'If you lie in wait there tomorrow, you can carry her off.' Well, they went ahead with this plan; but the next morning Shih's wife went out instead of his sister-in-law, so they carried off the wrong woman! Huang lives more than ten miles away, and he has already slept with her. When Shih went to ask for his wife back, Huang wouldn't give her up; so he has appealed to the court and the suit has just started. The trouble is that they never drew up a marriage certificate, so there is no proof; and now Huang wants to have one made out, but those villagers don't know how to do it. That's why I came to you, sir. He hopes you can also handle the yamen side for him, and he will send you a few taels of silver as a a present."

"Why get so exited over a little thing like this?" demanded Pan. "Sit down. I'm waiting for Huang the runner."

Soon Huang Chiu arrived with Wang Number Six.

"So Mr. Hao is here too," he said, when he saw the other man.

"That has nothing to do with you," said Pan. "He's here for something else."

Pan and the runner sat at one table, Wang and Hao at another.

"How do you plan to settle this business, sir?" asked Huang.

"How much is he willing to pay?"

"Mr. Hu says if he can get the girl, he'll pay two hundred taels—but that must cover all the costs."

"How much do *you* want to make out of it?"

"If you can pull this off, sir, I'll be satisfied with a few taels. You don't think I'm going to wrangle with you, do you?"

"That's all right then. There is a scholar from Yuehching County in our family who happens to be a friend of the county magistrate there. I shall ask him to get a report from the magistrate stating that this girl Lotus has been sent back to her own home. At the same time I shall find someone here to get authority from our magistrate to fetch her back, so that we can hand her over to Mr. Hu. What do you say to that?"

"Excellent!" said Huang Chiu. "But there's not a moment to lose: you will have to get busy at once, sir."

"I shall get authority from the magistrate today. Tell Mr. Hu to bring the money at once." When the runner had consented and left with Wang, Pan took Hao back with him to his house.

The gamblers were still there. When their game was over Pan saw them out, but kept Kuang Chao-jen behind.

"Won't you stay for the night?" he asked. "I have something to discuss with you."

Taking him to a back room upstairs, he drafted a marriage certificate for Kuang Chao-jen to copy, then showed this to Hao telling him he could have this the next day when he brought the money. This done, he sent Hao away.

After supper, Pan lit the lamp and dictated a faked writ to Kuang Chao-jen, then chopped it with one of the many false seals made of dried beancurd which he had in the house. Next he produced a vermilion brush and asked Kuang Chao-jen to write out an order of recall. And when all their work was done, he brought out wine and they drank together. "These are what I call worthwhile jobs, which won't be wasting your time," said Pan. "Why play about with those fools?"

That night Pan kept Kuang Chao-jen there. And the next morning when the two lots of money arrived, he gave him twenty taels to take back with him. Kuang Chao-jen accepted the money gladly, and sent some home through a friend to increase his brother's capital. Various bookshops asked him to edit essays for them, and from now on he had a share in all Pan's profits; so he was gradually able to cut a better figure. He also took Pan's advice and kept away as much as possible from the scholar-poets.

One day about two years after this, Pan Number Three called on him.

"I've not seen you for a long time," he said. "Let's go and have a drink."

Kuang Chao-jen locked his door and accompanied Pan; but they had not walked many yards when a servant from Pan's house came up to them.

"There is a guest waiting for you, sir, at home," he said.

"You had better come with me," Pan told Kuang, then took him to his house and asked him to wait in a inner room while he talked to the caller in the hall.

"I haven't seen you for a long time, Li Number Four," said Pan. "Where have you been?"

"I have been at the examiner's yamen," replied Li. "I have something to talk over with you, and was afraid you might not be at home. Now that I've found you, I'm sure we shall be able to pull this off."

"What are you up to now?" demanded Pan. "I've never worked with anyone so close-fisted. You can't bear parting with a cent!"

"There's money in this."

"What is it?"

"Well, the imperial examiner will soon be coming to Shaohsing, and there is a man called Chin Tung-yeh who has been a clerk in the Board of Civil Office for a number of years and made some money, who wants his son to take the examination. But his son Chin Yao is an absolute idiot. So now, with the examination coming, his father wants to find a substitute. The trouble is that this examiner is very strict: we shall have to think out a new way. That's why I've come to talk it over with you."

"How much is he prepared to pay?"

"To pass the examination in Shaohsing is worth a cool thousand taels. If he takes this short cut, we can ask at least five hundred taels. The substitute will be difficult to find though; and there's the problem of how to disguise him, how much to pay him, how much to spend in the yamen, and how to divide what's left between ourselves."

"If it is only five hundred taels altogether and you want a share of it, I am not interested," declared Pan. "You can get a little money out of Mr. Chin for your trouble, but you can't touch this five hundred."

"All right. I'll do anything you say. But tell me how to manage it."

"You needn't trouble your head over it," said Pan. "I shall find a substitute and settle with the yamen. All you need do is tell Mr. Chin to give you the five hundred taels to deposit in a pawnshop, just paying me thirty taels first for minor expenses. I guarantee that his son will pass. If he doesn't, I won't touch the five hundred taels. Will that suit you?"

"There can be no objection to that," said Li.

So the matter was settled, and a date fixed for the payment. When Pan had seen Li out, he rejoined Kuang Chao-jen.

"I'm counting on you for this, my friend," he said.

"I heard what you said, and I'll do what I can for you. But will I have to write the essay outside and try to pass it in, or go in to take the examination for him? I must say I haven't the courage to pass myself off as someone else."

"Don't you worry. I'll look after you. You don't think I'd let you get into trouble, do you? When he brings the money, I'll go to Shaohsing with you."

Kuang Chao-jen then returned to his lodgings.

A few days later Pan called for him with his luggage, they crossed the Chientang

River, travelled straight to Shaohsing and found quiet lodgings in an alley near the examiner's office. The next day Li brought the candidate to see them. When the examiner had announced the time of the examination, Pan took Kuang Chao-jen at midnight to the gate-house of the examination school, where he made him take off his scholar's costume and put on a tall black hat, a blue cloth gown and a red belt. Then he whispered some urgent instructions and left him, taking Kuang's clothes away with him.

At dawn three cannons were fired, the examiner entered the hall, and Kuang Chao-jen, holding an usher's stick, mingled with the other ushers who bustled noisily in to stand on guard by the second gate. When the examiner called the roll and reached the name of Chin Yao, Kuang winked at the young man—who was forewarned—and instead of going to his appointed cell he slipped into the shadow while Kuang stepped back to join him. Behind the backs of the others, Chin took off his cap and they exchanged caps and clothes. Then Chin picked up the stick and joined the ranks of the ushers, while Kuang Chao-jen took the paper to the cell and wrote an essay. He handed in his paper rather late, then returned to his lodging without anyone discovering the imposture. And when the results were published, Chin Yao had passed with distinction.

Pan Number Three accompanied Kuang Chao-jen back to Hangchow and gave him two hundred taels as his reward. . . .

Kuang Chao-jen was about to choose an auspicious day for his return to Yuehching when Ching Lan-chiang called to see him and invited him out to a tavern. While they were drinking, Kuang told him all that had happened; but after expressing his admiration Ching steered the conversation round to Pan Number Three.

"Have you heard the news?" he asked.

"No. What has happened?"

"He was arrested last night and is now in gaol."

Kuang Chao-jen was aghast.

"Surely not!" he exclaimed. "I was with him at noon yesterday. Why should he be arrested?"

"It's quite true," declared Ching. "I wouldn't have known, but for the fact that I have a relative who is a police officer in the district yamen. It's his birthday today, and when I went to congratulate him everybody was talking about this. That's how I heard. It seems that the order came down from the provincial governor, so the county magistrate dared not delay but sent to arrest him at midnight, fearing he might escape. They surrounded the house and arrested him then and there. The magistrate didn't ask a single question, simply tossed the warrant to him to read. And when Pan saw it he didn't even attempt to defend himself, but kowtowed to the magistrate and let himself be taken away. He had walked to the door of the hall when the magistrate called the runners back and ordered them to put him in the inner prison with the bandits. He's in for trouble all right. If you don't believe me, I can take you to my relative's place to see the warrant."

"That would be best," said Kuang. "May I trouble you, sir, to take me there? I wonder what he was accused of?"

They paid the bill, left the tavern and went straight to the house of the police officer, whose name was Chiang. He was entertaining friends; but when he saw them he invited them into the library and asked the reason for their visit. Ching Lan-chiang told him: "My friend would like to see the warrant for that man, Pan, who was arrested last night."

Chiang produced a notice pasted on a board, which read: "It appears that Pan Tze-yeh is a local criminal who has been making use of his official position and concealing his real character to practice legal chicanery, lending money at exorbitant rates of interest and injuring the people—there is no crime of which he is not guilty. Such a criminal should not be tolerated for a moment. See that your county magistrate loses no time in arresting this man and trying him, in order to bring him to justice. This is extremely urgent."

Then followed the accusations against Pan Number Three. First, he had embezzled large sums of money; secondly, he had hushed up several murders; thirdly, he had used the official seal of the county yamen and the vermilion brush for fraudulent purposes; fourthly, he had forged several official seals; fifthly, he had kidnapped women; sixthly, by usury he had driven people to suicide; seventhly, he had bribed the school officers and found substitutes for candidates for the examinations. . . . There were other accusations too. When Kuang Chao-jen read this, he nearly took leave of his senses. . . .

"Sir," he asked when the wine had been poured, "is your present post as tutor one likely to lead to promotion?"

"It certainly is," replied Kuang. "Scholars like myself who reach officialdom through proper channels are imperial tutors whose pupils are the sons of nobles."

"Is it like ordinary teaching?"

"Indeed not! Our college is just like a yamen, with official seats, vermilion ink, brushes and inkstones set out in proper order. When I take my seat there in the morning, if a pupil sends in a composition I have only to mark it with my vermilion brush for him to retire. My lowest-ranking students are officers of the third rank by inheritance, and if they accept official posts, they become provincial governors or generals; but they will always have to kowtow to me. Take the libationer of the Imperial College, for instance, who is my tutor. He's the son of the present prime

PROVERBS

Ten gold coins will move the gods; a hundred will move Heaven itself.

The mud Buddha scolds the clay Buddha.

An honest magistrate has lean clerks; a powerful god has fat priests.

Blessings never come in pairs; misfortunes never come singly.

Good deeds are not known out of doors; evil deeds are known a thousand miles away.

If a gambler can reform, there is a cure for leprosy.

At steady gambling even the gods and immortals lose.

Water can support a ship, and water can sink it.

The farmer hopes for rain, the traveler for fine weather.

It is the beautiful bird that is put in the cage.

minister, so the prime minster counts as my grand-tutor too. The other day when the prime minister was ill, he refused to see all the court officials who went to inquire after his health, but asked me alone in to sit on his bed to talk to him for a while."

When Kuang had finished speaking, Chiang said slowly: "Our friend Pan Number Three is still in gaol. The other day he told me very eagerly that he had heard you had come back, sir, and that he would like to see you to talk over his troubles. I don't know how you feel about it."

"Pan Number Three is a stout fellow," said Kuang. "Before this trouble of his, when he invited us to taverns he would order at least two ducks, to say nothing of mutton, pork, chicken and fish. He wouldn't touch the kind of set meal this place serves. It's a pity he's in this fix! I would have gone to the gaol to see him, but my position has changed. As a servant of the throne I have to abide by the law; and to call on him in such a place would show no respect for the law."

"You are not a local official," countered Chiang, "and you would only be visiting a friend. What harm can there be in that?"

"Gentlemen," said Kuang, "I shouldn't say this, but to friends it doesn't matter. In view of what our friend Pan has done, if I had been in office here I would have had to arrest him. If I were to go to the prison to call on him, it would look as if I disapproved of the sentence. That is not the way of a loyal subject. Besides, all the yamens here know I have come back for my testimonial. If I were to go to the gaol and the story reached my superiors, my official reputation would be ruined. How can I do such a thing? I will trouble you, Mr. Chiang, to send my regards to Pan Number Three and tell him that I shall remember him. If I am lucky enough to be appointed to some profitable post on my return to the capital, I shall be glad to send him a few hundred taels in a year or so to help him." . . .

"So you are the famous Chekiang editor," said Feng. "I have read much of your distinguished work."

"I have my share of literary fame," responded Kuang. "During the last five or six years since I went to Hangchow I have selected essays by students and scholars and written commentaries on the *Four Books,* the *Five Classics* and the *Anthology of Ancient Essays*. According to the record I have kept at home, I have produced ninety-five volumes in all. Each time a book of mine is published, ten thousand copies are sold; and travellers from Shantung, Shansi, Honoa, Shensi and Peichih fall over each other in their eagerness to buy, all dreading the possibility that it may have sold out. One of my works published the year before last has already been reprinted three times. To tell you the truth, gentlemen, scholars of the five northern provinces respect my name so highly that they often light incense and tapers to me on their desk, calling me 'Master Kuang of sacred memory.' "

"Sir!" Niu Pu-yi laughed. "That must be a slip of the tongue. Only the dead are described as 'of sacred memory.' Since you are still among us, how can they refer to you in that way?"

"No, no," insisted Kuang, flushing. "It is used as a sign of respect!"

Niu Pu-yi decided not to argue with him.

"A certain Ma Chun-shang selects essays too," said Feng. "What do you think of him?"

"He is a good friend of mine," answered Kuang Chao-jen, "but although he understands the rules, he lacks genius and therefore his books don't sell too well. And the circulation is most important, you know; for if a book doesn't sell, the bookshops lose money. My selections, however, are read even in foreign countries." . . .

He was turning home when he met a nephew who insisted on taking him to their house. His niece, dressed in her best, came out to wish him a happy New Year and kept him to tea at which dumplings of glutinous rice were served; and though Old Pu did not want to eat more than two, his niece pressed him to take another two. On his way home the wind was against him and he felt rather unwell; and by evening he had a headache and high fever so that he had to go to bed. Physicians were sent for. But some said that owing to worry he was suffering from phlegm, some that he ought to perspire, others that a warm sedative was needed, and yet others that being old he required stimulants. They could not agree on their diagnosis. . . .

As they were talking, two scholars in square caps walked up the stairs. The one in front was wearing a yellow silk gown, the front of which was stained with grease, and the one behind a black gown with tattered sleeves. "Isn't that Wang Yi-an," cried the scholar in yellow, "the pimp for that brothel in Feng Family Lane?"

"It is," agreed the scholar in black. "How dare he strut about here in a scholar's cap?"

He walked over, tore off Wang's cap and gave him a resounding slap in the face. Wang grovelled on the ground, kowtowing as fast as a pestle pounding onions; but that only made the two scholars more angry than ever. And when Niu Yu-fu spoke up for Wang they spat at him.

"A scholar to share a meal with a pander!" they said. "It might be excusable if you didn't know who he was; but to plead for him now that you know is unforgivable! Get out of here, before we make things hot for you!"

When Niu Yu-fu saw that nothing could be done he nudged Niu Pu, hurried downstairs to pay the bill and went quickly back to the junk.

The two scholars gave the pander a thorough beating. Even though the restaurant owner intervened and made Wang Yi-an apologize, they would not stop but threatened to take him to the yamen. Only when Wang in desperation produced three taels and seventy cents of silver and gave this to them did they let him go. . . .

There were three cases that day, the first involving the murder of a man's father, the plaintiff being a monk. This monk stated that he had been gathering firewood on the mountain when he noticed that one of the cows grazing there kept staring fixedly at him. Strangely moved, he went up to the cow, whereupon tears gushed from the beast's eyes; and when he knelt down before it, the cow licked his head, its tears falling faster and faster. The monk realized that this must be his father whose soul had entered the body of a cow. He pleaded tearfully with the owner of the cow to give him the beast in order that he might keep it in the temple. Then, however, a neighbor had taken the cow away and killed it. The monk had now come to court with the man who had given him the cow as his witness.

When Magistrate Hsiang had heard the monk's story, he questioned the neighbor.

"Three or four days ago this monk led the cow over and sold it to me," said the neighbor, "and I killed it. But yesterday the monk came back to claim that this cow was his father so I must pay him some more, because he had sold it too cheaply. When I wouldn't give any more money, he started abusing me. I've heard say that the cow wasn't his father at all. For years now this monk has shaved his head and put salt on it; and whenever he sees cattle grazing, he picks out the fattest cow and kneels before it, so that the cow licks his head. Any cow licking salt will shed tears. Then he declares that this cow is his father and goes crying to the owner to ask to have it given him; and when he gets it he sells it. He has done this many times. Now he is accusing me. I beg Your Honor to decide between us!"

The magistrate called the owner of the cow. "Did you really give him the cow for nothing?" he asked.

"Yes. I didn't ask for a single cent."

"Transmigration has always been considered a mystery," declared Magistrate Hsiang. "But this is simply incredible. Besides, if he really believed that the cow was his father, he ought not to have sold it. This bald-pate is a scoundrel!"

Having sentenced the monk to twenty strokes, he dismissed the case. . . .

"I have to go to the examination school to invigilate," Prefect Hsiang told Pao Wen-ching and his son. "If I take my servants as inspectors, there is bound to be cheating. But I trust you both completely—will you help out for a few days?"

Acting on the prefect's instructions, Pao Wen-ching and his son inspected the grounds of the examination school and searched each cell. There were three examinations at Anching. Some of the candidates had found substitutes, others slipped essays to each other. In fact, they were up to every conceivable trick: passing notes, throwing bricks, winking and making signs to one another. When soup dumplings were served, Ting-hsi was disgusted to see how they pushed and jostled for the food. One candidate, on the pretext that he must go to the latrine, slipped over to the mud wall which surrounded the school, knocked a hole in it, and put his arm through this hole to receive an essay from an accomplice. Ting-hsi, who caught him red-handed, wanted to hale him before Prefect Hsiang. But his father stopped him.

"My son is only an ignorant boy," he said to the student, "while you, sir, are a respectable scholar. Hurry back to your cell now to write your paper. If the prefect found you here, that would be awkward."

Having scooped up some soil to stop up the hole in the wall, he escorted the candidate back to his cell. . . .

"The scholars of this generation are going from bad to worse," declared Prefect Hsiang. "If you talk to metropolitan graduates and academicians about studying the classics and continuing our best traditions, they will call you a pedantic visionary; while if you speak to them of understanding the new and gaining a wide knowledge of the old, they will accuse you of being a dilettante. They are loyal neither to their sovereign nor to their friends!" . . .

Tu kept Chi for a meal, and when the wine was served they began to talk freely.

"Are you fond of climbing, or visiting rivers and lakes?" asked Chi.

"My health is not up to it," replied Tu. "I find climbing mountains or visiting lakes too strenuous."

"Are you a music-lover?"

"I like to listen to music occasionally; but if I hear it too often it jars my ears."

A few more cups, and Tu was a little tipsy.

"Wei-hsiao!" he said, and heaved a long sigh. "Since ancient times men have been the slaves of love!"

"No love is greater than that between the sexes," replied Chi. "Yet you said just now you had no interest in women."

"And is love confined to that between men and women? No, the love of friends is stronger! Just look at the story of the Lord of Ngo[1] and his embroidered coverlet. And in all history I consider Emperor Ai of Han, who wanted to abdicate in favor of his friend, showed the truest understanding of love. Yao and Shun were no better than this, for all their polite deferring to others. But what a pity that no one understands this lofty love today!"

"True," rejoined Chi. "Have you never had a friend who really understood you?"

"If I could live and die with such a man, I would not be grieving and pining away like this! But I have not been lucky enough to find a true friend, and that is why I so often give way to melancholy!"

"You should look for a friend among the actors."

"That proposal is even more wide of the mark, Wei-hsiao! To seek a true friend among actors is like looking for a grand romance in the courtesans' quarter. Nothing could be more impossible. No, they alone deserve unqualified praise who require a spiritual affinity and a friendship transcending the flesh. Their friends must be some of the greatest men of the time!"

He struck his knee and sighed.

"But there's no such man in the world. No, Heaven has condemned gallant Tu Shen-ching to pine away alone!"

With this, he shed tears.

"Why, the man is possessed!" thought Chi. "Let me play a trick on him."

"You mustn't say there is no such man in the world, sir," he declared. "I know a young man who is neither an actor nor a scholar, but a Taoist priest. He is handsome and elegant, but not in any feminine way—his is true masculine beauty. It always irritates me to hear people praise a handsome man by declaring he looks like a woman. How ridiculous! Anyone who likes a feminine beauty can look at women. But there is a masculine beauty too, which is seldom recognized."

"A truer word was never spoken!" cried Tu, clapping the table. "But tell me more about this man."

"He is so fastidious that, although many people have tried to make friends with him, he holds himself aloof. He loves genius, though. Because I am a few years older than he is, I don't feel good enough for him, so I have never ventured to make any advances. Would you care to meet him, brother?"

"When can you bring him here?"

"He wouldn't be the extraordinary man I said he was if I could bring him over just like that. You must call on him yourself."

"Where does he live?"

1. The Lord of Ngo was devoted to a singer in the state of Yueh, and covered him with an embroidered coverlet. Later this incident was used as a classical allusion to describe love between men.

"In Divine Pleasure Temple."

"What is his name?"

"I can't tell you that now. If word of this came to his ears, he would keep out of your way and you would never see him. I'll write his name on a piece of paper and give it to you sealed, but you mustn't open it till you reach the gate of Divine Pleasure Temple. If you open it there, you'll have no difficulty in finding him."

"Very well," agreed Tu with a laugh.

Chi Wei-hsiao went inside, closed the door, wrote for some time, sealed up his paper carefully and inscribed a Taoist magic formula on it. He gave this to Tu.

"I will leave you now," he said. "After you have seen this marvellous man, I shall come back to congratulate you."

His host saw him out.

"You must take a message to Big Foot Shen tomorrow morning," Tu told his servant. "Tell her I have no time to go to see the girl at Flower Arch, but will go the day after tomorrow. And call the chair-bearers tomorrow morning. I am going to Divine Pleasure Temple to see a friend."

The next morning he washed with soap, changed into new clothes and scented himself lavishly; then, with Chi Wei-hsiao's paper in his sleeve, went by sedan-chair to Divine Pleasure Temple. He left the chair at the gate, and stepped over the threshold to open Chi's note.

"Go to Cassia Pavilion at the end of the north corridor," he read, "and ask for Lai Hsia-shih, who is newly arrived from Yangchow. He is your man."

Tu ordered his chair-bearers to wait, and took a winding path through the temple grounds. From a building in front he heard the sound of music, and through the open doors could see three rooms. In the central room sat a eunuch in charge of the imperial tombs, dressed in a dragon-embroidered gown. A dozen actors on the benches to his left and seven or eight young acolytes on the benches to his right were singing and playing musical instruments.

"Can Lai Hsia-shih be here?" wondered Tu.

He took a good look at the young Taoists in turn, but none of them was particularly handsome. Then he looked at the players, but they were quite commonplace too.

"Lai Hsia-shih has too much self-respect to mix with a group like this," he decided. "I must go to Cassia Pavilion to find him."

Arrived at Cassia Pavillion he knocked at the door, and a priest invited him in and gave him a chair.

"I have come to call on Mr. Lai, who recently arrived from Yangchow," said Tu.

"He is upstairs," replied the priest. "Please wait here, sir, while I fetch him."

He went away, and presently a fat priest came downstairs. He wore a Taoist's cap and brown robe, had a dark, greasy face, bushy eyebrows, a big nose and thick beard, and looked over fifty. He bowed to Tu and sat down.

"May I know your name and where you come from?" he asked.

"I come from Tienchang, and my name is Tu."

"Do you belong to the honorable Tu family of Tienchang which gave us such a handsome donation?"

"I do."

The Taoist's face broke into a smile.

"I did not know you were here, sir, or I would have called to pay my respects," he said obsequiously. "How dare I put you to the trouble of visiting me, sir?"

He immediately called for fresh tea and refreshments.

"This must be Lai Hsia-shih's master," thought Tu.

"Is Lai Hsia-shih your pupil?" he asked. "Or your pupil's son?"

"I am Lai Hsia-shih."

Tu gave a start.

"What! *You* are Lai Hsia-shih?"

He could not help himself. Hiding his face in his sleeve he shook with laughter. The mystified Taoist placed refreshments on the table and busied himself with the tea; then he produced a volume of poems from his sleeve and asked for Tu's criticism. The young man had to read the poems, but after two bowls of tea he rose to go. Lai insisted on walking hand in hand with him to the main entrance, where he asked:

"Do you live at the Temple of Kindness Repaid, sir? I will come tomorrow to spend a few days with you."

He saw Tu right out, and watched his chair leave before turning back himself.

As for Tu, he laughed all the way back.

"That dog, Chi Wei-hsiao!" he thought. "What a liar he is!" . . .

The next day Chi Wei-hsiao called to offer his congratulations, and Tu went out to greet him.

"Excuse me for not coming yesterday to congratulate you on your marriage," said Chi.

"I did not prepare for guests yesterday," replied Tu.

"Did you find that marvellous man the day before?"

"You dog! You deserve a beating, but I'll let you off because your trick was not too vulgar!"

"Why do I deserve a beating? I told you he had masculine, not feminine, beauty. You can't deny that, can you?"

"I'm really going to beat you now!"

While they were laughing the Taoist arrived with Ting-hsi to offer congratulations, and Tu and Chi were hard put to it not to laugh; but Tu signed to his friend to keep quiet. They all exchanged greetings, and Tu kept his guests to a meal. After the meal Tu mentioned the eunuch he had seen in Divine Pleasure Temple with actors on his left and acolytes on his right singing and playing to him.

"Why should a man like that have all the luck?" asked Chi. "It's too bad!"

"I want to consult you, Wei-hsiao," said Tu, "about a rather amusing scheme I have in mind."

"What is it?"

"How many opera companies are there, Ting-hsi, by West Water Gate and along the riverside?"

"Over a hundred and thirty."

"I want to choose a date and hire a big place for a contest, at which all the men who play girls' parts shall perform a scene each. Wei-hsiao and I will watch them and take notes of each; and a few days later we'll publish a list of their marks, ranking them according to their looks and acting. We'll post these results in some public place. We can't ask them to come for nothing, though. We'll give each actor fifty cents, two new pouches, and a fan inscribed with a poem. Wouldn't that be amusing?"

"Why didn't you tell me this wonderful idea earlier?" cried Chi, leaping up. "This is too marvellous for words!"

"Let me go and notify them," said Ting-hsi, smiling. "They'll get fifty cents each, and when you gentlemen have marked them and posted up the results, they'll be famous. I shouldn't be saying this, but the truth is, whoever comes out high on the list, even though he's had a powerful patron all along, will be able to make his patron cough up more. They'll be falling over each other in their eagerness to come!" . . .

On the day appointed, two property boxes were taken to Carefree Lake. Chi and Tu as hosts arrived first, then the guests assembled, and Pao Ting-hsi brought about six dozen actors playing women's parts who had put down their names for the contest to pay their respects to Mr. Tu. Tu bade them have a meal, then dress up and walk through the pavilion so that the judges could have a good look at them, and finally go up to the stage to perform. The players assented and left. The scholars, looking round the pavilion, saw that it had windows on all four sides and was surrounded by water. A soft wind had raised ripples on the lake. After putting on their costumes, the actors were to cross the bridge to the pavilion. Tu ordered the middle door to be closed, so that when the actors had crossed the bridge they should go round by the corridor to the latticed gate on the east, and then through the pavilion to leave by the gate on the west. In this way the spectators could see them clearly and judge of their charm and looks.

When the actors had finished their meal, they put on their costumes and make-up. They were all wearing brand-new head-dresses and jackets. One by one they crossed the bridge and walked across the pavilion while Tu and Chi, who had paper and brushes concealed in their hands, made notes. Soon the feast was served, and music sounded as the first actor ascended the stage. One acted "The Feast," another "The Drunken Singer," yet others "Borrowing Tea" or "Killing the Tiger." No two scenes were the same. Wang Liu-ko presented "The Nun Longs for Earthly Pleasures." When night fell hundreds of lamps were lit, high and low, making everything as bright as day. And the melodious singing lingered in the air. Rich yamen officials, merchants and shop-keepers in the city, hearing of the contest, hired fishing boats, fixed up awnings and hung up lanterns, then had themselves rowed to the middle of the lake to watch. When they were pleased, they applauded and cheered. This went on till dawn, by which time the city gates were open and they went home.

A day later, the results were posted up outside West Water Gate. First on the list was Cheng Kuei-kuan of the Fragrant Wood Company; second, Ko Lai-kuan of the Divine Harmony Company; third, Wang Liu-ko. The remaining sixty-odd actors were listed in order of merit. When Pao Ting-hsi took Cheng Kuei-kuan to call on Tu and thank him, Tu gave Pao two taels of gold to take to the silversmith and have them made into a gold cup with the inscription: "Brighter than Cherry Chen."[1] This cup was the actor's prize. All the others received pouches, silver, handkerchiefs and fans.

1. Girl favorite of Prince Shih Hu of the fourth century.

When the men who were friends with the first ten actors on the list saw the notice, they were delighted. Some of them invited their protégés home to celebrate, others gave parties in honor of the occasion in taverns. One feast followed another, the festivities continuing for three or four days. News of this travelled from West Water Gate to Huaiching Bridge, and the fame of the seventeenth Mr. Tu spread throughout the Yangtse Valley. . . .

In the afternoon, Sixth Master arrived with his two cousins, who were wearing silk caps and black shoes with white soles. One had a red gown embroidered with gold, the other a pale grey gown embroidered with gold. Though it was broad daylight, the four servants with them were carrying lanterns bearing the inscriptions "The Brigade General's Household" and "The Successful Nanking Candidate." The two young men came in and sat in the seats of honor. The prostitutes kowtowed to them, while Sixth Master stood at one side.

"Here's a bench, Sixth Brother," said Tang Yu, the elder of the two. "Why don't you sit down?"

"Yes, yes. I was just going to ask you—shall we let these girls sit down?"

"Why not?" demanded Tang Shih, the younger brother. "Sit down."

Gingerly and coyly, giggling behind their handkerchiefs, the two prostitutes sat on a bench.

"How old are these girls?" asked Tang Yu.

"One is seventeen," said Sixth Master. "The other's nineteen."

Wang Yi-an brought in tea, the prostitutes took the cups, wiped the water from them with their handkerchiefs, then offered them to Tang Yu and Tang Shih. The brothers took the tea and drank it.

"When will you young gentlemen be setting out?" asked Sixth Master.

"Tomorrow," replied Tang Yu. "The chief examiner has already gone to Nanking, so we mustn't delay any longer."

While Sixth Master was talking to his brother, Tang Shih pulled Miss Hsi to his bench and cuddled her.

Presently wine was brought in. They had hired a Mohammedan cook, who served Mohammedan dishes: birds'-nests, duck, chicken and fish. Sixth Master poured out the wine himself, and made his cousins take the seats of honor. He himself sat at the lower end of the table, and the two prostitutes one on each side. One dish was brought in after another. Sixth Master sat there awkwardly, drinking.

"Will you go straight to the examination hall when you reach Nanking?" he asked. "At the fifth watch on the eighth day they start by calling the roll of candidates from Taiping Prefecture. Won't it be late by the time they get round to our Yangchow candidates?"

"Who says they call the roll for Taiping Prefecture?" retorted Tang Yu. "First they fire three salvoes in front of the hall and open the palisade. Then they fire another three salvoes and open the main gate. Then they fire another three salvoes and open the dragon gate. There are nine salvoes altogether."

"Those guns aren't as big as the one at our father's headquarters," put in Tang Shih.

"A little smaller—not much," rejoined his brother. "When the guns have been fired, an incense table is set out in the Hall of Supreme Justice, and the mayor of Nanking in sacrificial headdress and serpent-embroidered robe bows, stands up and hides his face behind two umbrellas. The secretary of the finance commissioner's office kneels to invite the God of War to the hall to keep order and the God of War's bodyguard to make an inspection. The umbrellas are parted and the mayor bows. Next the finance commissioner's secretary kneels to invite the God of Literature to preside over the hall, and his bodyguard—the star of successful candidates—to come to the hall to shed light."

Sixth Master shot out his tongue in dismay.

"What! You invite all those gods and Buddhas! One can see what a big event it is!"

"How brave you gentlemen are to go into a place with all those Buddhas!" said Miss Shun. "We'd sooner die than go!"

"These gentlemen are stars in heaven," replied Sixth Master gravely. "They can't be compared to girls like you."

"After inviting the God of Literature," continued Tang Yu, "the mayor bows again three times to heaven, and the secretary invites all successful ancestors."

"What do you mean by successful ancestors?" asked Sixth Master.

"Successful ancestors are those who have passed the metropolitan examination and held office," replied Tang Shih. "They're the only ones invited. What would be the use of asking common people or those scholars who grow old taking the district examinations?"

"There's a red flag at the door of each cell, with a black flag beneath it," said Tang Yu. "Under the red flag squat the spirits of those the candidate has helped, under the black flag the spirits of those he has wronged. Now the mayor takes his seat. The secretary calls out: 'Enter the ghosts of all those helped or wronged!' Paper coins are burnt on either side and with a sudden gust of wind—whoosh!—in tumble the spirits and fly with the burnt paper to under the red and black flags!"

"Amida Buddha! It shows you've got to be good!" cried Miss Shun. "At a time like that men appear in their true colors!"

"Your worthy father must have no end of grateful ghosts," said Sixth Master. "Look at all the good deeds he has done at the frontier and the number of lives he has saved. There won't be room for them all under one red flag."

"It's lucky *you* aren't taking the examination, Sixth Brother," said Tang Yu. "If you showed your face there, the ghosts of those you've wronged would carry off!"

"What do you mean?"

"Look at my friend Yen of Yihsing at the last examination. He's a learned scholar. He had finished seven essays and was reading them at the top of his voice when a sudden draught set the flame of his candle guttering, the curtain was drawn aside and a head thrust in. Yen looked hard, and saw it was a prostitute he had known.

" 'You're dead,' said Yen. 'What are you doing here?'

"The prostitute looked at him and laughed.

"Yen lost his head and banged his fist on the desk, upsetting the inkstone so that ink poured over his papers, making great black blotches.[1] Then the prostitute disappeared.

1. Candidates were disqualified if there were blots on their papers.

" 'This must be fate!' sighed Yen.

"It was pouring with rain, poor man, as he handed in his papers and left through the downpour. He was laid up for three days with a cold, and when I went to see him he told me what had happened.

" 'You must have abused her,' I said. 'That's why she came to find you.'

"How many people have you abused, Sixth Brother? Are you fit to enter the examination hall?"

The prostitutes clapped their hands and laughed.

"We're the people Sixth Master likes to abuse," they said. "If he goes to the examination hall, we'll be the spirits of those he has wronged!"

After eating for some time, Sixth Master sang a catch in his husky voice; and the Tang brothers sang as well, beating time on their knees. That the girls sang goes without saying. They made merry till midnight, when the brothers left with their lanterns.

The next day they boarded a junk for Nanking, and Sixth Master saw them to the boat. Then the brothers spoke of the excitement that attended entering the examination hall.

"What question d'you think will be set this year?" asked the younger.

"My guess is it's bound to be something connected with our father's suppression of the Miao tribesmen in Kweichow last year."

"That would be set in Kweichow."

"Well, then, it must be either the search for worthy scholars or exemption from taxes, one or the other. There's nothing else it could be."

So they chatted all the way to Nanking. Their steward Whiskers Yiu met them there, and had their baggage carried to lodgings in Fishing Lane. Upon entering, the brothers skirted a two-storey building and went in by a side door to three neat rooms overlooking the river. Sitting down, they saw a row of houses on the opposite bank, with scarlet balustrades, green lattice windows, and speckled bamboo blinds. Successful district graduates from all parts of the province were lodging there and could be heard intoning essays.

The brothers had no sooner sat down than they ordered Whiskers Yiu to buy them two new square caps, as well as baskets, bronze receptacles, awnings, door-curtains, stoves, candlesticks, candle-scissors, and bags for their papers—two of each. Then they hurried to Vulture Peak Temple to hand in their names. They also prepared food for the session: moon cakes, honeyed-orange cakes, lotus seeds, dragon's eyes, ginseng, popped rice, pickled cucumber, ginger and salted duck.

"Take some of that asafoetida from Kweichow," the elder brother advised the younger. "You'll need it to calm your nerves if you write a word wrongly."

It took them a whole day to settle matters to their satisfaction. And they checked everything themselves, remarking:

"We can't afford to take chances when our whole careers are at stake!"

On the morning of the eighth they gave their old square caps to two servants, so that these could attend them to the examination hall. The road from Huaiching Bridge onwards was lined with stalls set up by poor scholars for the sale of gay editions of essays compiled by Hsiao Chin-hsuan, Chu-ko Tien-shen, Chi Tien-yi, Kuang Chao-jen, Ma Chun-shang or Chu Hsien-fu. Their turn did not come till late in the evening after the roll of all the scholars from Yicheng had been called. The servants could go no further than the first gate: now the two brothers had to take their own baskets and shoulder their own bedding. Bonfires on either side lit up the sky as they sat on the ground to unfasten their coats and take off their shoes. From within they could hear someone shouting: "A thorough search must be made!"

They went in with the other candidates, took their papers at the second gate, then passed through the dragon gate and went to their cells. On the tenth they emerged, exhausted, to eat a duck apiece and sleep for a whole day. The three sessions were over. On the sixteenth they bade a servant take a card from the brigade general's yamen to requisition a company of players to thank the gods. . . .

Over twenty days later, when ink and paste were taken into the examination hall to write the blue announcement of those who had failed, they knew the results would soon be out. Two days later the lists were published—neither of them had passed. They sat sulking in their rooms for seven or eight days, then collected the rejected papers—three for Tang Yu, three for Tang Shih. Not a single paper had been read to the end! They fell to inveighing against the stupidity of examiners. . . .

While feasting, Yu mentioned his intention to look for a burial ground for his parents.

"Sir," said Chih Heng-shan, "if the ground is dry and warm and free from wind and ants, you can bury your parents safely. All that talk about wealth and fame is nonsense."

"Exactly," replied Yu. "Yet where I come from they take it very seriously. And people are often so hard to satisfy that they delay their parents' burial. I have never made a study of geomancy. Can you gentlemen tell me the origin of Kuo Pu's teachings?"

"Since the ancient practice of appointing an officer in charge of graves was abolished," replied Chih with a sigh, "and the rule of burial by clans no longer observed, many cultured men have been taken in by all that talk about dragons' lairs, mountains and water. Men want their families to prosper; but in their attempts to achieve this, they actually prove most unfilial."

"What do you mean?" asked Yu, much shocked.

"Let me recite you a verse, sir:

> Can spirits live where cold winds blow?
> What logic can your science show?
> A bloody death you had to die;
> Yet on your book men still rely!

This was written by an earlier poet at Kuo's grave. Nothing enrages me more than the way geomancers nowadays, who quote Kuo as an authority, say: 'This plot will ensure that your descendants come first in the palace examination and are Number One Palace Graduates.' I ask you, sir: Since the rank of Number One Palace Graduate was instituted in the Tang Dynasty, how could Kuo Pu, who lived in the Tsin Dynasty, know of this Tang title and decree that a certain type of ground would produce this rank? This is absolutely ridiculous! If the ancients could foretell honors and rank from the soil, how is it that Han Hsin, who chose a high and spacious burial ground for his mother, first became a noble and then had three branches of his clan wiped out? Was that site good or bad? It is even more ridiculous when these charlatans claim that the site for the first Ming emperor's sepulchre was chosen by Liu Chi of our dynasty. Liu Chi was the most talented man of his time, but he was so busy studying military science, agriculture, ceremony and music that he had not a single day's leisure. What time did he have to choose a burial site? No, when the First Emperor ascended the throne, he merely relied on the geomancers to choose an auspicious burial ground for his line. Liu Chi had nothing to do with it!"

"Your arguments, sir," said Yu, "would make a deaf man hear and a blind man see."

"Mr. Chih is entirely right," remarked Wu Shu. "A curious thing happened here the year before last, which you might care to hear."

"I should be most interested," replied Yu.

"This happened to the household of Censor Shih, who lives in Shih Family Lane by Lower Floating Bridge."

"I heard some talk of that," put in Chih, "but never knew the details."

"Censor Shih has a younger brother," continued Wu Shu, "who maintained that the reason his brother had passed the metropolitan examination and he had not was because their mother's burial ground was no good—it aided the first son only, not the second. He kept one of these wind-and-water men in his house, and spent his whole time discussing where to move her grave.

" 'She's been buried some time,' said the censor. 'Better not move her.'

"He wept, bowed and pleaded with his younger brother, but the latter insisted that the grave must be moved. And the geomancer frightened him by saying: 'If the grave is not moved, not only will the Second Master never become an official—he will grow blind!'

"The second son became more and more frantic, and sent this geomancer all over the place in search of a site. Now if you keep one wind-and-water man in your house, you get to know a lot of others outside. When his private geomancer found a site, the second brother called in others to check on it. And, oddly enough, the way of these wind-and-water men is for son to scoff at father and father to scoff at son. No two of them can agree. Whenever this geomancer found a site, the others who checked on it would prove it was no good.

"At last the home-kept geomancer grew desperate. He produced another plot; and this time he bribed a man living to the left of it to say that one night he had dreamed that old Mrs. Shih in ceremonial dress had pointed out this plot to him and signified that she wanted her grave moved here. Since the old lady had chosen this plot herself, the other geomancers couldn't oppose it; and the younger brother insisted on moving the coffin.

"On the day of the removal, Censor Shih and his brother knelt by their mother's grave. As soon as the grave was opened and they saw the coffin, a puff of hot air from the tomb rose straight into the younger brother's eyes. He was blinded on the spot! But that only convinced him more than ever that this wind-and-water man was a living immortal, who knew both past and future; and later he paid him several hundred taels."

"People in our parts have a passion for moving graves too," said Yu. "Is this right or not, Shao-ching?"

"I'll tell you what I think," said Tu. "The government should enact a law requiring anyone who wants to move a grave to hand in a petition at the yamen, and the geomancer to put down in black and white just how many inches of water there are on the coffin, and how many pints of ants. If they prove right when the grave is opened, good. If not, then the executioner, who must stand by when the grave is opened, shall cut off that dog of a geomancer's head. And the man who wanted to move the grave shall be executed like a parricide, by being sliced into pieces. Then this craze might die out by degrees." . . .

One day, before Chang had chosen a date and when they had nothing to do, Yu Yu-ta bought two catties of wine and six or seven dishes, intending to have a good talk with his brother. That afternoon, however, they received a note from the fourth Mr. Yoo, who lived on the main street.

"I have prepared a simple meal for this evening," wrote Yoo Liang. "Please come over for a chat. Don't refuse now."

"Very well," said Yu Yu-ta to the servant. "Give our respects to your master. We shall come."

As soon as the servant had left, a native of Soochow who was a brewer here sent a messenger to invite them both to his brewery for a bath.

"This fellow Ling must be asking us to a meal too," said Yu Yu-ta. "Let's go to Ling Feng first and then to Yoo."

When they reached Ling's gate, they heard shouting and cursing inside. Because the brewer's family was not here, he had hired two big-footed countrywomen, and was carrying on with both of them. All the men in Wuho are accustomed to sleeping with these big-footed maids. Even at feasts in respectable families, when this custom is mentioned people laugh till their eyes are slits, thinking it a great sport and nothing to be in the least ashamed of. But the two maids in Ling's house had grown jealous. Each suspected the other of getting more of their master's money, and through jealousy started scrapping. They made a clean breast of things, both admitting to sleeping with the assistant, and the assistant joined in the quarrel too. After smashing all the bowls, plates and dishes in the kitchen, the maids with their big feet kicked over all the tubs. Instead of the feast and bath they had expected, the Yu brothers spent a

PROVERBS

The fish that escaped is the big one.

A whitewashed crow will not remain white long.

He who rides a tiger will find it hard to dismount.

He uses a cannon to shoot a sparrow.

When beating a dog, first find out who his owner is.

The conquerors are kings; the losers are bandits.

One speck of rat's dung spoils a whole pot of rice.

Straight trees are felled first; sweet wells are drained first.

When with dwarfs do not talk about pygmies.

The tongue is soft and remains; the teeth are hard and fall out.

Alive, we know not the soul; dead, we know not the body.

long time as mediators, then took their leave of their host. Ling, much embarrassed, poured out a thousand apologies, and promised to invite them another day. Then the two brothers went to Yoo's house, only to find the feast there at an end and the gate closed.

"Let's go home," said Yu Yu-ta with a laugh. "We shall have to eat our own feast."

Yu Yu-chung laughed too, and going home together they called for the wine. But the two catties of wine and six dishes had been finished by their wives—there were only an empty pot and some empty dishes left.

"We had three feasts today but weren't able to eat one," said Yu Yu-ta. "This proves that every bite and sup is predestined!"

Laughing, they made their supper off pickled vegetables and rice, and after a few cups of tea each went to his room. . . .

"When are your chaste women to be enshrined?" he asked. "I want to go down for the sacrifice."

"When we go back we will fix a date," they told him. "Your Honor will naturally be invited."

After the meal they left. The next day they sent in cards to take their leave, and went back to their district.

The day after Yoo reached home, Yu Yu-ta came to him.

"The third of next month has been settled on," said Yu, "to celebrate womanly virtue. There are several great-aunts and aunts in our two families who ought to be enshrined. We should prepare a sacrifice and gather together all our clansmen to escort their shrines to the ancestral temple. I suggest we go and pass the word around."

"Most certainly," agreed Yoo. "My family has one to be enshrined, your family has two. Our two clans must have nearly a hundred and fifty members. We should all assemble in official dress to welcome the retinue, as befits two distinguished families."

"I'll go to tell my kinsmen. You tell yours."

Yoo made the round of his relatives, and was absolutely enraged. He was much too angry to sleep that night. Early the next day Yu arrived, rolling his eyes in fury.

"What did your clan say, cousin?" asked Yu.

"Well! What did *your* clan say? Why are you so angry?"

"Don't remind me of it! I went to tell my kinsmen, and if they'd refused to come it wouldn't have mattered. But they said since old Mrs. Fang is being enshrined, they must join in her procession! They urged me to join it too! And when I took exception to this, they jeered at me for being old-fashioned. Have you ever heard anything so infuriating?"

"My family was the same," said Yoo with a smile. "I couldn't sleep for rage! Tomorrow I shall prepare a sacrifice, and escort my own great-aunt's shrine without them."

"I shall have to do the same."

So the matter was settled.

On the third, Yoo put on new clothes and a new cap, and ordered a servant to carry a table of offerings to his eighth cousin's house. He found the place deserted, without a soul to be seen. His eighth cousin, who was a poor licentiate, came out in a ragged cap and gown to greet him. Yoo Liang went in to bow before his great-aunt's shrine, then carried it to the stand. They had hired an old, sedan-like stand and two shoulder poles. And four country fellows carried this lopsidedly along, without any retinue. Four musicians blew a ragged fanfare in front as they carried the shrine to the street, while Yoo and his cousin followed behind. From the door of the ancestral temple they could make out two other derelict stands in the distance, escorted by no musicians but followed by Yu Yu-ta and Yu Yu-chung. When the Yu brothers reached the temple, the four scholars greeted each other. Honoring the Classics Pavilion before the temple was hung with lanterns and streamers, and there a feast had been laid. This was a high pavilion in the middle of the road, commanding a fine view on every side, and actors were carrying up their properties.

"Mr. Fang's actors have come!" the stand-bearers said.

They stood there for a little, till they heard three cannon shots.

"Old Mrs. Fang has started!" said the bearers.

Presently gonging and drumming filled the street. Two yellow umbrellas and eight flags appeared, as well as four groups of horsemen bearing placards inscribed: "The Minister of Ceremony," "The Hanlin," "The Provincial Director of Education," and "The Number One Graduate." These had been lent by the Yu and Yoo families. As the procession drew near, gongs and trumpets sounded, incense was burnt, and the crowd thronged round Mrs. Fang's shrine, which was carried by eight big-footed maids. The sixth Mr. Fang in a gauze cap and round collar followed respectfully behind. After him came two groups: the gentry and the scholars, the gentry including the second, third, fifth and seventh Peng brothers. Then came the metropolitan and provincial graduates, senior licentiates and college scholars of the Yu and Yoo families—sixty to seventy in all. In gauze caps and round collars, they followed respectfully behind the Pengs. In their wake came another sixty to seventy licentiates from the Yu and Yoo families, in scholars' caps and gowns, who scuttled hastily after them. The last of the local gentry, Tang Erh, held a notebook in which he was writing down a record. The last of the licentiates, Tang San, also carried a notebook in which he was writing a record. Because the Yu and Yoo families had a scholarly tradition and some proper feeling, when they reached the ancestral temple and saw their own aunts' shrines there, seven or eight of them came over to bow. Then they all surged after Mrs. Fang's shrine into the temple. Behind them were the magistrate, local teacher, district police warden and sergeant, who came with the retinue to play music and set up the shrine. The magistrate, teacher, police warden and sergeant each sacrificed in turn. Then the local gentry and scholars sacrificed, and last of all the Fang family sacrificed. When this was over, they all rushed noisily out and mounted Honoring the Classics Pavilion for the feast.

When the crowd had left, Yu and Yoo carried their shrines inside and set them in the proper places. Yoo had prepared a table of sacrificial objects, Yu Yu-ta three offerings. The sacrifice at an end, the table was carried out; but since there was nowhere to enjoy the food, they decided to go to a college attendant's house. Yu Yu-ta looked up at the richly dressed men on Honoring the Classics Pavilion, who were toasting each other. The sixth Mr. Fang seemed uncomfortable after such a long ceremony. He replaced his gauze cap and round collar with a head-cloth and ordinary gown, then wandered up and down the balconies. Soon a flower-seller named Chuang came along, and with her big feet climbed the pavilion stairway.

"I came to see the old lady enshrined!" she chuckled.

The sixth Mr. Fang fairly beamed. He stood beside her, leaning against the railing, watching the flags and musicians, pointing out this and that and explaining things to her. The flower woman kept one hand on the railing, and with the other undid her clothes to search for lice, which she popped in her mouth as she caught them. Yu Yu-ta was completely disgusted. . . .

Mr. Wang walked six or seven miles to his son-in-law's house, and found the young man seriously ill. A doctor was there, but no drugs were of any avail. A few days later his son-in-law died, and Wang mourned bitterly for him; while his daughter's tears must have moved both heaven and earth. When her husband was in his coffin, she paid her respects to his parents and her father.

"Father," she said, "since my elder sister's husband died, you have had to support her at home. Now my husband has died, will you have to support me too? A poor scholar like you can't afford to feed so many daughters!"

"What do you want to do?" her father asked.

"I want to bid farewell to you and my husband's parents, and follow my husband to the grave."

When the dead man's parents heard this, their tears fell like rain.

"Child!" they cried. "You must be out of your mind! Even ants and insects want to live—how can you suggest such a thing? In life you're one of our household, in death you'll be one of our ghosts. Of course we'll look after you, and not expect your father to support you! You mustn't talk like that!"

"You are old," said the girl. "Instead of helping you, I should just be a burden to you, and that would make me unhappy. Please let me have my own way. But it will be a few days before I die. I'd like you, father, to go home and tell my mother, and ask her to come so that I can say goodbye to her. This means a lot to me."

"Kinsmen," said Wang Yu-huei to his son-in-law's parents, "now that I think this over, I believe, since my daughter sincerely wants to die for her husband, we should let her have her way. You can't stop someone whose mind is made up. As for you, daughter, since this is the case, your name will be recorded in history. Why should I try to dissuade you? You know what you must do. I'll go home now and send your mother over to say goodbye to you."

Her parents-in-law would not hear of this, but Wang Yu-huei insisted. He went straight home, and told his wife what had happened.

"You must be in your dotage!" she protested. "If our daughter wants to die, you should talk her out of it, instead of egging her on. I never heard such a thing!"

"Matters like these are beyond you," retorted Wang.

When his wife heard this, the tears streamed down her cheeks. She immediately hired a chair and went to reason with her daughter, while her husband went on reading and writing at home as he waited for news of his child. In vain did Mrs. Wang argue with her daughter. Each day the girl washed and combed her hair, and sat there keeping her mother company; but no bite or sup passed her lips. Though the old folk begged and implored her, and used all the wiles they could think of, she simply refused to eat. And after fasting for six days she had not strength to get up. The sight of this nearly broke her mother's heart. She fell ill herself, and had to be carried home and put to bed.

When three more days had passed, torches appeared at the second watch, and some men came to knock at their door.

"Your daughter fasted for eight days," they announced. "At midday today she died."

When the mother heard this, she screamed and fainted away. And when they brought her round, she would not stop sobbing. Her husband walked up to her bed.

"You're a silly old woman!" he said. "Our third daughter is now an immortal. What are you crying for? She made a good death. I only wish I could die for such a good cause myself."

He threw back his head and laughed.

"She died well!" he cried. "She died well!"

Then, laughing, he left the room. . .

"Ma Chun-shang is my sworn brother: of course I know him. He has gone to Peking now. Once in the capital, he is sure to go far."

"Why has he gone to Peking?" asked Wu Shu quickly. "He has not yet passed the provincial examination."

"When the last provincial director of education completed his three years in office, he recommended Ma for his excellent conduct. He has gone to the capital now to take a short cut to officialdom. That's why I say he will go far."

"When all's said and done," remarked Censor Shih, "these unorthodox careers won't take one very far. A man of character should stick to the examinations."

"During his visit last year," said Chih Heng-shan, "I was struck by Ma's genuine knowledge of his subject. It is strange that after all these years he is still a licentiate. It looks as if the examination system is not infallible after all."

"You are wrong there, Mr. Chih," protested Kao. "This is the only matter in which there has been not the slightest change for the last two hundred years. Scholars who deserve to come first will always come first. Ma Chun-shang's writings on this subject are merely superficial: of the finer points he knows absolutely nothing. If he were a licentiate for three hundred years and came first in two hundred prefectural tests, he would still fail every time in the prefectural examinations!"

"Do you mean to say," asked Wu, "that the examiners and the provincial director of education don't see eye to eye?"

"Certainly!" answered Kao. "All the students that rank high on the provincial list will fail in the real examinations. That's why before I passed I gave all my attention to the examinations. The provincial director often placed me in the third rank!"

"That essay of yours, sir, which won the first place," said Wan, "has been carefully studied by everyone in our province."

"Careful study," responded Kao, "is the golden key to success. In my three essays for the district examination, not a single phrase was written at random: each was culled from the classics. That is how I succeeded in passing. Without careful study, even a sage cannot pass. Mr. Ma has been expounding essays all these years; but what he teaches simply cannot pass muster. If he understood the meaning of 'careful study,' he would be a high official!"

"Your words are a guide to the young, sir," answered Wan. "But I still consider my friend Ma Chun-shang a fine scholar. I saw his edition of *The Spring and Autumn Annals* in a friend's house in Yangchow, and I thought he had made a very good job of it."

"How can you say such a thing!" protested Kao. "There is a Mr. Chuang here, who was summoned by the court for a special appointment and who works at home on a commentary of *The Book of Change*. Not long ago, a friend of mine met him at a feast and heard him say: 'Mr. Ma knows how to advance but not to withdraw, like the dragon in *The Book of Change*.' Of course, Ma Chun-shang can't be compared to a dragon; but how ridiculous, also, to use a living licentiate to illustrate a point in the sage's works!"

"Mr. Chuang was simply joking, sir," observed Wu. "If you say living men can't be used as illustrations, why did King Wen and the Duke of Chou refer to Wei Tzu and Chi Tzu? And why did Confucius later refer to Yen Tze? These men were all contemporaries."

"Your comment displays your erudition," said Kao. "My field is *The Book of Songs* not *The Book of Change:* hence there are points on which I am not too clear."

"Your mention of *The Book of Songs* reminds me of another ridiculous thing," continued Wu. "Those who take the examinations nowadays cling blindly to Chu Hsi's interpretations, growing more confused the more they try to explain them. Four or five years ago, when Tu Shao-ching compiled a commentary on *The Book of Songs* and made use of certain Han commentators, his friends were quite amazed. There is obviously no true scholarship today!"

"That is only partly true," put in Chih Heng-shan. "As I see it, scholars should stick to scholarship without trying to become officials, and officials should stick to officialdom without trying to be scholars too. A man who wants to be both will succeed in neither!"

"I hear your cousins asked you to go to Fukien, Mr. Chen," said the monk. "Why haven't you started yet?"

"That's why I came to see you," said Chen. "I wanted my fortune told. When shall I be able to go?"

"Our fortune-telling is nothing but a trick, sir," said Ting. "Just choose a good day and start. You don't need to have your fortune told." . . .

By the twenty-third year of the Wan Li period [1595], all the well-known scholars had disappeared from Nanking. Of Dr. Yu's generation, some were old, some had died, some had gone far away, and some had closed their doors and paid no attention to affairs outside. Pleasure haunts and taverns were no longer frequented by men of talent, and honest men no longer occupied themselves with ceremony or letters. As far as scholarship was concerned, all who passed the examinations were considered brilliant and all who failed fools. And as for liberality, the rich indulged in ostentatious gestures while the poor were forced to seem shabby. You might have the genius of Li Pai or Tu Fu and the moral worth of Yen Hui or Tseng Shen [disciples of

Confucius], but no one would ask your advice. So at coming of age ceremonies, marriages, funerals or sacrifices in big families and in the halls of the local gentry, nothing was discussed but promotions, transfers and recalls in the official world. And all impecunious scholars did was to try by various tricks to find favor with the examiners. . . .

Flowers in the Mirror (extracts)

Li Ju-chen (1763–1830?) / Lin Tai-yi

Trying to explain to the Western readers what Flowers in the Mirror *is like, in her introduction to the following translation Lin Tai-yi says (p. 6): "It is one of the most original works in Chinese literature, and there is nothing like it in Western literature either, unless we think of a work which has the combined nature of* Grimm's Fairy Tales, Gulliver's Travels, Aesop's Fables, *and the* Odyssey, *with* Alice in Wonderland *thrown in for good measure."*

The story takes place in the seventh century but actually satirizes the China of Li's own day. A disappointed scholar named Tang Ao travels by sea with his brother-in-law Merchant Lin and has a number of incredible adventures, visiting such lands as the Country of Two-Faced People, the Country of Women, the Country of Sexless People, and a number of other places difficult to locate on maps but readily recognizable. The transitions between adventures are often abrupt, and the narrative changes in the latter part of the book to allegory. But the reader by that time has willingly suspended disbelief in exchange for a delightfully whimsical satire.

The streets appeared to Tang Ao and Old Tuo to be much like those in the Kingdom on Earth, and were full of people buying and selling. Going up to an old man, Tang Ao inquired whether it was true that to the people of this country, other people's desires always mattered more than one's own. But the old man could not understand what he was talking about. Tang Ao asked him what was the meaning of "gentlemen" and again, the old man could not reply. Finally, Old Tuo said, "You are asking him to judge his people by the standards of other countries, therefore asking him questions he cannot answer. He does not know what being a gentleman means, because he does not know what it is to be anything else."

When they came to the market, they overheard a soldier talking to a shopkeeper. He was holding something in his hand and saying, "What a lovely thing this is! But you are charging too little for it! How could I deprive you of it? Please do me the favor of making it more costly, so that I may buy it with an easy conscience. If you refuse, it will only mean that you do not consider me your friend."

"I suppose this is an example of what is meant by other people's interest mattering more than one's own," whispered Tang Ao to Old Tuo.

The shopkeeper replied, "You know that we are not allowed to haggle here. All prices are one! I am afraid I shall have to ask you to shop elsewhere if you insist on paying more than the fixed price, for I cannot oblige."

"You are putting me in an extremely difficult position by refusing to charge more," said the soldier. "I should not be kind if I agreed. How dare I take advantage of you?"

The shopkeeper still would not give in, so the soldier had no choice but to pay him what was asked, but took only half of what he had paid for, and started to go. But the merchant pressed the rest of the goods on him, and would not let him go until he had taken more than his money's worth. The dispute was finally settled by two passers-by, a pair of old men, who said that the soldier should take not less than eighty per cent of what he paid for.

Tang Ao and Old Tuo thought that it was just.

After a few steps, they saw another soldier who was trying to buy something. He was telling the merchant, "I asked you the price of this, and you would not tell me, but kept asking me to name my own price. Now I have done so, you tell me it is much too much, so I have lowered it and still you say the price is too high. What shall I do?"

"Truly, I dare not charge too much for my articles, which are inferior in quality to what they sell in other shops, and none too fresh, either. How can I think of charging you even half of what you want to pay?"

"Really," thought Tang Ao, "customer and shopkeeper have changed places. Each is saying what the other would say in other countries."

"What are you talking about?" said the soldier. "I recognized the quality of your goods, and they are not inferior at all. How could you think of charging me only half price?"

"I can only charge you half price," replied the merchant, "if you insist on paying more, I am afraid you will have to take your custom elsewhere, for I honestly cannot let you pay so much and feel easy about it."

When the soldier saw that this was the highest price the merchant was willing to charge, he paid it, took only a few items of inferior quality, and started to walk away.

The merchant hurried after him, saying, "Why are you such a difficult customer? Why do you take so little, do you want me to make a profit from it? I didn't think that you would be so hard to please!"

The soldier said frantically, "I didn't want to take the best quality. I only took the worst, because I would not feel right about it otherwise, since I had paid so little."

"But if you only wanted the inferior quality, you should have given me even less money. How can you pay me so much and take so little?"

The soldier did not heed him, and went away. The people on the street thought that he had not given the merchant a fair deal, so he had no course but to come back, and exchange half of what he had taken for goods of the best quality.

Then there was a farmer who had finished his purchases, and was in the act of paying for them. The merchant was weighing the silver and said, "Please, brother, don't go away. Here in the city we deal in second-grade silver only, and you have given me the best grade. I know you don't mind over-paying, but I don't want to be over-paid, either. Please take some of this back."

"It is only a small sum," said the farmer. "Why don't you keep it, and we shall even up next time I come to do business with you."

The merchant said, "No, no. Last year there was a customer who wanted to do the same thing, but he never came back! I owe him to the next incarnation! What shall I do if you don't come back either? Shall I become a horse or donkey in the next life and work for you to repay what you have left me, when I must already be reincarnated once as a horse or donkey to pay back what I owe the other fellow? Please, take what is yours, to save ourselves trouble later on!"

Put this way, the farmer obliged, and took a few things from the shop in place of the silver, and went away, while the merchant continued to complain that it was not fair, that he had taken too little. But the farmer was gone now, and there was nothing he could do.

A beggar happened to come by. The merchant weighed out the silver he thought he owed the farmer, and gave it to him.

"Now I have seen everything," thought Tang Ao. "This is truly a country of gentlemen!"

He was so thinking when down the road strutted two gentlemen of style, smiling and bowing. Tang Ao and his friend shied to one side to let them pass, and the two gentlemen asked their names.

Tang Ao learned that these two were brothers, Wu Tseho and Wu Tsehsiang, and after Tang Ao and Old Tuo had identified themselves, the brothers invited them to their home for a chat. Their home was covered with climbing wisteria, and there was a pond full of water caltrop in front.

It was soon evident that the two gentlemen were learned in scholarship and appreciated the fine arts of living, as well as possessing the most original and sensible opinions on the values and customs of society. They spoke eloquently against the custom of choosing propitious burial places for one's parents, and against the killing of fowl and pigs and lamb for feasting to celebrate the birth of a child. For, as Wu Tsehsiang said, "Is it heaven's will to sacrifice many lives in order to celebrate the birth of one, human though that one may be?"

The brothers were especially against the custom of placing a high value on a commodity simply because it is rare, such as birds' nests, which are considered to be the finest of foods in the Kingdom on Earth, because they are rare, and yet tasteless, without nutritional value, and not unlike wax in substance, and had to be cooked in the best chicken soup to be palatable. Birds' nests abounded in the Country of Gentlemen, but no one would eat them.

In fact, the brothers were against most of the rituals which were attendant upon eating, living, being born and dying, considering them to be senseless and extravagant.

Tang Ao and Old Tuo listened with great appreciation. Then an old servant hurried in and said, "Begging your pardon, gentlemen, but the King is coming to discuss some urgent matters with you."

"In our country when we want to get rid of guests, we give the servant a wink, and he comes in to say that someone is calling, or awaits our presence, so that the guests will leave," thought Old Tuo. "I wonder if this is the same trick."

He and Tang Ao both rose, and left, only to find that the road leading to the house was being swept, and that people were keeping clear of it for the king, proof that it was no excuse at all.

"These gentlemen surely have my admiration," said Old Tuo. "How vulgar our own officials seem in comparison!"

"They are really worthy to be called 'gentlemen' in the truest sense of the word," said Tang Ao.

When they returned to the junk, they found Merchant Lin had already come back, having failed to make any profit because it seemed that the Country of Gentlemen had plenty of everything. Just as they were about to cast off, messengers came from the Wu family, bearing gifts of fruit and pastry, and for the sailors, ten piculs of melon and ten piculs of bird's nest.

The messengers had just left when Wu Tseho himself came, and after being welcomed on board, said, "I am sorry my younger brother has not come, but the King is in our house, and he is entertaining him. My brother has informed the King of your presence, and he has sent me especially as emissary to convey his respects. I should wait to see you off, but as the King is waiting for me, I must take my leave now. I hope you will return." Then he hurried away.

The sailors stowed the melon and the bird's nest in the ship's hold. They sailed soon after, and when evening came, cooked a mess of melon and a mess of bird's nest. The sailors were delighted to taste this food, which they could not afford to eat in ordinary times, but when they put the bird's nest in their mouths, they frowned and cried, "What is this stuff? It is like glutinous noodles! Have we been tricked?"

At the end of the meal, they had eaten all the melon, but there was still a lot of bird's nest left, and Merchant Lin was delighted, and told Old Tuo to buy what was left in the hold from the sailors at the price of noodles, thinking that he would make a handsome profit when he went back to the Kingdom on Earth. . . .

After a few days of travelling, they arrived at the Country of Giants. If the reader wants to know what happened there, please read the next chapter.

Lin did not want to trade in the Country of Giants, because he knew the people here were very much like those in the Country of Gentlemen which they had just left, and where he had made no profit. But he accompanied Tang Ao on a tour of the country.

Tang Ao said, "I have heard that the people of this country walk on clouds. I cannot wait to see them!"

"We'll have to walk more than twenty *li's* before we see anybody," said Old Tuo, "and it will be late before we come back. The roads are confusing, and it won't be easy to find the peak where the people make their city."

They walked for some time, and saw a few farms, and a few people living on them, who were taller than most people by two or three feet. Everyone walked on his own cloud, which was about half a foot from the ground, and when a person stood still, the cloud remained under his feet.

The travellers climbed up a hill, crossed two peaks, and found that they were nowhere near where they wanted to go.

"We must be lost," said Old Tuo. "Let us go over to that temple there and ask the way."

They approached the temple, and knocked on the door. But before anyone opened it, an old man came by, holding a pot of wine in one hand, and the roasted head of a pig in the other.

"We beg your pardon, sir," said Tang Ao. "Could you tell us the name of this temple, and whether any monks live in it?"

The old man put his wine and roast pig's head down and said, putting his hands together in supplication, "This is the Kuan-yin Temple, and I'm a monk."

Merchant Lin could not conceal his surprise. "Why, how could you be," he said, "when you have not shaved your head, and obviously you have been buying meat and wine to enjoy yourself? From the looks of things, would I be unreasonable to conclude that monks and nuns live together in this temple?"

"There is indeed a nun, and she is my wife," said the old man. "Apart from us two, no one else lives here. We are keepers of the temple, but in our country, we do not know anything about monks and nuns. It is from your illustrious country that we heard that those who live in temples must shave their heads and be called monks and nuns. Accordingly, we follow the custom, but we have not bothered to observe the other requirements. I wonder where you are going and where you came from?"

Old Tuo told him, and the old man said, bowing, "Oh, I was not aware that I was in such distinguished company! Please come in and have a cup of tea!"

Tang Ao demurred, saying that they were anxious to get across the peak. Merchant Lin said, "I am wondering what you call a child who has a monk for a father and a nun for a mother?"

The old man laughed. "We are only keepers of the temple," he said. "What would you expect our children to be called? What do you call the children of the keepers of your temples?"

"I hear that in your country, everyone walks on a cloud. Is this cloud born with a person?"

"These clouds are born with us," said the old man. "They are not man-made. It is best if one has a rainbow-colored cloud. Yellow is second, and black is the worst."

"We have far to travel before returning to our ship," said Old Tuo. "If you would be so kind as to point the way, we should be going along."

The old man told them which way to go, and they took a winding path, and crossed the peak.

When they found the city, they saw that everything looked much the same as in the Country of Gentlemen, except that everyone was walking on clouds of different colors. A beggar went past walking on a rainbow-colored cloud.

"Isn't that odd," said Tang Ao, "since the rainbow-colored cloud is supposed to be best, and the black cloud the worst."

"And that old fellow at the temple was obviously a monk who had not kept his vows," said Lin. "Yet he, too, had a rainbow-colored cloud."

"When I came here before, I was told that the color of one's cloud depends not on whether he is rich or poor, but on the way he conducts himself," said Old Tuo. "If a man is open with people, straightforward and honest, he has a rainbow cloud, but if he is secretive and conniving, he walks on a black cloud. The color of one's cloud changes with his temper, and so you may find a rich man walking on a black cloud, and a poor man on a rainbow cloud. However, look! Hardly a soul is walking on a black cloud! The people of this country must all be kind-hearted and good-natured—doubtless, because they would be ashamed to be seen with a black cloud under their feet, and are proud when they can show off a good-colored cloud. This country is called the Country of Giants. People who don't know think that the people are really giants. Actually, it refers to the largeness of their hearts."

"But I have often heard that there is a country abroad somewhere where the people are very tall," said Tang Ao. "Can I be mistaken?"

"Oh, you must mean the Country of Tall People," said Old Tuo, "which is different from this one."

Suddenly the pedestrians shied to either side of the street, and someone who was obviously an important official swaggered past, wearing a black turban and an elaborate costume. He carried a red umbrella, and had a retinue of subordinates behind and in front of him, who shouted to the people to make way. But the official's cloud was surrounded by a red curtain, so that no one could see it.

"I suppose this official doesn't need a carriage to ride in, since he is already walking on a cloud," said Tang Ao. "But I wonder why he has hidden his cloud behind a curtain?"

"Sometimes a man will get an attack of stormy grey cloud," said Old Tuo, "because he has done something which conscience tells him is wrong. This man has hidden his grey cloud behind a curtain because he doesn't want people to see it, but of course by hiding it behind a curtain he is only calling attention to it. Luckily, a cloud changes color when a man changes heart, and a man who persistently walks over a dark cloud is ostracized by everyone in this country, and even punished."

"Oh, how unfair!" said Lin.

"How unfair?" asked Tang Ao.

"How unfair it is that only the people of this country have clouds under their feet! If everyone in the world had to carry a self-advertisement like this, how wonderful people would be!"

"We may not have clouds under our feet, but when we do something wrong, the smoke which rises from our heads can be seen from far away. Isn't that just as effective?" said Old Tuo.

"What do you mean?"

"Whatever we do, old Father Heaven always knows," said Old Tuo. "He knows exactly who has done right and who has done wrong."

"I suppose heaven is not unjust after all," said Lin.

After walking about a little more, they returned to the junk before dark.

After a few days, the junk arrived at the Country of Restless People. The people here had black faces, and were so restless that they moved about all the time. Even when they sat down or stopped walking, they could not keep their arms and legs still.

"They look like epileptics," said Lin. "I wonder if they keep moving when they are asleep! It's lucky I don't live here, I'd fall apart in a couple of days."

"Do they live to an old age for all their ceaseless activity?" Tang Ao inquired.

"Yes, they do," said Old Tuo. "They all live to a ripe old age, because they exercise their muscles so much, and because, being too restless to farm, they live on fruits and nuts, and being too nervous to cook, fried food never touches their mouths. But I am getting dizzy watching them. I would like to go back."

Tang Ao thought that he had seen enough, too, and they all went back after Lin had bought a pair of two-headed birds which could make marvellous sounds, which he thought he would sell at the Country of Split-tongued People.

After a few days, they came to the Country of Long-eared People, where the people's ears hung down to their waists, and they walked about holding their earlobes in their hands.

Then Tang Ao and his companions arrived at the Country of Intestineless People, who considered eating a social embarrassment, much as people in other countries considered defecation, and ate only when no one was looking. This was because as soon as they ate something, it passed through their bodies undigested to emerge at the other end.

Next to the Country of Intestineless People was the Country of Dog-headed People, who, on the other hand, spent all their time in the enjoyment of food and drink, and did not know how to do anything else. Tang Ao wanted to go and look at them, but Old Tuo thought that they should not, since the people had no pupils in their eyes and were so greedy that they had lost their sense of judgement, and could not tell a good man from a bad man.

One day, the travellers arrived at the Country of Black-bottomed People. The skin of the people was black from the waist down, although the upper part of their bodies was fair. They were a country of fishermen, and the place was desolate and poor. The sailors, however, wanted to buy some fish, so they tied up, and went up along the seashore. The people wore capes and fish-skin trousers, and were bare-footed. One man was hauling up his net which had a queer fish in it with one head and ten bodies.

"Is this the *Chih* fish from the *Chih* waters which tastes like spice and smells like orchids?" asked Tang Ao.

Before Old Tuo could answer, Merchant Lin crouched down, took a sniff of the fish, wrinkled up his face and retched.

Old Tuo laughed. "You should not have been so hasty," he said. "Give it a kick, and it will bark like a dog."

Lin did so, and the fish barked.

"This, then, is the other one, the *Holo* fish," said Tang Ao.

"Yes," said Old Tuo. "Both the *Holo* fish and the *Chih* fish have ten bodies to a head, but one smells heavenly, and the other extremely foul. Our brother here should have found out which one this one was first."

As they were watching the fisherman haul a big net in, an old man with white hair came over and said, "Brother Tang! Do you remember me?"

He was wearing a fisherman's hat of woven bamboo, with a fish-skin cape around his shoulders, and his legs were as black as the bottom of a kettle. Tang Ao took a good look at him, and got the shock of his life.

In fact it was his old teacher Yin Yuan, the Imperial Censor. "What are you doing here, Master, and in this garb?" he cried. "Can I be dreaming?"

"It's a long story," said Yin Yuan. "I live not far from here. I'd be happy to tell you all about it if you come to my house."

It was a very small thatched-roofed house of two rooms, but clean and tidy, although there was no furniture in it. So they sat on the floor.

Yin Yuan explained that when the Emperor was banished from the throne by Empress Wu, he had incurred the displeasure of Her Majesty when he submitted three official memoranda to her, advising her to abdicate and allow the Emperor to come back. He resigned from his post, and had lived a quiet life from then on. However, at the time of the Rebellion, some minister at Court brought up his past record and called it to the Empress's attention. He had no choice, then, but to escape overseas.

The people of this country were poor, and they did not like to have strangers living among them. But luckily, Yin Yuan had a daughter who was skilled at making fishnets, and they sold these for a living. After some time passed, the people came to take pity on them, and told Yin to paint his legs black. When he did this, he passed as a native, and was allowed to fish along with the rest of the people. . . .

After passing several other countries, the travellers arrived at the Country of Sexless People.

Tang Ao said, "I have heard that the people of this country do not give birth to children. Can that be true?"

"I have heard that it is so," said Old Tuo, "because there is no distinction between men and women among them. I have been here before, and, indeed, the people look like neither men nor women."

"But if they don't give birth to children, shouldn't they have all died out long ago?" asked Tang Ao.

"No, because their bodies not do corrupt after death, but they come back to life again after a hundred and twenty years. Thus, their numbers neither increase nor decrease. They think of death as sleep and life as a dream, for well they know that all mortal strife ends in a long sleep. Therefore, they don't crave fame and power and personal gain. They know that these things don't last, and that if they succeed in winning them in one life, they will only wake up a hundred and twenty years later to find that they have to struggle for them anew. Needless to say, these people also eschew violence."

"How foolish we must seem to them then," said Merchant Lin, "when we don't even come back to life again, and yet struggle so hard for wealth and fame!"

"If you can look at things that way," said Tang Ao, "all you need to do is to place a different value on these very things."

"That's easy to say, and, theoretically, I can see that wealth and fame are of dudious value when we think that life is like a fleeting dream. Yet, when I find myself embroiled in a real situation, it is as though I were crazed, and I cannot help becoming excited and engaged in the struggle and the strife. However, in the future, when I find myself in that state, I should be happy if someone pinched me. Then I would wake up at once and see the futility of it all."

"Ah, but when you are in that state, I am afraid that you would not listen if I tried to remind you of the futility of it all, but on the other hand, would turn around and blame me for interfering!" said Old Tuo.

"That's true," said Tang Ao. "Lust for fame and fortune are like an intoxication.

While a man is intoxicated he doesn't realize it. It's only after it is all over that he realizes that everything is like an illusion. If men could realize this all the time, there would be much less trouble on earth, and there would be much happier people, too."

"But I hear that these people eat the soil, is that true?"

"Yes," said Old Tuo. "They don't farm, and they don't like the fruit which grows on trees, but prefer to eat the soil...perhaps because by nature they are really an earthy lot." . . .

When the travellers arrived at the Country of Deep-eyed People, they discovered that the eyes of the people grew on their hands, and that it gave them great freedom when they wanted to look at things high and low, as well as an advantage when they came to a crossroads, and wanted to know which was the right road to take.

"I wonder why their eyes are in their hands?" said Merchant Lin.

"No doubt because they are a cautious people," said Old Tuo, "who like to look at things from every different angle before they decide to do anything."

At the country of Black-toothed People, Merchant Lin sold a lot of cosmetics, and Tang Ao discovered that the people loved scholarship above wealth. There, they met two girls, Lee Red Rose and Lu Purple Lily, who were so learned that they put Tang Ao to shame.

In the Country of Little People, the citizens were only seven or eight inches tall, and the children about four inches. But these were a contrary people, who called everything by their opposites, saying sweet was bitter, and salt had no taste. Crochety, mean, caustic, and cunning, they carried rifles wherever they went for fear of big birds pecking at them.

Tang Ao did not like them much. "I didn't know people could be so small," he said.

In the Country of Tip-toeing People, the inhabitants, who were eight feet tall and eight feet wide, walked about on tip-toe all the time.

Tang Ao took one look at them and said, "What squares!" and did not bother to go ashore.

When they arrived at the Country of Tall People, they saw a vast mountain with a city built upon it, and men who were seventy, eighty feet tall. . . .

After a few days' sailing, Lin and Tang were standing on the bridge-tower one day when they saw an apparition ahead which was like neither smoke nor cloud. From its misty outlines, there seemed to be a city. There seemed also something very fragrant.

Old Tuo looked at the compass and the basin of incense (to tell the time) and said, "I think we have come to the Country of Scholars."

As they approached it, they saw that thousands of tall plum trees enclosed the city. The travellers went ashore, and walked into the forest of plum trees. Leeks were growing everywhere on the ground.

Soon they saw farmers wearing scholars' costumes. After walking for a long time, the travellers came to a pass. On the city gate was a couplet inscribed in gold which said:

Kindness elevates a family's social position.
Learning makes good sons and daughters.

"The King of this country is supposed to be a descendant of Chuan Hsueh, who is a descendant of the Yellow Emperor," said Tang Ao.

Before they could enter the city, however, soldiers came forward and asked them who they were and searched them.

When they were allowed to enter the city, Merchant Lin said, "I suppose they thought we were thieves. We should all have taken some walk-on-air plant and leaped over the wall."

The people on the streets all wore the scholars' blue or green costume, and the scholars' scarf around their heads. Even the merchants were dressed like this, and the shops were very simple. Apart from books, paper and ink, spectacles and toothpick shops, there were only a few wine and grocery shops which sold mostly green plums and leeks.

The three went into a wine shop and sat down at a table. Soon they saw an old man come in and sit down near them.

"Give me half a pot of light wine, and a dish of salted beans," the old man said to the proprietor.

Tang Ao asked the old man's name, and was told that it was Ru. They introduced themselves and said, "Would you have a drink with us?"

"How dare I impose on you when we have just met?" said the old man.

"Then what if we come and drink with you?" said Old Tuo, and told the waiter to move their wine and food to the old man's table. After toasting each other and eating a little, Tang Ao said, "Could you tell us why the people in your country, no matter what their business, all dress like scholars? Do your officials all dress this way, too, so that one cannot distinguish between high and low?"

"We all dress alike, but we make a differentiation in color and material," said Ru. "Yellow is for the man of the highest rank, red is next, then purple. Blue is lower, and green is lowest. He who is not educated is called a 'vagrant' in our country, and is ostracized. So even the merchants and farmers are at least scholars of the lowest or second to lowest ranks. It is only after a man qualifies as a scholar that he may pursue his livelihood with any self-respect."

"But in such a vast country as this, can it be possible that everyone passes?"

"The subjects are various. A man may qualify in any one of the subjects; classics, history, poetry or prose; calligraphy, music, rhyme scheme, law, mathematics, painting or medicine. One needs to pass only one subject to wear the green costume, but to wear the blue, one must pass in one of the literary subjects."

When it was dark, Tang Ao paid the bill, and as the old man rose, he took a towel from his person and spread it on the table. He emptied the few salted beans which remained on the plate into it, and wrapped it up. There were two cups of wine remaining in the pot, and he said to the proprietor, "Keep this for me for tomorrow. If I find one cup less in this pot when I come back, I will make you pay for it ten times."

Then he scraped the left-over sauced beancurd and wine-cured beancurd into a dish, and gave it to the waiter. "Keep this for me," he said.

On his way out, the old man saw a used toothpick lying on one of the tables. He picked it up, wiped it, and slipped it into his sleeve. . . .

When they arrived at the Country of Two-faced People a few days later, Young Shu remained on board, as he was afraid that the Royal Son-in-law might have sent men ahead to catch him.

The three travellers therefore went on shore, but after walking a little, Old Tuo complained of a pain on his leg, and turned back. Tang Ao and his brother-in-law decided to go a little further to look at the people, and it was not until then that Merchant Lin discovered that he had forgotten to change his clothes in his hurry to come ashore, and looked like a poor man next to Tang Ao in his scholar's scarf and silk costume.

Old Tuo returned to the junk, took some medicine, and had a nap. When he woke up, he felt much better, and saw Tang Ao and Merchant Lin coming back.

"Why, you are wearing each other's clothes," he remarked.

"We walked over ten *li's* after you left us before we met any two-faced people," said Tang Ao. "But everyone was wearing a turban at the back of his head, so we could not see both their faces at once. I went up to some of them and had a nice talk. I asked them about the customs of the country, and they were all smiles and spoke to me most respectfully and in the most cordial manner. I thought they were charming, lovely people, quite different from the people we've met anywhere else."

"But as soon as I put in a few words, they all looked at me and stopped smiling, and became cold and reserved and were most reluctant to have anything to do with me," said Lin. "Afterwards we wondered if it might have had something to do with our clothes, so we changed, and sure enough, they began to treat me with the utmost respect, and to give Brother Tang the cold shoulder."

"So that is what is meant by being two-faced," said Old Tuo.

"Not only that, but when Brother-in-law was talking, I sneaked around the back of one of these people, and stealthily lifted his turban. When I saw what was underneath, I received the shock of my life and screamed. There was an ugly face with rat's eyes, hooked nose and a furious expression on it, and when this face saw me, the bush-like eyebrows gathered in a deep frown. It opened its huge basin of a mouth, and stuck out its long tongue at me. I was overpowered by an extremely vile smell which made me almost faint. When I turned around again, Brother-in-law was on his knees."

"Why were you doing that?" asked Old Tuo.

"You see, this man was talking to me in a most pleasant manner when Brother Tang lifted his turban and revealed not only his other face, but his true self. Then his good face turned green, too, and stuck out its tongue at me. I was so surprised I didn't know if he was going to kill me next. My knees buckled, I sank to the ground and kowtowed to him repeatedly, and then ran for my life. Have you ever heard of such a thing, Old Tuo?"

"It is not surprising," said Old Tuo. "I have met many people of this kind in my long life. The difficulty lies in recognizing them for what they are. But if you are more careful about whom you speak to, you can save yourself many an unpleasant surprise." . . .

The junk headed back to the Country of Intelligent People. It was the Autumn Moon Festival, and the sailors all wanted to go ashore to have a few drinks and celebrate, so Lin had the junk tied up early in the day, and they all went ashore to enjoy themselves.

When they approached the town, they discovered that the people were actually celebrating New Year's Day, and not the Autumn Moon Festival. When Tang Ao asked the reason why, Old Tuo said that being intelligent people, they thought that the biggest festival of the year should be celebrated when the weather was fine and there was a full moon, and not when it was freezing cold.

"I remember you said once that the natives of the Country of Restless People live to a grand old age, and that the people here are shortlived," said Tang Ao. "But they all look like old fellows to me."

"They may look old, but they are in fact only thirty or forty years old," said Old Tuo. "The reason for this is that since they are intelligent people, their minds never stop working. They are forever trying to outwit one another. Although they are skilled in a hundred arts, and wonderfully educated in astrology, mathematics, sorcery and fortune-telling, their hair turns white before they are thirty years old, and when they are forty they look eighty. But compared to the natives of the Country of Worried People, they may be said to enjoy a long life, for those people seldom reach the age of forty."

"No wonder they called me 'little brother'," said Lin. "They would never guess from my appearance that I am older than they are!"

Tang Ao learned that the people here were all wizards at mathematics, and that there was one man called Mi who was best at it. They went to call on him, but discovered that he had taken his daughter Orchid Fragrance back to visit relatives in the Kingdom on Earth.

Nevertheless, they all enjoyed themselves guessing riddles and watching the fireworks, and did not return to the junk until it was dawn, where they had a few further cups of wine. When the sun rose, the sailors cast off once more.

After a few days, the travellers arrived at the Country of Women. If the reader wants to know what happened there, please turn to the next chapter. . . .

When Tang Ao heard that they had arrived at the Country of Women, he thought that the country was populated entirely by women, and was afraid to go ashore. But Old Tuo said, "Not at all! There are men as well as women, only they call men women, and women men. The men wear the skirts and take care of the home, while the women wear hats and trousers and manage affairs outside. If it were a country populated solely by women, I doubt that even Brother Lin here would dare to venture ashore, although he knows he always makes a good profit from sales here!"

"If the men dress like women, do they use cosmetics and bind their feet?" asked Tang Ao.

"Of course they do!" cried Lin, and took from his pocket a list of the merchandise he was going to sell, which consisted of huge quantities of rouge, face powder, combs and other women's notions. "Lucky I wasn't born in this country," he said. "Catch me mincing around on bound feet!"

When Tang Ao asked why he had not put down the price of the merchandise, Lin said, "The people here, no matter rich or poor, from the 'King' down to the simplest peasant, are all mad about cosmetics. I'll charge them what I can. I shall have no difficulty selling the whole consignment to rich families in two or three days."

Beaming at the prospect of making a good profit, Lin went on shore with his list.

Tang Ao and Old Tuo decided to go and see the city. The people walking on the streets were small of stature, and rather slim, and although dressed in men's clothes, were beardless and spoke with women's voices, and walked with willowy steps.

"Look at them!" said Old Tuo. "They are perfectly normal-looking women. Isn't it a shame for them to dress like men?"

"Wait a minute," said Tang Ao. "Maybe when they see us, they think, 'Look at them, isn't it a shame that they dress like women'?"

"You're right. 'Whatever one is accustomed to always seems natural,' as the ancients say. But I wonder what the men are like?"

Old Tuo discreetly called Tang Ao's attention to a middle-aged woman, who was sitting in front of her doorstep, sewing on a shoe. Her hair was braided and coiled smoothly on top of her head, and decorated with pearls and jade. She was wearing long golden loops of earrings with precious stones in them, and wore a long mauve gown with an onion-green shirt underneath, from which peeped the toes of tiny feet shod in red silk shoes. With long, tapering fingers, the woman was doing embroidery. She had beautiful eyes and was carefully powdered and rouged, but when she lifted her head, they saw that her lip was covered by a thick moustache.

Tang Ao and Old Tuo could not help laughing out loud.

The 'woman' looked up and said, "What are you laughing at, lassies?"

The voice sounded as deep and hoarse as a cracked gong. Tang Ao was so startled that he took to his heels and ran.

But the "woman" shouted after them, "You must be women, since you have whiskers on your faces. Why are you wearing men's clothes and pretending to be men? Aren't you ashamed of yourselves! I know, you dress like this because you want to mingle with the men, you cheap hussies! Take a look at yourselves in the mirror.

PROVERBS

Pretending becomes truth.

There is no Superior Man in hot weather.

When there is enough to eat and to wear, manners and morals appear.

A hen can roost better than a phoenix.

One who knows many subjects is liable to be shallow; one who knows only one subject is apt to be perverse.—LUSIN

A bee gives a sting and loses its life; a satirist gives a sting and preserves his.
—LUSIN

Chinese people love compromise. If you say to them, "This room is too dark, we must have a window made," they will all oppose you. But if you say, "Let's take off the roof," they will compromise with you and say, "Let's have a window."
—LUSIN

Have you forgotten that you are women? It's lucky for you you only met up with me! If it had been somebody else who had caught you casting those sneaky glances, you would have been beaten almost to death!"

"This is the first time I have ever had such an experience," muttered Tang Ao. "But I suspect Brother Lin will receive better treatment at their hands."

"Why?" said Old Tuo.

"Well, he is very fair, and since he lost his beard at the Country of Flaming People, he may be mistaken by these people for a real woman. But come to think of it, isn't it worrying?"

As they walked further on, they saw some "women" on the streets as well as "men." Some were carrying babies in their arms, and others leading children by the hand. All the "women" walked on dainty bound feet, and in crowded places, acted shy, as if they were embarrassed to be seen. Some of the younger ones were beardless, and upon careful study, Tang Ao discovered that some of the ageing or middle-aged "women" shaved their lips and chins in order to appear younger.

The two returned to the junk before Merchant Lin. But when the latter did not come back at supper time, and it was past the second drum, Mistress Lu began to get worried. Tang Ao and Old Tuo went on shore with lanterns to look for him, but discovered that the city gates were shut for the night.

The next day, they went to look again, but found not a trace of Lin. On the third day, some sailors went with them, but still they could not find him.

When a few days had passed, it seemed as if Merchant Lin had vanished, like a rock sinking to the bottom of the sea. Mistress Lu and Pleasant wailed with grief. Tang Ao and Old Tuo went to make inquiries every day.

They could not know that Merchant Lin had been told by one of his customers that the "King's uncle" wanted to buy some of his goods. Following instructions, he went to the "Royal Uncle's" residence in the Palace, and handed his list of merchandise to the gatekeeper. Soon, the gatekeeper came back and said that it was just what the "King" was looking for for his "concubines" and "maids", and asked Lin to be shown into the inner apartments.

The attendant led Merchant Lin through guarded doors and winding paths until he was at the door of the inner apartments, where a guard told him, "Please wait here, madam. I shall go in and inquire what the royal wishes are." She took Lin's list, and after a short time, returned and said, "But madam hasn't put any prices on her list. How much do you charge for a picul of rouge? How much is a picul of perfumed powder? And hair lotion? And hair ribbons?"

Lin told her the prices, and the guard went in and came out again and asked, "How much is a box of jade ornaments, madam? And your velvet flowers? How much is a box of your fragrant beads? And what about the combs?"

Merchant Lin told her and the guard again went to report, and came back and said, "The King has been choosing imperial concubines and wants to buy some of your goods for them. He invites you to go inside, since you come from the Kingdom on Earth and we are friendly allies. However, madam must behave with courtesy and respect when she is in the presence of His Majesty."

Merchant Lin followed the guard inside, and was soon in the presence of the "King". After making a deep bow, he saw that she was a woman of some thirty years old, with a beautiful face, fair skin and cherry-red lips. Around her there stood many palace "maids."

The "King" spoke to Lin in a light voice, holding the list of articles in her slender hands, and looking at him with interest as he answered her questions.

"I wonder what she is staring at me like this for," Merchant Lin thought to himself. "Hasn't she ever seen a man from the Kingdom on Earth before?"

After a while, he heard her say that she was keeping the list of goods, and ordered palace "maids" to prepare a feast and wine for the "woman" from the Kingdom on Earth.

In a little time, Merchant Lin was ushered to a room upstairs, where victuals of many kinds awaited him. As he ate, however, he heard a great deal of noise downstairs. Several palace "maids" ran upstairs soon, and calling him "Your Highness", kowtowed to him and congratulated him. Before he knew what was happening, Merchant Lin was being stripped completely bare by the maids and led to a perfumed bath. Against the powerful arms of these maids, he could scarcely struggle. Soon he found himself being anointed, perfumed, powdered and rouged, and dressed in a skirt. His big feet were bound up in strips of cloth and socks, and his hair was combed in an elaborate braid over his head and decorated with pins. These male "maids" thrust bracelets on his arms and rings on his fingers, and put a phoenix headdress on his head. They tied a jade green sash around his waist and put an embroidered cape around his shoulders.

Then they led him to a bed, and asked him to sit down.

Merchant Lin thought that he must be drunk, or dreaming, and began to tremble. He asked the maids what was happening, and was told that he had been chosen by the "King" to be the Imperial Consort, and that a propitious day would be chosen for him to enter the "King's" chambers.

Before he could utter a word, another group of maids, all tall and strong and wearing beards, came in. One was holding a threaded needle. "We are ordered to pierce your ears," he said, as the other four "maids" grabbed Lin by the arms and legs. The white-bearded one seized Lin's right ear, and after rubbing the lobe a little, drove the needle through it.

"Ooh!" Merchant Lin screamed.

The maid seized the other ear, and likewise drove the needle through it. As Lin screamed with pain, powdered lead was smeared on his earlobes and a pair of "eight-precious" earrings was hung from the holes.

Having finished what they came to do, the maids retreated, and a black-bearded fellow came in with a bolt of white silk. Kneeling down before him, the fellow said, "I am ordered to bind Your Highness's feet."

Two other maids seized Lin's feet as the black-bearded one sat down on a stool, and began to rip the silk into ribbons. Seizing Lin's right foot, he set it upon his knee, and sprinkled white alum powder between the toes and the grooves of the foot. He squeezed the toes tightly together, bent them down so that the whole foot was shaped like an arch, and took a length of white silk and bound it tightly around it twice. One of the others sewed the ribbon together in small stitches. Again the silk went around the foot, and again, it was sewn up.

Merchant Lin felt as though his feet were burning, and wave after wave of pain rose to his heart. When he could stand it no longer, he let out his voice and began to cry. The "maids" had hastily made a pair of soft-soled red shoes, and these they put on both his feet.

"Please, kind brothers, go and tell Her Majesty that I'm a married man," Lin begged. "How can I become her Consort? As for my feet, please liberate them. They have enjoyed the kind of freedom which scholars who are not interested in official careers enjoy! How can you bind them? Please tell your 'King' to let me go. I shall be grateful, and my wife will be grateful."

But the maids said, "The King said that you are to enter his chambers as soon as your feet are bound. It is not time for talk of this kind."

When it was dark, a table was laid for him with mountains of meat and oceans of wine. But Merchant Lin only nibbled, and told the "maids" they could have the rest.

Still sitting on the bed, and with his feet aching terribly, he decided to lie down in his clothes for a rest.

At once a middle-aged "maid" came up to him and said, "Please, will you wash before you retire?"

No sooner was this said than a succession of maids came in with candles, basins of water and spittoon, dressing table, boxes of ointment, face powder, towels, silk handkerchiefs, and surrounded him. Lin had to submit to the motions of washing in front of them all. But after he had washed his face, a maid wanted to put some cream on it again.

Merchant Lin stoutly refused.

"But night time is the best time to treat the skin," the white-bearded maid said. "This powder has a lot of musk in it. It will make your skin fragrant, although I dare say it is fair enough already. If you use it regularly your skin will not only seem like white jade, but will give off a natural fragrance of its own. And the more fragrant it is, the fairer it will become, and the more lovely to behold, and the more lovable you will be. You'll see how good it is after you have used it regularly."

But Lin refused firmly, and the maids said, "If you are so stubborn, we will have to report this, and let Matron deal with you tomorrow."

Then they left him alone. But Lin's feet hurt so much that he could not sleep a wink. He tore at the ribbons with all his might, and after a great struggle succeeded in tearing them off. He stretched out his ten toes again, and luxuriating in their exquisite freedom, finally fell asleep.

The next morning, however, when the black-bearded maid discovered that he had torn off his foot-bandages, he immediately reported it to the "King", who ordered that Lin should be punished by receiving twenty strokes of the bamboo from the "Matron". Accordingly, a white-bearded "Matron" came in with a stick of bamboo about eight feet long, and when the others had stripped him and held him down, raised the stick and began to strike Lin's bottom and legs.

Before five strokes had been delivered, Lin's tender skin was bleeding, and the Matron did not have the heart to go on. "Look at her skin! Have you ever seen such white and tender and lovable skin? Why, I think indeed her looks are comparable to Pan An and Sung Yu!" the Matron thought to himself. "But what am I doing, comparing her bottom and not her face to them? Is that a compliment?"

The foot-binding maid came and asked Lin if he would behave from now on.

"Yes, I'll behave," Lin replied, and they stopped beating him. They wiped the blood from his wounds, and special ointment was sent by the "king" and ginseng soup was given him to drink.

Merchant Lin drank the soup, and fell on the bed for a rest. But the "King" had given orders that his feet must be bound again, and that he should be taught to walk on them. So with one maid supporting him on each side, Merchant Lin was marched up and down the room all day on his bound feet. When he lay down to sleep that night, he could not close his eyes for the excruciating pain.

But from now on, he was never left alone again. Maids took turns to sit with him. Merchant Lin knew that he was no longer in command of his destiny.

Before two weeks were over, Lin's feet had begun to assume a permanently arched form, and his toes begun to rot. Daily medical ablutions were given to them, and the pain persisted.

"I should have thought that Brother-in-law and Old Tuo would have come to my rescue by now," he thought one day as he was being led up and down his room. "I have endured all I can! I'd be better off dead!"

He sat down on the edge of the bed, and began to tear off his embroidered shoes and silk bandages. "Go tell your "King" to put me to death at once, or let my feet loose," he told the Matron.

But when he returned, the Matron said, "The King said that if you don't obey his orders, you are to be hung upside down from the beam of the house."

"Then do it quickly! The quicker the better!" said Lin, impatient to have an end put to his agony.

Accordingly, they tied a rope around his feet and hung him upside down from the beam. Merchant Lin saw stars before his eyes. Sweat poured out of his body, and his legs became numb. He closed his eyes and waited for death to come to the rescue. But it did not come. At last he could stand it no longer, and began to scream like a pig being led to slaughter.

The order was given to cut him down.

From now on, Lin was completely in the power of the maids. Wanting to complete the task their "King" had assigned them as soon as possible, they tied the bandages around his feet tighter than ever. Several times, Lin thought of committing suicide, but with people watching him constantly, he had not a chance.

In due course, his feet lost much of their original shape. Blood and flesh were squeezed into a pulp and then little remained of his feet but dry bones and skin, shrunk, indeed, to a dainty size. Responding to daily anointing, his hair became shiny and smooth, and his body, after repeated ablutions of perfumed water, began to look very attractive indeed. His eyebrows were plucked to resemble a new moon. With blood-red lipstick and powder adorning his face, and jade and pearl adorning his coiffure and ears, Merchant Lin assumed, at last, a unot nappealing appearance.

The "King" sent someone to watch his progress every day. One day, the Matron announced that the task of foot-binding had been completed. When the "King" herself came upstairs to have a look, she saw a Lin whose face was like a peach blossom, whose eyes were like autumn lakes, whose eyebrows suggested the lines of distant hills, and who stood before her in a willowy stance.

She was delighted. "What a beauty!" she thought to herself. "If I hadn't seen her hidden possibilities beneath her ridiculous man's costume, her beauty might never have come to light!"

She took a pearl bracelet and put it on Merchant Lin's wrist, and the maids persuaded him to sink down on his knees and give thanks. The "King" pulled him up and made him sit down beside her, and began to fondle his hands and smell them and look appreciatively at his dainty feet.

Lin went red with shame.

Extremely pleased, the "King" decided that Lin should enter her chambers the very next day. When Merchant Lin heard this, he saw his last hopes vanish. He was not even able to walk without someone to help him, and spent the whole night thinking about his wife and shedding tears.

In the morning, the "maids" came especially early to shave off the fine hairs from his face, and to powder him and comb him in preparation for his wedding. Supported by a pair of red embroidered high heeled shoes, his longer-than-ordinary "golden lotuses" became not obtrusively large. He wore a bridal crown and gown, and with jewels dangling and waves of perfume issuing from his person, was if not notably beautiful, at least a rather charming "bride."

After breakfast, "Imperial Concubines" came to congratulate him, and he was kept fully occupied until the afternoon, when maids came again to straighten his clothes and freshen up his appearance before escorting him to the Reception Hall.

Soon, palace attendants holding red lanterns came in and knelt before him and said, "The propitious hour has come. Would madam please come to the Main Reception Hall to await His Majesty? The ceremonies will be conducted there."

Merchant Lin was stunned. His body and soul almost parted company.

The attendants seized him and escorted him downstairs. Countless officials and guests had come to witness the ceremony in the Main Reception Hall, which was brightly lighted with candles. As Lin walked toward "His Majesty", swaying on the arms of attendants, he was like a sprig of fresh flowers waving in the wind. When he was standing directly in front of the "King", he had no alternative but to tug at his sleeves and make a deep bow.

Congratulations were showered upon the "King" by the attendants.

As Lin was about to be ushered into the "King's" chambers, there came a great hubbub of noise from the outside. The "King" was startled.

It was Tang Ao, who had come to the rescue. . . .

[Tang Ao repaired the broken canals of the country in exchange for Lin's freedom. The "King," disappointed by Lin's lack of affection, let him go.]

[The following passage occurs after the travelers return to China. The character Tang Min is speaking.]

. . . "To celebrate the Female Emperor's birthday, she had issued twelve decrees, besides granting official promotions and scholastic honors to the meritorious. These twelve decrees all concern women. That is why I say it is unprecedented."

"Please tell me what these decrees are," said Little Hill.

Tang Min said that they all had to do with women's welfare. Those who performed distinguished service in the home to their parents or parents-in-law would be publicly honored. Widows who remained chaste all their lives would be publicly recognized. Homes to care for aged and infirm women, orphanages to take care of girls, and allowances for the support of widows would be set up.

To girls who were twenty years old but not yet married because they lacked dowries, the Empress would give dowries. Women's clinics would be set up throughout the country by renowned physicians who would travel its length and breadth. The Empress would provide funerals for women who left no money behind, and if a woman had no family to remember her in prayers, she would be publicly remembered in official memorial rites held in the spring and autumn of each year, provided she had been a virtuous and filial woman.

"But best of all," said Tang Min, "the Empress has decided to hold Imperial Examinations for Women in order to discover talented girls to come and help her in the affairs of the country. She thinks that there is no reason why women should not bring glory to their families as well as men. Title and rank will be awarded according to merit. Here is your chance, Little Hill! You asked me last year whether there were official examinations for women. Now your wish has come true. If you study hard, I am sure you can pass."

Little Hill was very happy, but she said, "I wonder when the examinations are to be held? If they are not to be for some time, I may have a chance. But how can I hope to pass if they are to be held very soon? I have such a lot of studying to do. And besides, I may be too young to participate."

"Everything depends on yourself," said Tang Min. "But as far as age is concerned, the younger the better. I urge you to work very hard from now on. There is no reason why you should not take part in the Examinations if they are held next year."

From then on, Little Hill studied very hard. The following year, details of the Examinations for Women were issued by the Empress. Little Hill read the Empress's declaration eagerly:

By Divine wish the Empress declares:

That Heaven is not discriminating in endowing human beings with the pure essences and fine savours of the Universe. Although men may be as brilliant as jade, women are no less so. In my search for people to help me with affairs of the nation, a ministry is given to fine men of learning and ability. But so far, the source of talented women has not been explored. Although talented men have been recommended to me, and there are none too many of these, no talented woman has been singled out.

Now since the pure essences and fine savours of the Universe have been concentrated upon a woman (myself) for so long, it follows that the glory and talent of women should be promulgated and propagated.

After consultations with my officials, I have decided to hold Imperial Examinations for Women in the Third Year of *Sheng Li.* May the Ministries and Officials take heed of the following rules.

Among the rules for the candidates were these: that the name, date, place of birth and family background of candidates should be submitted to county officials in the

Second Year of *Sheng Li,* and that County Examinations should be held in August of that year. Successful candidates would participate in District Examinations, which would be held in October. Candidates must not be accompanied by their teachers or advisers, but may be accompanied by one or two women relatives.

Successful candidates of County Examinations will be known as "Damsels of Literature." Successful candidates of District Examinations will be known as "Virtuous Ladies of Literature." These will participate in Ministerial Examinations. Successful candidates of Ministerial Examinations will be known as "Talented Ladies of Literature", and participate in Palace Examinations at the capital. Those who pass the Palace Examinations with the highest honors will be known as "Lady Scholars." Those who pass with second-class honors will be known as "Lady Doctors," and those who pass with third-class honors will be known as "Lady Masters," and all will be invited to attend the Banquet of Literary Celebration. Those who wish to serve in the Palace in their literary capacities may do so on a trial basis for a year. Those who fail in the Palace Examinations will receive a length of satin and may, if their age permits, take the Examinations when they are held again.

The parents, parents-in-law or husbands of Lady Scholars will be promoted one grade in rank if they already hold official positions of the fifth rank or above. Those who hold official positions below the fifth rank will be promoted to be officials of the fourth rank. Those who do not hold official positions will be awarded titles of the fifth rank, and all will be given appropriate official robes. The parents, parents-in-law and husbands of Lady Doctors will be awarded the title and robes of officials of the sixth rank. The parents, parents-in-law and husbands of Lady Masters will be awarded accordingly the title of officials of the seventh rank, and appropriate official robes will be presented.

All County, District and Ministerial Examinations will be held on the subjects Poetry and Prose. Candidates will enter Examination Hall between four and six a.m. and leave between five and seven p.m. Candles are forbidden. All Examination papers will be copied before they are submitted for grading, in order to avoid partiality.

Those who fail to attend County and District Examinations due to illness may take them when they have recovered, while those who fail to take the Ministerial Examinations due to illness or failure to arrive at the capital on time may take them at a later date if the official responsible thinks that the candidate merits it.

Palace Examinations may not be taken at a later date than that designated.

Passage will be given to those participating in Ministerial Examinations who have far to travel. The successful candidate of District Examinations and her family will be exempt from government service.

Sixteen years is the age limit of candidates. Girls who are divorced, disfigured or who come from dishonorable families are disqualified.

In order to give time for the necessary preparations it is decided that the Ministerial Examinations will be held in March of the Third Year of *Sheng Li* and Palace Examinations in April of the same year.

Yea! Those whose prose is like brocade and whose calligraphy is as beautiful as a maiden with flowers in her hair will attend the Banquet of Flowers! From now on talent will fill the Court. Is it possible that a female Hsiangju will be left out?

May all officials take heed and act accordingly to accomplish this worthy task. . . .

[In the following allegory all the characters are new.]

. . . When Honeybush and his men arrived at the Treasure Pass, Wu Number Six was ready for them. He stood at the edge of his spell-bound area and shouted, "Come and try to break the spell!"

Prince's Feather advanced on horseback, and engaged Number Six in battle for two rounds, and then galloped into the area.

As soon as he was in it, the smell of money invaded his olfactory senses. He sighed and thought to himself, "Scholars are always warning people of the evils of money, but that is because they cannot appreciate its lovely smell. What a pity!"

The roads were paved with jade, and the bridges which Prince's Feather crossed were made of silver. There were scarlet portals and golden gates, and the air of affluence overflowed from every quarter. He dismounted, and led his horse toward a high archway with the words "Money Is My Brother" written in gold letters on it.

Going through the arch, he saw many people on the other side, with very happy expressions on their faces, all holding coins of different sizes in their hands. Walking further on, he saw a huge coin (suspended in the air) which was giving off a dazzling golden light. Millions of people were struggling to get up to it. Some of them were scholars, others were farmers. There were laborers, merchants, and the representatives of the three religions and nine schools of thought. There were officials stretching out their palms, and lesser officials and clerks in the act of extortion. There were some who were trying to falsify evidence and blackmailing each other in their attempt to claim the coin, and gamblers who were trying to accept bets. There were men with angry faces making terrifying threats and smooth talkers who were making false promises. People were setting traps and forging papers and swindling each other. Every kind of evil was going on.

Countless ladders were suspended from the huge coin, and bodies and white skeletons were strewn across them, and piled up like a mountain beneath.

Prince's Feather saw it all, and understood, and sighed. From the hole in the coin could be seen a vista of coins shining in every direction, and jade and gold. He tied his horse at the side of the road, and climbed up a ladder himself. When he came to the hole in the center of the coin, he crept through it, and saw jade pavilions and fairy caves beyond, and golden altars and fairy ponds. The ground on the other side was paved with green jade, and jade walls lined the street. He had never seen anything like it on this earth.

He came down on the other side of the coin, and went to look around. The more he saw, the better he liked it. "If I could have a few rooms in this glorious place and live here for a little while, I will not have lived in vain," he thought.

As he was so thinking, he saw a very large mansion, and went in to have a look. There were jade towers and many chambers in the front and back, with painted beams and red balustrades. The rooms were furnished with every kind of luxury. Prince's Feather was extremely taken with it all, and thought, "To live here, one would need to have clothes to go with it, and good food."

Then he saw that in the chambers there were piles of silk and embroidered curtains and bedding, and jade, silver, and pearl treasures, and all the delicacies of the mountains and sea. Nothing that he could think of was lacking.

"If I had known this, I would have brought my servants!" he thought.

An old man-servant appeared at that instant with a list in his hand, followed by a large retinue of other servants and errand boys. An old woman-servant also appeared, leading a retinue of maids and slave girls, and everyone bowed to him.

"What is the name of the old man-servant, and how many are there of you?" said Prince's Feather.

"I am called Old Wang," said the old man-servant, "and there are sixteen under me who are ready to serve you. Here is a list of their duties. Please look it over."

Prince's Feather read the list, and discovered that Twenty Columns and Forty Columns were the Accountant and Assistant Accountant. The former checked the receipts against the payments, and the latter did the actual calculation, for the Accountant could not count. Checking Cash was in charge of the expenses of the kitchen.

"Cooks like to falsify their accounts," said Prince's Feather. "If you are in charge, you must see that they do not do it. But you must not falsify the accounts yourself, or else you will be dismissed."

Checking Cash said, "I would not dare to . . . except for such little items as tea, wine and bath."

"As long as you retain a sense of reality," said Prince's Feather, "who can keep track of every penny? And furthermore, you are not aspiring to become a model of honesty, are you?"

"You are truly enlightened, Master," said Checking Cash.

The next names Prince's Feather saw on the list were Five Per Cent and Four Coppers, who took care of the silver.

"Why are you called Five Per Cent and Four Coppers?" Prince's Feather asked.

"I am very honest," said Five Per Cent. "Of all the money that passes through my hands, I only take five per cent of every ounce, and never more. That is why Old Wang put me in charge of the silver."

Four Coppers said, "I am also very honest, and of every thousand coppers which pass through my hands, I only take four. I would never short-change anyone."

Prince's Feather nodded and said, "Five per cent of each ounce of silver, and four coppers out of every thousand coppers cannot be said to be unreasonable."

The man who was in charge of the wine was called Half-Ounce.

"Why is he called Half-Ounce?" Prince's Feather asked Old Wang.

"In looking after Master's wine, he is not unscrupulous, and takes only half an ounce for himself every day, and that is why he is in charge of the wine."

Prince's Feather said, "Half an ounce is not much, but he must not take more."

Half-Ounce said, "I have a very small capacity. Even if I indulged a little, it would not be more than a few cups a day."

"I think I can bear that," said Prince's Feather. "But if your capacity increases, and you throw away the ounce measure for the catty measure, and then after each cask is opened you drink half the cask, I shall not tolerate it."

The servants all bowed, and Prince's Feather turned to the old woman and said, "What is your name, and what are the names of the others?"

"I am called Penny Farthing," said the old woman. "It is not an attractive name. Would Master care to give me a more sexy one?"

Prince's Feather looked at the old woman and saw that she was trying to flirt with him, although she had not a black hair left on her head. "Why not call yourself Greenback?" he said. "Green has an air of youth about it. Maybe after you change your name the color of your hair will also change."

Penny Farthing said, "Thank the Master very much!"

"What are the duties of these maids?" said Prince's Feather.

Penny Farthing said, "One is in charge of the Mistress's powder, and another looks after her rouge. This one takes care of the Mistress's foot-binding cloth, and this one removes the corns from the Mistress's feet. These two look after her ornaments and jewels, and this one paints the Mistress's picture."

Prince's Feather said, "A person is needed to look after the foot-binding cloth, but you have assigned someone just to remove the Mistress's corns. This is very thoughtful of you, and I shall tell the Mistress to reward you. What do the eight slave girls do?"

Penny Farthing said, "The one in white looks after the Mistress's silver, and the one in green looks after her copper coins. The one in red looks after her gambling account, and the one in yellow looks after her food bills. Their names all have the same meaning as Four Coppers and Five Per Cent, because they only pocket a very little money and never take more."

She pointed to the four younger girls and said, "Little Currency looks after Mistress's silk, and Little Money takes care of the tea and hot water. Little Spade looks after her towels, and Little Knife looks after the scissors which cut the Mistress's corns."

Prince's Feather cried, "A special person to look after the Mistress's towels and another who is in charge of the scissors for cutting her corns! This is a truly well-managed household! As they would say in official jargon, you are 'clear-headed and efficient, and attentive to details in the execution of affairs'."

The servants, with their duties before them, bowed and withdrew.

The slave girls made tea, and made the bed ready for Prince's Feather. With teacup in hand, he wondered which girl he should ask to spend the night with him. As he was trying to decide, four extremely beautiful girls appeared to keep him company. Prince's Feather dined with them, and retired with them.

In the morning when he awoke, the four beauties were still by his side. Day after day, he enjoyed their company, ate the finest food, and wore the finest garments, and enjoyed all the blessings which life on this earth could yield. Soon, all four beauties were pregnant. They burned incense and bowed and prayed to the gods of heaven, earth and water, and Prince's Feather gave each of them a "male coin" to wear, to ensure the birth of a son. The four beauties in time did indeed present him with five boys.

Prince's Feather felt that he had too many sons and wanted a daughter. So he gave several of the beauties some "female coins", and in time, two girls were born to him. When the five boys and two girls were a little older, Prince's Feather had a tutor teach them. After a few years, the boys and girls were of marriageable age, and he arranged matches for them. In the twinkling of an eye, his grandchildren were grown up, too, and he also arranged their marriages. Before he knew it, he was eighty, and surrounded by great-grandchildren.

One day, he looked in the mirror, and saw that he was an old man whose hair was as white as snow. Suddenly, he remembered having climbed through the hole in the coin. What happened sixty years ago seemed like only yesterday. He was strong and full of spirit then, and now he was old and decrepit. Life was like a dream! Had he known that this was all that a man could hope for in life, he would have been able to detach himself from many of the cravings he thought he had to satisfy! Now it was too late. He wondered if he could find the way back to the ladder up which he had climbed so many years ago.

Prince's Feather found the coin, but when he put his head through it to look out the hole became narrower and narrower, until he was trapped, and could neither move forwards nor backwards. . . .

[One of the Fairy Princesses orders an emissary from heaven, a fairy gibbon, to find a scholar on earth who will write about the previous events.]

. . . The gibbon looked everywhere, and it was not until there was peace in the land in the present (Chin) dynasty that he found a descendant of Laotse, who had a reputation of sorts. Because the gibbon was weary of his search, he handed the record to this man, and returned to the fairy mountain.

When this man saw the scribbling in the book, he knew that it would not be easy to tell the story which had to be told. Luckily, there was peace in his time, the officials were not exacting, and left the people alone. In the harmony of the seasons, and under the peaceful rule of the land, he read some stories of adventure, and enjoyed some pleasures of life. When the spirit moved him, he took up his brush and wrote. In the long summer nights and on cold wintry ones, under the lamplight or in the moonlight, he wrote for his own amusement. One year followed another, and in the end he wrote a hundred chapters of *Flowers in the Mirror,* and had told only half the story. But those of his friends who were worried and suffering from melancholy burst out laughing upon reading it, and recovered their good spirits. They urged him, "Since you are so lazy and write so slowly, who knows when you will ever finish the story! Why don't you send the first hundred chapters to the printers and have them blocked, so that other people can enjoy them, while you go on writing the rest?"

Well! What does it matter! The novelist has worked for more than thirty years, and what has he produced but a small, small literary work in the three thousand universes? Perhaps he has made a few flowers bloom on paper, and those who read the novel will smile, and pluck a few blossoms, and that would be destiny, too.

ESSAYS

Born in Sin

Hsun-tzu (3rd cen. B.C.) / Herbert A. Giles

By nature, man is evil. If a man is good, that is an artificial result. For, his condition being what it is, he is influenced first of all by a desire for gain. Hence, he strives to get all he can without consideration for his neighbor. Secondly, he is liable to envy and hate. Hence, he seeks the ruin of others, and loyalty and truth are set aside. Thirdly, he is a slave to his animal passions. Hence, he commits excesses, and wanders from the path of duty and right.

Thus, conformity with man's natural disposition leads to all kinds of violence, disorder, and ultimate barbarism. Only under the restraint of law and of lofty moral influences does man eventually become fit to be a member of regularly organized society.

From these premises it seems quite clear that by nature man is evil; and that if a man is good, that is an artificial result.

Flunkeyism

Tsung Ch'en (16th cen.) / Herbert A. Giles

I was very glad at this distance to receive your letter which quite set my mind at rest, together with the present you were so kind as to add. I thank you very much for your good wishes, and especially for your thoughtful allusion to my father.

As to what you are pleased to say in reference to official popularity and fitness for office, I am much obliged by your remarks. Of my unfitness I am only too well aware; while as to popularity with my superiors, I am utterly unqualified to secure that boon.

How indeed does an official find favor in the present day with his chief? Morning and evening he must whip up his horse and go dance attendance at the great man's door. If the porter refuses to admit him, then honied words, a coaxing air, and money drawn from the sleeve may prevail. The porter takes in his card; but the great man does not come out. So he waits in the stable among grooms, until his clothes are charged with the smell; in spite of hunger, in spite of cold, in spite of a blazing heat.

At nightfall, the porter who had pocketed his money comes forth and says his master is tired and begs to be excused, and will he call again next day. So he is forced to come once more as requested. He sits all night in his clothes. At cock-crow he jumps up, performs his toilette, and gallops off and knocks at the entrance gate. "Who's there?" shouts the porter angrily; and when he explains, the porter gets still more angry and begins to abuse him, saying, "You are in a fine hurry, you are! Do you think my master sees people at this hour?" Then is the visitor shamed, but he has to swallow his wrath and try to persuade the porter to let him in. And the porter, another fee to the good, gets up and lets him in; and then he waits again in the stable as before, until perhaps the great man comes out and summons him to an audience.

Now, with many an obeisance, he cringes timidly towards the foot of the dais steps: and when the great man says, "Come!" he prostrates himself twice and remains long without rising. At length he goes up to offer his present, which the great man refuses. He entreats acceptance; but in vain. He implores, with many instances; whereupon the great man bids a servant take it. Then two more prostrations, long drawn out; after which he arises, and with five or six salutations he takes his leave.

On going forth, he bows to the porter, saying, "It's all right with your master. Next time I come you need make no delay." The porter returns the bow, well pleased with his share in the business. Meanwhile, our friend springs on his horse, and when he meets an acquaintance flourishes his whip and cries out, "I have just been with His Excellency. He treated me very kindly, very kindly indeed." And then he goes into detail, upon which his friends begin to be more respectful to him as a *protégé* of His Excellency. The great man himself says, "So-and-so is a good fellow, a very good fellow indeed"; upon which the bystanders of course declare that they think so too.

Such is popularity with one's superiors in the present day. Do you think that I could be as one of these? No! Beyond sending in a complimentary card at the summer and winter festivals, I do not go near the great from one year's end to another. Even when I pass their doors I stuff my ears and cover my eyes and gallop quickly past as if some one was after me. In consequence of this want of breadth, I am of course no favorite with the authorities; but what care I? There is a destiny that shapes our ends and it has shaped mine towards the path of duty alone. For which, no doubt, you think me an ass.

PROVBRBS

People hate Buddhist monks and nuns, Mohammedans and Christians, but no one hates a Taoist. To understand the reason for this is to understand half of China.—LUSIN

When the Chinese are in power, and see that others cannot do anything to them . . . they are autocrats and have no use for moderation; when they talk of "moderation" they know they have to be moderate; and when they are out of luck, then they begin to talk of "fate." They would be contented even with being slaves and find themselves in perfect harmony with the universe.—LUSIN

Both talking and writing are the signs of those who have failed. Those who are engaged in fighting the evil forces have no time for these, and those who are successful keep quiet.—LUSIN

In defense of concubinage: Whereas you always see a teapot with four teacups, you never find a teacup with four teapots.—KU HUNG-WING (19th cen.)

China's Enemy Within

Teng To and his accusers / "Mainichi Daily News," Tokyo

At the time of the publication of these essays and rebuttals, in 1966, the existence of powerful adversaries of Mao Tse-tung was becoming steadily clearer as the purges continued and hammering propaganda in favor of the "great proletarian cultural revolution" grew ever louder—accompanied by the uncontrolled actions of its adolescent promoters, the Red Guards. This opposition was called "revisionist," "bourgeois," "treacherous" by the Mao regime. The proofs most frequently cited at the time were two collections of essays entitled The Night Talks Around Yenshan *and* Notes of the Three-Home Hamlet, *published serially beginning in 1961, by Teng To, Wu Han, and Lao Mu-sha. Before being purged in 1965, Teng was the chief editor of the* Peking Evening News *and, along with Lao, a member of the Executive Committee of the Communist Party of Peking. Wu, a noted historian, was Deputy Mayor of Peking. None has been heard of since May, 1966.*

The essays, on the surface mild social and historical commentaries, were, according to sensitive partisans of Mao, virulently seditious. Ironically, without the "Accusations" that appeared in the official daily Renmin Ribao *five years after the essays' first appearance, most of the selections would have seemed little but innocuous cautionary tales or bits of off-beat history. With the "Accusations," they indeed add up to a devastating, if sometimes subtle, commentary on the shortcomings of a despised tyrant.*

Below is a selection of the essays by Teng To with their angry rebuttals, as translated from Chinese for one of Tokyo's English-language newspapers, the Mainichi Daily News.

The Great Empty Talk / Somebody likes to talk. At nearly every meeting he attends, he talks. And his speech is so long that words flow out of his mouth like a waterfall incessantly rolling down. But no impression remains in the minds of the listeners when they recollect what he said.

His speech may last several hours with explanations repeated time and again. But the explanations can only increase ambiguities about what he means; at best, they are inconclusive. This is characteristic of the Great Empty Talk.

It cannot be denied that the delivery of such empty talk on certain occasions is unavoidable insomuch as it seems to be needed at that moment. If the talker, however, believes he is a gifted orator and his style of talk is a special art and he delivers such talks here and there, the result will certainly be horrible. Even worse than this: if he insists on inflicting such talks on the mass of people and bequeathing his art to the next generation, the aftermath will be simply catastrophic.

Coincidentally, my neighbor's child, who tries to imitate the tone of the writings of great poets, wrote, not so long ago, some Great-Empty-Talk-style verses, of which one with the title "Wild Grass" is quoted here:

The aged heaven is our father,
The great earth is our mother,

The sun is our nurse,
The eastern wind is our benefactor, and
The western wind is our enemy.

This verse contains many noted terminologies such as heaven, great earth, father, mother, sun, nurse, eastern wind, western wind, benefactor and enemy. Nevertheless, they become a kind of circumlocution, and his verse consequently becomes a heap of worn-out words and exaggerated expressions.

Even admitting that the words and terminologies he employed are most noteworthy, they do not help the merits of his verse. The opposite effect may result: the more such words and terminologies are used, the less merits his verse may gain. Therefore, I wish to advise my friend, the Great Empty Talker, hereafter to read and think more, but talk less. And whenever there is occasion for you to speak, you had better retreat instead somewhere to take a rest in order to avoid wasting not only your own time and energy, but that of others.—[*Forefront,* 21st issue, 1961]

THE ACCUSATION: The insidious attack on our great Party [the Chinese Communist Party].

Upon the scientific conclusion of "The eastern wind is our benefactor, and/The western wind is our enemy," Teng To insidiously attacked the great empty talk and worn-out words and exaggerated expressions.

The implied scientific conclusion of "the eastern wind beats the western wind" came from a speech delivered to the congress of Communist workers' parties of twelve Socialist countries, November 18, 1957, by Chairman Mao Tse-tung. He substantially pointed out that the international situation had reached a stage where the strength of Socialism overcame that of capitalism. "Eastern wind" represented the revolutionary force of the proletariat and the oppressed peoples against the imperialists, while the "western wind" represented the rotten and corrupt imperialists and all the reactionaries. To praise the eastern wind and rebuke and hate the western wind is perfectly correct. Why did Teng To deliberately ascribe the writing of "the eastern wind is our benefactor" and "the western wind is our enemy" to "the Great Empty Talk" and "circumlocution and excessive expressions"? Khrushchev, the revisionist, castigatingly said that with resoluteness we must uncover the absurdity in the sectarianism of "the eastern wind beats the western wind." Here Teng To sings in the same tone as Khrushchev.

Is Shrewdness Reliable? / Man's knowledge is definitely not unlimited. If a man believes he can understand everything and command all kinds of knowledge, he must either be a blockhead or full of delusions. Besides, it is absolutely impossible for a man to understand every field of knowledge. . . . Someone appears quite clever, but through analysis his cleverness is shown to be merely falsehood or petty slyness. He is, in fact, neither clever nor skillful on important matters.

The ancient philosopher, Lao Tzu, and the later-age Princes of the Six States, took opposite and extreme attitudes on the question of knowledge. The former maintained that knowledge should be discarded and wisdom abandoned. He apparently denied everything. The latter governed the people with dogmatism and blind self-belief. As a result, both were led astray by the wrong conception. The fault of both derived from the fact that they both had disrespect for the concerted wisdom of the people.

True shrewdness can be produced only from popular (or public) opinion. During the reign of Emperor Yuan of the Han Dynasty, the Premier, Kuan Hang, in a memorandum to the Emperor advised him: "Through studies I learned that to consult widely and adopt the opinion of the majority is conforming to the heart of Heaven." . . . The famous scholar, Cheng Shing, during the reign of Emperor Kuang Wu of the same dynasty, also gave advice to the effect: "Put the people's will into deed, and accept the suggestions offered by your aides of the different ministries."

Fan Yao-fu, the son of Fan Chung-ian, of the Sung Dynasty, advised the prominent statesman Tzu Ma-kuang: "I wish you to accept public opinion with an open mind; do not be anxious to display your own capability. Flattery would take the chance to erode you if your own capability would be anxious to be known." All these ideas of our forefathers, particularly those of Fan Yao-fu, are commendable. Fan Yao-fu's "Do not be anxious to display your own capability" is most noteworthy. Man always likes to show his own ability in the false belief that he is wise and that he need not hold respect for the people. In disposing of any public affairs, he insists on doing so in accordance with his own way. Presuming that success can be reached through unconventional measures, he disregards the good ideas of the majority.

If a man has this kind of drawback in his character, he should reform himself. If not, he will eventually suffer irreparable errors.—[*Peking Evening News,* February 22, 1962]

THE ACCUSATION: Teng To attacks our leader with the words "delusion of being self-wise; treat the people with disrespect." This kind of attack equals holding poisonous sand in the mouth and spurting it at our leader.

Now, what does Teng To mean in his description of Kuan Hang advising Emperor Yuan of the Han Dynasty "to consult widely and adopt the opinion of the majority" and Cheng Shing advising Emperor Kuang Wu of the same dynasty "to take the concerted opinions of his aides"? From his description we can find that he hints that our great party is "pretending to be wise and disrespecting the interest of the common people." Comparing his wording to that with which Khrushchev, the revisionist, mocked us, the intention of Teng To's utterance is evident. Does not his writing insult us as much as that of the revisionist, and are not both just like two similar wagons rambling on the same track?

The Forgetful Disease / There are many people suffering from various diseases with strange symptoms. Among them is one called Forgetful Disease. Anyone who is taken with this disease will be very miserable and worry about the difficulty of curing it.

Many different symptoms appear in the patient: he will very quickly forget what he has seen or what he has said; as for what he has done, it is less possible for him to remember. Therefore this kind of person often backs down on his promises and never keeps his word, causing people to wonder whether he is pretending to be stupid or is a maniac.

According to ancient Chinese medical books, the Forgetful Disease has two causes and consequently two different symptoms will appear. In accordance with "The Book of Nervous Pivot," one of the causes is that the sufferer's nervous system and pulse become abnormal by being upset because of his sentiments. As a result he will be not only forgetful but also become unreasonably happy or angry, inarticulate, easily lose his temper, and eventually become a madman. The other cause is that his brain and marrow are damaged. Then he will feel numb from time to time and sometimes will faint. Without an early cure, he would become an idiot. If either of these two extreme symptoms appears, the sufferer should immediately take complete rest. He should not make any speech or do any work. If he tries to speak or work, great trouble will result.

Is there any effective treatment for this kind of disease? Certainly there is: for instance, in ancient China there was a magical physician who poured a pot of dog's blood on the head of the patient immediately after the disease attacked him, and then washed the blood off. In case one treatment could not bring him back to his mind, another one or two might be given. This is a magical art which, however, lacks scientific background. The modern medical method to heal this disease is to use a specially made wooden club to give the patient a hard strike on the head as a shock, and later bring him back to consciousness. Yet, people generally hesitate to give this kind of treatment. . . .

Recently, I read "Huang Ti Dialogue on Medicine" from which I find more interpretations about Forgetful Disease. The over-throbbing, it is said, of the Spring Pulse could cause forgetfulness, confusing feelings and diminution of all restraint. It adds, "The abnormal rise of pulse, blood and breath will cause forgetfulness," and "the exhaustion of the strong breath contained in the muscles is also a cause of forgetfulness."

THE ACCUSATION: This is evidently an essay filled with hatred against our Party to a certain point that Teng To must have gnashed his teeth when he wrote it. Reading through all kinds of medical books we can never find that the symptoms of Forgetful Disease are "backing down on one's own promises, not keeping one's own word, unreasonable happiness and anger, madness and violence." Moreover, there is no such thing as treating the patient by pouring dog's blood upon his head or striking his head with a wooden club to the point of faintness. The Ai Tzu Hou Yu by Lu Choh of the Ming Dynasty is a politically sarcastic book which is irrelevant to medical studies. Therefore, what Teng To wrote about here is hinting at political affairs but not medical problems. All of these are hard facts.

The Three Types of Chu Ko-liang / [Chu Ko-liang was premier of the Kingdom of Shu during the Three Kingdoms period, 220–80. Because of his highly praised and respected strategy and statesmanship during his lifetime, his name became the symbol of wisdom.]

"A Chu Ko-liang with Juice" is a nickname given to a person who is most despised by others. In a chapter of vol. 15, under the title of "Kuo I likens himself to Chu Ko-liang," by Ting Shih, the grandson of Yueh Fei, this nickname was invented. In that chapter Yueh Ko said, "Kuo I was arrogant in talk and proud in demeanor and consequently nobody liked to counter him. One day he inscribed on his fan these words: 'Being called at his home three times for consulting with him about State affairs, and becoming elder statesman of two succeeding Reigns (the historical event of Chu Ko-liang),' which implied that he was as wise and admirable as Chu Ko-liang. . . . Once I sojourned at Tzu during the summer, happened to see the fan on the table of his parlor, and confirmed that what I heard about the above inscription was true. When Chueh was defeated in Fu Li and Chuan was defeated in I Chen, he realized that the situation was hopeless and could not control his sad emotion but burst into tears in the presence of his visiting friends. Around that time a court judge named Peng, who was witty and ironical, sat among a group of friends, including myself, and made a remark on Kuo I, saying, 'This is a Chu Ko-liang with juice.' All of us laughed excitedly and clapped our hands. On hearing this remark, Kuo I became angry and contemplated punishing that jurist. It happened, however, that he was dismissed from his position, so could not do so."

"The Chu Ko-liang with Juice" like Kuo I can only be the object of laughter and despising. But this indicates that anybody who pretends to be a Chu Ko-liang can never be awed by others, and someday when his real shape is uncovered, he will be mocked and laughed at by all the people.—[*Peking Evening News,* March 1, 1962]

THE ACCUSATION: By the same writer, Teng To, the leader of our Party is described and ridiculed as "A Chu Ko-liang with Juice."

Teng To seriously insults somebody by using the nickname "the Chu Ko-liang with Juice," saying, "The counterfeit Chu Ko-liang, the pretending Chu Ko-liang, whose real shape someday would be uncovered." After all, to whom does Teng To's writing apply? If his implication points to bourgeoisie or landlords, there is no need to write in such a veiled way. Thus his mockery is aimed straight at the leader of our Party.

The Man's Family Wealth: One Egg / It is true that any great fortune is accumulated from little sums of money. Their first amount may be very small. This conforms to the old sayings: "A great fur robe is made from under the forelegs of animals" and "The water of rivers and seas is gathered from drops of liquid." This does not, however, mean that anybody under any circumstance can make a fortune by merely obtaining one egg.

During the reign of Wan Li, Ming Dynasty (1573–1620), a novelist named Kiang Ying-ko wrote some short stories and collected them into an anthology with the title of "Snow Wave Short Stories." Contained in the anthology is a story entitled "One Egg's Family Wealth." It reads, "A man living in the city is very poor. One day he picks up an egg lost by somebody along the street. He is delighted. On returning home he tells his wife that now he can get the family wealth. She inquires 'Where is it?' In reply, he shows the egg to her, saying, 'Here it is, but ten years are needed before it becomes the family wealth.' Then he explains his scheme to her:

" 'I shall ask a favor from our neighbor and use his hen to sit on the egg in order to bring forth a chick. When the chick has grown up into a hen, she can produce eggs. From the eggs fifteen chicks can be born every month. As hen will bear hen, 300 chickens, worth 10 ounces of silver, will be attained within three years. With the 10 ounces of silver I can buy five cows. In turn, the cow will give birth to a calf. And within another three years we can have twenty-five cows. In three more years the number of cows will reach, by reproduction, 150. By selling all of them we can get 300 ounces of silver. To use the total sum of silver as security for raising more money we can have 500 ounces of silver in the last three years.' "

In his scheme, however, he plans to take a concubine. On learning of this, his wife becomes furious and strikes the egg sharply with her fist. Thus the whole family wealth, based on the egg, is crushed.

After reading this story, don't you see some problems? This man, crazed for wealth, also knows that in order to build up family wealth, the time factor is necessary. Therefore, his plan for attaining it, as explained to his wife, needs ten years to accomplish. This seems to be possible and reasonable. But his plan is based entirely on hypothesis: each step takes the last conclusion as a premise. For all the succeeding developments of his plan he takes illusions as facts, which thoroughly manifest his mental outlook of the wealth-crazed pursuer. It is natural that his wife is angered to such an extent that one strike by her fist completely destroyed his dream of family wealth.

THE ACCUSATION: This piece of work hints that our Socialist reconstruction has completely failed. It is slanderous!

At the time when our Party announced the Socialist reconstruction plan, Khrushchev, the revisionist, remarked: "There are some truthful elements in it, but we must wait and see its development." Later, when we encountered temporary difficulties, the revisionists calumniated our Great Leap Forward as having "failed" or "collapsed."

In his present essay, Teng To applied such phrases as "rely on illusion instead of reality" and described our plan as allowing fancy ideas to run wild by saying, "One egg's family wealth is completely crushed." Is this not an attack against our Great Leap Forward as being a failure? Does he not sing a duet with Khrushchev?

The Ancient Caricatures / The Chinese people started early to utilize drawings as a kind of weapon against evil persons and wanton actions on the one hand and a kind of publicity for good persons and virtuous conduct on the other. Thus the pictures of artists in ancient China can be regarded as an expressive pattern of public opinions. Their functions are not different from those of modern caricatures.

Generally speaking, however, the artists (we may call them caricaturists, though they were not professional) in different dynasties could neither freely analyze and criticize the social evils, nor dared openly expose political malpractices. Therefore, some of them chose to draw the most hidden form of caricatures to express their discontent toward the political and social conditions.

The caricatures by the so-called Eight Strange Persons of Yang Chow were most outstanding. These eight persons were intellectuals from the northern and southern parts of China. And they happened to be all staying in Yang Chow. Drawing was their hobby, but also described their true feelings. They detested the current political and social evils. Under tyrannical rule, to draw sarcastic pictures was the only way for them to point out to the people the current events which concerned all of them. These intellectuals looked like cynics, but actually they were not; they simply did not wish to be political opportunists for their own selfishness. The word "strange" given to them by the people was an epithet, and they accepted it with gratitude. With profound knowledge of political situations and deep sympathy for their countrymen, their drawings were bound to be "strange" enough to touch the bottom of the human heart.

The works of Loo Liang-feng, one of the Eight Strange Persons, gives an illustration of the nature of the whole school. He was fond of drawing bogies and made fame from such drawings. His masterpiece was "the pictures of bogies' interests," which could be regarded as typical ancient Chinese caricatures.

Loo's works on bogies clearly show that the bogies ridiculed in the drawings were living men who were hated by the common people. Under the current tyranny, if Loo expressed the common people's feelings other than by drawings, he would certainly encounter disaster. To describe the evil doings of a living person in the name of a bogy would save him from hazards. To do so might be the conclusion he reached after many considerations.—[*Peking Evening News,* November 2, 1961]

THE ACCUSATION: Teng To, the writer of the above essay, intends to incite intellectuals to draw caricatures as a means of spreading discontent over current social conditions.

The essay itself stated that ridiculing a bogy is actually ridiculing a living person. This means that the caricatures are camouflage under which to propagate discontent over current social conditions. The whole book of "The Night Talks Around Yenshan" is of the same design.

JAPAN

ON JAPANESE HUMOR

Unlike the classical tradition in Western literature, which emphasizes neatly organized structure and logical unity, the literature of upper-class and scholarly Japanese writers accepted a very different aesthetic. As Makoto Ueda demonstrates, the assumptions of the Japanese literary hierarchy were clearly not those of Aristotle, Horace, and Racine. "Japanese arts," says Ueda, "generally shun logic as the principle of unity and try to minimize the role of intellect in the structure of a work. When talking about the work of prose, which is supposedly more logical than poetic language, Japanese aestheticians never emphasize the importance of tight, logically coherent structure. Lady Murasaki speaks only of natural smoothness, the rhythm of life, which is never logical. . . . A tragedy could certainly make effective use of a logically constructed plot, but Chikamatsu seldom does so. . . . A comedy would be quite effective, too, when it has a tight plot unfolding itself toward a single denouement, but Toraaki teaches that there should be two or three climaxes in each work of the Comic Interlude.

"Perhaps beneath all this lies a view of life . . . traditionally Japanese: human life is essentially irrational and the universe is not logically constructed. The work of art, if it aims to copy life and nature faithfully, cannot have a logical structure. . . . Japanese aesthetic writings tend to be metaphorical rather than analytical, and impressionistic rather than rationalistic."[1]

This analysis is supported by an Englishman who spent his adult life in Japan. "The Japanese mind and speech," says R. H. Blyth, "have a certain jelly-fish quality, an interpermeable character which finds it difficult to call a spade a spade or even an agricultural implement, because after all it may be used for an infinite number of purposes."[2] Of the Japanese character, Blyth says: "The Japanese have these qualities: first, they are intuitive, with a distrust of logic and science; second, they are temperamentally anarchistic in their attitude to society. Thirdly, though subtle, they are innocent. . . . Fourth, they love beauty rather than goodness, and in the last event, truth more than beauty." To make one such generalization about a whole nation requires some tendency to arbitrary expression; to compound the dictum four times, even for the sake of parallelism, is awesome.

Modern scholars agree that China had a prodigious influence on Japanese culture and that many significant elements of Japanese culture can be traced back to Chinese sources. What remains debatable is the degree to which the Japanese adapted the borrowings to make them fit the needs of uniquely Japanese characteristics. Donald Keene, for example, emphasizes the dissimilarities between Chinese and Japanese

1. Ueda, *Literary and Art Theories in Japan*, pp. 224–25.
2. This and the following quotation are from Blyth's *Oriental Humour*, pp. 211, 147.

patterns of art: "We shall find that Japanese poetry is in most ways unlike Chinese, that the Japanese were writing novels of magnitude and beauty centuries before the Chinese, and that the Japanese theater, far surpassing the Chinese, ranks with the great dramatic achievements of the world."[1]

Keene contrasts the upper-class literature of Japan, "prevailingly aristocratic in tone," elegant, "smoothing away the rough edges of emotions, as something indecorous and rather vulgar," and the "popular" literature "designed to meet the tastes of the lower classes." It is from this popular literature that most of the Japanese humor and satire comes, in the works of Saikaku and Jippensha Ikku, the anonymous authors of Kyogen, and the creators of satiric anecdotes and jokes.

By the seventeenth century the greatest of Japan's comic theorists, Okura Toraaki, had formulated most of the concepts about comedy which the Western world by that time had independently evolved. His standards were high, particularly so since he was an actor by profession and specialized in the production of the comic interludes which were offered between Noh plays. "To be delightful is better than to be funny," Toraaki wrote. "To be superb and moving is even better. . . . Everything ends in pathos."[2] Toraaki recognized three grades of laughter—high, middle, and low—and bewailed the fact that the low kind was the easiest to get from an audience.

Although the comic interlude was often played merely for laughs, Toraaki castigated that approach. He denounced laughter at the expense of deformity and vulgarity, "because these do not properly represent the true nature of things. . . . Such is a pitiless, unhealthy, superficial laughter." Imitation and elegance were two principles which Toraaki felt both the Noh play and the comic interlude should share. The laughter of the Kyogen should not be of the low type found in farce or burlesque; instead of laughing at physical deformity or abnormality, the Kyogen should deal with the common foibles of ordinary people. Laughter depends on the distance from which one looks at things; with sufficient perspective, everything can be made comic.

A number of Western scholars who have lived in Japan have commented on the nature of Japanese humor. Their conclusions do not always agree, but the variety of viewpoints provides a more comprehensive understanding than reliance on a single person's judgment would offer. Basil Chamberlain, for example, tries to define Japanese humor by contrasting it with several European species. "Japanese fun does not in the very faintest degree resemble French *esprit,* that child born of pure intellect and social refinement. . . . Shall we compare it with the grim mixture which we Northerners call humour—the grotesque suffused with the pathetic? It may seem a little nearer to that. But no—it lacks alike the hidden tear and the self-criticism of humour:—it has no irony, no sidelights. It is more like . . . the old Roman saturnalia—the broad jest, the outrageous pun, the practical joke, the loud guffaw . . . buffoonery, tomfoolery, high jinks of every sort."[3] So much for the Western myth of decorous, polite Japan. Chamberlain suggests that it is because official formalism, in life and literature, hung so heavily on the Japanese that "the national spirits sought

1. Keene, *Japanese Literature,* p. 2.
2. Makoto Ueda, "Toraaki and His Theory of Comedy," *Journal of Aesthetics and Art Criticism,* vol. xxiv (1965), pp. 19-26.
3. Chamberlain, *Things Japanese,* p. 214.

a vent in the lower strata of society," and for genuine amusement one has to turn from the books written for the upper classes and associate with more vulgar companions.

R. H. Blyth wrote more about Japanese humor than any other Westerner, and his translations offer a rich source of jokes, anecdotes, and poems. But his pronouncements are erratic, sometimes brilliant and sometimes merely eccentric, sometimes informative and sometimes peculiarly biased, and his dogmatic generalizations are sometimes open to obvious refutation. "One great difference between Japanese and European humour is that there is no spitefulness or rudeness or personal animus in Japanese humour," Blyth says,[1] but he admits elsewhere that *Hizakurige* is the funniest novel in Japan, and that book clearly disproves every claim in the above statement. Blyth believes that Japanese satire, unlike European, is more interested in diverting the world than in vexing it, and in general this is true, though Akutagawa is clearly working in the European tradition in *Kappa* and Natsume sometimes loses his geniality in *I Am a Cat*. "Facetiousness is unknown" in Japanese humor, says Blyth, "and sarcasm is forbidden, or at least dangerous," but again *Hizakurige,* the jokes Professor Blyth himself has translated, and even the Tokyo periodicals available to tourists offer abundant evidence to the contrary.

But Blyth is always stimulating. "Japanese humour is more subtle, more poetical than Chinese. It avoids vulgarity and obscenity on the one hand, and the excessively high tone of Chinese literature on the other. . . . Japanese literature is pre-eminent in puns and playing on words, and most expert in parody."

Anyone who still thinks that the Japanese do not indulge in vituperation, vulgar abuse, and obscene insults might read Saikaku's seventeenth-century *This Scheming World,* or the nineteenth-century *Hizakurige,* or the twentieth-century *Botchan.* These books are full of vile insults, diatribe, vilification. It is true that "proper" Japanese literature has none of this billingsgate, and upper-class Japanese do not publicly use language of this kind. But aggressive vulgarity is not absent from Japanese culture; it is simply concentrated into lower-class expression and proletarian communication. Admittedly, profane language is rare in Japan, paradoxically, W.G. Aston suggests, "probably owing to the want of any deep-seated sentiment of piety in the Japanese nation. Their language is equally deficient in such phrases as 'God bless you' and 'Thank God.' "[2]

Among the many sources of Japanese humor and satire not included here are Bunraku (the famed puppet theater) plays; Shikitei Samba's collection of satiric sketches, *The World's Bathhouse* (1811); other works of Saikaku, Kiseki, and Akutagawa; and Natsume's *Botchan,* a novel about the misadventures of a naïve young schoolteacher, very popular in Japan. Recently, black humor found Japanese expression in Akiyuki Nozaka's novel *The Pornographers.*

1. The quotations in this and the following paragraph are from Blyth's *Oriental Humour,* pp. 202, 204, 209.
2. Aston, *Japanese Literature,* p. 375.

JOKES

translated by R. H. Blyth and Norbert Kaneko

A Miser's Death / There was in the country of Mikawa a rich man named Sokei. Born stingy, even on his deathbed he would not drink any expensive medicine. His friend tried to get him to swallow a medicine called Gooen, but he refused to open his mouth, so his friend said, "This Gooen cost nothing! It was free!" and the sick man then opened his mouth and gulped it down.

•

Countereffect / A very thin man came to the chemist's, sat down painfully, sighed, and then asked: "Haven't you any medicine to reduce the energy?" The chemist said: "You look rather weak; what on earth do you want such a medicine for?" "No, no! It's not for me; it's for my wife and concubine."

•

A Go-Between's Thoughtlessness / A certain go-between arranged a marriage between two people, and the parents were perfectly satisfied with it. The son, however, called the go-between secretly, and said, "I hear you have chosen my wife-to-be, and I appreciate the trouble you have taken very much, but is she a good-natured girl?" The intermediary began to praise her to the skies, and said, "She is the most beautiful girl in the world, clever with her needle, and well-read. Her waist is as graceful and slim as a willow. Her mouth is sweetness itself, and her eyes as slender as the pampas grass." The son said, "That sounds fine, but for one thing. I don't like narrow eyes. A woman's eyes should be as round as a berry." The go-between was startled, and said hurriedly, "Only one of her eyes is thin; the other is large."

•

Politeness Among Familiars / An old father came downstairs in the evening, when even for ordinary people things are a little dim. Mistaking his son for a visitor, he invited him up very courteously. After a while the son said, "It's me, you know." The father said, "I knew it was you from the beginning, but I treated you like that to teach you how to behave in this world."

•

Reliable Evidence / Someone sent a messenger many times to Mr. Dozen to borrow money, but the other was always out, so he went there personally, and said he wanted to see the master, Dozen. The master came out and said, "Dozen is not at home now." "What, you are Dozen, aren't you?" "How on earth can you doubt his word, when the master himself tells you personally that he is out!"

The Model of a Ridge-End Tile / (To understand this story it is necessary to know that the roof-end tile is the representation of an ogre.)

There was a man who lived near a tile-maker, and who had an unusually ugly daughter. This girl died at the age of twenty-four or -five, and the tile-maker went to the father to offer his condolences. But he wept so much the father asked him why he was so upset, whereupon he answered through his tears, "What shall we do now? We have lost our model of the ridge-end tile!"

•

Long Dog / A blind man trod on a dog, which barked at him fiercely. Going on a few steps he trod on the dog again. Bewildered, he cried, "What an extraordinarily long dog!"

•

Memory / A flower-seller was walking along the street calling, "Forget-me-grasses! Forget-me-grasses!" (The Japanese have not only forget-me-nots, but also forget-mes.) Some inquisitive passer-by stopped him and said, "They have no flower or special charm; are they good for anything?" "Yes, indeed! When you look at them, you forget all your troubles, the heat in the hottest summer, the cold of midwinter, the old year at the end of the year." "Really! Then I'll buy a bunch. How much are they?" "Er...I'm sorry...I've forgotten!"

•

Buns / A pale, thin man came running and all out of breath to a group of people, and said, "A bun-seller is after me! I'm so afraid of buns, please hide me somewhere." So they hid him in a shed nearby. "What a funny chap, to be afraid of buns!" and they bought all the buns from the bun-seller, and threw them in the holes in the door. The man seemed to be going crazy. "O how awful! How awful!" he cried, and at last was quiet. They began to think they had gone too far, and wonder whether he had died of fright, so they opened the door, and found only a few buns inside. The man came out, licking his lips, and saying, "Now I'm afraid of a cup of tea!"

•

The Fencing Gymnasium / A very dignified-looking samurai came to a school of fencing that said outside it, in enormous letters: GYMNASIUM OF FENCING: EVERY SCHOOL. He said, "Please teach me whatever school may suit me; I wish to become your disciple." "Did you come here after looking at the signboard?" "That is so." "Good Heavens! It's just to keep robbers away!"

•

Role Change / There was a flood on the River Kanda, and the firewood on the bank was all swept down the river. A beggar of Yanagiwara came to the riverside and pulled up the bundles with a fire-hook. And suddenly the beggar became a dealer in firewood, and the dealer in firewood became a beggar.

•

A Likely Story / A priest was found plucking a fowl. He stammered out, "It wanted to become a monk, and asked me to shave it!"

•

Appearances Are Deceiving / A certain man was wading across a river, the water coming up to his breast. Those who came after him, seeing this, took off all their clothes and entered the river. But the water came only up to their knees. When the other man reached the farther bank they found he was a cripple.

•

Adaptability / A thief, discovered by the master of the house, was at a loss what to do, being unable to run away. He stood with his arms outstretched on the wall, and said, "This is your shadow, sir."

•

Hospitality / A man and wife were toasting rice-cakes, when a visitor happened to come. "Oh, how nice to see you!" They called him in, but the wife said, "Now eat them quickly before someone else comes!"

•

The Hatchet / A man visited somebody one snowy day. As he entered the house, from light to dark suddenly, "It's very dark!" he said. Just then his foot touched something, and when he picked it up it was a hatchet, a thing he had wanted for a long time, so he put it under his coat. But as his eyes got used to the darkness, the inside looked lighter, and he felt ashamed when he thought that the people must have seen him putting the hatchet under his coat. But it would be still more funny if he put it back, so he was at a loss what to do. Just then another man came in and said, "How dark it is!" Taking advantage of this he handed him the hatchet, and said, "Put this under your coat, and it will get lighter!"

•

The Black Dog of Hyogo / While a certain stupid man was passing along a street in the town of Hyogo, a big black dog suddenly appeared and bit him severely in the leg. He was much chagrined at it, till he reached Amagasaki, when he came across a black puppy which he trod on and kicked. People were indignant and gathered round him threateningly, but he explained, "I kicked it to pay back an old score. I had my leg bit in Hyogo by a black dog."

•

Star-Catching / There was a certain priestling who, when night came, swung a long pole here and there in the temple garden. The priest happened to come by, and asked what he was doing. "I am trying to get a star in the sky, but they don't seem to fall down." "What a fool you are! The pole is not long enough; get on the roof and try!"

•

A Dream / The husband groaned in his sleep and his wife shook him awake, and the husband said, "Oh, did I groan?" "Yes, you were having a nightmare, weren't you?" "No, no, it was nothing terrifying. A superb woman took me by the hand and asked me to come into a beautiful bed, and I was resisting her, and groaning." The wife said, "If I hadn't woken you up, most likely. . ."

•

Love in the Water / A carp fell in love with the daughter of a crucian, but there seemed no prospect of marriage in the water. Their vows became like the bubbles, and they both felt it better to die, so they twined themselves together with their fins and jumped out of the water into a fishing boat.

•

"Yajiro, Whom I Saw in the Land of the Living" / What does this mean? Years ago there was a gold mine in the Island of Sado, and many people lived round it. One of them was a sage, who ate no grain, kept the commandments, was always chanting the sutras, was indeed a living Buddha, so that people came from near and far to revere him. His servant was a man named Yajiro. Now after some years the sage announced that the time had come for him to depart to the next world. When they heard this, all shed tears. On the twentieth of the month, the date decided, he dug a deep hole on the moor and entered it, all clad in his Buddhist robes. He told them to shovel in the earth, and was thus buried alive. A wonderful thing indeed! But there were some who said that he had given a certain mine-worker a lot of money to make a secret tunnel by which he got away safely.

Three years later, Yajiro, who venerated his master as a saint, went to Echigo, and ran across him there. He accosted him and asked him if he were not that sage who had pretended to die. Like Peter, he denied it thrice, but after Yajiro pointed to clear proofs of it, he admitted the fact, and said, "Yes, now I remember, you are Yajiro, whom I saw in the land of the living."

•

Forced Not to Be Divorced / A man got tired of his wife after many years of married life, and said to her, "I feel sick when I just see you. Please go away." The wife replied, "Well, it can't be helped. If you feel like that I will go back to my mother's home," and she took out the clothes she had been married in, put them on, oiled her hair, and dyed her teeth. Looking at her, the man suddenly began to want her not to go, but he could not unsay what he had said, so he went to see her off. They had to cross a river, and when they reached the other side he had an idea, and said to her, "You must pay the ferry fee." The wife said, "How is that possible, between man and wife like you and me?" "That's only when we are married. When we're divorced we have no relation. You can't go without paying the fee, and you can't pay the fee, so let's go back!" So he rowed her back in his boat and lived with her five and eighty years.

•

Octopus / Some priests and laymen held a party, and were talking and laughing together. A priest coughed suddenly and brought up something like hard phlegm. One of the men looked at it and found it to be a piece of octopus. "What a strange thing you brought up!" he exclaimed. "Yes," said the priest, "the octopus that I ate when a child has just come up. They say with truth that octopus is indigestible!"

•

A Profit-Making / A gambler came home at midnight, woke his wife up, and said, rocking to and fro with self-satisfaction, "I've never had such a bit of luck in all my life!" His wife thought he had won a lot of money that night, and said, "How much did you make?" "I lost the same as usual, but I gave my sword for a two thousand debt, but I bought the sword for five hundred the other day, so I made a clear thousand five hundred!"

•

A Stingy Snore / Hearing the sound of rain at dawn a priest who was in bed with a young man thought, "Good heavens! I ought to give him some breakfast, as it's raining. . . . Well, I'll pretend to be sound asleep, and then I won't have to." After a while the young man got up quietly and went out. The priest waited a bit, and when he thought the young man must be outside the temple, got up and looked out, and found the young man still there inside. The priest was so surprised, he shut his eyes and snored loudly, standing there.

•

A Feline Failure / Whenever the husband was not at home her paramour came to the wife's house. They had arranged previously that he should enter secretly from the roof by a ladder the wife had prepared, and if the husband came back and asked, "What is the sound on the roof?" he should imitate a cat. One day the husband came home unexpectedly, and asked, "What is that noise? It sounds like a man." The wife said, "Oh, no, it must be a big cat like a man." The paramour on the roof was very surprised, and forgot to cry "Miaow," and said in weak voice, "I'm a c-a-a-a-t."

•

Stuck-Up / There was a proud man who got even more puffed up when he was praised. When he showed his handwriting to people, they admired it highly, saying "How wonderful! It's just like that of the great priest Kobo. You must be the reincarnation of Kobo Daishi!" At that the man murmured audibly, "Yes, dying's no joke!"

•

Beggars' Conversation / As I passed over the Bridge of Sanjo, the beggars were talking under the balustrade. "What do you think? There are many rich people in this town. It must be nice for them, they can do what they like. How much money do they have?" "They don't have so much as they are supposed to have, just as we don't." "What do you mean?" "Oh, they say in the capital that a beggar has a bushel of lice, but we each have at most a peck."

•

The Sound of Rain / There was once a scatter-brained fellow who went out to the verandah one rainy night and did not come back to his bed though day had dawned. His wife wondered what had happened, and went out to look. There he was standing on the verandah, all exposed in front. "What on earth are you doing?" she said. "I'm making water," he replied, "but so much is coming out!" He was standing by the rain-pipe from the eaves.

•

The Aid of Others / There once was a man who redecorated the drawing-room of his house. He invited his neighbours to the new room, and while they were enjoying the sakè, his wife appeared and greeted them. "We have no dainties, but please drink sakè in our new room." The guests said, "It must have cost you a lot to make such a fine room as this." The wife said, "We could not have done this by ourselves. We are grateful for the aid of you neighbours." Yosaku, coming back home, praised her to his wife and said, "She is such a clever woman! She never says anything wrong. With their fortune it was not necessary to ask the aid of others, and yet she talked like that!" His wife protested that anybody could have said such an easy thing. A fortnight after, there was a feast at their own house; they had invited the neighbours to celebrate the seventh night of the birth of their baby. The guests said, "Congratulations! Your wife must be very glad. She was very fortunate in her confinement, and got a boy to crown it all." The wife came out and said, "The baby was born, not due to my husband alone. I am grateful for the aid of the young men in the neighbourhood."

The Sham Centipede / While a group of people were talking about different things, someone said, "If a man carries cuprite [red copper ore], no centipede can approach him." The host said eagerly, "I was given a cuprite knife. I'll show you it." The other looked at and said, "Oh, this is only a sham one; this is no good." The host got angry. "This is no imitation! The person who gave it to me valued it highly. You just don't know what cuprite is!" Just then, because the roof was a thatched one, a centipede fell down from the ceiling. "This is a good chance!" they cried, and put the knife near it. The centipede crept onto it. "Look! It must be a sham!" The host became all the more vehement. "This cuprite is the real one! The centipede is probably a sham centipede!"

•

No Women Know No / A certain man married a beautiful woman, and all day long they were canoodling, and all night long embracing. The maid-servant, Natsu, saw and overheard all this, and felt correspondingly envious and uneasy. One day the wife went back to her old home. To comfort his loneliness the husband invited all his friends. As they were going back one of them said, "We know how you feel. You'll miss her tonight!" The husband laughed, and said, "Well, it can't be helped. Tonight I must lie on Miss Natsu's breast."

In her bed Natsu thought, "How lucky it is my mistress is away! My master is going to sleep with me!" And she waited there as children wait for the New Year. But still he didn't come, so she thought, "Perhaps he has fallen asleep. I'll go and wake him up." So she went to his room and opened the sliding screen very quietly.

"Who is it?" "It's Natsu, if you please." "What have you come here for?" "I came to say 'No,' because you said you would come and lie on my breast."

•

The Illiterate Father / A father who couldn't read was at a loss what to do when his sons were out of the house and letters came. "We'll leave some answers behind." "That's impossible!" "All right, I have an idea." He went down to the bottom of the garden and prepared some plaster. When a letter was brought by a messenger, requiring an immediate reply, he would stick his hands in the plaster and then show them to the messenger and say, "As you see, my hands are like this, so I will write the answer later."

•

Sham Dumb / A dumb beggar was going round the houses beating his begging bowl. Someone said, "He's not dumb, he's only pretending." The master of the house said, "Oh, don't say such a cruel thing! Pitiful creature! How troublesome it must be for you to be really dumb!" The dumb man was touched by his human feeling, and said, "Yes."

•

No-Talking Penance / Three men decided to perform the ascetic practice of absolute silence until midnight, when they would gaze at the harvest moon. One of them happened to say, "It's difficult not to say anything at all!" The second said, "Aren't you speaking during the time of silence?" The third man said, "I'm the only one who hasn't spoken yet."

•

The Width of Japan / Father and son came down from their mountain village to see Kyoto. They passed over Amanogawa and the Moor of Ikuno. The prosperous capital, the busy merchants, the crowded streets amazed them, and the son said, "Father, I have seen many places, but never such a one as this! Is this what they call 'Japan'?" The father replied "Oh, don't talk so silly, people will laugh at you, and I shall be shamed. Listen, Japan is three times bigger than this!"

•

The Unlendable Ladder / There was once a very stingy man. Someone sent a messenger to borrow a tea-mortar from him, but he replied, "A tea-mortar gets into a habit of being used in a special way, so please come and use it here." Later on, the stingy man sent a servant to borrow a ladder, but the owner replied, with great relish, "A ladder has a special way of being used, so if you want to climb up somewhere, please use it here."

•

Two Temples and Their Dogs / In a certain town there were a temple of the Hokke (Nichiren) sect and another of the Jodo (Pure Land) sect next door to each another. At the temple of the Nichiren sect they had a dog which they called Honen. The priests in the next-door temple of the Jodo sect said to each other, "What a nasty thing to do! They call their dog by the name of the sacred founder of our sect. Let's pay them out!" So they also kept a dog which they named Nichiren. After they had made it very thin by giving it no food at all, they called the children of the neighbourhood and told them to set the next-door Honen and their own Nichiren on each other. The children all came and called, "Come on Nichiren!" and "Come on Honen!" and the dogs began to fight. As Nichiren was such a lean dog, it was soon bowled over, and the children jeered, and cried, "Nichiren lost! Honen won!" The monks in the temple of the Hokke sect were furious about it, and soon after got rid of their Honen.

•

A Stingy Father / A child had died, and the old man said to his son, "My son! don't cry so loudly. People may hear you and come to the funeral service and we shall have to give them some tea. That would be a pity, so say nothing about it. Put the body in a hamper and take it and bury it yourself. When you fill in the hole, some earth will remain over, so bring back the soil in the hamper and we can use it as the final coating of the cooking-range."

•

Righteous Indignation / A man and his wife were sitting in a room, when unknown to them a burglar broke in, and hid himself under the verandah. Late at night the wind made a sound at the back door, and the husband asked his wife, "Did you fart?" "Certainly not!" said his wife indignantly. She was so angry the husband was troubled and said, "Oh, well, perhaps a thief has broken in and is hiding somewhere, and *he* did it." The thief came out from under the verandah and said, "Now I must protest. . . ."

•

Miser / A white-haired, mean-looking old man was passing over a bridge wearing new clogs. He happened to drop one clog over into the river bed. Looking round he saw a beggar on the bridge, and asked his name. "Chobe." "Chobe, just go and get that clog for me." "No, not for nothing," the beggar grumbled. Then the old man got a mean idea. He kicked off the other clog into the river bed and said, "Chobe, go and get them and I'll give you a penny."

The Servant Dispossessed of a Fox / A new servant boy was possessed by a fox. After the prayers and exorcisms, he was dispossessed of it at last, but he seemed to be still absent-minded. The master got angry, and shouted, "You became a big fool since you were possessed by a fox!" The fox stuck his head in the window, and said, "He was like that from the beginning!"

•

The Stolen Bundle / "Santa, we are in the capital, where a thief may steal something from you even during the daytime if you are careless. So be careful how you carry this bundle." Saying these words, the master set out with his servant. When they got to a busy place in front of the theatre, the servant pulled the sleeve of the master and said to him, "As it is so crowded, please be careful of your purse." "Well said! I'm being careful of course, and you too with your bundle." "Yes, I had it stolen just now, so I told you to be careful."

•

The Servant's Pulse / There was a maid-servant who was excessively humble. Her mistress caught a cold and sent for the family doctor. He came, and after he had seen her she called the servant and said to her, "You don't seem quite well either; show the doctor your pulse." The maid-servant said self-depreciatingly, "How should a woman like me have a pulse?"

•

A Doctor's Self-Praise / A certain doctor used to boast how he had brought the dead to life, and cured one after another the most difficult cases that no other doctor could have any effect on. An intimate friend of his said, "It may be as you say, but you are speaking only of your successes. Haven't you ever killed any of your patients?" The doctor replied, "That sort of thing is spoken of at the houses of my clients, so I needn't mention it."

•

Her Past Betrayed / A ragman came to a back slum where a woman lived by herself. When he bought some rags from her, he found three *koto* plectra in the basket. The ragman said, "Since you have these plectra, you must have known better days. It is a pity that you have to live like this; times have changed." The woman replied, "Yes, I used to live handsomely before. What a pity! I kept the whole set of five plectra until very recently."

(The actual number of plectra which makes a set is three, not five as the woman supposes. She thus shows she had never played the *koto* [harp], which is plucked with three fingers only.)

•

A Cowardly Samurai / There was once a very cowardly samurai who one evening wanted to go to the (outside) lavatory, but felt afraid, so he told his wife to bring a candle and go with him. From inside the lavatory he called to her, "Aren't you frightened?" "What is there to be frightened of?" she replied. He said admiringly, "You are indeed worthy to be the wife of a warrior!"

•

The Wrestling Hall / There was a match between Shakagatake and Niodo, so the hall was record-makingly full. Even those with tickets could not get in. "It can't be helped," thought one man, went round to the back, broke the fence, and tried to get through it like a dog. The manager saw him and pushed him out, saying, "No, this is not the way in!" So the man thought it over for a while, and pushed backwards with his hindquarters. The manager saw him, and pulled him in, saying, "No, that is not the way out!"

•

Money / A certain samurai came to Kyoto from a distant province to improve his health, and employed a man-servant in a house he rented there. The year drew to its close, and 30 ryo was sent to him from his native place, and when the man servant saw this he began to think that 30 ryo was just the sum he needed to set himself up in business, so with some bloody thoughts in mind he approached his master and said, "What would happen to a man who killed his employer and robbed him of his money?" "A man who murders his master and takes his money will be searched for all over Japan, arrested, bastinadoed, and crucified. That's the law." "Well, I think I'll go to bed."

•

The Copper Torii / The wife next door was having a very difficult delivery. Oh, it was such a nuisance, sending for a doctor, or buying some expensive ginseng! At last, her husband took off all his clothes, ran to the well, poured bucket after bucket of water over himself, and cried, "Oh, god of Kompira, please give her an easy delivery, and I will present you with a copper torii for your shrine!" Hearing his prayer, his wife called to him, "But dear, even if I have an easy delivery, how can we offer a copper shrine gate? Why do you talk such nonsense?" "Sh! Have the baby quickly while I am deceiving the god!"

•

The Kite / A little boy was trying in vain to fly his kite. The father came out of the house, saw him, and said, "Come along, I'll fly it for you. Let's go to the other side of the stream." He went there with the boy and when he ran a little, the kite flew wonderfully. The father was interested, and got absorbed in drawing it back and letting it out. The child urged, "Daddy, give it to me now. Let me have it!" The father answered, "Hold your tongue. I wish I hadn't brought you with me!"

•

Widows Are Best / Whenever men get together, they are sure to begin to talk about love. "I myself choose innocent girls in long sleeves." "Oh, no, I prefer ripe beauties to young ones." "No, I don't like non-professionals. Courtesans are more attractive." One of them said, "I like none of these. No woman is equal to a widow. A widow is best of all." On hearing this, all agreed unanimously. "Yes, that's true. A widow is the thing." Then one man said, "Ah, I wish my wife were a widow!"

•

Suicide / The keeper of the Ryogoku Bridge was summoned to court, and reproached. "Every night someone drowns himself from your bridge. Why aren't you more careful? From tonight you must keep a sharp look-out!" On that very night, while he was keeping a strict watch with eagle eyes, along came a suspicious-looking chap who tried to get under the parapet. The keeper seized him from the back and cried, "No mistake about it, you are the one that keeps on drowning himself every night!"

Big Characters / A courtesan wrote a letter in very big Chinese characters. "Are these big characters to be put on a paper screen?" "No, no! It's a letter!" "From the time of Buddha, I've never seen such a letter. It must be requesting something enormous." "No, it's to a man who is deaf."

•

A One-Sen Prayer / A stingy old man visited a temple with a boy servant. He wanted to offer a three-sen coin, but when he searched in his purse he found only four-sen coins, so he offered one very unwillingly, and said to the boy, "You'll have to pray, too!"

•

The Death Verse / A thief was at last caught, and was going to be executed, but he said, "Wait a bit, I want to write my death poem." "Well, that's no bad thing. Please tell us it." So the thief recited:

"At this time
How I would regret
To leave this world,
Had I not known from the first
That I must die."

Those who heard it cried, "Hey! that's by Ota Dokan!" The thief said, "Yes, and this is my last theft."

•

The Day of Abstinence / A certain man was given the first bonito of the season by a neighbour of his. How lucky! But unfortunately it happened to be the day of abstinence for his late father. He wondered for a while what to do. Then he carried the bonito before the altar where his father was enshrined, and, "Father," he said, "I received this bonito from someone. But as it is a day of abstinence for you, I can't have it. Do you mind my eating it? If you don't mind, it is not necessary for you to say so."

•

Yoritomo's Skull / Treasures were being exhibited at Edo-in. "The sacred treasures are shown on the left. This is the skull of Lord Yoritomo. Approach near, and look closely at it." Hearing this, one of the viewers said, "I thought the skull of Yoritomo would be larger. This looks too small." The explaining priest answered, "This is the skull of Lord Yoritomo when he was three."

•

Letter from Edo / A man was sent two salted bonitos from his relative in Edo. As he was illiterate, he was at a loss, not knowing how to read the letter. In came the landlord. Jumping at this opportunity he said, "Well, I have got these from Edo. Would you kindly read the letter for me?" The landlord couldn't read either, but he concealed the fact and said, "All right, I will read it for you. Listen to me. Er . . . I hope you are quite well. I am sending you these two salted fish and five straw bags of millet." "Sir, these bags of millet are ours." "Oh, yes, that's true. So he writes in the postscript."

Imitation Cat / A man couldn't sleep well, being alone; and also the rats were making a scuffling noise. As they ran about altogether too freely, he miaowed, and a rat on the shelf became still and silent. He thought he had succeeded, but another rat said to the rat on the shelf, "Why do you stand still?" And it answered, "Come and listen to this imitation of a cat!"

•

Hell / A very ugly woman died suddenly after a quarrel caused by jealousy and went to Hell. She wished to become a ghost to haunt her husband and asked Yama, the King of Hell, to this effect. Yama looked at her and grumbled at her, saying, "You are so ugly that I cannot allow you to be a ghost." The devil attending her pulled her by the sleeve and whispered, "Ask to be a goblin."

•

The Bill-Collector / On the very last night of the year, "Hello!" "Who is it?" "It's the rice-dealer." "Oh, the master is not at home." The voice sounded just like that of the master himself. So the bill-collector made a hole in the paper sliding door and peeped inside. The master was warming himself in the kotatsu (foot-warmer). "Hey, you said the master was not at home, but there you are!" The master got angry. "Why did you make a hole there? This is my house, you know." "I'm sorry; I will repair it." He repaired the hole. "Now it's all right." "You can't see me any more?" "No, sir." "Then, I'm not at home."

•

Half-Price / A woman of about thirty years of age came to the New Great Bridge. Throwing down one mon, she began to pass over the bridge in haste. The bridge-keeper called her back, saying she had to pay another mon. The woman answered, "I am going to drown myself from the middle of the bridge."

•

Lantern-Viewing / A countryman who was staying at a courtesan's house went to see the lanterns, and wanted to come back. But he forgot both the name of the house and the direction. At last he managed to find something he remembered, and asked a young man of a certain house if there was a guest who had gone to see the lanterns, in blue clothes. "Yes," he replied, "there was, but he is not back yet." "Am I the one? Look at me."

•

A Big Lie / "Listen! When I went to the mountains the other day, a huge wild boar rushed out and I took it by its horns!" "What? How can a wild boar have horns!" "Ah yes, I took it by its tail." "Nonsense! It has no tail!" "Then what did I take it by?"

•

A Mean Man / A stingy old man who was about to die made his last request, that they should not spend much money, and that they should send him to the temple before daybreak for cheapness' sake. The relatives gathered together, and said they couldn't do this and that. The old man sat up and said, "Well, I won't die then!"

•

The Watch-Tower / A thief climbed up a watch-tower and was going to steal the bell there. The watchman woke up and challenged him. He pretended innocence, and said, "I want to ask you, how can I get to Honcho Street?" "Ah, Honcho Street! You come down this ladder, and . . . "

•

Half-Sleep / A man stayed at his friend's house. He woke at midnight and found him sleeping deeply, so he got up and went into the wife's bed. The husband then woke, saw them, and got very angry. The friend begged his forgiveness, saying, "I'm so sorry; it was all a mistake. I was half-asleep—please forgive me!" "Well, it's not altogether impossible," he said, and they went to bed again. The friend regretted his mistake very much and got up again, and finished it safely this time. Hearing their excited breathing, the husband woke again, and called out, "Now then, wake up! Wake up!"

•

Father and Son / The father came back home intoxicated, and said to his son, "Hey, Magoroku, you've got three heads. I'm not going to leave my fine house to a monster like you!" The son, just as drunk, retorted, "That's all right with me. Who'd want a house going round and round like this one?"

•

An Express Messenger / A big wolf was lying in the road with its mouth open. An express messenger came running along right into the wolf's mouth, and without knowing it passed through the wolf's stomach and came out of the anus, still crying, "Essassa! Essassa!" The wolf muttered, "I should have worn a loincloth!"

•

A Wedding Present / A man, having heard that a friend of his had got married, called on him with a fish he had bought on the way as a wedding present. "Hello, Hachiko, I hear you have married. I've come to congratulate you."

"That's very kind of you," he answered, "But I divorced her yesterday."

"That's too bad. I bought a fish for you. But luckily another friend of mine married lately. I'll take this fish to him." He went off with the fish.

"Hi, Gonshichi, someone told me that you are married. Congratulations!" "No, she went away yesterday," was the answer.

So the man was disappointed, and thought he had better take the fish back home and have it with his wife. He went back home, to find the owner of the house waiting for him.

"I say," he said, "I just had someone go and look for you. Your wife has run off with her lover." "Good heavens!" he cried. "Is there nowhere I can take this fish?"

•

The Thief / The wife aroused her husband, and whispered, "Dear, a thief has broken into the kitchen!" The husband jumped out of bed and seized him. But the thief was so strong that he grappled with the husband desperately for about an hour. In the end, the husband was stronger, and at last got the thief under his knee. He panted to his wife, "Dear, give me a glass of water!" The thief from under him gasped out, "And one for me too."

•

In a Bustle / A chamber-maid asked the lady of the house to let her attend on the lady in a visit to a festival of the shrine. But the lady declined the young girl's request with the pretext that a decent young girl should keep away from such congested premises.

"But," added the lady out of pity, "if you particularly wish it, just come here."

So saying, the lady gave the girl a pinch or two on the buttocks, and remarked, "So, you see, this is as good as your visit to the festival."

•

Boozer / There was once a man who continually complained of not having enough money with which to buy sakè wine. His faithful wife was so sorry for him that she cut part of her hair and sold it to a wig shop for 24 mon and bought some wine for him.

"How could you buy this?" asked her husband.

"Darling, I cut off some of my hair for you and sold it."

"So, you did that, dearest!"

The unworthy husband was moved to tears, and then fondling his wife's hair, he added, "But you still have half a bottle to drink!"

•

Reasoning / Son: "My sister is a lovely girl. If she can marry me, father, you can save much money, can't you?"

Father: "What a wretched simpleton! That is incest. It is the way of brutes!"

Son: "How dare you talk to me like that, father? You married my mother, didn't you?"

•

Like Draws to Like / Lad: I'm sorry to say this to you, but I'm a born woman-hater. I detest them. I swear, I'll keep single.

Girl: That can't be! What a coincidence! I hate men—they are just disgusting.

Lad: Can that be possible? We two have much in common. Let's get married. What d'you say?

•

Request / "Will you do me a favor, friend?"

"I'm always at your service, so please don't hesitate."

"You are awfully kind. Will you please lend me 1,000 yen?"

"Oh, with pleasure! But, I have a favor to ask of you in return."

"What is it? I can refuse you nothing, of course."

"It is very awkward to say, but . . . may I beg you to oblige me by cancelling the request you just made of me?"

•

Domestic Scene / After a quarrel the husband gave a letter of divorce to his wife.

"So, I'm through with you, I hate to see you any longer."

The sad wife was offended at these spiteful words, and after making her toilet and dressing up, she bid good-bye to her husband with swimming eyes.

As she was very beautifully done up, the husband felt sorry to part with her. But he could say only, "Get out of here," by force of circumstances. When the wife was about to go dolefully out the front door, he exclaimed, "No, you shouldn't go out the front door!"

Then, as the wife was going out the back door, he cried again, "No, no. You cannot use that door, either!"

"Then, there is no other door for me to get out," complained the wife.
"If there isn't any, why don't you stay here?"

•

Priest / "Your cheek is stained with rouge, father."
"Really? It is the ointment I applied to a cut on the cheek." So saying, the Buddhist priest wiped his cheek.
"But, father, your lips are smeared with something red, too."
"Save your breath to cool your porridge! It is blood I licked, as it ran from the cut on my cheek!"

•

Peddler / A peddler went on through a crowded thoroughfare, crying, "Puddings, sugar puddings! The most delicate morsels in all Japan!"
But a passerby chanced to overhear the peddler grumbling that he was so hungry.
"Why don't yer eat some of your puddings?"
"My puddings? Are you crazy? How on earth can I eat such sour stuff as these!"

•

Under a Bridge / It was New Year's Eve and bitter cold. A beggar and his wife were huddled together as usual under a bridge, listening to the endless bustle of people walking on the dribge. The wife asked, "What is this endless parade on the bridge, my dear?"
"Why, it's the bill-collectors running about all the night trying to clear accounts for the year."
"I see. They may get a large sum of money, I don't doubt, but it must be a rather hard job going round on such a cold night as this. I'd rather be here all night."
To this, her husband responded proudly, "Well, you know whom you may thank for your happy lot, don't you, woman?"

•

Stammerer / During the ceremony of New Year's Day a stammerer was scattering parched beans to drive out evil spirits from the house and to bring new luck in.
"In w-w-with l-l-luck! Out w-w-with th-th-the d-d-de-m-m . . . "
The demon, standing in the doorway, asked impatiently, "Look alive! Shall I go out, or shall I stay?"

PROVERBS

A rosy face in the morning; white bones in the evening.

Even new tatami [floor-mats], when thoroughly beaten, will give out dust.

Meeting is the beginning of parting.

There is no medicine for a fool.

The poor have many children.

What you wish for is the size of a stick and what you are granted is only the size of a needle.

He that hates a monk hates his surplice too.

A nail that sticks out is hammered.

Fellow patients pity one another.

A group of blind men feeling an elephant.

Dumplings rather than blossoms.

Believe only half what you hear.

Charming women who have a smile for everybody are cold-hearted.

Soft-Hearted / Three hen-pecked husbands were drinking together and complaining about their situation. Finally they reached an agreement to fight for improvement of their matrimonial standing.

At that juncture, the shrews stormed in and were about to strangle their chicken-hearted husbands. Two of the terror-stricken husbands ran away, but the last one remained behind sitting upright in his chair.

The runaways peeped in the room and were immediately moved to admiration.

"Really and truly, he is a dashing hero! A real man!"

After the vixens' raid was over, the two men quietly approached their hero.

"Bravo, you are a courageous man. You're a hero."

So saying, they came nearer to him, only to find him dead from fright.

•

Teetotaler / "I heard you took the pledge."

"Yes, I did. I signed the pledge for five years' abstinence."

"It must be very inconvenient. How would it be if you made it ten years and abstained from drinking for the daytime only?"

"That's not a bad idea, but I think I'll make it twenty years and drink day and night."

•

Poor Preacher / The long boring sermon of the head priest was over at last. After the audience left the hall of the temple, a woman, seemingly on the wrong side of forty, remained alone. The priest was greatly moved by the religious piety of the woman, and was about to accost her. At that moment, the woman looked up at the priest with sleepy eyes, and whispered:

"My gracious! The priest of yesterday is still here!"

•

Fire Guard / When the night-watchman returned to the guard-shed after his round, he discovered a man by the shed who was preparing to hang himself with a rope. Challenged by the watchman, the would-be suicide begged, "Please, for mercy's sake, let me die. Please go and let me alone."

When some cash was slipped into the hand, the guard urged, "I understand. Hang yourself quickly and be off!"

•

Everyday Use / A girl came to a man and said, "I heard your cat has kittens. Won't you give one to me?"

"Sure, take this."

"But this one is not very pretty. Please give me a prettier one."

"Bear with it, miss, and I'll get you a better one before long. Until then, make it a week-day cat."

POETRY

Senryu

translated by R. H. Blyth

The senryu is a satiric poem with the same form as the haiku, five syllables in the first line, seven in the second, and five in the third. Just as some Western scholars have contended that the satiric verse of Swift, Pope, and Dryden is not really poetry, so some Japanese scholars have argued that senryu also belong on a lower level of aesthetic achievement than genuine poetic expression attains. The argument is as relevant—or as irrelevant—in Japan as in the West, and its resolution remains largely subjective. People who like satiric verse and senryu accept them as poetry; people who dislike them are entitled to their blind spot.

The senryu is often pure satire—criticism, exposé, cynical realism permeate its content. There is no sentiment in the senryu-writer's temperament, no romanticism in his motivation, no illusion in his image of the world. He focuses on the seamy side of existence, debunks the affectations of society, exposes the rationalizations of mankind, and parodies the gentleness of haiku. Like Western satire, the senryu concentrates on man and society rather than nature and infinity, and, simply by its choice of material, exaggerates the unhappiness and duplicity of man, the defects of his institutions, and the inadequacy of philosophy and religion to provide consolation.

Obviously, the epigrammatic quality of senryu intensifies its effect—a flash of insight, then nothing. The reader has to do the judging for himself, has to make his own evaluations, for the writer of the senryu is not didactic. The poet simply gives us a glimpse of reality; we have to evaluate it ourselves, in terms of our own temperament and philosophy. Still, it is revealing to observe how many of the most effective senryu depend primarily on the expression of an unexpected truth.

All the following verses are from R. H. Blyth's Senryu: Japanese Satirical Verses.

He is a winter fly,
Disliked,
But long-lived.
—KIKAKU

In winter,
People say,
Summer is better.
—ONITSURA

The wife of the cricket
Bemoans, perchance,
His being eaten by a ca.
—KIKAKU

In the New Year,
About midnight,
I met a coffin.
—SHIKI

Even when the courtezan farts,
She does it
As a favor.

Someone trying his sword on a chance wayfarer,
Jizo[1]
Calmly gazing on.

Snow viewing—
Till we tumble to the fact
That we are fools.[2]

Welcoming the emperor—
Right in front of my nose
Comes a horse's hindquarters!

Round the roast sweet-potatoes,
Speaking ill
Of other people.

—EISHI

They [children] do not become
Mad
For their parents.

When she dresses it well
She is spoken ill of—
The widow's hair.

"If you want to die, die!"
The daughter says,
Cruelly.

The lap-dog barks
At the matrimonial quarrel—
How funny it is!

The bachelor
Kills the mosquitoes
In earnest.

—SANTARO

"The one behind is not crowded,"
Says the tram conductor,
As he goes off.

—KANAME

The pawn-shop,
Seeing his intention,
Won't lend what he asks.

She stops playing the harp,
And takes away
Some of the fire-wood.

On the scaffold;
Seventy million—
Now one less.

While they are out cherry-blossom-viewing—
Quietly, calmly,
Looking for lice.

Time was,
When in this mirror
I was charmed by myself.

—MAMEBO

All the town
Knows about it,
Except the husband.

The widow's pawning;
She begins
With the man's things.

The wife was sent away;
But her mother
Makes out she just left.

"Do take out your teeth
Once more!"
Begs the grandchild.

—SHUNU

The *Kamuro* [young prostitute]
Offers up a prayer:—
Not to be pinched!

The Zen sect;
Catching the fleas
After the religious meditation.

1. Stone statue of Jizo, god of mercy, patron of children and travelers. His statues are usually in lonely places.

2. Parody of a famous haiku by Basho: "Now then / Let's go snow-viewing / Till we tumble over!"

When the teacher turns
  To the blackboard,
He yawns.
—ISAN

A difficult piece of work;
  The dentist
Opens his mouth too.
—GOROSUKE

The rickshaw-man
  Gives another rickshaw-man
A ride.
—ITTO

Farting—
  There's nothing funny about it
When you're living alone.

When we want to cherish
  Our parents,
They are no more.

The place of suicide being decided,
  There is nothing left
To say.
—EMPEKI

While having
  His fortune told,
His pocket was picked.
—URATO

The candidate
  Sets up his temporary office
In his concubine's house.
—KURAKU

At the bargain sale of toys,
  Adults only
Gather.
—ISORO

Four or five people,
  Inconvenienced
By the horse farting on the ferry-boat.

He is seen by the doctor's assistant,
  Thinking in his heart,
"What can this ignoramus do?"

Kindly giving advice,
  The pickpocket also
Got on the train.
—GOYO

Buying a prostitute
  That told no lies,
I felt lonely.

Losing his job,
  He tries reading
Marx.
—SAZANKA

The night
  She goes to the theater,
She dislikes her husband.
—HAMMONSEN

The farewell note,
  Left
Where it can be easily found.

Gathering together the ashes,
  Weeping, weeping,
Looking for the gold teeth.
—AMEMBO

Calling to offer condolences,
  And bringing a child dressed
Like the dead child.
—SANGEN

Business at its lowest ebb—
  But the cherry blossoms
Come out just the same.
—KENKABO

The servant is most respectful,
  Not knowing
He is the insurance man.
—KAHYO

Too much affection;
The doll's head
Has come off!
—SHUMMU

Already neither the excuse
Nor the length of the sash
Will reach.

The one who only taps
At the doctor's door
Must have come on some ordinary business.

The parasite;
What he says in his sleep
Is the truth.

When the cook
Becomes a guest,
He talks too much.

When the courtezan "comes out,"
She is popular
For seventy-five days.

Recovering,
He became just as stingy
As before.

For the dependent,
It is miserable to eat,
And painful not to eat.

"Why can't he say it
In plain words?"
Thinks the widow.

There is a useless laughter
In the greetings
Of women.

The cherry-blossom season;
They put more food
In the dish for the cat.

She blows the nose
Of the playing child,
As if screwing it off.

The convalescent
Gets into the habit
Of expecting everything to be done for him.

Even with thunder and lightning,
Some is well done,
Some unskillfully.

How different the teasing
Of the father-in-law,
And the mother-in-law!

During the sermon
She consults with her mother
About going to the toilet.

The one who pays the rent
Early in the month
Is a concubine.

The hanger-on
Goes next door
To get angry.

Nothing intimates
In the appearance of the just-washed hair
That it will turn white.[1]

A flea
Makes the most faithful woman
Undo her sash.

The day after the divorce
He keeps on having
To look for things.

For a courtezan,
One pillow
Is the most shameful of all things.

1. This may be a parody of Basho's famous haiku: "Nothing intimates, / In the voice of the cicada, / That it will soon die."

Even Buddha
  Cannot save
Those without money.

The disciple of the surgeon
  Wishes somebody
To get hurt.

A visitor came,
  So the scolding stopped,
And was put off for a while.

The well-digger comes up
  And the roofer comes down
To have a meal.

There they sit in the boat,
  Floating over a suicide's watery grave,
Playing the samisen romance.

The flea
  Chooses just the place
We can't reach to scratch.

—KABAN

The lady teacher
  Does not look as though
She would ever fart.

They do not treat their daughter-in-law
  As gently
As they do the kutani.[1]

—AIKYOSHI

Insects too
  Think that this world
Is theirs alone.

—TOMEI

The Bible
  Can be read in such a way
As to permit the atomic bomb.

—GYOTEN

The tongue yearns
  For the pulled-out tooth,
Going there so often.

—TSUMETO

"I am at a loss
  About the lavatory,"
Says the armoured warrior.

"It was a mistake!"
  The pock-marked courtezan
Sits down again.

The laundryman eats
  By the dirt
Of his neighbours.

If you hang round
  Your wife too much,
She will think little of you.

I look into the mirror
  At my old age,
With trepidation.

He returns from abroad,
  Having seen
All he understands.

—JUGOYA

Something lost:
  The policeman asked about it in detail,
And that was all.

—GAKUJIN

"Be like me!"
  "Be not like me!"
Thoughts for the child.

—MICHIRO

The New Year greeting card;
  It reminds me
I owe him a small sum of money.

—JAKURO

Blind people
  Wipe away one another's
Secret tears.

—KOHO

Afraid of death,
  But not surprised
At that of others.

—UYURO

1. Kutani-yaki is a kind of pottery made in the Kanazawa district. It is rather elaborate and ornamental.

A dog
  Bringing up the rear
Of a short funeral procession.
—SOEI

Opening the window,
  The owner of the house
Intends to make him buy the view too.
—OKAKI

They were once
  In love with each other;
Now they are yawning.
—IKUO

How sensitive
  The bottom of the socks:
A grain of boiled rice!
—AMEMBO

Yes,
  I said I didn't mind poverty,
But . . .
—YOSHIKO

Long, long ago,
  How delighted I was
To have a fountain-pen!
—REIGETSU

Giving in, giving in,
  Serving in an office
For twenty years!
—AMEMBO

There is no word
  "Buffoon"[1]
In the Education Department reader.
—YONEMBO

When we give back
  What we borrowed,
We feel as if we have been robbed.
—SANKAKUSHI

Other Verse Forms

translated by R. H. Blyth and Kenneth Rexroth

The following poems are typically brief, wryly detached, tinged with melancholy. Like most Japanese poets, the writers of these verses tend to avoid direct moralizing and explicit commentary. The purpose of the Japanese poet has traditionally been to imply, to hint, to let the reader complete the meaning of the poem himself. This kind of delicate innuendo is very hard to convey in translation, and all of these poems are more subtle in their original form. The technique of the Japanese poems suffers in English presentation, but the relevance and universality of the content come through clearly enough. The first five translations are by R. H. Blyth and the rest by Kenneth Rexroth.

When I say, "I love you!"
To get some money out of him,
He says he would give me his life—
  That I don't want in the least.

1. The *hokan* is the man who makes visitors laugh at the Yoshiwara [a pleasure quarter of Tokyo]. Such words are never found in schoolbooks. That is to say, these books are lying and hypocritical; that is to say, the whole school system is lying and hypocritical.

On the way to death—
  But he is avoiding
The mud of the road.

To see Mount Fuji
  In a dream—
What a blessing!
  No weariness of the journey,
  No travelling expenses.

No parents,
  No children,
Not much money.
  I don't wish for anything,
  But I don't want to die.

Though I should live
  To be a hundred,
The same world, the same cherry-blossoms;
  The moon is round,
  The snow is white.

I think of the days
Before I met her
When I seemed to have
No troubles at all.
—FUJIWARA NO ATSUTADA (10th cen.)

A strange old man
Stops me,
Looking out of my deep mirror.
—HITOMARO (7th–8th cen.)

May those who are born after me
Never travel such roads of love.
—HITOMARO

I dreamed I held
A sword against my flesh.
What does it mean?
It means I shall see you soon.
—LADY KASA (8th cen.)

I may live on until
I long for this time

In which I am so unhappy,
And remember it fondly.
—FUJIWARA NO KIYOSUKE (12th cen.)

I have always known
That at last I would
Take this road, but yesterday
I did not know that it would be today.
—NARIHIRA (9th cen.)

You say, "I will come."
And you do not come.
Now you say, "I will not come."
So I shall expect you.
Have I learned to understand you?
—LADY OTOMO NO SAKANOE (8th cen.)

She said she would come
At once, and so I waited
Till the moon rose
In the October dawn.
—SOSEI (9th cen.)

That spring night I spent
Pillowed on your arm
Never really happened
Except in a dream.
Unfortunately I am.
Talked about anyway.
—LADY SUO (11th cen.)

No, the human heart
Is unknowable.
But in my birthplace
The flowers still smell
The same as always.
—TSURAYUKI (10th cen.)

DRAMA (KYOGEN)

The following six plays are all Kyogen, taken from Shio Sakanishi's book of translations The Ink-Smeared Lady and Other Kyogen. *Kyogen are short plays performed in the intervals between Noh plays to provide comic relief for the audience. They are in colloquial speech, the comic plot always depends on situation rather than character, and the humor is often physical. In spite of the insistence by scholars that Kyogen are never farces and should never include vulgar words or gestures, many of the performances have in fact made use of low humor and obscene innuendo. Since Kyogen-like entertainments were well known on the Japanese stage a thousand years ago, they are considered by some critics the earliest form of humorous literature in Japan.*

In the introduction to her book, Shio Sakanishi suggests that the Kyogen originated in "some primitive forms of religious worship. . . . To beguile the sun goddess, Amaterasu, from her hiding place in a rock cave, the lesser deities gathered before her cave and made merry with mimic dances and music." Whatever its origin, critics continued to demand for the Kyogen a higher aesthetic achievement than in fact it ever provided. Zeami, for example, thought that the Kyogen should exhibit subtlety, understatement, and refinement; the dialogue should be appropriate even for aristocratic audiences and vulgarity should never be introduced.

Okura Toraaki, a seventeenth-century actor, had an even nobler objective in mind: truth should be the source of Kyogen material; the comic interlude should provide genuine laughter by drawing upon the lives of ordinary men and women, transforming "the real into the unreal" by exaggerating familiar defects, not to reform or to moralize but simply to provide a detached observer's perspective.[1]

Among the most frequent types in the Kyogen are the stupid master, the shrewd servant, the cowardly warrior, the shrewish wife, the fool, the sensual monk—stereotyped characters whom the audiences immediately recognize and to whom they feel superior.

The Ink-Smeared Lady

Anon. / Shio Sakanishi

CHARACTERS: Feudal Lord, his attendant Taro, the Lord's Mistress.

LORD: I am a famous feudal lord of a distant province. I have been in the capital

1. Ueda, "Toraaki and His Theory of Comedy." *Journal of Aesthetics and Art Criticism,* vol. XXIV (1965), pp. 19–26.

very long on a lawsuit, but finally it was decided in my favor, and luckily a vast new territory was added to my possession. Nothing delights me more than this. First I will call Taro boy and share the joy of this auspicious event with him.

Yai, Yai! Is Taro boy around?

TARO: Ha!

LORD: Where are you?

TARO: In your presence.

LORD: It is nothing special. Our long stay in the capital comes to an end with the court decision in my favor. A vast new territory was added to my possession. Is not this a very happy day?

TARO: It is indeed a happy day. I wish to congratulate you.

LORD: Now this means that I have to go home soon. That, by the by, reminds me I must make a farewell call on my lady in town, for once back in the province, I do not know when I can see her again. What do you think?

TARO: That will be a very good plan, sir.

LORD: Then I shall go. You accompany me.

TARO: Very well.

LORD: Come!

TARO: I am coming!

LORD: When my wife in the province hears this good news, she will be waiting for my homecoming day and night.

TARO: She must, indeed.

Oh, sir, we are already here. Shall I announce your arrival? Please wait here.

LORD: All right.

TARO: Please, your lord has come.

MISTRESS: Ha! There is an unfamiliar voice outside.

Oh, is that you, Taro? My lord is here, did you say?

TARO: Yes, madam.

MISTRESS: Oh! This is most unexpected. Pray, what lucky wind has brought you here? How have you been? As I had not seen you for a long while, I had certain misgivings.

LORD: Oh, I am happy to find you well. I have not seen you for a long while, have I?

By the by, Taro boy, shall I tell her about our news?

TARO: I believe there is no harm in telling her that.

MISTRESS: What could it be? Oh, I have fears.

LORD: Oh, no! It is nothing very important. We have been in the capital for a long while about the lawsuit, but finally it was decided in our favor today. As I must be going home soon, I came to say farewell.

MISTRESS: Alas, what do I hear? Going back home! Then I shall not be able to see you again. How sad this is! *(She secretly draws to her a little water basin in the writing box. Putting a few drops on her face, she pretends to cry bitterly.)*

LORD: Your deep grief touches me, but even if I go home, I shall be coming back soon. Therefore be of good cheer and wait for me. *(He weeps too.)*

MISTRESS: You say so now, but once back home, you will not even think of me. This is very sad indeed.

TARO: What do I see? I thought she was really crying, but she is just putting water on her face. What an odious shrew she is!

Pardon me, my lord! Will you come this way, just a moment?

LORD: What is the matter?

TARO: Do you think she is really weeping? If you do, you are wrong. That's only plain water from the writing box.

LORD: Don't talk such nonsense to me! The poor thing is really crying because she must part with me.

MISTRESS: Oh, my dear lord! Where have you gone? 'Tis only a little while together we can be. Please come here.

LORD: I am sorry. Taro boy had something to tell me, so I went over there. The fool was talking nonsense.

TARO: It's incredible not to see through the woman's trick. Well, I have a scheme. We will see who is right. *(Removing the water basin he puts an ink-well in its place.)*

MISTRESS: I am so loath to part with you even a few hours, but now this is going to be our last meeting! Oh, so very sad and miserable!

TARO: This is fun. Not knowing my trick, now she is putting ink all over her face. Just look at that face!

Oh, please, my lord! Will you step this way just a moment?

LORD: What is the matter?

TARO: Because you did not believe what I told you, I replaced the water basin with an ink-well. Just look at that face, please!

LORD: You are right, my boy! I was a fool to be so easily tricked and duped. What can I do to that deceitful woman? Oh, yes. I will give her my hand-mirror as a keepsake. That ought to put her to shame.

TARO: That is a splendid idea.

LORD: Well, when I go home and settle down, I shall send for you as soon as possible, but till then I shall leave this mirror as a keepsake. Treasure it. Here, please accept my gift.

MISTRESS: Oh, I am so wretched! I never thought I should have to accept a keepsake from you. This is a melancholy life indeed. *(She looks in the mirror.)* What! Who smeared ink on my face? How maddening! Did you do it?

LORD: Oh, no! I know nothing about it. That's Taro's devilment.

MISTRESS: That's not going to excuse you. You cannot get away so easily as that. I must smear your face. *(She smears him.)*

LORD: It is outrageous to blacken my face. Forgive me, forgive me. *(He runs away.)*

MISTRESS: Hey, Taro, where are you? I will blacken your dirty face, too. *(She catches Taro.)*

TARO: It is terrible to have my face blackened like this. Pardon, pardon!

MISTRESS: Never, never! Don't let the rascal get away. Catch him, catch him!

The Ribs and the Cover

Anon. / Shio Sakanishi

CHARACTERS: Priest, Novice, First Visitor, Second Visitor, Third Visitor.

PRIEST: I am the priest of this temple. I have something to say to my assistant. Is the novice around? Where are you?

NOVICE: Right here. What do you wish?

PRIEST: It is nothing special. But as I grow older I feel weary of bearing many burdens. This very day I am going to retire and make you responsible for the temple.

NOVICE: I am indeed greatly obliged to you for this honor, but I have not gone very far in my learning. Perhaps it would be better not to decide upon this important matter just now.

PRIEST: I call that a very gracious answer. But even if I retire, I shall be right here, and if any important matter comes up, you can always consult me.

NOVICE: In that case, I will obey your command.

PRIEST: Needless to say, you must try to find favor in the eyes of our patrons and make the temple prosperous.

NOVICE: Rest assured. I shall do my best.

PRIEST: That's good. I am retiring now. If you wish to ask me anything, come and do so. If any patrons call, let me know.

NOVICE: Very good, sir.

Well, well! I have been wondering when the priest intended to retire, but never suspected that such good luck would befall me this very day. The patrons of the temple will be happy to hear this, and I shall do my best to win their good will.

FIRST VISITOR: I am a villager who dwells in this vicinity. I am on my way to do an errand. But the sky turns dark suddenly, and I fear it is going to rain. I will stop at my temple and borrow an umbrella. Oh, here I am. Please! Please!

NOVICE: How do you do? I am very happy to see you.

FIRST VISITOR: I have been neglecting to call, but how is the priest? And you? I hope you are both well.

NOVICE: We are both very well. By the by, the priest has decided to retire, giving me full responsibility for the temple. Please come often.

FIRST VISITOR: I congratulate you! Had I known, I should have come especially to wish you success.

As to my present visit, I was on my way to the village, but suddenly it looked as if it were going to rain. Could you let me have an umbrella?

NOVICE: Certainly. Please wait a moment.

FIRST VISITOR: Oh! Very many thanks.

NOVICE: Here, then! I will let you have this.

FIRST VISITOR: Thank you so much.

NOVICE: If there is anything of any kind that I can do for you, please let me know.

FIRST VISITOR: Certainly. I will call on you for assistance.

NOVICE: Are you going?

FIRST VISITOR: Yes. Good-bye!

NOVICE: Good-bye!

FIRST VISITOR: I am much obliged to you.

NOVICE: I am glad you came in.

FIRST VISITOR: Ah! Well! I am glad I did.

Now I must hurry.

NOVICE: The priest told me to let him know if any of the patrons came. I will go and tell him.

Please, sir! Are you in?

PRIEST: Yes, I am here.

NOVICE: You must be feeling very dull.

PRIEST: No, not very.

NOVICE: Somebody has just been here.

PRIEST: Did he come to worship, or was it that he had some business?

NOVICE: He came to borrow an umbrella, and I let him have one.

PRIEST: That was quite right, but tell me. Which umbrella did you let him have?

NOVICE: The new one that we got the other day.

PRIEST: You are a careless fellow. Would anybody ever dream of lending an umbrella which I have not used yet? The case will present itself again. When you do not wish to lend it, you can always find a good excuse.

NOVICE: What would you say?

PRIEST: You should say: "It would be no trouble to lend it to you, but recently my master went out with it and encountered a gust of wind at the crossing. The storm tore the ribs and the cover apart. So I tied them both by the middle and hung them up to the ceiling. I am afraid they would be of little use to you." You should say something like that, with an air of truth about it.

NOVICE: I understand. Next time I shall certainly remember what you have told me.

Now I must go.

PRIEST: Must you go? Good-bye!

NOVICE: Good-bye!

That is very queer. Whatever my master says, it does seem strange to refuse to lend a thing when you have it by you.

SECOND VISITOR: I live in this vicinity. As I have to go to a far-off place, I mean to stop at the temple and borrow a horse. I will go quickly. Ah! Here I am. Please! Please!

NOVICE: There is someone calling at the gate again. Who is asking for admittance? Who is calling?

SECOND VISITOR: It is I.

NOVICE: How do you do? I am happy to see you.

SECOND VISITOR: My present reason for calling you is just this. I am going to a far-off place today, and although it is a bold request to make, I should be greatly obliged if you could let me have your horse.

NOVICE: Nothing could be slighter than your request. But unfortunately a few days ago my master went out with it and encountered a gust of wind at the crossing. The storm tore the ribs and the cover apart. So I tied them by the middle and hung them up to the ceiling. I am afraid they would be of little use to you.

SECOND VISITOR: But I am speaking of the horse.

NOVICE: Precisely. I, too, am speaking about the horse.

SECOND VISITOR: Well! Then there is no help for it. I must be going.

NOVICE: Must you go?

SECOND VISITOR: Yes! Good-bye!

NOVICE: I am so glad you dropped in. Good-bye!

SECOND VISITOR: Well! I never! He says things that I cannot at all understand.

NOVICE: As I told this man exactly what the priest told me to say, I am sure my master will be pleased.

Pardon me! Are you in?

PRIEST: Yes, I am in. What can I do for you?

NOVICE: Someone has just been here to borrow a horse.

PRIEST: Fortunately no one is using it today. Did you let him take it?

NOVICE: Oh, no! I told him exactly what you had instructed me to say.

PRIEST: What! I do not remember saying anything about the horse. What did you tell him?

NOVICE: I said that a few days ago my master went out with it and encountered a gust of wind at the crossing; that the storm tore the ribs and the cover apart. So I tied them by the middle and hung them up to the ceiling. I was afraid they would be of little use to him.

PRIEST: What do you mean? That was what I told you to say when someone came to borrow an umbrella. But would anybody ever dream of saying such a thing to a person who would come to borrow a horse? When you do not wish to lend it, you can make a fitting excuse.

NOVICE: Tell me what I should say.

PRIEST: You should say: "We have recently put our horse out to spring grass, and he has gone stark mad, breaking his hip bone. Just at present he is lying in the corner of the stable under a straw mat. I fear he is not going to be of much service to you." You should say something like that, with an air of truth about it.

NOVICE: I shall keep it in mind. Next time I shall say something like that.

PRIEST: Be sure you do not say anything stupid.

NOVICE: What can this mean? I was ordered to say it, and when I did say it, I got a scolding! This is the most troublesome thing.

THIRD VISITOR: I am a resident in this neighborhood, and I am on my way to the temple where I have some business.

Ah! Here I am. Please! Please!

NOVICE: There is someone calling at the gate again. Who is that asking for admittance? Who is it?

THIRD VISITOR: It is I.

NOVICE: Oh, I am so glad you came.

THIRD VISITOR: I have not called on you for a long time. I hope both the priest and you have been well.

NOVICE: Oh, yes! We both continue well. By the by, I do not know what prompted the priest, but suddenly he has turned the whole responsibility of the temple to me and retired. I hope you will come as often as before.

THIRD VISITOR: I congratulate you indeed. Had I known it, I should have come especially to congratulate you.

Today I came on business. Tomorrow is the religious anniversary of our family, and I shall be greatly honored if both the priest and you can come.

NOVICE: To be sure, I can. As to the priest, I am afraid he cannot come.

THIRD VISITOR: Has he a previous engagement?

NOVICE: No! But recently we have been putting him out to spring grass, and he has gone stark mad and has broken his hip bone. At present he is lying in the corner of the stable under a straw mat. I fear he is not going to be of very much service to you.

THIRD VISITOR: But it is the priest that I am talking about.

NOVICE: Precisely! I am speaking about the priest.

THIRD VISITOR: Well! I am very sorry to hear that. Then you will come?

NOVICE: Most certainly, I will come.

THIRD VISITOR: Now I must go.

NOVICE: Must you? Good-bye!

THIRD VISITOR: Well, well! He says things that I cannot make out at all.

NOVICE: This time I did as I was instructed, and the priest ought to be pleased.

If you please, are you in?

PRIEST: Yes, I am in. Is it on business that you come?

NOVICE: Somebody has just been here to ask both you and me to go to him tomorrow to attend a religious anniversary in his family. So I said that I would go, but that you would hardly be able to do so.

PRIEST: Luckily, I have no engagement tomorrow, and I should like to go.

NOVICE: But I said what you had instructed me to say.

PRIEST: I do not remember. What did you tell him?

NOVICE: I said that you had been put out to spring grass, but had gone stark mad and broken your hip bone. At present you were lying in the corner of the stable under a straw mat. I said I feared that you could not come.

PRIEST: Did you really and truly say that to him?

NOVICE: YES! Really and truly.

PRIEST: Well, I never! Say what you will, you are a perfect dunce. No matter how many times I say a thing, nothing seems to make you understand. I told you to say that when anyone came to borrow a horse.

The end of all this is that it will never do for you to become a priest. Get out!

NOVICE: Oh!

PRIEST: Won't you get out? Won't you get out? Won't you?

NOVICE: Ouch! Ouch! O-u-c-h!

But sir! Even if you are my master, it is a great shame for you to beat me like this. For all you are the man you are, you cannot tell me that you have not gone stark mad.

PRIEST: When have I ever gone stark mad? If I ever was, out with it quick! Out with it!

NOVICE: If I were to tell it, you would be put to shame.

PRIEST: I know nothing that could put me to shame. If there is, out with it quick, quick!

NOVICE: Well then, I will tell it.

PRIEST: Hurry up!

NOVICE: Well! A while ago Mistress Ichi who lives across from the temple gate came to call . . .

PRIEST: What has Ichi got to do with me?

NOVICE: But please listen! You beckoned to her and disappeared with her into your dwelling quarters. Do you not call a priest who did such a thing stark mad?

PRIEST: You rascal! Inventing things I never did, you put your master out of countenance. After this, by the Hachiman God with his bow and arrows, I shall not let you escape me.

NOVICE: Even if you are my master, I cannot be put down so easily as that.

BOTH: Ah! Ah! Ah!

NOVICE: Have you learned a lesson? Oh! I am happy. I've won. I've won.

PRIEST: Hey, hey! Where are you going after putting your master in such a plight? Is there no one there? Catch him! Do not let him get away!

Plop! Click!

Anon. / Shio Sakanishi

CHARACTERS: Koto, Kikuichi, Passerby.

KOTO: I am a Koto[1] who dwells in this vicinity. Now I will call Kikuichi and consult with him. Is Kikuichi around?

KIKUICHI: Coming!

KOTO: Where are you?

KIKUICHI: Right here.

KOTO: It is nothing very special that I want you for. As I have not been out for a long while, time seems to hang heavily on my hands. I wish to take a short sight-seeing trip. What do you think about it?

KIKUICHI: To tell you the truth, I was just going to suggest it to you. It is an excellent idea.

KOTO: Then let us go. Get ready a sakè flask.

KIKUICHI: Very well. The sakè flask is ready.

KOTO: Let us go at once. Come!

KIKUICHI: I am ready.

KOTO: What do you think? It must strike some people as ridiculous to see blind men like us go on a sight-seeing trip. But going to a new place changes one's mood and is pleasant.

1. By an edict of 1547, two official ranks were created for educated blind men, such as musicians and scholars, the first being Kengyo and the second Koto.

KIKUICHI: No one, I am sure, will think us ridiculous. Therefore, whenever you are so moved, we must have as many such jaunts as possible. They do you much good, Master.

KOTO: Already we are out of town. We must be out in the open fields. It is rather lonesome here.

KIKUICHI: This is indeed an open field.

KOTO: When I am in the open plain my heart expands, and I feel light-hearted.

KIKUICHI: As you say, it is very delightful.

KOTO: Listen! I have long been intending to tell you that you cannot forever be singing little ditties and reciting light tales. How about practicing the *Battle of the Heike,*[1] the famous epic?

KIKUICHI: I have been hoping to ask your help in that matter. Fortunately now you have brought the subject up yourself. If you can teach me that, I shall be exceedingly grateful to you.

KOTO: Then I will. Since there seems to be no one around, I will recite a verse for you.

KIKUICHI: That is very kind of you. I shall listen.

KOTO: "Now the battle of Ichi no Tani had come to a crisis, and there was a great combat. The noble Heike, alas, were defeated, and the warriors of the Genji, eager to win fame, crashed forward in their attack. The Heike fell like wheat before the scythe. What bloodshed! What confusion! Some had their chins cut off; some their heels. Confused amidst the din of cries and groans, they clapped the severed heels on their bleeding chins and the severed chins on their bleeding heels. Ah, the strange sight indeed! Three or four hundred battle-scarred soldiers with beards on their heels and blisters on their chins! . . ."

KIKUICHI: That is indeed very marvelous. I am happy to have heard it.

KOTO: Let us go a little further. Come, follow me!

KIKUICHI: I am following.

KOTO: There are many who chant the *Heike,* but none I know can do it well. So you must practice hard.

KIKUICHI: I will practice very hard, and I hope you will again instruct me.

KOTO: If I should be appointed to the position of a "Kengyo," I shall try to make you a "Koto."

KIKUICHI: That is very good of you, to be sure.

KOTO: What? I hear the ripple of water. We must be near a river.

KIKUICHI: True, it seems like a river.

KOTO: We must cross over. What had we better do?

KIKUICHI: Indeed what should we do?

PASSERBY *(aside):* I dwell nearby here. As I have a little business across the mountains, I must hasten. What! Two blind men are going to cross the river. I wonder how they are going to do it. I will stop and watch them a while.

KOTO: Come! Throw a stone and try the depth of the river.

KIKUICHI: Very well. Eh, there it goes. *Plop!*

KOTO: Very deep there.

1. Fought in the province of Settsu in the year 1185.

KIKUICHI: It is exceedingly deep there.

KOTO: Try another direction.

KIKUICHI: Very well. Eh, there it goes. *Click!*

KOTO: Shallow there.

KIKUICHI: Indeed, it seems shallow there.

KOTO: Then let us wade through. Come!

KIKUICHI: But, master, will you wait just a moment?

KOTO: What is the matter?

KIKUICHI: I will carry you on my back.

KOTO: Oh, no. That is not necessary. You follow me.

KIKUICHI: But I am here with you to do just such service. It is for the good of my soul. Please let me carry you.

KOTO: No, no. Since you too cannot see, there might be an accident. We will hold on to each other and wade. Come!

KIKUICHI: But this is my only chance to be of real service to you. I must carry you on my back.

KOTO: Since you insist, I shall let you carry me. But first we must get ready. Prepare yourself then.

KIKUICHI: Very well.

PASSERBY *(aside)*: How clever the blind men are! They try the depth of water with pebbles. I am a lucky dog. I am going to be carried across. *(He climbs on Kikuichi's back.)*

KIKUICHI: Please hang on to me tightly. Now I am going to wade into the water. I hope it is not going to be very deep.

Very good indeed. I have done it with perfect ease, and I am glad we had no accident.

PASSERBY *(aside)*: This was really an unexpected fortune. I am very happy.

KOTO: Hello, Kikuichi! How about it? Are you ready? No answer? I cannot understand this. Ki-ku-i-chi! Where-are-you?

KIKUICHI: Y-e-s!

KOTO: Why don't you carry me across quickly?

KIKUICHI: But I have just carried you across.

PROVERBS

Poor preachers talk long.

When you see a stranger, suspect him to be a thief.

Even the face of Buddha must not be slapped a third time.

Trials in Hell too depend on money. (Even Yama, king of hell, is influenced by money.)

Ten men, ten colors. ("So many men, so many minds.")

New Year gate decoration pines are a milestone in life's journey to Hades.

To have one's hand bitten by one's own dog.

Jizo's face in borrowing, Emma's face in repaying. (Jizo, guardian deity of children, is cheerful. Emma, or Yama, is king of hell and judge of the dead.)

When victorious, the imperial army; when defeated, a rebel army. ("Might is right.")

KOTO: Carried me across? I was just getting ready. You have not carried me across yet. The miserable wretch has gone over all by himself.

KIKUICHI *(hurrying back to the other side)*: When did you cross over on this side again, Master?

KOTO: When, indeed! The wretch! He is backing out. Come quickly and take me over.

KIKUICHI: I cannot understand this at all. Well, I will cross over again. Now please climb up on my back.

KOTO: Be steady.

KIKUICHI: I am going to wade. This seems very deep.

KOTO: Be careful and steady.

KIKUICHI: Yes, yes. But how deep this is! Oh, help, help!

PASSERBY: This is highly entertaining. Poor wretches!

KOTO: Well, well, this is annoying. I am soaked to my bare skin. That was why I refused to be carried across.

KIKUICHI: I am very sorry. I will wring you out. Though I was going very cautiously, I stumbled. Please forgive me.

KOTO: It was pure accident, and no one can help that. Did anything happen to the sakè flask?

KIKUICHI: What did you say? Oh, the flask is here, quite safe.

KOTO: I am getting chilly. Pour me out a drink.

KIKUICHI: Very well.

PASSERBY: Another piece of good luck. I shall get a drink.

KIKUICHI: I am pouring. Glug, glug!

KOTO: Oh, that's enough. I shall forget the chill when I take this.

KIKUICHI: Of that I am quite certain.

PASSERBY *(aside)*: How delicious this is!

KOTO: Kikuichi, my boy! Why didn't you give me some?

KIKUICHI: But I did pour you some just now.

KOTO: I thought you did, but there is not a drop in my cup.

KIKUICHI: I simply cannot understand this. I will pour you some again. Have a cup brimful.

KOTO: All right. Be quick.

KIKUICHI: Very well. Glug, glug!

PASSERBY *(aside)*: Another treat! Marvelous sakè indeed!

KOTO: That is enough. You take some too.

KIKUICHI: May I? That is very kind of you. Wonderful sakè!

KOTO: Now why don't you pour for me?

KIKUICHI: But really I have just poured a cupful for you.

KOTO: I thought so, but again there is not a drop in it. You are a hateful rascal. Without giving me a drop, you are drinking it all by yourself.

KIKUICHI: That is not at all like my master's word. Why should I drink all by myself without giving it to my master? I fear you are falsely accusing me. You have had two cups already.

KOTO: You are a scoundrel. You not only cheat me of my drink but also accuse me of drinking behind your back. Pour me another.

KIKUICHI: Very well. But sorry! There is no more left.

KOTO: What! Not a drop left?

PASSERBY *(aside):* This is very amusing. I will make them quarrel. Bang! Bang!

KOTO: Ouch, ouch! This is outrageous. After cheating me of my drink, now you beat me.

KIKUICHI: What did you say? Beat you?

KOTO: You certainly did beat me.

KIKUICHI: I was just putting away the flask. My hand was not even pointed in your direction.

KOTO: Not even pointed in my direction? Who else do you think would beat me? Who else, I ask you.

KIKUICHI: Ouch, ouch! Not only do you accuse me of all things which I have no idea of doing, but you also beat me. Why do you beat the innocent?

KOTO: My hand was not even pointed in your direction.

KIKUICHI: Not even pointed in my direction! But who else could beat me? Pray, who else?

KOTO: Ouch, ouch! Hey, Kikuichi, why do you torture me?

KIKUICHI: My hands were right on my lap.

KOTO: Right on your lap? Whose hands could they be, indeed?

KIKUICHI: Ouch, ouch! Alas, my master abuses the innocent.

KOTO: What? Abuse you?

KIKUICHI: Indeed you do.

KOTO: My hand never even touched you.

KIKUICHI: Not even touched me? Who else would beat me like this?

KOTO: Ouch, ouch!

KIKUICHI: Ouch, ouch!

PASSERBY *(aside):* This is really fun. I am going to play all sorts of tricks on them. But look here! They are really fighting now. To stay here may be a bit dangerous. I must be going while there is still daylight.

KOTO: I have exhausted my patience. I shall not let you get away so easily.

KIKUICHI: Why should I be beaten?

BOTH: Oh-h-h!

KIKUICHI: Now shame on you, Master. I have got you. Goody, goody!

KOTO: Wait, wait! After beating his master to a pulp, he is running away. Is there no one here? Catch him, catch him! Do not let him get away!

Seed of Hojo

Anon. / Shio Sakanishi

CHARACTERS: Nephew, Uncle.

NEPHEW: I am an inhabitant of this vicinity. I have an uncle over across the mountain whom I often call on. He is such a clever storyteller that I am always taken in, and it is very provoking. But today I intend to make up a few good stories myself to dupe him.

Indeed, my uncle is a clever person. He tells so many stories that once in a while I should think he would repeat himself, but not so. I have never heard him tell a story which even resembles others. Tonight I have made up tall ones, and I am sure he cannot beat me this time.

As I amble along, here I am already. I must inquire.

Pardon me! Are you in?

UNCLE: Well, well! I have not seen you for a long while. What has been the trouble?

NEPHEW: Oh, I made a pilgrimage to Mt. Fuji recently, and that is why I had not called on you before.

UNCLE: That was very commendable of you. Was the journey up exciting?

NEPHEW: Indeed, it was very jolly.

By the by, Fuji is much larger and higher than I imagined.

UNCLE: It should be, for it's the most famous mountain in the world. Was there anything interesting?

NEPHEW: No, nothing special, but after we entered the province of Kai, we stayed overnight at the foot of the mountain. There was a crowd of pilgrims, and in the course of conversation, we younger men thought it would be fun to put a paper bag over Fuji. The older folks thought it impossible and laughed at us. Then we said we could.

Immediately the fellows brought out bamboo spoons, and each holding one in his mouth, two in his hands, and two more in his feet, we began to make paste. In no time we made it as high as the mountain. Next we collected all the paper from the provinces of Idzu and Suruga. First I thought we were to make a huge bag, but the fellows began to paste paper on the mountain, and in no time we were at the top of Fuji, which was all clothed with a paper bag. Wasn't that an unheard-of thing?

UNCLE: Oh, no! That is not so unusual. Last year when I went down to Omi Province, the young men brewed tea in Lake Biwa and drank up the whole lake.

NEPHEW: There you are up to your old tricks. How could they possibly drink the lake dry?

UNCLE: Listen. They said, "Let's make tea in the lake," and gathered up all the tea leaves, irrespective of their quality, from the five neighboring provinces. In no time there was a pile of tea leaves as high as Mikami Hill. Then they put it in the lake, and young fellows with mulberry brooms with handles one hundred feet long began to stir it. When it was done, they blew off froth and drank it up. In fact, they drank the whole lake dry, but the froth they blew off still remains and is known as Awazu ga Hara, Plain of Froth.

NEPHEW: Oh, but you are telling an old yarn again. The Plain of Awazu appears in the heroic tale of Kiso Yoshinaka.

UNCLE: But you don't know the New Plain of Awazu right beside it, which appeared last year.

NEPHEW: That's a lie.

UNCLE: If you think it a lie, you just go and look for it yourself.

NEPHEW: I shall not argue with you.

But please listen! A few years ago, when I went to the western part of the country,

I saw a bull that lay down in Innami Plain of Harima Province, and fed on the pastures of Awaji Island. Imagine feeding himself across those mountains, rivers, and sea. Don't you think it was an enormous beast?

UNCLE: That's not so wonderful. When I went to Kwanto last time, I saw a drum nine miles in circumference.

NEPHEW: How ridiculous. You can make the frame of a drum by joining pieces of wood, but I fear you cannot find a hide nine miles large.

UNCLE: Oh, but how do you know there is not? To tell you the truth, I verified the fact that it was made of the bull hide which you saw on Innami Plain.

NEPHEW: Great Scott! I am taken in again.

I confess, because you always fool me so successfully, that I decided to trick you once and made up these stories, but you are too clever for me.

Tell me how you manage to collect such marvelous stories.

UNCLE: At your pace, you will never be able to beat me. Though I shall never tell any outsiders, you are an exception. I will tell you the secret.

NEPHEW: What is it?

UNCLE: There is a seed for such stories known as the Hojo no Tane. Would you like to have one?

NEPHEW: Oh, please give me one.

UNCLE: Just wait there a few minutes.

NEPHEW: Very well.

UNCLE *(aside)*: What do you think of this? There are some fools in this world. He wants to have a seed of lies, and I am going to have some fun with him.

Here, my dear nephew! I will give you a seed.

NEPHEW: Please!

UNCLE: I buried it in the garden. Dig it up.

NEPHEW: Very well.

UNCLE: I think it was by that stepping stone.

NEPHEW: Here?

UNCLE: Yes, dig there.

NEPHEW: No, it is not here.

UNCLE: Dig a little deeper.

NEPHEW: I cannot find it.

UNCLE: Now I remember. It was under this pine tree.

NEPHEW: Very well.

UNCLE: There, right there.

NEPHEW: I cannot find it.

UNCLE: Dig deeper.

NEPHEW: Yes, I dug deep, but it was not there.

UNCLE: You are indeed a silly fellow. That which you cannot find is called the Hojo no Tane.

NEPHEW: Was that a lie too?

UNCLE: Of course! What did you think it was? Ha, ha, ha!

NEPHEW: Even if you are my uncle, this is too much. I cannot let you get away. Catch him! Catch him!

The Deva King (Niwo)

Anon. / Shio Sakanishi

CHARACTERS: Shite, Waki, Spectators.

SHITE: I dwell in this vicinity, but recently I have met reverses of fortune, and it has become exceedingly difficult for me to live here. Therefore I will go to a distant country to try my luck anew. However, as I have a friend who has been very kind to me, I will first call to bid him farewell. Also he may have a good scheme that will enable me to stay here. I must hurry. I hope he is at home. As he is a very busy person, even though I have come thus far especially, I may be unable to see him. Here is his establishment.

Pardon, pardon! Is anyone home?

WAKI: Someone is at the gate. Who is it?

SHITE: It is I.

WAKI: Oh, is it you? I am glad to see you.

SHITE: I have not seen you for a long while. I hope you have been well.

WAKI: Thank you. We have all been well. But you look as if you are ready to take a long journey. Where are you going?

SHITE: I came to call on you today to talk about that. I must confess that recently I have met reverses of fortune so that I cannot stay in this city any longer, and I have decided to go to a distant country. Therefore I have come to bid you farewell. You have been good to me and I am very grateful to you.

WAKI: I am exceedingly sorry to hear that. Instead of going to a far-off country, isn't there any way of trying out your fortune in this city?

SHITE: I fear not. All possible avenues are closed to me. I cannot very well stay here any longer.

WAKI: But have you someone in a distant country upon whom you can depend?

SHITE: Unfortunately no one, but in desperation, I just hit upon that idea.

WAKI: You are a reckless man. What will you do in a strange country with no friends?

SHITE: Precisely.

WAKI: I can't let you do that. I certainly should like to help you out.

SHITE: Please assist me.

WAKI: I have a good idea. Are you a good mimic?

SHITE: That depends on what I am to mimic.

WAKI: Niwo, the Deva King, I am thinking.

SHITE: You mean Niwo whose statue stands in the temple gate?

WAKI: Precisely.

SHITE: Fortunately I have lived in the neighborhood of the temple, and as I remember the statue well, that will be easy.

WAKI: That's splendid! I shall dress you up as an image of Niwo and then send word around that a wonderful image of Niwo has descended in Uyeno Park. I am sure people will come to pay homage.

SHITE: I am certain of that.

WAKI: With what offering you get, you can start out afresh. What do you think of this idea?

SHITE: Excellent indeed, and I am greatly obliged to you. Please go ahead with your scheme.

WAKI: Then come this way. I shall dress you up as an image of Niwo.

SHITE: Very well.

WAKI: First put this hood on.

SHITE: Very well.

WAKI: Slip this over your shoulders.

SHITE: Does this look all right?

WAKI: It's almost done. Let us go to Uyeno Park! Come.

SHITE: Very good! I am a thousand times obliged to you for your kindness.

WAKI: Needless to say you must be careful not to be detected.

SHITE: Rest assured on that point. I will do my utmost to safeguard against that.

WAKI: Oh, before we know it, we are already in Uyeno Park. Where do you think will be the best place?

SHITE: Where indeed do you think is the best place?

WAKI: This looks good. Come here and mimic a Niwo.

SHITE: Very well.

WAKI: Listen, folks! Just now here in this park has descended a new and wonderful Niwo. So come and worship him.

FIRST SPECTATOR: Are you all there?

CROWD: Here we are.

FIRST SPECTATOR: Did you hear that just now a new and wonderful Niwo descended into this park?

CROWD: So we hear.

FIRST SPECTATOR: Then let us go and pay homage to him.

CROWD: Very good.

FIRST SPECTATOR: Then come.

CROWD: We shall follow you.

FIRST SPECTATOR: The descent of a Niwo in this day and age is indeed a miracle.

SECOND SPECTATOR: As you say, it is really a miracle.

SHITE: People ought to come very soon. Well, that crowd looks as if they come to worship. I'll get myself ready.

FIRST SPECTATOR: Here we are already in the park. Where is the image?

SECOND SPECTATOR: Indeed, where is this Niwo?

FIRST SPECTATOR: Oh, there he stands.

SECOND SPECTATOR: Let us pay homage. But first let us give an offering.

CROWD: Certainly. Very well.

FIRST SPECTATOR: First let us offer some coins.

CROWD: Very well.

FIRST SPECTATOR: Please protect me from all diseases and calamities.

SECOND SPECTATOR: Please grant me health and wealth.

THIRD SPECTATOR: Grant peace, happiness, and long life to my family.

FIRST SPECTATOR: Give me strength, and I will offer this precious sword to you.

SECOND SPECTATOR: I will present this.

FIRST SPECTATOR: This is a miraculous Niwo.

CROWD: This certainly is wondrously miraculous.

FIRST SPECTATOR: Well, we must be getting home.

SECOND SPECTATOR: I will tell this wonder far and wide, and urge people to come and worship him.

CROWD: We will all do so.

FIRST SPECTATOR: Come, folks.

CROWD: Coming!

SHITE: Ha, ha. How wonderful! I am very happy. What an abundance of treasure! I must carry the gifts home and examine them.

Hello, hello! Where is my friend?

WAKI: I am here. What is the matter? Were there any devotees?

SHITE: Oh, indeed. There was an enormous crowd, and not only did they offer coins, but also these treasures.

WAKI: Well, well! This is very fortunate. Now you have a little capital to start afresh.

SHITE: Quite true. Now I have some capital. First I wish to ask you to keep the valuables for me.

WAKI: All right. I will keep them for you.

SHITE: Thank you. But if you please, I'd like to try this game again.

WAKI: Oh, no! You have enough now.

SHITE: I shall be careful not to be detected. Please let me try again.

WAKI: No, that's too dangerous.

SHITE: Oh, please let me try this once.

WAKI: Well, if you must, I suppose you must.

SHITE: Thank you very much.

WAKI: I will let you carry a sceptre this time.

SHITE: I am greatly obliged to you.

WAKI: Do not get caught.

SHITE: Rest assured. I shall take care of that.

WAKI: Let us hurry.

SHITE: Very good. My good luck is all due to your kindness, and I shall be eternally grateful to you. Here we are in Uyeno Park again. This time I shall try a Niwo with his mouth closed. Is there no one to worship me? Oh, I see people coming!

FIRST MAN: Is everybody here?

CROWD: Here we are!

FIRST MAN: I am told that a new Niwo appeared in Uyeno Park, and I wish to pay homage to him. What do you think?

SECOND MAN: That is excellent. I shall accompany you.

FIRST MAN: Then let us go. Come, one and all.

CROWD: We are following.

FIRST MAN: The descent of a Niwo is wonderfully miraculous!

SECOND MAN: As you say, it is a miracle.

FIRST MAN: We are already in the park.

SECOND MAN: So we are.

FIRST MAN: Where, I wonder, has the noble image descended?
CROWD: Where, indeed?
FIRST MAN: Here he is!
SECOND MAN: Indeed here he stands.
FIRST MAN: Let us first offer some coins.
CROWD: Very well.
FIRST MAN: Now let us worship him.
CROWD: Very well.
FIRST MAN: Grant me fortune and all good virtues.
SECOND MAN: Make my sons and daughters and their sons and daughters prosperous.
FIRST MAN: This indeed is a noble image.
SECOND MAN: Noble he is!
FIRST MAN: Like a living Buddha!
SECOND MAN: Quite so.
FIRST MAN: Quick! Come this way.
SECOND MAN: What is the matter?
FIRST MAN: What do you think? If you look into his eyes closely, you will see that his noble eyeballs are moving. Have you noticed that?
SECOND MAN: As you say! I see his head is moving, too.
FIRST MAN: This is very strange. I can't understand it. There are many false and wicked monks and priests who take unfair advantage of the public. To find whether this is the real image of Niwo or not, shall I tickle him? What do you think?
SECOND MAN: Excellent idea, indeed.
FIRST MAN: Then come closer.
SECOND MAN: This is a wonderfully wrought image.
SECOND MAN: Truly it is.
FIRST MAN: His head seems to be moving.
SECOND MAN: Moreover, his eyeballs are rolling in their sockets.
FIRST MAN: Just like a living man's.
SECOND MAN: Just so.

PROVERBS

A fire across the river. (Speaking of a thing which can be looked on with unconcern, a Japanese uses this proverbial expression, meaning, "It's no business of mine any more than is a fire across the river.")

To go up a tree to seek fish.

A paradise on hearsay, a hell at sight.

Praying to God only when in distress.

Kyotoites ruin themselves through extravagance in dress, Osaka people in food.

Yield to the powerful.

Inscrutable are the ways of providence.

As for wife and tatami, the fresher the better.

Woman's heart is as changeable as a cat's eyes.

Parents' are partial eyes.

Pleasure will be followed by pain.

Proof rather than argument.

He reads the *Analects* but knows not what he reads.

Sakè is the best of all medicines.

FIRST MAN: Tickle, tickle!
SECOND MAN: Tickle, tickle!
SHITE: Ouch, ha, ha! Ouch, ha, ha! Forgive me, forgive me!
FIRST MAN: You naughty monk! You wicked imposter!
SHITE: Pardon, pardon! Oh, please spare my life.
CROWD: You cheat! You scoundrel! Is there no one here to catch him? Do not let him get away! Catch him, catch him!

An Unfair Exchange

Anon / Shio Sakanishi

CHARACTERS: Blind Man, his Wife, Monkey Man.

BLIND MAN: I am a blind man who dwells in the capital. I hear the cherry blossoms are at their height now. Every year my wife teases me to take her to see them, but since I cannot see anything, I am loath to go, and every year she loses her temper. This year, however, I will take her to Kiyomizu, and though I cannot see them with eyes, I will try to smell them.

Hello, my wife! Are you there?

WIFE: What is it that you call me for?
BLIND MAN: Oh, it is nothing very special that I called you for. I hear the blossoms are at their best now. Because you have been wishing to go every year, I have decided to take you to see the flowers. You look and enjoy while I smell them.
WIFE: I am very happy to hear this. It will be a pleasant diversion. But flowers are for the eye, and I have never heard of smelling them.
BLIND MAN: No, no. It is all right to smell them. Listen, there is an old poem on the matter.

In moonlight night
The white blossom is out of sight;
Yet by her fragrance, I can tell
Where she does dwell.

So you see, it is perfectly all right to smell flowers.

WIFE: Indeed I am convinced. Let us go then!
BLIND MAN: Lead me by the hand, please.
WIFE: Very well.
BLIND MAN: Listen! To go with you hand in hand thus is perfect bliss. To me it is better than looking at cherry blossoms.
WIFE: Oh, please do not be so loving. People might hear us.
BLIND MAN: What a crowd! I suppose they are all going to see the cherries.
WIFE: I believe so.
BLIND MAN: Did you prepare a little flask for us?
WIFE: Yes, I sent it to the temple at Kiyomizu. It will be waiting for us there.

BLIND MAN: That's excellent.

WIFE: Oh, please! Strolling along, we have already come to the temple ground of Kiyomizu.

BLIND MAN: Already? Let us pick out a secluded place.

WIFE: Here is a nice place. Come this way and sit down. The flowers are indeed marvelous.

BLIND MAN: I shall sit down. You sit here too. Well, first let us have a little sakè. Take the bottle out.

WIFE: Very well. Here is a cup.

BLIND MAN: All right. Please pour me some.

WIFE: Here!

BLIND MAN: This is delicious. Somehow it does taste better out-of-doors than at home. You have one too.

WIFE: Thanks. I will.

BLIND MAN: Take a full cup. How about a little song?

BOTH: Zan-za! The waves of Hamamatsu roar. Za-zan-za!

WIFE: Have another cup!

BLIND MAN: Good! The more I drink, the better it gets. Let us sing some more.

MONKEY MAN: I am a monkey man who has been making the rounds of the capital recently. Today I have been visiting my patrons, but I hear the cherry blossoms are at their height. As the temple of Kiyomizu is on my way home, I think I shall stop there.

Oh, already I am at Kiyomizu. What a crowd, indeed! Ha, there is a blind man looking at the flowers with his wife. What an uncommonly beautiful woman she is! *(He goes toward her stealthily, and speaks to her in a low voice.)*

Oh, hello, my dear lady! I want to ask you something.

WIFE: What is the matter, I wonder. Were you speaking to me?

MONKEY MAN: Yes, indeed. I was talking to you. Is that your husband?

WIFE: Yes, and we have known each other ever since we were so high.

MONKEY MAN: It is a great pity that such a singularly pretty girl like you is married to a blind man. I will arrange an infinitely better match for you. So you come with me.

WIFE: That is very good of you. Though I am tempted, I have known my husband so long that I feel sorry to leave him.

BLIND MAN: Hey, my wife! Where have you gone?

WIFE: I am right here.

BLIND MAN: I cannot understand this at all. Where have you been?

WIFE: I just went over there to get a little more sakè.

BLIND MAN: I still can't understand this. Give me some more. Pour it for me, quick!

WIFE: There you are. Have as much as you like!

BLIND MAN: Ha! This is good. Now you have one. I will pour for you.

WIFE: I fear I shall get light-hearted. But then, what does it matter! I'll have a cup. As there is no one around, how about a little dance to relish the sakè?

BLIND MAN: Just as you say. To get a little light-hearted and to dance! That's excellent.

WIFE: I am so happy! Do dance, please. *(The blind man dances while his wife chants.)*

In this blessed land of Yamato,
Peace reigns o'er land and sea.
May thy reign, my sovereign lord,
Last ages, myriad ages. . . .

MONKEY MAN: What do I see? The blind man is dancing. *(He motions to the wife.)* Listen, dear lady! Please come here a moment.

WIFE: What is it?

MONKEY MAN: I will arrange the best possible marriage for you. So you get out of this right away and come with me.

WIFE: I am not uninterested in your proposal, but will it be a very good house?

MONKEY MAN: Oh, sure! It is an excellent family. Furthermore, the man is very handsome.

WIFE: If that is the case, I think I can manage to come with you.

BLIND MAN: Oh, oh, my dear wife! Where have you gone? Wife, my wife!

WIFE: I am right here.

That was a splendid performance of dancing you gave. A very pretty show!

BLIND MAN: You are getting up and down and up and down all the time. I cannot understand why all this fuss. I have an idea.

I will tie her with this sash and fasten her to my belt.

WIFE: What under the sun are you doing?

BLIND MAN: Now I have no need to be anxious about her. Come, come! I want to drink more sakè.

WIFE: There, I have poured it for you. I am afraid you are going beyond your limit.

MONKEY MAN: What is this? Sure enough, the blind man is clever. He has tied his wife to his belt.

Now come, please! Oh, I see! She means she is tied and cannot come. Of course! But I have a scheme. I will tie my monkey to that sash instead. I must be very quiet so that he will not hear me. Ha, that's done. *(After tying the monkey to the sash, he goes off with the wife to a corner of the stage.)*

Listen! I told you that I would arrange a marriage for you, but that is a lie; I want you to marry me. We will live together one thousand, nay, nay, ten thousand years happily. Get on my back, and I will carry you home. Oh, how happy I am! Let us hurry home! *(They go off.)*

BLIND MAN: Ha, my wife! I want to drink more sakè. Pour it for me. But why don't you say something? Well, well, she is angry because I tied her. Does that make you so mad? Come, come! Be good. *(He pulls the sash.)*

MONKEY: Kya, kya, kya!

BLIND MAN: Now, now, wife! Why do you scratch me so? What is the matter?

MONKEY: Kya, kya, kya!

BLIND MAN: Oh, how sad! My wife has turned into a monkey and is hairy all over. Alas, alack! What can I do?

MONKEY: Kya, kya, kya!

BLIND MAN: Alas, alack! Do not scratch me so! Do forgive me, my dear wife!

STORIES AND SKETCHES

The Tale of Seijuro from Himeji (extract)

Ihara Saikaku (1641–93) / Ivan Morris

Ihara Saikaku, the author of the next seven selections, was a successful merchant in Osaka, but when his young wife and daughter died tragically, he gave up business and became a wandering Buddhist monk. He has been called by some scholars the Defoe of Japan, as he introduced into Japanese literature a realism and middle-class perspective which no previous Japanese writer of fiction had done. Among his works translated into English are This Scheming World *(a series of sketches describing what a number of people were doing on a particular New Year's Day),* The Life of an Amorous Man *(adventures of a wealthy, presumably typically amoral Japanese of the seventeenth century),* The Life of an Amorous Woman *(confessions of an old nun who had been a courtesan), and* Five Women Who Loved Love.

Onatsu wrote a petition begging that Seijuro's life be spared, and this she presented to the Mount Myoshin Shrine at Murotsu. Strange to relate, there appeared by her bedside at about the middle of that very night an old man who imparted to her ears a wondrous message: "Heed well what I say. The people of this world, when they find themselves in distress, are wont to make such utterly unreasonable requests that even I, the deity of Mount Myoshin, do not find it in my power to grant them. Some pray for sudden prosperity, or again, that they may enjoy a secret tryst with some other man's wife. Some pray that their enemy may be haunted to death, others that a rainy day may turn to fine weather, still others that the short nose with which they were born may grow longer. One after another they come with these selfish requests which cannot possibly be realized, and by praying to the Gods and Buddhas who can in no wise serve them, they only make thorough nuisances of themselves. At the last festival I was visited by eighteen thousand and sixteen worshippers, but of this great company there was not one but prayed for his own selfish ends. It was odd indeed to hear them. Yet the offerings which they threw into the box were pleasing to me, and, as such is the duty of a God, I listened to their prayers. Among all these visitors there was but one who showed real piety—a servant from a charcoal dealer's in Takasago. 'I have no special favour to ask,' she said, bowing to me. 'Just let me continue in good health. I shall come here again to worship you.' She left, but had not gone more than a few yards when she returned and addressing me again, said, 'Grant also that I get myself a handsome man.' " —FROM "FIVE WOMEN WHO LOVED LOVE"

A Bonze's Wife in a Worldly Temple

Ihara Saikaku / Ivan Morris

Now this period was the very "noonday of Buddhism"—and indeed even at noon the priests disported themselves with their temple pages. Repressing my shyness, then, I shaved my head in the centre to look like a young man's, simulated a male voice and committed to memory the general bearing of a man; when I came to put on a man's loincloth, I was amazed how well I could resemble the other sex. I also changed my sash for an ordinary one of narrow width, and thrust a pair of swords by my side. These made me unsteady in my gait, and though I covered myself in a coat and a sedge hat, I could not but feel strange.

Having heard of an affluent Worldly Temple, I made my way thither. On arrival, I pretended to admire the cherries that blossomed in the temple garden; then I entered the precincts through a gate in the wall. The drumholder went to the private apartment of the priest, and, finding him at leisure, whispered in his ear. Thereupon I was invited into the guest chamber....

Thereafter we all became fuddled with sakè, while from the kitchen was wafted the aroma of fish and meat. The fee for my services was fixed at two rectangular gold pieces a night.

In the course of time I urged this one religion on temples of all the eight sects, and I may say that I never found a single priest who was not ready to slash his rosary. Later it happened that the bonze of another temple became infatuated with me. It was agreed that I should be paid twenty-five pounds of silver for a three years' period of service, and thus I assumed the role of a bonze's wife.

Dwelling there day after day, I came to understand the strange ways of a Temple of the Floating World. In earlier times it used to happen that a group of priests who were on friendly terms would live together in a temple. These men would mark the Six Days of Fasting in the month, and, so long as these did not fall on the anniversaries of the various Buddhas or of the founders of their temple, they would regard them as the occasions when they might freely break their holy vows; at the same time, they would swear to respect these vows during the remainder of the month. On the appointed days they would partake of fish and fowl, visit the gay quarters, consort with trollops on the Third Avenue and give themselves over to other such license. Yet, since their normal conduct was befitting to the cloth, no harm was done, and even Buddha would surely understand and forgive them their lapses.

In recent years, however, with the growing prosperity of the temples, the priests have become ever more licentious. In the daytime they wear their vestments, but at night they sally forth dressed in short coats. Furthermore, they install women in their temples. For this purpose the priest will have a deep recess built in the corner of his private apartment; this is provided with a narrow skylight, so designed as to be invisible from the outside. In order that no sound of voices may escape, he has his apartment built to a considerable depth, with earth piled heavily on the roof, and the walls a foot in thickness.

It was in such a place that I was now immured each day; only at night I would emerge to visit the priest's bedchamber. This was indeed a constrained existence, and it was grievous to think that it was not love that had brought me to it, but the need to gain a livelihood.

The priest to whom I had entrusted myself was a disagreeable man. He indulged ceaselessly in fornication, until all my interest in these matters stopped and all my pleasure died away. Gradually I became wasted and thin from overmuch indulgence. Yet the bonze had not the slightest mercy on me, and would regard me with a baleful look, as though to say, "If you die, I shall simply bury you in the precincts of this temple."

In the evenings a vendor came with various relishes. I would then prepare a dinner of stuffed teal or swellfish broth, or fish baked on splints of cedar. Lest I attract attention by the smell of cooking, I would place a cover over the charcoal brazier. But in due course I learned of the temple's slovenly ways, and found that even the acolytes would wrap dried sardines in old scraps of paper, on which they had scribbled the Sutra of the Names; they would hide these packages in the sleeves of their vestments and later bake the fish. It was just because they indulged day and night in such pursuits that the inmates of the temple were lustrous and fleshy in appearance and apt for the performance of their offices. How different they looked from those men who, renouncing the world, retire to mountain groves to live on the berries of the trees, or again, from those priests who, being poor, cannot do other than observe religious abstinence! One can recognize this latter sort at once, for they come to look like dried-up bits of wood.

Now my service in this temple continued from spring until about the beginning of autumn. At first my priest regarded me with deep suspicion, and never left without first locking the door. But, as time passed, he relaxed his guard; he allowed people to visit him in his quarters, and even when parishioners called at the temple, he no longer made haste to conceal me.

One evening, as the wind whistled in the branches and soughed through the leaves of the plantains, I lay by myself on the bamboo veranda, resting my head on my arm and drearily thinking of this world in which all is doomed to change. While I lay dozing, an old woman appeared before me like a ghost. There was not a single black hair on her head, her face was furrowed as though with waves, and her limbs were as thin as a set of fire-irons. She tottered up to me, and in a thin, pathetic voice addressed me as follows:

"I lived in this temple for many a long year with the priest whom you know, and had people believe that I was his mother. I myself am not of such humble origin, but on purpose I made myself seem unsightly. Being twenty years older than the priest, I felt my position to be a shaming one. Yet this was a way to gain my livelihood and I gave myself to him with no reserve. As an outcome of our deep intimacy, we exchanged the most tender vows. Yet in the end the priest renounced these, telling me that, since age had made me as I was, he no longer had use for me.

"He had thus thrust me aside to live on the offerings of rice that people make to Buddha, and he looks reproachfully at me when yet I fail to die. You may regard all this as brutal usage; but it is not the worst. What really makes me pass my days in bitter thought is—you. You do not know it, but every night I listen as you and the priest lie in bed engaged in your intimate converse. Even though age has withered my body, the path of love is a hard one to forsake. Finally I have resolved that the only way to calm my spirits is to get my hands on you—and so I will do this very night!"

The old woman's words hit home, and I realized that it was bootless for me to stay in this place any longer. I adopted a droll way to make my departure from the temple. In the front underfold of my everyday kimono I stuffed some wadding. Then, feigning a cumbrous gait, I approached the priest and told him, "I have managed to hide things until now. But the months of my pregnancy have piled up and soon my time will come."

Hearing this, the priest was much distraught and said, "Go home with all haste, I pray you, and return here when all is well again."

He then collected the alms that had accumulated in the collection box and gave them to me, together with various warnings regarding my confinement. Some unhappy couple in the parish had lost their child and, being unable to bear the sight of the infant's tear-stained clothes, had offered them to the temple. These the priest now gave me to use for swaddling clothes. Finally, he held a service in celebration of the expected birth, assigning the name Ishichiyo to the unborn child.

I had become utterly weary of this temple, and, although my period of service was not yet elapsed, I did not return. Unfortunately for my bonze, he could enter no action against me.—FROM "THE LIFE OF AN AMOROUS WOMAN"

The Nun's Robe

Ihara Saikaku / Masanori Takatsuka and David C. Stubbs

The other woman, who is older, once served as a maid in an inn on the Tokaido highway, near the town of Seki. While working there she mistreated the young men making secret pilgrimages to the shrine at Ise, and would pilfer their scanty supply of rice. Divine retribution overtook her while yet in this world, however, and she is now a poor mendicant nun. Pretending to be pious, she chants sutras devoid of devotion. A nun in form, she is but an ogre in spirit, a veritable wolf in sheep's clothing. So impious is she that it never even occurs to her that she ought to abstain from eating meat. Yet for the past fourteen or fifteen years she has, by the mercy of the Buddha, managed to eke out a living, only because of her black clerical robe made of hemp. For as the saying goes, "Even a sardine's head will shine if believed in." Each morning as she walks about the streets begging rice she receives alms from an average of two houses per street, which means that to gather even a single go of rice she must visit as many as twenty houses. She cannot hope to garner five go of rice until she has walked through at least fifty streets. It surely takes a healthy person to be a mendicant nun!

Unfortunately, during the previous summer, she suffered a sunstroke, which necessitated her pawning the clerical robe for one momme and eight. Since then, as she has been unable to redeem the robe by any means, she has lost her means of livelihood. Of course we should not jump to the conclusion that people have become any less generous in almsgiving for the sake of their souls in the afterlife. Yet now that she is without the clerical robe, she cannot expect to collect even two go of rice a day; whereas formerly when wearing it she usually received five go. "December priest and priestess" runs the well-known saying. Yes, especially in December when people are so busy that they forget even the services in memory of their departed parents, it is no wonder that they do not care to give alms to a mendicant nun. So, with only eight mon in hand, she must somehow tide over the year end.—FROM "THIS SCHEMING WORLD"

When Ise Lobsters Were Scarce

Ihara Saikaku / Masanori Takatsuka and David C. Stubbs

Now this particular year of which I write it happened that everyone in the city, vowing that his New Year decorations would be incomplete without an Ise lobster, determined to buy one even if it cost a thousand kan. The result was that by December 27th or 28th the supply of Ise lobsters was so exhausted that in every fishmonger's shop in Osaka they were as scarce as imported articles. And by New Year's Eve not even a whiff of one was to be detected, high or low; all along the shore and in every fisherman's hut you could hear the plaintive voices of buyers asking if there were any Ise lobsters for sale.

At a fishmonger's shop called the Era, located in the middle of Bingo Street in Osaka, there happened to be just one Ise lobster left. The bidding for it began at one and a half momme and finally rose to four momme and eight. Even at that exorbitant price, however, the fishmonger refused to part with it, claiming that its like could not be found anywhere else.

Since it was far beyond the authority of a mere servant to buy it at such an inflated price on his own responsibility, he returned home hastily to his master and explained the situation. Whereupon the master frowned and said: "Never in my life have I bought anything that was too expensive. I make it a rule to buy firewood in June, cotton in August, rice before the sakê-brewing season starts, and hemp just after the Bon season. In brief, my principle is to buy for cash when the price is cheapest. The only exception (and one which I have ever since remembered with regret) was made when my father died: I bought an expensive coffin at the price quoted by the cooper. There is no reason in the world why, willy-nilly, we should have to greet the New Year with an Ise lobster installed in our house. I'll make up for its absence this year by buying two of them next year when the price comes down to only three mon apiece. I don't mind in the least if due to the absence of an Ise lobster the New Year god is reluctant to visit my house. No, not in the least! I wouldn't buy one if the price were reduced to four momme—no, not even if it were only four bu!"

Despite the master's wry face, his wife and son both thought it just wouldn't do at all to be without an Ise lobster. They could bear up under the thought of losing face publicly, but when the daughter's husband would make his first New Year's call on his wife's parents and see no Ise lobster crowning the New Year decorations—that scene was simply unthinkable. They must have one at any cost. Back went the servant posthaste, but he was too late, for another servant of a wholesaler from Imabashi had already bought the Ise lobster. The price quoted had been five momme and eight, but since it was appropriate to usher in the New Year with round figures, an even five hundred mon had been paid for it. The last lobster having been sold, then, all further forays of the servant to hunt lobsters were fruitless; so he had to return home, empty-handed, a sadder but wiser man, more conscious than ever of the great size of Osaka, and confess all to his master and mistress.

The mistress looked sorrowful, but the master laughed and said: "I feel uneasy about any wholesaler who would buy a lobster at so fancy a price. He's bound to go bankrupt before long. His financial backer, unaware of his real circumstances, is sure to have a nightmare over the holiday season. If a lobster is indispensable for the decoration, I have an idea for making one that will keep much longer than a live one." So saying, he commissioned an artisan to fashion a lobster of crimson silk, which cost him only two and a half momme. "Look," he pointed out, "it will be useful as a toy for the baby even after the season is all over. That's the way a wise man does things. A thing that would have cost you four momme and eight has been provided for two and a half momme. And what's more, it can be used over and over again."

Since there was no gainsaying the master's proud boast, everyone was forced to listen to him and acknowledge the rare wisdom of one who could attain to such wealth as he possessed.

While all this was going on, the master's old mother, who was ninety-two years of age, but was still able to see well and to walk as well as ever, entered the room from her quarters in the annex. "I hear that you're making a lot of fuss over the price of a lobster," she remarked. "It was foolish of you not to have bought one ahead of time. With such negligence how in the world can you expect to keep this shop? You should remember that always just before the New Year season lobsters are expensive, not only because the Grand Shrine at Ise and all its subordinate shrines, including the temporary offices where the underling priests are sent, need lobsters, but also because at this season there are millions of them in demand by every household in every town and countryside that holds a festival to the gods—and truly this is a land of the gods! The lobsters brought into Kyoto and Osaka each year are those left over, after the gods have had their fill. Now it just happens that I took all this into consideration and about the middle of the month I bought two lobsters as fresh and natural as they came out of the sea. Perfect specimens: even their feelers have never been joined together. And the price I paid for them? Just four mon apiece, you see."

Admiring applause greeted the old mother's announcement, but some ventured to criticize her extravagance in buying two lobsters when really one would have done. "I don't spend my money to no purpose," she retorted. "There's a man who every year presents me with five bundles of burdock—three, if the burdock is thick—and I must give him in return something of like value. My plan was to give him a lobster that cost me four mon in return for the burdock which ought to be worth about one momme. It's pretty lucky for you that he hasn't come yet with his usual year-end present. I tell you what I'll do: I'll let you have one of my lobsters, but remember that business is business even between mother and son. If you really want the lobster, then you'll have to send somebody to me with five bundles of burdock. I don't care who gets the lobster, just so long as I get my burdock in exchange for it. And anyway, you can't celebrate the New Year without it. Not that I'm speaking from any selfish motive, understand. It's just that in giving and receiving presents on the five annual festival days you have to make rather careful calculations of what you receive. In return, you have to give things which, while seeming to be equal in value, actually allow you a slight margin of profit.

"For example, every year the Ise priests present our family with a good-luck charm, a set of dried bonito, a box of face powder, a folding calendar, and five bundles of green lave. If you make a close calculation of their value it comes to about two momme and eight. Now from our house we always used to offer three momme, which meant that the difference of two odd bu represented a profit for the Grand Shrine of Ise. For thirty years this was our practice, but since you've become master of this house, each year you have offered one piece of silver. That's unconscionably too much!—even if it is an act of devotion. Why, even the shrine gods themselves would frown with disapproval upon anyone who spent money without due consideration. Take for example that offertory coin called a Pigeon's Eye. Contrary to what most people think, one kan of these round lead coins with a hole in the middle is actually worth only six hundred mon. From this it is quite apparent that the gods themselves are concerned that pilgrimages be made with economy."—FROM "THIS SCHEMING WORLD"

It's Expensive to Lie When You're Lying Low

Ihara Saikaku / Masanori Takatsuka and David C. Stubbs

The entertainer who had been called into the inn for the customer's comfort feigned gaiety as part of her service. Although she did not feel happy, she spoke with a smile on her face: "What a pity it is that the years flit by one after another!" she said. "Last year the arrival of the New Year was delightful to me, for I could play battledore and shuttlecock, but now I'm nineteen years old. It won't be long before I'll have to sew up the slits in my kimono sleeves and be addressed as 'Madame.' I'm sorry to say that this may be the last year I'll be able to wear long-sleeved kimono."

Unfortunately for the entertainer, the customer had a good memory, and replied, "The last time I met you at the Hanaya you were wearing kimono with round sleeves and saying you'd be nineteen that very day. That must have been about twenty years ago. So by now you must be at least thirty-nine, but you're still wearing long-sleeved kimono. What in the world could you have to regret? It's all to your advantage to be of small build, because it makes you look young." Thus unsparingly he reminded her of her old line of talk, while the woman could only sit quietly, with hands folded in apology. So the man gave up being particular about her age, and the two of them had a peaceful sleep in a friendly bed.—FROM "THIS SCHEMING WORLD"

The Night of Insults

Ihara Saikaku / Masanori Takatsuka and David C. Stubbs

Every New Year's Eve in Kyoto at Gion, a divine service of half-shaven sticks is observed. First the sacred lights are dimmed until the faces of visitors are unrecognizable in the darkness. Next they divide the company into two groups, who then proceed to exchange insults, each side heaping as gross abuses as possible upon the other, much to the merriment of all the participants. For example:

"On one of the first three days of the New Year a rice cake will stick in your throat, and you'll be cremated at Toribeno."

"You are a partner in crime with a slave trader: both of you'll ride bareback to Awataguchi for your execution."

"On New Year's Day your wife will go crazy and throw your baby down the well."

"Messengers of Hell will carry you off in their fiery cart and eat you up."

"Your father was a town watchman."

"Your mother used to be the concubine of a Buddhist priest."

"Your sister will go out to buy bean paste without wearing her panties and tumble head over heels in the street."—FROM "THIS SCHEMING WORLD"

Hirataro

Ihara Saikaku / Masanori Takatsuka and David C. Stubbs

"We trust in the Buddha to make a living," is an old proverb which still holds good.

Every year on the evening ushering in the first day of spring, the story of Hirataro is told in all the temples of the Shinshu Sect of Buddhism. Year after year the story does not vary, yet each time people hear it they are impressed anew. So usually many people, old and young, men and women, gather to listen to it.

One year the eve of the vernal equinox happened to fall on New Year's Eve. As a result, the voices of the bill collectors were mingled with the incantations of the men casting out devils, while the clink of money balances blended with the sound of bean throwing. This rather weird atmosphere reminded one of the expression, "A demon in the dark." At a Shinshu temple in Osaka the priest beat a drum, offered the sacred tapers before the altar, and awaited the arrival of worshipers. Yet even after the midnight bell had tolled, and the priest had gone through all the rituals, only three visitors were to be seen in the hall. The priest being forced to acknowledge that the world was utterly worldly, addressed the worshipers in these words:

"Because tonight happens to be the deadline for the settlement of all debts of the old year, worldly people seem to be too busy to attend the services. I should think, however, that even tonight any grandmother who has retired from active household management would have nothing to do. When that boat arrives from the other world to ferry her across the river, she cannot refuse to board it. How foolish people are! What a pity, what a shame to neglect the services of the Buddha! But now it seems of little use to preach a sermon to only three people. Although these are spiritual services to the Buddha, a few material considerations must also be taken into account. Since the offerings of you three will scarcely pay for the candles burned, it seems uneconomical to preach. Would you kindly take back your offerings and go home? To have come here at a time when people are so absorbed in their worldly affairs is none the less praiseworthy on your part. You may rest assured that the Buddha will see to it that your attendance tonight will not have been in vain. He will have it recorded in his golden ledger to balance your accounts in the future life. So I beg you not to think that your piety tonight has done you no good at all, for the Buddha is all charity. This I speak in earnest. You may depend upon it absolutely."

An old woman who had been listening began to shed tears and said, "Your inspiring words have made me thoroughly ashamed of myself. I must confess that I did not come here from any pious motive. My only son has been neglecting his business, and every year end until now he has managed to get by with some excuse or other, but this year he was unable to think of any. At last he asked me to come here, so that after I was gone he could make a racket, crying out that his old mother was missing. Then while the neighbors beat drums and gongs all night long, he could go around pretending to be searching for me. Such was his scheme for tiding over the year end. He boasted that it was an original idea he had just thought up in order to outwit the year-end bill collectors by crying, 'Come back! Come back, Grandma!' It is unfortunate for me that I have a son who is so good-for-nothing, but what a pity it is that I should sin unwillingly by giving my neighbors so much trouble!"

Another person, a man from the province of Ise, spoke up: "Fate is forever a mystery," he said. "At first I was quite a stranger in this big city for I had no relatives here. But since I was employed by a clerk of the Grand Shrine of Ise responsible for the subscribers living in the Osaka district, I would visit this city carrying on my back things to be delivered to them. Seeing what a prosperous city Osaka was, I thought that a family of two or three might easily make a living here doing something or other. Fortunately I made the acquaintance of a widow of a haberdasher who used to peddle his wares in Yamato Province. She was a plump, fair-skinned woman, with a two-year-old son. I married her, thinking that with both of us working we might live comfortably, and that when I grew old I could depend upon the boy to provide for me.

"But in less than a year after our marriage I lost what little money we had due to my lack of experience in peddling, and from the first of December I have had to think seriously of finding another job. Meantime my wife, neglecting me entirely, doted on her son exclusively, often saying to him, 'Listen to me carefully, for you have ears. You must know that although your dead papa was a small man he was clever. He even cooked, which is a woman's task. He would let me go to bed early, while he sat up until dawn making straw sandals. He wouldn't buy himself a kimono, but he had new ones made for you and me to wear in the New Year season. This bluish-yellow one here brings back fond memories of him. In fact, everything reminds me of that dear old man. Son, you do well to cry for your papa who is gone forever.'

"Hearing her talk like this vexed me because of my position as the spouse of an heiress, but all I could do was to put up with it. I had a little money due me from some people in my native province; so thinking that I might be able to tide over this year end by collecting it, I went all the way back to Ise. Quite unexpectedly, however, I found that my debtors had all left for parts unknown. So I returned this evening just before supper, without any money in my pockets.

"When I entered the house I found rice cakes and firewood. Moreover, the table to be dedicated to the New Year god had been properly decorated with ferns. There must still be some hope left, I thought, for the world was as kind as it was cruel. However that may be, I had my wife's good husbandry to thank for all these things prepared in my absence. I felt pleased, and when my wife saw that I had returned, she seemed more affable than usual. First she brought me water to wash my feet with, and then set before me a supper of sardines, some vinegared and some broiled. Just as I started to eat them, she asked me if I had brought the money from Ise. No sooner did she learn of my failure than she began bawling me out:

"'How dare you come back empty-handed! The rice you are eating was obtained by mortgaging my very person. Unless I pay ninety-five momme by the end of February I shall be lost. Other people's rice costs only forty momme, while ours costs us ninety-five momme solely because you are good-for-nothing. You came to this house with no dowry but your breechcloth, so you'll lose nothing by clearing out right now. It will be dark tonight, so you'd better leave before it's too late.'

"So saying, she took away the dishes from before me and urged me to be on my way. Meantime neighbors had come thronging in, and siding with my wife, they said, 'It must be embarrassing to you, but your position as spouse of the mistress is a weak one. If you are a man at all, you'd better leave this place and try your luck somewhere else.' At the time I was too sad even to cry. Tomorrow I shall return to my home province, but I was so completely at a loss as to where to spend tonight that I came here, even though my denomination is Nichiren."

When his story, at once funny and pitiful, was finished, the last of the three temple visitors laughed aloud and said, "Now it's my turn to tell my story, but please excuse me from telling you who and what I am. I can't stay at home without being tormented by bill collectors, and nobody will lend me even one red cent. I felt chilly and wanted a drink, so I hatched up first one scheme and then another, but in the end could think of none that would tide me over the year end. At last I concocted a shameful plan: tonight the story of Hirataro would be told at the temple and crowds of people would come to hear it. While they were listening I would steal their geta to get drink money. Contrary to my expectations, however, very few people are to be seen tonight in any temple, and so the job that was to be done under the very eyes of the Buddha is just impossible."

The man shed tears as he told his story. The priest was deeply moved and said,

"Well, well! Though all of you are endowed with the body and mind of the Buddha, it appears that your poverty begets all manner of evil schemes. But such is the sad way of the world."

As with a sigh he was deploring the world of men, in rushed a woman to inform him that his niece had just given birth in an easy delivery. On her heels came a man with a message that the funeral of Kuzo the boxmaker, who had hanged himself after a quarrel with a bill collector, would be held after midnight. The priest was cordially invited to come out to the burial ground. In the midst of the ado caused by this good news and bad news, a tailor entered to report that the white padded silk kimono which the priest had asked him to make had been stolen by a thief. The tailor promised that if after a search he was unable to recover it, he would reimburse the priest to spare him any possible loss.

Then a man who lived just east of the temple came in to ask the priest to allow him to draw water from the temple well during the first five days of the New Year, because his own well had run dry. After him came the only son of an influential parishioner who, because of his dissipation, had been disinherited by his father. Finding it absolutely necessary for him to leave his father's house at once and go elsewhere, his fond mother had thought of placing him under the care of the priest until the fourth day of January. Such a request as this from so rich a parishioner no priest could deny.

So we see that the "priest in December," so long as he lives in the world of men, is far from being free from involvement in human affairs.—FROM "THIS SCHEMING WORLD"

Characters of Worldly Young Women

Ejima Kiseki (1667–1736) / Howard Hibbett

Ejima Kiseki, the author of the next three selections, was the son of a well-to-do Kyoto businessman. After running through his inheritance, he turned to writing about the subject he knew best, the fleshpots of Japan in the late seventeenth and early eighteenth centuries. At times he ghost-wrote for publishers on order, until his own popularity was established. His later writings, says Howard Hibbett in The Floating World in Japanese Fiction, *all had "an element of scandalous wit. His greatest success was* Courtesans Forbidden to Lose Temper *(1711), which won especial favor for its impudent parody of the Buddhist sermon style. There are sermonizing stories to illustrate the virtues of courtesans, along with controversies, in theological terms, about whether they make better lovers than* kabuki *young men."*

Kiseki considered Saikaku the master whom he imitated, sometimes expressing his admiration by plagiarizing the master's material. He lacked Saikaku's originality, but he developed an entertaining, realistic style that enriched Japanese satire.—LF

Kiseki begins his second character-book in customary fashion with a lively tirade. And he treats that most ancient subject of satire: feminine perversity. In the Characters to

follow all its latest varieties will be illustrated. Here, then, is the long censorious passage (in part borrowed from Saikaku) with which he introduces his book of sketches of these modern hussies.—HH

It was once believed that excessive virtue is typical of young ladies. Now, however, mother and daughter alike behave immodestly: they ape the manner of harlots and courtesans, and of the actors who play female roles; they wear their sashes so high one thinks of the pictures of Ling-chao (without her fish-basket); their sleeves hang open in the masculine style; and on promenade they saunter with a seductive gait. They do everything for effect, caring only how others see them. A facial blemish is hidden by choosing the right profile; thick ankles are concealed in a long skirt; a large mouth is abruptly closed, at the cost of swallowing a remark. Ah, the women of today go to extraordinary lengths! If their husbands could bear it, these ladies would no doubt scrape and polish into their very nostrils, regardless of pain. They abhor stray hairs straggling at the back of the neck, and pluck every one of them, down to the slightest fluff. In their own tidying-up they all but heap ornamental mounds of sand.

And since, as people say, inferiors learn from their betters by imitating them, it is natural that all the maids—personal attendants, parlour-maids, even kitchen-girls whose right hands bear the mark of the ladle—should whet the fish-slicer, shave their eyebrows, cut the short hairs in the hollow of the neck, put rice bran in an old tea-bag, and after soaking for hours in a hot tub (each heedless of the others), scrub themselves furiously. Having no idea when to stop, they end with a hideous inflammation of the skin.

Few women of former times—courtesans excepted—used oil of aloes-wood, but now young ladies smear it on down to their navels. To think of keeping a wife these days you must be prepared to increase your expenses, not only by the cost of her food, but also by a round box of five ryo in gold, handed over the first thing every morning. 'A fair skin hides ten defects,' she says, and masks herself in a thick coat of powder, even if her face would be bearable undisguised. Still the result is unfortunate. Neglecting what seems out of sight, she gives her neck and shoulders the two-toned colouring of an Anraki-an brocade.

And the reason why modern girls have become altogether too smart, till indeed they are as gaudy as harlots, is that their mothers, being soft-headed, pride themselves on daughters of quite mediocre looks. They dress them in striking clothes, take them along to shrines and temples where large crowds gather, and delight in having licentious men stop to stare after them. Noses high, they walk on, thinking, 'Doubtless no one else in the world has such a daughter!' And there are mothers still worse. . . .

A woman who is mistress of a large household may be known to have had five children—one a year, the eldest now thirteen. Yet for sightseeing and temple-visiting she decks herself out in gorgeous clothes, and adopts the wanton air of a courtesan. Though her wailing children run after her (crying, 'Mamma, can't we go?'), she shuts them up in the house, assumes an expression as unmatronly as possible, and sets out to display herself to fashionable men.

Thus, no matter if she happens to be chaste at heart, her inclination to love finery more than her children, and to seek out crowded places, causes her to forget home, children, and parents, and, not unnaturally, to win a spicy reputation among the young rakes.

In general, it may be said that a woman's morals nowadays are as changeable as a cat's eyes. When she returns in the evening from a picnic to look at flowers, if you notice, she appears to have lost character since morning. She has nimbly removed her cotton socks and stuffed them into her sleeves; she has thrust a wooden skewer into her hair, to replace the silver bodkin, and put the tortoise-shell comb away in her purse; she has tucked her scarlet crepe underskirt into her sash, and lowered the (to her) unpleasantly high neck-line of her outer garment. Her silk veil has been put in the travelling-box, and the blind-stitched white satin band of her Kaga hat rolled in with a supply of towels and paper handkerchiefs, and given to a servant to carry. At dusk she gleefully hitches up her skirt like a peasant girl going to weed a rice-field, and her conduct becomes so loose that you can hardly tell Madam from kitchen-maid. Tipsy on sakè, and chanting ballads in a shrill voice, she goes home by way of Yasaka-hakken and Nawate where she knocks on tea-house doors and peers in at the courtesans. Kyoto women cannot be equalled for boldness—certainly not by their men!

Again, leggings used to be worn only by the firewood-selling women of Yase and Ohara; but in recent years, thanks to the advance in sophistication, even ladies of prominent family have grown tired of ordinary underthings: each step (to the secret chagrin, surely, of their maids) reveals a glimpse of red silk gaiter. To protect their collars in the back, they use pale blue pongee wraps; to keep the dust from their oil-still, pinned coiffures, they order waterproof hats in the style worn by nobles at Court. One supposes that they dress for a solitary trip to the country as if going to hear the oracle at Kashima. Lately, too, ladies wearing oiled-paper raincoats, in the fashion of maidservants from samurai households, have been seen in the capital.

With the modern urge to be fashionable, little girls of seven or eight have precocious whims. Bored with the way their hair has been done, they say, 'A "hanging Shimada", please, the back hair drawn in; and tie it with one of those smart hidden cords.' And a girl going off to marry no longer drenches her sleeves in tears, weeping at the farewell. The young lady of today is cheerful enough, if a bit impatient with the go-between. She hurries to get ready, jumps into the sedan chair (which she has eagerly awaited), and radiates joy from the very tip of her nose. In particular, the girl brought up in Kyoto acquires a knowing air long before the provincial one: she becomes an expert in coquetry. Should she lack a teacher, looking around would soon teach her to look out for herself.

In a world where such manners prevail, a girl who asks, "Mamma, where do babies come from?" and who, at sixteen or seventeen, has been so sheltered by her parents that she is unfamiliar with the paths of love, thinks of men only as terrifying creatures, blushes violently at the slightest touch, and, if anyone snatches at her sleeve or skirt, does not hesitate to scream—a girl of this sort embarrasses men, and is referred to as 'That old-fashioned simpleton.'

But should a proper young lady behave otherwise?

A Wayward Wife (extracts)

Ejima Kiseki / Howard Hibbett

In this little tale, with its typically abrupt ending, Kiseki offers a Genroku (1688–1703) variation on the traditional theme of the spoiled, restless wife. There is also her indulgent husband, 'his nose tilted as triumphantly as if he were the Emperor Hsuan Tsung.'—HH

'Obviously morning-glories are best at morning,' declares the mistress, 'not to say how much cooler it is.' And so that night she leaves orders to fill tiers of lacquer boxes with savoury rice and a variety of titbits, prepared exactly to her taste, to arrange several chairs at a back hedge as far as possible from the house, and to lay a floral carpet. 'Cedar picks for the food, a gold lacquer tray . . . be sure to use that exquisite tea from Toga-no-o! Have the bath ready before six. As to my hair, you may do it in three folds, and please take out a sheer gown with wide sleeves and a pink lining—the sash ought to be dark grey satin, covered with huge dots, the underskirt white, but with a speckled pattern. It must all seem quite perfect: you know how the neighbours stare. So put the maids in fresh summer kimono, won't you? And so send a sedan chair to Kama-no-za for my sister, at the usual rising time.' After issuing a bewildering set of instructions to her housekeeper, who has long had charge of kitchen affairs, she retires to lie at ease in the shelter of an ample mosquito net; and tiny bells tinkle at its corners as the servants fan her, by turns, till she drops off to sleep.

Such are her airs merely to look at flowers in her own garden.

And modern matrons have their other caprices, too. They reserve three boxes for the latest play, but then, stopping at Choraku Temple to hear ballads chanted when an image is on view, become so absorbed they omit to go to the theatre. Yet their boredom is not easily dispelled by the suitable feminine pleasures of incense-guessing, poem cards, playing the koto or the samisen, painting, and flower-arranging. 'There's wrestling at Makuzu-ga-hara, and Shichigoro takes on the Thunderbolt!' they cry. 'We can't miss it!' Off they dash, in sedan chairs decorated by autumn landscapes of sprinkled gold.

Did anyone hear of women at wrestling matches in former times? But since men now dote on their wives, and meet each request with a nod, and a smile of fatuous tolerance, these ladies do not hesitate to display their morbid zest for outings—with picnic lunch—to watch the beheading of criminals at Awataguchi. It recalls how Chieh-chi, consort of King Chou of the Yin Dynasty, having exhausted her notable repertoire of diversions, found a superior pastime in seeing executions by the 'wrapping and roasting' process; or how King Yu of Chou, infatuated with Pao-ssu, had the signal-fires set off to amuse her. Indeed, these are only classic examples of the familiar petticoat tyranny. The greengrocer need simply say, 'Madam's orders', to be paid off in large coins for water-melons costing 365 momme; and no sooner has he gone than two stout bearers are dispatched to Yakichi's, on Shijo, to settle a 28,326 mon account for vegetable jelly. You may imagine the other luxuries. Smoking, for instance, used to be unknown as a feminine practice, except among courtesans; yet today women who abstain are as few as monks who fast.

Now there was a certain man who, though of merchant lineage, was highly esteemed, being known throughout the capital for his wealth. Generations ago his family had withdrawn from all but the infrequent business of handing down superb heirlooms. When snow fell he performed the tea ceremony; at blossom time he wrote poems in a traditional vein. He was careful to ignore whatever might be considered practical.

As a husband, he behaved with impeccable lordliness, never glancing into the kitchen. His wife, a radiant beauty, was the irregular offspring of a person of rank. Not only was she adept in the poetics of an ancient school, she had a rare gift for music, and particularly for the reed-pipe; frost gathered in midsummer when she blew winter melodies; with longevity tunes she made her husband utterly feeble. She was addicted to the pursuit of elegance, whether in arts or manners. For summer nights she had her room screened from mosquitoes by panels of silk gauze: inside were placed a five-foot-square tray-garden and a floating lamp, as well as fireflies specially procured from Uji and Seta. Thus she relieved the discomforts of hot weather. In winter she warmed herself at a covered brazier large enough for eight people, and had little girls with bobbed hair chafe the soles of her feet. Husband and wife slept in the perfume of precious incense, while its smoke, in all the varieties of Fuji, Asama, and Muro-no-yashima, curled through their clothing. Devotees of the cult of fragrance, they lived in a style of unfailing splendour. Where the father had strewn the seeds of riches the son now possessed mountains wooded in silver-bearing trees. Interest money clattered incessantly in his scales—a vulgar sound, to be sure, but better than party music at a poor man's house. No one carrying an account book visited his mansion on the last day of the year: all bills were paid early in November, as if the New Year (not greeted by the customary gate-pines) had arrived too soon.

Yet his wife was unhappy. Though she lived in luxurious fashion, and though her husband was handsome and urbane, a man who, far from counting among the Twenty-four Paragons of Filial Piety, was more devoted to wife than mother—despite all this good fortune, which would seem to have left no desire unfulfilled, she perversely disliked being a woman.

One thought obsessed her: 'Why was I cursed with this sex? Tied down to a skinny devil, and no chance to enjoy myself as I please!"

Boldly she extracted her husband's consent to have her hair trimmed in masculine style, the rich pinned coiffure replaced by a boyish arrangement in two folds, with the back hair drawn up. In dress, too, she flouted convention: a short skirt (exposing an edge of lining), a coat of 'eight-roll' cloth, a gold-mounted sword, medium long, and a wide rush hat of the 'Mist-on-Fuji' kind. Thus attired, and accompanied by her husband, she set out each day on another, more distant excursion. 'Let's climb Mount Koya', she would say. 'Those monks are so terribly woman-shy they'll be fun to tease.' Or: 'Now let's go to the whale-spearing at Kumano Bay.' Her demands were endless. Surely if men yielded to all such whims, these hussies would insist on going to China. . . .

But since the poor husband had a genius for being hoodwinked, he delighted in her singular conduct ('How original to dress up like a man!'), and even took her along to the Shimabara. When they were shown into a reception-room at Hana-bishi-ya, he said, 'See what a dashing wife I have! You won't find such a curiosity-seeker in all China; and as for looks—well, I'm afraid your famous beauties are a little outclassed.

Smart, isn't she?" And he engaged the most celebrated courtesans, for his wife as well as himself. They gave pleasure their undivided attention: doubtless the voluptuous joys of Paradise were exceeded. . . .

The jesters worried about the annual reckoning, which was not yet near, and thought, 'Better to run away from all this, or hang yourself and be done with it!' They dropped their game of capping humorous verses. 'It's a miserable life,' they sighed. 'We jesters have to drink when we'd rather not; we have to praise the tiresome little songs of our patrons, hear ourselves called fools by real blockheads, force a smile if we're offended, and tell a roomful of people what even a woman would keep secret. No, there's nothing so bitter as to entertain for a living. If you happen to please, you may be hired five times and get only one bu, or two at most. In this wide world, is there no country where it rains hard cash?' Folding their hands, they contemplated the vanity of all things. . . .

A Prig

Ejima Kiseki / Howard Hibbett

In this sketch, appropriate as to moral if in somewhat doubtful taste, Kiseki takes up the seemingly harmless affectation of Chinese-style learning. Scholarship is often merely one of those polite accomplishments (like the tea ceremony) that may easily be carried to extremes. Here, the young man has a misplaced sense of filial piety, along with a knack of quoting Confucius to confound his elders. And Kiseki implies that most Confucianists are tireless, supercilious bores—Sinophiles who disdain not only Buddhism and the businessman's point of view but indeed all opinions except their own. —HH

A learned man once declared: 'Such accomplishments as calligraphy, kemari [football], and singing immediately become known—after all, people have eyes and ears. In particular, a young man lionized by society for his wealth will find that his other talents, however numerous, will be hidden by an awkward script. And scholarship is certainly the prime concern, after calligraphy, of anyone who wishes to become a superior person.'

These words, as it happened, were addressed to just such a young man. He at once abandoned all the many arts and skills which he had been pursuing. Hastily providing himself with books, he went to study under a ronin Confucianist.

As soon as the young man had nearly mastered the Four Books (by rote, that is), he announced that he had begun to practise Confucianism, and in fact showed it to the very tip of his nose. He considered other people to be in error, paraded his own wisdom, and scorned Buddhism as a heresy. When he heard his father read the Sutras morning and evening, he asserted that all this talk of Heaven and Hell (the last word in stupidity) came from a pack of lies told by corrupt priests to earn their bread. His character was transformed overnight, and he adopted an extremely consequential air.

'Dear me!' a regular customer would exclaim, coming to borrow money. 'Even in this fine weather our young gentleman doesn't go out to amuse himself. I should think you'd feel pent up, just staying inside. Still, behind your back everyone praises your behaviour enormously—it's a model for all the sons in the neighbourhood!'

To this flattery he would make no reply, except to say, tilting his Chinese fan affectedly: 'It is written that "Fine words and insinuating wiles are seldom associated with Virtue." People of your sort who make insincerity their guiding principle miss my true character—"two-faced" is the word for you. It would be a shame for the clerks to follow your example, so don't let me see you around here any more.'

And as he spoke a disturbing gleam would come into his eye; so that even old customers stopped visiting the shop, and hesitated so much as to pay their respects at Bon and the New Year. The house trade, which had been thriving, grew remarkably quiet. 'The young master's studies will ruin us', the clerks complained to his father. 'He's always talking about the Way of the Five Duties, but never thinks of his own duty to help in our business. It would be better for this house if he'd practice the abacus, instead of quoting Confucius by the hour.'

The old man nodded agreement, and sent for his son. 'It's a great mistake for you to neglect the Way of the Merchant, on the pretext of scholarship', he scolded, knitting his brows. 'Besides, do Confucianists teach their students to be out-and-out fools—to go to brothels in the evening, come home in the middle of the night, and give free rein to their drunken whims, waking up all the servants? What nonsense to "Read the Analects and be ignorant of the Analects!" Hereafter, give up your books—use your head to balance accounts.'

The son, maintaining his pedantic air, promptly replied: 'In the words of Confucius, "A father conceals the misconduct of his son, and a son conceals the misconduct of his father; Morality demands this." Hence, for a son to conceal his father's guilt, and a father his son's—this is Natural Propriety in the relation of parent and child, as well as the acme of Human Feeling. To observe Propriety is to be Moral. You however, in a flagrant breach of Propriety, have just now permitted a group of clerks to hear you expose your son's unfortunate addiction to visiting brothels. How can you call that being Moral?'

The old man was disgusted. 'Moral or moronic, that gibberish interferes with business. In plain language, get down to your abacus!' This was the precept he gave his son.

Now on one occasion the classics teacher told the young man, 'To quote Master I Ch'uan, "Anyone who has been granted human life—of high rank or low—ought to be acquainted with the art of healing." The reason is that it would surely be a gross default of filial piety and compassion to put a sick parent or child in the hands of a bungling quack—being unaware, from one's own lack of medical knowledge, whether a physician is good or bad.'

When the young man returned home after hearing this, he immediately fitted out a handsome medicine box, for which he procured a rich assortment of drugs. To begin his practice he used the servants—the apprentice Kyusaburo, the maid Tama, and the others—as if they were scraps of waste paper; and he found as much pleasure in administering needless drugs or massaging bellies which were entirely without pain as in viewing the moon or flowers. Delighted that he made no charge for his services, they loudly acclaimed him an expert. Tenants, wives, and old women who frequented the house—all came to beg for treatment. The young man threw away the abacus he had been calculating on, and took pulses; he put aside business already undertaken and compounded medicines. Neglecting the family trade, he gave his attention wholly to medical practice.

The next morning someone came to the shop at dawn. A clerk, thinking it might be an early customer, hurried out at once to ask, 'What can I do for you?'

'I been suffering from them pills he had me take yesterday,' the visitor answered. 'I vomited, my feet got a chill, and I couldn't pass water. Let me have a different prescription—I'm not ready to go to the next world!'

At this point the wife of a man named Shichibei, a back-alley neighbour, made her appearance. 'The physic my husband took last evening made his bowels run, and gave him a terrible fever. All night long he paced the floor of our little room. He was well enough yesterday, but he raved about passing out sakè-money to a couple of men at the Yakko tea-house. Near dawn he weakened till he hadn't the strength to turn over in bed. I didn't think a man could sink so fast. For heaven's sake, give him back his health!'

With that, she sat down in front of the shop and waited; but just then a tenant's wife came up, wiping her eyes with one hand. 'How can anybody be so cruel, even to the child of a miserable tenant!' she shrieked, as her tears flowed freely. 'What kind of medicine leaves you speechless and goggle-eyed at a single dose? Maybe it doesn't matter if a poor man's children are killed, but landlord or not—if my little one dies I'll see that he pays for it!'

The clerk felt sorry for her. 'The young master's asleep at the moment,' he said soothingly. 'When he wakes up I'll tell him about it, and then we'll engage a fine children's doctor to give a remedy. For the time being, please go home.'

'A precious child's being murdered,' she howled, and her voice rose till it could be heard all over the neighbourhood. 'Is that a time to sleep late? Get him up! I never heard of such a wicked thing—forcing down unwanted medicine, and poisoning for amusement!'

Her words reached the ears of the old master. 'This is the height of foolishness', he thought. Sympathetic to the neighbours, he promptly disowned his son and turned him straight out of bed.

NOVELS

The Life of an Amorous Man (extracts)

Ihara Saikaku / Kengi Hamada

"Illicit affairs," said Yonosuke's elderly confidant, "are common enough. Once one yields to the temptation, it is difficult to forego. But young widows," and here he smiled reminiscently, "are perhaps the easiest to seduce.

"Consider the young widow's plight," he continued. "At the time of bereavement—if she feels so depressed—she probably can commit suicide, or she may want to become a nun. But as time goes on, she may want to acquire a new husband. Some do. Usually, out of sheer self-preservation, she decides to carry on the family responsibility and hangs on to her children, if any, and to the property left by the deceased.

"But while holding the keys to the warehouse she neglects the rusting lock, and her sense of insecurity increases. Willy-nilly she depends on others. Dead leaves pile up in her garden, and she forgets to have her house reroofed. On stormy nights the roof leaks, the thunder rolls, and she remembers how, in her fear, she used to nestle close to her husband and cover her head with a blanket. She has bad dreams, and she remembers how she used to awaken her husband to dispel fear and forebodings. And then she realizes that nothing can be more miserable than a widow's life.

"Out of sheer spiritual need she next turns to religion. On her trips to the temple she feels there is no need any more to wear silk robes embroidered with the family crest, and she discards the use of such finery altogether.

"Meanwhile she must keep up her late husband's shop and flatter long-standing customers if she is to survive. In so doing, she sits at his old desk, flicking away at his abacus and counting the profits and losses. But no matter how intelligent she may be, her efficiency is not quite up to what a man can do. She knows it, and inevitably she turns over the responsibility to the chief clerk. That turns the chief clerk's head. He becomes cocky, and he speaks to her without the respect due his employer. She swallows her pride, tries the art of wheedling, but to no avail. She becomes a mere figurehead.

"Then, in this falling state, she degenerates into unseemly familiarity with her servants, male and female. She joins their ribald jokes. Illicit thoughts enter her own mind. And then, in a final crash, she gets involved in a scandal with a young man of her own shop.

"That, at any rate," Yonosuke's confidant concluded, "is the usual road to degeneration. In my own time I have had pleasant relations with many a young widow.

This is the technique I have used. Upon hearing that a funeral had taken place, I would first investigate the family situation. Then, wearing formal garments, including a hakama and a wing-shouldered jumper, I would present myself to the sorrowing widow. I would gently offer her my condolences, saying that her late husband and I had been bosom friends. Later I would renew my acquaintance with her, asking after her children. If there was a fire in her neighborhood, I would hasten to her home, easing her fears and assuring her of my protection. In this way I would inspire confidence. Then, as our friendship deepened into intimacy, I would address her in the final alluring phrases. It has never failed." . . .

Then he saw a fresh grave marker made of bamboo, and his sympathy grew. He thought: "Whoever has been laid to rest there must have died suddenly of some awful disease—smallpox, maybe."

Suddenly, rising beside the fresh marker were two crouching figures, peasants evidently, digging up a coffin! Horrified, Yonosuke rushed forward and demanded reproachfully: "What are you two trying to do?"

The grave robbers, caught unawares and visibly embarrassed, refused to commit themselves.

"Answer me!" Yonosuke demanded, unsheathing his sword. "If you don't come out with the whole truth, I'll drive this sword into both of you and bury you in there."

Trembling, with hands in the attitude of prayer, the elder of the two men begged: "Forgive us. . . please. We are poor and desperate. We did not know which way to turn. Then we found out that a beautiful young woman had just been buried here. We . . . we dug her up to get her hair and fingernails."

"You beasts! What profit do you make by mutilating the dead like that?"

"We . . . we can sell the hair and fingernails in the gay quarters of the city."

Astonished at so base a motive, yet somehow curious, Yonosuke said: "What possible use can the buyers put them to?"

"It is this way. When courtesans pledge their fidelity to a favorite patron, they usually clip off strands of their hair and fingernails too and let the favorite keep them as a kind of memento. . . . "

"Yes, I know, but what has that got to do with dead women's hair?"

"Well, there are usually many other patrons whom the courtesans must please in order to keep up their popularity. So they buy clipped hair and fingernals from traders and pass them off as their own. The poor men don't know the difference. After all, it's a very secret affair. Those men, not knowing they have been fooled, slip the stuff into their charm holders. It is all so foolish, but then. . . it means money, so we. . . we planned to cater to that trade."

"Such deception," Yonosuke said dryly, "is the first I have heard. Anyhow," he added sternly, "you cannot rob graves, even to stave off starvation. It is an unforgivable sin. Cover up that coffin intact and bury it again. . . reverently now. And while you are at it, ask the forgiveness of the dead." . . .

While strolling in this manner on Sakai-machi he paused in front of a fashionable theater. The smooth-tongued barker at the entrance was clapping a pair of boards and shouting: "Here, here. . . here is where you can see and hear the only true Tango joruri." He was announcing the performance of a ballad-drama that had originated in the province of Tango. "Come one, come all! The show is just about to begin."

Yonosuke bought a ticket and was about to enter the playhouse when a young girl looking like a maid-servant accosted him from behind: "Moshi moshi, there is a woman who wants to speak to you privately."

He could think of no woman in this section of the town who might wish to converse with him, privately or otherwise.

"Who is she and what does she want to see me about?"

"She is waiting for you there." The girl avoided his question and directed him to a woman standing a few paces away on the street.

As Yonosuke approached wonderingly, this second woman said in a whisper: "I must beg your pardon for disturbing you in this way. I am a maid in waiting to a wealthy widow. My dowager mistress has been highly impressed by your physical appearance—so strong and handsome. She has a favor to ask of you. Only today she discovered the one who is regarded as her family enemy and on whom she must take revenge. She must kill that one. But being a woman, she cannot do it alone. She craves your assistance for the duel. Won't you please help her so that her mind can be set at ease?"

It was an appeal to his sense of chivalry, and to perform such a task was implicit in his new role. Besides, he could not very well ignore or spurn a request so desperately put to him, even by a stranger, even though he was not of the warrior caste and the enemy might be.

"This is a crowded place," he said. "Let us go somewhere near where we can have some privacy and discuss the whole thing."

He led the two women to a nearby tearoom. "Wait here for a while. I shall be back shortly."

Hurriedly Yonosuke returned to his quarters, put on armor for the sword duel, tied a white sweatband around his temples, picked up his sword, examined the sharpness of its edge, and in a few minutes more was back at the tearoom.

"Now tell me all about it," he said.

But the older woman, the rich widow's maid in waiting, seemed in no hurry to give Yonosuke the full details: who the widow was, where she lived, where he could meet her, the name of the family enemy, where that enemy was likely to be found, and for what particular offense the widow must kill him. Instead, she placed before Yonosuke a small brocade bag containing a mysterious object.

"Open it, please," she said. "When you see what it contains, I am sure you will understand what I mean." Then she hid her face behind her flowing uplifted sleeve.

Yonosuke untied the silken strings of the bag and opened it wide. His eyes bulged out in amazement. What he saw in there was an implement carved in an unmistakable form. Anger brought the blood to his face.

"You have deliberately deceived me!" he stormed. "I refuse to be caught in your web of intrigue. Go home and tell your mistress she can roast in hell for all I care. I am ready and willing to help anyone in jeopardy, even at the risk of my own life. But it must be for an honest cause, honestly approached. You have tried to make a fool of me. And I detest lies!"

Now the woman clung to him in mingled shame and appeal. "I . . . I can well understand your anger and distrust. But please believe me. My mistress is not to blame. This is my own scheme. She does not know about it. Still . . . still that thing in there is really her enemy. She asked me to buy it for her—a menace to her own life. Please . . . please help her conquer it." Yonosuke made no move to draw his sword on her, as perhaps he might or should have done. Again he was in torment.

The woman saw the hesitation, coolly disengaged herself, rummaged in her mirror bag. She slipped a number of gold coins to him. "We shall expect you, then, on the evening of the sixteenth of the seventh month."

She left the widow's address on his lap and departed hastily with her younger companion, leaving Yonosuke in a state of angry bewilderment.

"A male concubine!" he cursed to himself. But he knew he would keep that appointment. That was chivalry too. . . .

"Truly there is fun in playing with young actors."

Yonosuke finally yielded to this importunate suasion and visited the Ryosan Temple in Higashiyama.

But the Noh drama rehearsal was already over, and after everyone had left, there was not a sound save the sigh of the evening breeze among the pines and the sizzling of the wheat-gluten cake called fu being fried in deep oil in the temple kitchen. The frying of fu signified that a humble feast of abstinence, a vegetarian repast, was being prepared, which in turn called for abstaining from sakè drinking.

"This is indeed going to be a test of humility," said Yonosuke. "What will we do now? I'm ready for anything."

His host gave an order to a servant: "Go and fetch Tamagawa, Ito, and four or five others from Miyagawamachi. We'll have a different group this time."

Forthwith swift-traveling palanquins were requisitioned, and in no time at all, as it were, the good-looking youths arrived.

"Here they are! Who can resist them?" was the general exclamation.

Yonosuke's host put it this way: "Dallying with these youths is like seeing wolves asleep beneath scattering cherry blossoms, whereas going to bed with prostitutes gives one the feeling of groping in the dark beneath the new moon without a lantern. Truly," he continued, "that is the difference between the two types of indulgence. Almost every man is bound to be bewildered in either situation."

Forgetting their age, the assembled men played all sorts of indoor games with the youths, as though they themselves were boys again, until they became soaked with perspiration. To enjoy the cooling breeze, they all moved to the porch with a southern exposure. It was a night in May, and the moon was hardly bright. A Zelkova tree stood in the shadows, and from the thick foliage of its lower branches came myriads of leaping lights, like some bright glittering objects. Taken aback by this vision, the men ran back helter-skelter into the temple kitchen and administrative office, as though they had lost their minds. One of them, however, a husky chap with great muscular powers, fetched a bow and arrow and was about to leap out into the garden when Sansaburo Takii, one of the handsome youths, seized him from behind.

"Stop it!" said Sansaburo. "There is nothing up there that you should shoot at."

But when Sansaburo walked to the foot of the tree and looked sharply upward toward the leaf-laden branches, he saw a black object moving darkly against a starry background.

"Who are you?" he demanded. "And what are you doing up there?"

A voice from the treetop answered: "Mortifying! This is indeed mortifying! If I had been shot to death by an arrow, I would never be suffering like this. But you, Sansaburo-sama—you, out of your goodness—stopped it, and my agony has increased twofold. I feel as though my bones were cracking—a living hell, I tell you." Hot tears flowed from the eyes of the man in the tree as he said this, and he now wiped them with his sleeve.

"Well then," Sansaburo asked, "are you in love with someone?"

"You're making it harder for me when you ask me that," said the man in the tree. "It is you I have watched every day at the Noh play. How many times, indeed, have I followed you secretly to the gate as you left the theater! Really, I felt like dying when I heard you speak. Today I heard the sandal bearer Kongo and others whispering that you were coming out to Higashiyama again, and I wanted desperately to see you. So I came here and climbed this tree with the intention of forsaking this world by hanging myself. Now that I have had the good fortune of speaking to you, I have nothing to regret. If you have any pity for me, please burn incense for me after I am gone." So saying, he threw down the loose crystals of his broken rosary.

Sansaburo said: "I, too, have felt right along an emotion for you. Now that you have confessed to me, I am very glad. The feeling, I assure you, is mutual. How can I deny your wishes? Wait for the dawn, and your wishes shall be fulfilled. Come to my house in the morning."

The other men at the temple, ignoring this passionate confession of two homosexual males, surrounded the tree and, despite Sansaburo's pleas, dragged the man down from the tree. To the amazement of all, they found him to be a priest living at this temple.

When Yonosuke learned the truth of their attachment, he said: "Splendid!" and himself made arrangements so the two lovers could embrace each other in privacy right away.

The rest of the story came to Yonosuke's ears long afterwards in Edo at a gathering of men devoted to love among homosexuals—a gathering at which confessions were freely made. On that occasion, Sansaburo made a clean breast of his life with the priest. He even had the word Kei tattooed on his left arm as proof of his devotion to the priest, whose name was Keisu. This, therefore, is not fiction but a true story. . . .

At this moment the woman Yonosuke had chosen came in. It seemed she'd already had a few drinks at another table. She was considerably on the tipsy side.

Bedding was meanwhile prepared for the night. The woman said: "I haven't slept for a long time, so I'm going right to bed," and promptly slid into bed without even taking off her outer garments.

While she was seemingly fast asleep, someone yelled from the garden below: "Get up!"

Thereupon the woman awoke and said: "I'm going home, too."

Apparently she was still drunk and while prone on the bed she refused to engage

Yonosuke in conversation. Yonosuke tried to keep himself awake by remaining standing and puffing at his tobacco pipe.

The prostitute suddenly pushed out her buttocks from underneath the bed-covers. As Yonosuke stared at this in wonderment, she let loose a volley of smelly gas in an explosion that seemed to reverberate to the four corners of the room. So then Yonosuke bent down and pressed the bowl of his tobacco pipe on the spot from which the explosion came. If the explosion was deliberate, it was a sad state of affairs, indeed. But if it was spontaneous, beyond her power to prevent, then even the Lord Buddha would perhaps condone it. . . .

But intimacies rarely call for the exercise of one's wits and, as usual, the moment he had secured what he wanted, Yonosuke's interest in her palled. Ever seeking new faces, he found the charms of another Yoshiwara courtesan much more appealing. This meant that he had to sever his relations with the unsuspecting Yoshida.

Out of consideration for her feelings, he hesitated to declare his change of heart openly. He gave her hints instead; fairly obvious and brusque indications that his mind was already roving elsewhere. But she failed to take the hints, seemingly with sublime innocence. She showed no distress, no resentment.

So then one evening Yonosuke took Shohei of the Kozukaya along with him to the house of Ichizaemon. "Today," Yonosuke told Shohei, "it must be final. I am going to be very rude to Yoshida, so rude that she will never want to see me again. I can then visit the other courtesan freely. So you must bear witness and help me along. Let's hurry."

Three was indeed company among intimates, and the impertinent behavior of the two men at last seemed to convince Yoshida that she was going to be jilted. Yet she betrayed no anger, made no recriminative remark. She drank no more, no less than she had always done. She was imperturbably cool.

That confounded the two men. They gulped down their sakè, cup after cup. In their nervous excitement they began to feign drunkenness, the better to infuriate her. Shohei overdid it, knocking down the wine flask and spilling its contents. He tried to stop the flow of the sakè on the mat with his paper handkerchief, but to no avail. There was altogether too much of it. Just as it was about to soil the courtesan's immaculate robe, one of her girl attendants mopped it away with her own brown-and-black robe, soaking it up clean. The robe had to be discarded.

And then, just as the flowers in the garden were being lighted up by lanterns, Yoshida excused herself in order to go to the kitchen. Halfway down the exposed corridor, as she stepped firmly on an apparently loose floor board, there was a curious explosion of sound about her, loud enough for the two men watching in the room to hear. Without any show of embarrassment, however, she proceeded on her way.

"What an interesting sound!" Shohei exclaimed. Yonosuke nodded, laughing. "That gives us a splendid chance to make her really angry with you. When she comes back here we shall hold our noses, and if she does not take the hint . . . well?"

The courtesan took a very long time.

"She must be embarrassed," Shohei surmised.

Before the two men got through laughing, however, they saw her coming back up the corridor. She had changed her robe and she carried a sprig of cherry blossoms. She paused, sidestepped the spot where the sound had occurred, and frowned at it. Then she re-entered the room.

Her singular coolness awed the two men. Shohei hesitated to hold his nose. Yonosuke stood up and went out for an elaborate inspection of the corridor. He stepped vigorously on the floor boards, but no explosion resembling the previous sound could be heard. Just a small squeak. He, too, re-entered the room, silent, with a significant nod at Shohei.

It was the courtesan's voice that now exploded, with cold fury. "For some time now," Yoshida said, glaring at Yonosuke, "you have been acting very rudely. I have known your intentions right along. It was understood that we would keep up our relationship until one of us got tired of the other. Well, let me tell you now that I am fed up with you. Absolutely. I never want to see you again, ever!"

Without giving Yonosuke a chance to reply, she marched out of the room and down the corridor toward the front of the establishment. There, just as cool as ever, she began to play with a little dog. Totally taken aback by this unexpected reversal of the jilting process, the two men left forlornly by a side door.

Worse, the true account of this incident soon spread through the Yoshiwara district, and there was general condemnation of Yonosuke's behavior. The upshot was that the other courtesan for whose charms Yonosuke had tried to desert Yoshida refused to see him.

Later Yoshida called together the mistress of the establishment, the head man Shigeichi, the matron Oman, and all the courtesans to explain her action without equivocation. She said: "I purposely had the floor board loosened just a little at one spot so as to produce a sound when one stepped on it. If the two men were to assume—as I expected they would—that the explosion was of human origin, I would have confessed that such was my contempt for them. But when, upon returning to the room, I sidestepped the spot on the corridor floor, they were completely fooled. It was very, very funny. So I had the last word. Of course the sound did not come from the floor board."

Hizakurige (extracts)

Jippensha Ikku (d. 1831) / Thomas Satchell

Judging from the anecdotes about him, the man who wrote what is considered the funniest book in the Japanese language might have used his own experiences as source material for the novel. He was married at least three times, and his unsatisfactory marriages are clearly reflected in the remarks about women his two protagonists make throughout the book, and in the unflatteringly realistic way in which women are portrayed.

On one occasion, while Jippensha Ikku was visiting a wealthy man, he expressed admiration for the bathtub. His host presented it to him, and Ikku carried the tub home on his head, wittily insulting the pedestrians whom he jostled. The incident is used in

Hizakurige *(Shank's Mare), when his hero carries a door through crowded streets on one occasion, a large ladder on another. Once, when Ikku's publisher came to pay the formal New Year's Day visit, Ikku persuaded him to take a bath while the writer put on the publisher's ceremonial costume and went off to pay his own calls. His familiarity with liquor and brothels is clearly based on first-hand experience, and because he was often short of money his house was bare of furniture. Ikku made up for this dearth by hanging pictures of the missing articles on the walls. On festival days he offered to the gods gifts of the same immaterial nature.*

It is characteristic that he left instructions that certain packets he left were to be cremated with his body. When the funeral prayers had been read and the torch applied, his grieving friends were startled to hear a series of explosions and see shooting stars fly up from the corpse. The packets contained fireworks.[1]

Hizakurige *was published in twelve separate parts between 1802 and 1822. By the time the last section appeared, Ikku had forgotten some of the details in the earlier parts, so there are a few contradictions in the book. They don't matter. The story tells of the adventures of Yaji and Kita as they travel, mostly on foot, from Tokyo to Kyoto. Both are lower-middle-class rascals, amoral, earthy, and prankish, and though Yaji on one occasion masquerades as Jippensha Ikku, there is no substantial evidence to identify him as the author. They are rogues in the picaresque tradition, in Professor Aston's opinion "humble but not unworthy members of the illustrious fraternity which includes Falstaff, Sancho Panza, Sam Weller."*

The mention of Sam Weller is relevant. A number of scholars have chosen The Pickwick Papers *and* Hizakurige *as representative examples of their nations' humor and have considered the books revelatory of their cultures as well as their literatures. Dickens remarked that in* The Pickwick Papers *"no incident or expression occurs which could call a blush into the most delicate cheek." But R. H. Blyth notes: "The humor of* Hizakurige *is derived from sexual intercourse, eating, drinking, defecation, urination and . . . coprophagy."*[2] *He concludes:* "Hizakurige *and* Pickwick Papers *may be taken as typical of the Japanese and English sense of humor. . . . In English humor morality is the master, but Japanese humor is . . . much less limited by moral considerations." In the same vein, W.G. Aston says: "The most that can be said for them [Yaji and Kita] is that their grossness is the grossness of the natural uncultivated man . . . . With two continents and a wide gulf of social and racial differences intervening, their indecency somehow creates less disgust than if they were Englishmen or Frenchmen. Still, people of nice taste had better not read the* Hizakurige."[3]

The blunt fact is that Hizakurige *violates every generalization about the delicacy, subtlety, and propriety of the Japanese temperament. Only by divorcing the book from "proper" Japanese literature can one account for the vulgarity, obscenity, indignities, and frequent use of euphemisms for eating dung that fill the book. Yet* Hizakurige *is undeniably the funniest Japanese piece of extended fiction.*

"It is not far between the barriers, since fifty-three stages are all our country." Thus

1. See Aston, *Japanese Literature,* pp. 369-71.
2. This and the following quotation are from Blyth's *Japanese Humour* (Tokyo, 1958), pp. 98, 99.
3. Aston, p. 372.

wrote Sankoku, the poet, and I have heard that it was from this poem that the stages of the Tokaido came to be fixed at fifty-three.

Again, it is the song of the carriers about the Hakone hills that softens the hearts of the labour-masters, and it is the song of the postboys about the sparrows in the bamboos that awakens pity in the hearts of cut-throats.

Drinking in the virtue of these songs—along with something else—while turning over the leaves of the road-books on the journey to the capital;—using the staves of the carriers as my pen, and inspired by the music of their cries, here have I written a record of the fifty-three stages of the Tokaido.

You will find many bad jokes and much that is worthless in the book, which is moreover overburdened with many poems where sound and sense conflict. Along with this there is much of the one-night love-traffic of the roads,—in fact there is as great a variety of objects and everything is as mixed together as the goods in the shop of a general dealer.

This much by way of a preface. Now we will start on our journey. . . .

As Kitahachi had been turned out of the shop in which he had served so long and had again become a hanger-on of Yaji, and as both were tired of their way of living and were anxious to mend their luck, they decided to leave Edo. Thus it was that, having borrowed some money for the journey, they started in the middle of February along the East Sea route to welcome what they hoped would prove a lucky spring by making a pilgrimage to the Grand Shrine of Ise. . . .

The breeze murmuring through the pines on a beautiful spring day sounds like one singing to the harp of how the pine trees at the gate bring wealth, freedom and happiness. Then truly the highways seem like the hair of the head. Not a single hair is disturbed,—a sign of the glorious times in which we live, when the reputation of our warlike heroes survives only in the pictures of cock-crowing Adzuma;—when our bows and swords—even those made of wood—are hung up as an offering to the god of the thousand swift-brandishing weapons;—when the great exploits of the land rich in harbours,—the deeds of the Golden Age,—seem to pass before our eyes. Now is the

PROVERBS

Of the thirty-six tricks, flight is the best.	To count the age of one's dead child.
Even a monkey sometimes falls from a tree.	Put up a fence even between intimate friends.
Too many boatmen will send the boat up the hill.	The mean man at leisure does evil.
Preaching sermons to Buddha.	Youth may easily pass into age, but learning is hard to acquire.
Even a carriage and four cannot overtake the tongue.	He who mixes with vermilion becomes red.
Cultivate a rice-field rather than make verses.	While on a journey one need feel no shame.

time to visit all the celebrated places in the country and fill our heads with what we have seen, so that when we become old and bald we shall have something to talk about over the teacups. Let us accept the invitation of these bosom friends and go with them on their long long journey. Let us join this dissipated Yajirobei and his hanger-on Kitahachi, with their money kept warm in the loin-cloths round their navels; with their light foot-gear and their many shells of ointment, which will keep their feet from getting sore for thousands of miles; and their cotton robes dappled like the flesh of a clam. Let us go with them through foot-worn Yamato, welcomed by the divine wind that blows from the Grand Shrine of Ise, with the flowers of the capital and the plum-blossoms of Naniwa at the end of our journey.

Here they are already at Takinawa, which reminds them of the epigram

We remember we've forgotten
When we get to Takinawa.

But they have nothing to forget. Theirs is the easy life of the bachelor. No more than the rats are they required to waste money on rent, and as all the property they have is tied up in a bundle they have no anxiety about that. It is true that they had to make a small offering of rice at the family temple, and besides that pay a hundred coppers to get a travelling permit. Moreover, instead of paying what they owed to the landlord, they had to get their papers to pass the barriers. However, they made some money by selling to a second-hand dealer what they had of value, leaving the rubbish in the house for the next tenant to return thanks for. The stone weight for the pickle tub and the knife for scraping the pots and pans they left next door, and the house opposite got the torn sunshades and the oil jar. Nothing is left, but there is still the difficulty of paying the rice bill and the sakè bill. They are very sorry to go away without paying them, but then as the old poem says

Whether in this life or the next we cheat
In either case our punishment we'll meet.

This made them burst into laughter; after which Yajirobei began humming,

It is not right
To fly by night
To escape the dun,
The Edo dun;
But what can be done
Save tuck up your skirts
And cut and run.
So get you gone,
You Edo dun!
The water is deep and the river wide;
You can rave all you like on the other side.

Thus amusing themselves they quickly passed Shinagawa and Suzu-ga-mori, and reached Omori. . . .

Then they crossed the Rokugo ferry and went into the Mannenya to have a meal.

'Good morning,' said the maid.

'Let us have two trays, please,' said Yaji.

'I say, Yaji,' said Kita. 'Look at that girl. She used to be as slender as a willow and now she's like a mortar. Somebody's been pounding her. And isn't it strange that all the teahouses on the road should have dried up flowers in the alcoves. Look at that scroll. What is it?''

'That's carp going up a waterfall,' said Yaji.

'Is it?' said Kita. 'I thought they were eating vermicelli.'

'You'd better eat your food instead of talking nonsense,' said Yaji. 'The soup's getting cold.'

'Halloa!' cried Kita. 'I never knew they'd brought it.'

They quickly gulped down the beans and rice set before them.

'Well, we've cleaned up that dish,' said Yaji.

'Let's go a bit further and have something tasty,' suggested Kita.

They paid for their meal and were just starting off when they saw a daimyo's procession coming from the opposite direction. The running footmen in front were an old man of sixty and a boy of fourteen or fifteen. Both of them were inn servants.

'Down, down!' cried one of the footmen. 'Off, those with headgear.'

'Those with the head covered don't have to squat down, it seems,' said Kita.

'Why?' asked Yaji.

'Because he said off with them!' answered Kita.

'Postboy, hold that horse's mouth,' called out the footman.

'How's he going to hold the mouth of the horse?' said Kita. 'He-he-he!'

'That man behind is not bending low enough,' went on the footman.

'Does he mean me?' asked Yaji. 'Of course I'm not low enough. You wouldn't expect it of one who's as tall as Kumonryo on Atago Hill.'

'Don't make fun of them,' said Kita, 'or you'll get 'em angry.'

'Look,' said Yaji. 'Aren't those fine fellows? See how regularly their clothes are folded and how they keep in line. I know what they're like. They're like an airing of clothes in Yoshicho.'

'Halloa!' said Kita. 'Look at the helmets of those fellows with the bows. They look as though their heads were swollen.'

'And look at the length of their cloaks,' cried Yaji. 'You can see their whatyoumay-callems peeping out.'

'He's a fine fellow—the lord,' said Kita. 'I expect he's a great man with the maids.'

'There you go meddling with things you don't know anything about,' replied Yaji. 'You don't suppose people of that sort would stoop so low, do you?'

'Why not?' said Kita. 'There you are. Look at him. See how erect he is. Come on, we can go on now he's gone.'

They got up and went on, and at the end of the town met two postboys.

'Won't you ride, gentlemen,' they cried. 'We're on our way back.'

'We'll ride if it's cheap,' said Yaji.

'Just for a tip,' cried the postboys. 'Two hundred coppers.'

Having settled the price, Yaji and Kita got on the horses and rode along, the horses' bells ringing shan-shan-shan and the horses whinnying hin-hin-hin.

Then another postboy came past from the opposite direction.

'Halloa, you beast,' he said. 'You are early.'

'Go and eat dirt,' replied the other postboy.

'Ugh!' replied the first. 'Suck it.'

The only salutations of these kind of people when they passed each other seemed to be abuse.

'Here, Iga,' said the postboy of the horse Yaji was riding on, 'that fellow you were drinking with yesterday, that was Boshu of the upper stage, wasn't it?'

This kind of people never call each other by their names but only by the name of the provinces they come from.

'Last night,' said Kita's postboy, as he spat in the road, 'the wife of that chap Boshu was doing a job for herself outside the master's back door. The noise of it made me feel quite ill. She don't care where she does it, thinks I. I'll go out and give her one; for you see, I'd had just enough to make me feel like giving somebody one. So I lifted up my fist and was just going to give her one when she gives a jump. "Here, what are you doing?" she says. "What am I doing?" I says. "Do you think we're dogs' dirt?" I says, "Shut up," I says, and I give her one. "You rascal," she says, and she give me a shove that nearly sent me over, she's that big and strong. "Eh, what's that you're jawing about?" I says, and I give her a slap on the side of the face that sent her up against the stable wall and made her fall down. So I seized hold of her and as she was still jawing I shoved two or three pieces of rice-cake I'd bought for the master's kid into her mouth and while she was munching that I beat her. Then she said she wanted some more and I was feeling round for some and picked up a lump of horsedung by mistake and shoved it into her mouth and made her feel so bad that she got angry with me. So I had to promise at last that I'd give her a pair of clogs. What a bother!'

While they were amusing themselves by listening to this story they arrived on the outskirts of Kanagawa, and alighting from their horses continued their journey on foot. . . .

Leaving the teahouse they went along joking and talking at the tops of their voices and amusing themselves with one thing and another, till they caught up, at the end of the stage, with a boy of twelve or thirteen who was going to Ise.

'Please give me a copper, masters,' called the boy.

'Of course, of course,' said Yaji. 'Where do you come from?'

'I come from Oshu,' said the boy.

'Whereabouts in Oshu?' asked Kita.

'It's written on my hat,' said the boy.

'Chomatsu, village of Hatayama, district of Shinobu, Oshu,' read Yaji. 'Hatayama, eh? I've been there. Is Master Yojirobei in good health?'

'I don't know anybody called Yojirobei,' said the boy. 'But Master Yotaro lives next door to us.'

'Yes, yes,' said Yaji. 'That's him. And there should be an old gentleman named Nontaro living with him.'

'There is an old man,' said the boy.

'And Master Yotaro's wife is certainly a woman,' continued Yaji.

'Yes, Mistress Katsu's a woman,' said the boy. 'Your honour knows all about it.'

'I don't know how it is now,' said Yaji. 'but at that time the headman of the village was Denzaburo Kumano. His wife ran away after having had a love affair with a horse that her husband kept.'

'Your honour knows all about it,' said the boy. 'She went off with Master Horser as your honour says.'

'Wonderful! Wonderful!' cried Kita.

'Here, boy!' called Yaji. 'Why do you lag behind? Are you tired?'

'I'm so hungry I don't know what to do,' said the boy.

'Shall I buy you some rice-cake?' asked Yaji. 'Come along.'

He bought the boy five or six rice-cakes in great elation.

'There you are, my boy,' he said. 'You see I know all about your village.'

Then the companion of the boy, also a lad of some fourteen or fifteen, came running after them.

'Here, Chomatsu, Chomatsu!' he called.

'Come along,' said Chomatsu.

'Give me some rice-cake,' said the boy.

'Get that man in front to buy you some,' said Chomatsu. 'All you've got to do is to say "Yes" to everything he asks you about your part of the country.'

'I'll get him to give me some too,' said the boy. He ran after Yaji and caught him up. 'Please buy me some rice-cake too,' he said.

'Where do you come from?' asked Yaji, and he looked at the writing on his hat. 'Aha!' he said, 'you are from Oshu too. Imura, Shimosaka, eh? Look here, is there an old man named Yomosaku in your village?'

'Buy me the rice-cake first,' said the boy, 'or I shan't play up to you.'

'Get out,' said Yaji. 'Ha-ha-ha!'

'He-he-he! He had you that time,' laughed Kita.

Thus laughing and joking it was not long before they came to Hodogaya, where on both sides of the way the decoys were waiting, with their faces plastered with powder, just as if they were wearing masks, and all with blue aprons of the same pattern. . . .

'Wait a bit, Kita,' called Yaji. 'I've got something I want to talk to you about. Look here, they're sure to be always bothering us to take a girl at all the places we stop at. I've got a plan to prevent that. As I'm older than you I'll be the father, and as you're in the twenties you can be the son. Then at every place we stop at we can pretend to be father and son.'

'That's a good idea,' said Kita. 'It would be just the thing to keep them from bothering us. Must I call you father?'

'Yes, yes,' said Yaji. 'You must act like a son, you know, and do everything I tell you.'

'All right,' said Kita. 'But if there's a nice girl you mustn't try and keep her from your son.' . . .

Meanwhile the old woman had brought four or five dumplings on a tray.

'That dumpling's burnt,' said Yaji, but looking at it more closely he saw that it was a piece of hot cinder that had stuck to it.

'Here,' he said, passing it to Kita just as it was with the hot cinder on, 'try this one. You like 'em burnt, don't you?'

'Where, where?' asked Kita, and he stuck it in his mouth. 'Oh, oh!' he yelled. 'Look what you've done to me. There's a piece of hot cinder stuck to it. Oh, how it burns!'

'Ha-ha-ha!' laughed Yaji. 'I thought you liked 'em hot. That's why I gave you the one with the hot cinder on. Come, let's go.'

Kita followed grumbling and spitting after they had paid for the dumplings.

At Fujisawa they found each side of the road lined with the teahouse girls, who were calling out in chorus, 'Walk in, walk in. Our wine doesn't make you drunk. Try our hard-boiled rice.'

Then a postboy accosted them. 'Masters,' he said. 'Do you want a lively horse? I'll let you ride cheap. It's quite sound and warranted to kick.'

'Take a kago,' called a carrier. 'I'll carry you cheap as I'm on my way back.'

'How much?' asked Kita.

'Three hundred and fifty coppers,' replied the carrier.

'Too dear,' said Yaji. 'Why, I'd carry it myself for a hundred and fifty.'

'All right,' said the carrier. 'We'll make it a hundred and fifty.'

'You've come down, eh?' said Yaji. 'Very well, just hang my sandals up in front.'

'But you're not going to ride, are you?' said the carrier. 'You said you'd carry it yourself for a hundred and fifty, so I thought I'd get a hundred and fifty too for carrying the other end."

'That's a good one,' said Yaji laughing. 'Well, we'll make it two hundred then.'

'It's very cheap,' said the carrier, 'but we'll take it. What do you say, mate? Please get in.'

The price having thus been settled Yaji got into the kago and the men started.

'I say, mate,' said the carrier in front, 'the master's rather hard.'

'That's because he's strongly made,' said the carrier behind.

Just then the landlord of one of the teahouses called to the carriers. 'Hi!' he said. 'When you get to Umezawa just call at Sadoya's and tell him that the last wine had too much water in it. Tell him to put a little sakè with the next lot he sends. Look out, you've dropped something.'

'All right,' said the carriers, and started on their way.

'Do you come from Fujisawa?' asked Yaji. 'The town's got quite pretty. Is Master Tarozaemon, the merchant, in good health?'

'Master knows everybody,' said the carrier in front. 'Yes, he's quite well.'

'Is Master Magoshichi still working there?' continued Yaji.

'Yes, yes,' said the carrier in front. 'Master knows all about everybody.'

'You fool,' said the carrier behind. 'Of course he does. He's looking in the guide-book as he goes along. Ha-ha-ha!' . . .

At last they came to the inn, where the landlord hastened in and called the maids to bring hot water. The landlord's wife brought them some tea, and in the meanwhile the maid filled a bucket with hot water and brought it for them to wash their feet. Yaji looked at the girl out of the corner of his eye.

'Look at her,' he whispered to Kita. 'She ain't so bad.'

'I'll see what she's like tonight,' said Kita.

'What are you jawing about?' said Yaji. 'I'm going to do that.' . . .

Here the maid came back and told them that the bath was hot.

'Oh, the cold water's got hot, has it?' said Yaji. 'Then I'll go in.'

Taking his towel he went off to the bathroom.

Now, the landlord of this inn was a man from the West Country, and the bath resembled a Goemon bath, such as is common in his part of the country. He had constructed an oven of cement and over that placed a very thin piece of iron, such as is used to bake cakes on. On this he had placed the bath, and to keep it from leaking he had put mortar all round the sides. This is a very economical form of bath because it does not require much firewood to heat the water. Such baths have no lids, but there is a piece of wood to go on the bottom of the bath and as this floats on the top of the water when it is not in use, it serves as a lid and causes the water to get hot very rapidly. When the bath is used this piece of wood is, of course, pushed down to the bottom of the bath.

Yajirobei had never seen a bath like this before, and thinking the piece of wood floating on the top was a lid he took it off quite innocently and put it on one side. Then he plunged into the bath, but as there was only the red-hot iron of the oven to stand on he burnt his feet horribly and got a terrible shock.

'Oh, oh, oh!' he shouted, jumping out. 'This is a devil of a bath.'

As he didn't like to ask how to get into the bath, he turned over all sorts of plans in his mind, till it happened that his eyes fell on a pair of clogs outside the closet. 'Aha!' he thought. 'Those are just the things.' He put them on and got into the bath, and felt so happy at his discovery that he commenced to chant to himself.

'Her tears fell like dew,' he chanted, when Kitahachi, who had got tired of waiting, peeped in at the door.

'Halloa!' he said. 'That's why you've been so long in the bath. Aren't you coming out yet?'

'Here, just feel me,' said Yaji.

'Why?' asked Kita.

'Don't I feel as if I had been boiled?''

'You seem to have been enjoying yourself,' said Kita.

Kitahachi went back into the room and Yaji, getting out of the bath, hid the clogs and came back to the room with an entirely innocent face.

'Won't you have a bath?' he said.

'I'm off,' said Kita.

Quickly stripping himself he plunged one foot into the bath.

'Oh, oh, oh!' he yelled. 'Yaji, Yaji, come here a moment. It's awful.'

'What a row you are making,' said Yaji. 'What's the matter?'

'Look here,' said Kita. 'How did you get into this bath?'

'Fool!' said Yaji. 'There can't be more than one way of getting into a bath. You just swill yourself down and plunge in feet foremost.'

'It's no joking matter,' said Kita. 'How can you get in when the bottom's hot?'

'Of course you can,' replied Yaji. 'You saw me in the bath yourself.'

'How did you manage it?'

'What a persistent chap you are. What is there in getting into a bath?'

'Well, it's very strange,' said Kita.

'There's no difficulty about it,' said Yaji. 'It's a little hot at first, but bear it for a time and you'll soon get used to it.'

'Don't talk like a fool,' said Kita. 'While I'm getting used to it my feet will be burnt off.'

'What an unreasonable chap you are!' said Yaji.

Yaji was so tickled over Kita's plight that he had to go back into the room to have a laugh. Kita thought of all sorts of plans for getting into the bath, and while he was looking around he came upon the pair of clogs that Yaji had hidden. 'Aha!' he thought, 'I see now,' and putting them on he got into the bath. 'Yaji, Yaji,' he called.

'What is it now?' asked Yaji.

'It's just like what you said. It's not hot when once you get in. It feels fine. Do you not feel sorry for Ishidomaru? Tsunren, tsunren,' he began to chant.

Looking round Yaji saw that the clogs he had hidden had disappeared and knew that Kita had found them. He was just enjoying the joke when Kita, what with continually jumping up and down when he found a certain portion of his body was getting too hot and clattering about on the clogs inside the bath, broke the bottom out and sat down violently on the oven underneath, while the water running out of the bath turned into scalding steam. . . .

'Don't make a joke of it,' said Kita. 'You don't know how I feel.'

'Well, I'm sorry you feel it so much,' said Yaji, 'because I've got something to tell you that will make you feel worse still.'

'What's that?' asked Kita.

'I've arranged for the maid to come here secretly tonight,' said Yaji. 'It's all fixed up. As you're so low spirited now I'm afraid this will make you feel worse.'

'Really, is it true?' asked Kita. 'When did you arrange it?'

'I'm pretty smart at that sort of thing,' said Yaji. 'It was while you were in the bath. I gave her something in advance and sealed the bargain with a kiss. Ain't I clever? That's how lovers are. Ha-ha-ha! Shall we go to bed now?'

While Yaji was out doing something for himself the maid came in to make the beds.

'I say,' said Kita. 'You've made some arrangement with my companion, haven't you?'

'Ho-ho-ho!' laughed the girl.

'Well, it's no laughing matter,' said Kita. 'I'll tell you secretly that that fellow's suffering terribly from disease and you'd better be careful you don't catch it. It's out of pity for you that I'm telling you. You mustn't tell anyone else.'

As he was telling her as a secret the girl thought it was true and felt shocked.

'And his legs are always covered with boils,' Kita went on seeing the impression he had made, 'and they keep breaking like beggars' hats, and he has to stick ointment over them. And then the smell of his armpits! And he's such a terribly passionate fellow that he never lets go once he has caught hold of you. And his breath smells something horrible; that's because of his disease. It's really almost impossible for me to sit and eat with him. It makes me feel sick. Ugh!'

While he was speaking Yaji came back again and the girl said good-night and quickly went out. Yaji got into bed immediately.

'I'll just warm it up a bit,' he said.

'Botheration,' said Kita. 'Everything's gone wrong tonight. First I burn myself and then I have to pay two hundred coppers, and then on top of that I've got to lie here alone while you're embracing that nice girl. I'm being knocked about by the world something awful.'

'He-he-he!' giggled Yaji. 'You must be patient. I know it will be rather disagreeable for you tonight, but still . . . I wonder when the little beauty is coming . . . Kitahachi, are you asleep? Don't go to sleep yet.'

But Kita only snored by way of answer.

Yaji thought he heard the maid coming, but however long he waited there was not a sign of her, and he began to feel doubtful whether he had not wasted his money in giving her something in advance. At last he could bear the suspense no longer and clapped his hands. The landlady answered the summons.

'Did you call?' she asked.

'It's not about you,' said Yaji. 'I've got something I want to ask the maid. Would you mind calling her?'

'The girl who waited on you?' asked the landlady. 'She comes in from outside every day. She's gone home now.'

'Oh! said Yaji. 'Really? All right, all right.'

So the landlady said good-night and went back to the kitchen.

'Ha-ha-ha!' laughed Kita.

'What are you laughing at, you fool?' asked Yaji.

But Kita went on laughing. 'I've got level with you now,' he said. 'We can go to sleep peacefully.'

'Do as you like,' said Yaji sulkily.

The unfortunate Yaji, quite unconscious of the trick that Kita had played on him, knew that he had not only wasted his treasured money but that he was also compelled to lose time by lying alone that night. . . .

Soon after they had passed Nagasaka Oshigure they were overtaken by a traveller in a blue raincoat, who was carrying a bundle and a basket. After he had passed and repassed them several times, the traveller at last spoke to them.

'May I ask where you gentlemen hail from?' he said.

'We're from Edo,' replied Yaji.

'I also am from Edo,' replied the traveller, whose name was Jukichi. 'May I ask what part of Edo you come from?'

'From Kanda,' said Yaji.

'Why, that's where I live,' said Jukichi. 'I thought I'd seen you somewhere. May I ask what part of Kanda?'

'At Yajirobei Tochimenya's in Hatcho-bori,' said Yaji. 'It's quite a big place, with a frontage of a hundred and fifty feet and a backage of two hundred and fifty. It's a corner house, built of plaster.'

'I see,' said Jukichi. 'You live behind that house.'

'Nonsense!' said Yaji. 'Mine's not a house in a back lane. It's a detached house.'

'Oh, indeed!' said Jukichi. 'What's the value of the property?'

'One thousand eight hundred gold pieces.'

'Do you get the first commission on the sale? If so I'll split it with you.'

'Whatever are you talking about?' asked Yaji.

"I thought you'd got a commission to sell the place.'

'No, no, that's not it at all,' said Yaji. 'Why, when I go out I usually have five or ten retainers with me, but I got tired of that, so I just take this one fellow now. I've got a whim for roughing it when I walk.'

'Yes, yes, I see,' said Jukichi. 'By the way I met your respected mother the other day. I know her well. It was in Asakusa, just opposite the Monzeki Temple I saw her. She had a bundle in her hand and was walking with the aid of a stick. She must be very old.'

'Yes, yes,' said Yaji. 'She was probably going to worship at one of the temples. As she knows you she must certainly have spoken to you.'

'Yes,' said Jukichi. 'When she saw me she came hobbling up, and did me the honour to say,' Won't you give me a copper, kind master?'

At this Kita burst into a roar of laughter.

'You had me that time,' acknowledged Yaji. . . .

With the bed quilt drawn tightly over them, for a time they lay silent.

Meanwhile Kita's companion, Tsume, had also come, and there was more talk, but I will not repeat it. Already the night had deepened, and the sound of the horses' bells was stilled. All that could be heard was the far-off bark of the dogs chasing the wild boar, and the sighing of the night wind as it blew coldly round the inn. Soon the oil in the night-lamp became exhausted and the light went out, leaving the room in complete darkness.

Meanwhile the turtle, which they had left lying in the alcove wrapped in straw, had bitten its way through and crept out. Softly it crawled along the floor, but not so softly that it did not waken Jukichi, who lay and wondered what it was. Slowly the turtle crawled along, till finally it crept among Kita's bedclothes, causing Kita to wake up with a start.

'What's that?' he cried.

He lifted up his head, whereupon the turtle got alarmed and tried to run across his chest. At this Kita gave a yell, caught hold of it and flung it away. It fell on Yaji's face, and he also woke up with a start and caught hold of the turtle, which promptly bit his finger.

'Oh! Oh! Oh!' yelled Yaji.

This startled Take out of her sleep. 'What's the matter?' she cried.

'Light the lamp, yelled Yaji. 'Oh! Oh! Oh!'

'Whatever have you done?' asked Take.

Feeling about, her fingers came in contact with the turtle, whereupon, with an exclamation of surprise, she fell backwards, knocking over the screen with a bang as she did so. Then she began to clap her hands wildly.

'I can't see what's happening in the dark,' said Kita.

'Tatsudon! Tatsudon! called Take. 'The guests have been calling you for a long time. Bring a light quickly.'

'Quick, quick!' said Yaji. 'Oh! Oh! Oh!' and he began to howl in his anguish.

Meanwhile Jukichi had stolen the money in Yaji's loin-belt, which Yaji had placed under his bedding, and had substituted for the money a packet of pebbles which he had prepared beforehand, afterwards carefully putting the belt back where it was before under the bedding. In truth this Jukichi was a thief, who lived by robbing travellers on the road. He had seen that Yaji was carrying some money and had picked up an acquaintance with him in order to steal it.

At last the landlady appeared with a light and was much surprised to see the turtle. 'Dear me, how did that get in here?' she asked.

'That must be the turtle we bought last night,' Kita said. 'It's eaten its way through the grass and come out. It's caught you this time, hasn't it?'

'It's nothing to laugh about,' said Yaji. 'Look how it's made the blood come. Oh! Oh! Oh!'

'I was wondering what it was,' said Take, 'and it turns out to be a turtle. You must put your finger in water and it will soon let go.'

'Yes, that's what you must do,' said the landlady. The shutters were opened and Yaji rushed to the washbasin and stuck his finger into the water, whereupon the turtle let go.

'There,' said Yaji. 'Look what he's done to me.'

'Dear me,' said Kita. 'What an extraordinary thing! Wonderful, unheard of, most astonishing and inexplicable. Ha-ha-ha!'

After putting things straight, as it was still before dawn they went to sleep again, though not before Kita, half in fun, had composed the following poem:

> The turtle bit his finger till it bled
> From bashfulness when getting in his bed. . . .

'I thought I'd have some fun with that young palmer,' said Yaji, 'but the old woman's taken her upstairs. What a nuisance!'

'I squeezed her hand and pinched her while I was talking to her,' said Kita. 'You didn't know I was making love to her, did you?'

'None of your lies,' said Yaji.

'It's not a lie,' said Kita. 'I'm going to have that girl tonight.'

'Ain't he quick!' said Yaji.

They went in and shut the door, and so to sleep. The strangeness of the place where they were spending the night, the roughness of the accommodation, the broken plaster through which the wind whistled,—all these they thought would form a subject for conversation hereafter. The night deepened and at the sound of the midnight bell Kitahachi opened his eyes. He listened and heard them all snoring; they were worn out with their travels. 'Now's the time,' he thought, and getting up softly he felt round in the darkness till he had found the ladder. Now the floor of the attic was made of interlaced bamboos, on which mats were spread, and when anyone walked on the floor it made a great creaking. This startled Kita at first, but he crawled along on all fours, feeling about, till he came to the bed in which he thought the young girl was sleeping, although in reality it was the old woman's bed. He crept in and began shaking her gently to wake her up. The old woman soon opened her eyes.

'Who's that?' she called. 'What are you doing?'

At the sound of the old woman's voice Kita discovered his mistake and endeavoured to get away. He jumped up, but unfortunately ran a splinter of the bamboo into his foot, which made him fall down, whereupon the bamboos gave way and he fell with a crash into the room below.

'What's that?' called the old man.

'Whatever can it be!' called the old woman. 'What an awful noise! Get up all of you.'

The noise had also awakened the pilgrim and the palmer.

'What a terrible noise!' said the pilgrim. 'Light the lamp. We can't see what it is in the darkness.'

Meanwhile the unfortunate Kita, having broken through the ceiling, had fallen into what seemed to him like a box, though what it was he could not well make out. His feet seemed to be caught in something and feeling about he found it was the halo of a Buddhist saint. Then he knew that he had fallen inside the Buddhist shrine, a fact which tickled his sense of humour in spite of the pain that he was suffering from his fall.

Meanwhile the old man had been getting the lamp lit.

'Seems as if it fell inside the shrine,' he said. He opened the doors of the shrine, when, to his surprise, Kitahachi walked out.

'Oh! Oh!' he said, 'It's this man.'

'Can you tell me the way to the Minobu?' asked Kita.

'Don't talk nonsense,' said the old man. 'What are you doing in there?'

'Well, I got up to go somewhere,' said Kita, 'but I lost my way.'

'Lost your way? said the old man. 'You haven't been doing it inside the shrine, have you?' He peeped inside and saw the ceiling was broken.

'He fell through the ceiling,' he cried.

'Yes,' said Kita. 'I fell through while I was running away from the cat.'

'Are you a rat?' said the old man. 'Running away from the cat, indeed! What did you go upstairs for?'

'Well, the rats carried off my loin-cloth, and I thought it might be upstairs, so I went up to look.'

While Kita was making these excuses the old woman came down from upstairs.

'It's not that at all,' she said. 'I'm sixty years old, and I don't know what part of the country he comes from, but he came upstairs and crept into my bed.'

'What?' said the old man. 'He must be mad. Why, it's twenty years since I gave up that sort of thing. Creeping into the bed of a wrinkled old woman, indeed. It's disgraceful.'

'Please excuse me,' said Kita. 'Here, Yaji, don't lie there pretending you're asleep. Get up.'

Yaji thus awakened concealed his amusement. 'He's very young,' he said, 'and never thinks of what he's doing. Do forgive him.'

The pilgrim and the palmer also endeavoured to calm the old man, and finally Kita, by the sale of a kimono, raised enough money to pay for the repair of the ceiling. The affair was thus settled. . . .

'It will be fun going to buy a girl on horseback,' said Yaji.

Finally they set out on horseback.

This Abekawa-cho is in front of the Abekawa Miroku. Turning off the main road you come to two big gates, where you must alight from your horse. Inside are rows of houses, from each of which comes a lively sound of music, meant to attract people to the house. In fact it is much the same as in the Yoshiwara quarter in Edo. . . .

Let's go in somewhere,' said Yaji.

'Wait a minute,' said Kita. 'The girls all have different prices—some of them are one bu, some ten momme, and some two shu. I'll have that one over there by the wall. She'll be ten momme I expect. What's the name of that place? Shinonoya. And there's the Chojiya, and this is the Yamamotoya. But what do you do to get in? I don't know how they manage things here.'

While they were wandering about in front of the gates, they saw a guest arrive and go in.

'Oh, oh! I see now,' said Kita. 'Let's go in here. Yaji, have you chosen one?'

'Yes, yes,' said Yaji. 'Come on.' So they went in together.

'Welcome!' said a young man at the entrance. 'Please come up.'

He conducted them upstairs and soon led them to the room of the girls they had selected. Looking around they saw there was a harp in the alcove and also some flowers. Altogether it was like a small house in the Yoshiwara at Edo. Apparently it was the custom to pay some drink-money at this stage of the proceedings.

'Will you have some sakè?' asked the young man.

'Yes, bring some sakè,' said Kita.

Meanwhile the two girls they had selected had come in. Yaji's, whose name was Kozasano, was dressed in a wadded silk robe, with a striped satin girdle and a sky-blue overmantle; Kita's, whose name was Isagawa, was dressed in a striped crepe-silk robe and a gold embroidered girdle, with a black silk cloak. Both of them had silk lining to their clothes. . . .

Just then there was a noise in the passage, with the sound of many voices raised in dispute, and finally the persons disputing went into the next room.

'What's the row?' asked Kita.

'It's nothing,' said Isagawa. 'They've found a bad guest and brought him here.'

'Ah, that's amusing,' said Yaji. 'Let's have a look.'

He pushed open the sliding doors a little and peeped into the next room, where a large number of girls had surrounded one of the guests.

'Why do you never come here now?' they asked.

'You're always going to the Chojiya now,' said another girl, 'and you've got no reason for it. You've made Tokonatsu quite angry.'

'Well, look here,' said the guest, who seemed to be a country fellow. 'The day before yesterday and yesterday I was coming, but I had so much to do that I couldn't get here. Then my uncle asked me to accompany him to the Chojiya, and I went, but as I am under a vow to Tokonatsu I swear by Nitten I did not allow my heart to be turned.'

'Nonsense!' cried the girls. 'You went with Hanayama of the Chojiya. We know all about it.'

'No, no, that's not true,' said the guest looking hurt. 'You mustn't say such things.'

Then an elder girl of the name of Tokonatsu came in. She had thrown a mantle over her shoulders and came in solemnly carrying a pipe and a tobacco pouch.

'You are welcome, Master Yatei,' said she.

'I'm sorry I haven't been able to come and see you lately,' said Yatei. 'You must excuse me.'

'There's no excuse for you,' said Tokonatsu. 'I'm the oldest here, and the girls call me elder sister. How do you suppose I'm going to maintain my position here if I'm put to shame like this? I'm going to punish you just as a warning to other false guests like you. Here, Natsugiku, bring that razor.'

'What are you going to do?' asked the guest.

'What am I going to do?' said Tokonatsu. 'I'm going to cut off your hair.'

The razor was brought and the girl stood up to carry out her threat.

'Spare me, spare me,' cried the guest as he tried to shield his head. 'Wait, wait.'

'There's nothing to wait for,' cried the girls.

'I can't let you cut a hair of it,' said the guest. 'Forgive me, forgive me.'

'Forgive you, indeed!' said Tokonatsu.

'Well, but look here . . .'

'We must cut it off.'

'Here, here,' cried the guest. He tried to run away, but they all got round him and caught hold of his head, whereupon all his hair came off. In truth the man had very little hair of his own and was wearing a false queue and side locks, which all fell off when they pulled it.

'There,' said the man, feeling his head, 'You've pulled off all my hair.'

At that all the girls burst into laughter. 'Ho-ho-ho!' they laughed.

'It's no laughing matter,' said the guest. 'Give me my hair and I won't go to the Chojiya again.'

'I don't know anything about your hair,' said Tokonatsu.

'Natsugiku's hidden it,' said the guest. 'Please give me my hair quickly.'

'Will you promise not to go to the Chojiya again?'

'Yes, yes. I won't go again.'

'Solemnly promise?'

'By Ten Shoko Daijingu I promise not to go again.'

'Then give him his hair, Natsugiku,' said Tokonatsu. . . .

Yaji and Kita laughed till their sides ached. 'That happens all over the place,' said Yaji, 'but it's very amusing. It was only last spring that Ikku was tied up by Katsuyama at the Nakadaya, although he doesn't like people to know about it.'

Then a maid came in. 'Shall I spread the beds?' she asked. 'Please move a little over here.'

Kita went with his companion into another room, and the maid spread the bed, and in a short time they were asleep. But their dreams were short, for the dawn soon came, with its parting. Yaji got up, and Kita came in rubbing his eyes. Their companions accompanied them downstairs, where all were assembled, and after a hurried farewell, they hastened to Temmacho, to find their breakfast at the inn ready for them. . . .

Just then a ferryman came to meet them. 'Are you going up to the capital, gentlemen?' he asked.

'Who are you?' asked Yaji.

'I'm the waterman,' he replied. 'I'll take you across the river cheap.'

'How much?' asked Kita.

'The rain yesterday has made the river rise,' said the waterman, 'so it will be sixty-four coppers each.'

'That's dear,' said Kita.

'Well, just go and look at the river, then,' said the waterman.

'It is running fast,' said Yaji. 'Don't let us fall in.'

'Never fear,' said the waterman. 'Just get in.'

The two got into the hand-barrow, and the watermen commenced to carry them across the river.

'Oh lor'!' said Kita. 'It makes my eyes go round in my head to look at it!'

'Keep hold of my head,' said the waterman. 'Here, you're putting your hand in front of my eyes and I can't see where I'm going.'

'It is deep,' said Yaji. 'Don't let us fall.'

'There's no chance of your falling,' said the waterman.

'What would happen if you were to let us drop?' asked Yaji.

'You'd only be carried away by the current and drowned, that's all,' said the waterman.

'Don't talk of it,' said Yaji. 'Here we are, here we are. Thank you, thank you.'

He got out of the hand-barrow and paid the men. 'There's sixteen coppers each extra for you,' he said.

'Thank 'ee, your honour,' said the watermen, and went back across the river lower down where it was shallow.

'Here, Yaji, look at that,' cried Kita. 'They took us across the deep part and charged us sixty-four coppers each for it.'

From there they reached Tegoshi, where it started to rain again and soon was coming down in torrents. But they put their raincoats over their shoulders and trudged along till they got to Mariko. Here they entered a teahouse.

'Shall we have a meal?' suggested Kita. 'This place is famous for its potato stew.'

'Landlord,' called Yaji. "Have you got any potato stew ready?'

'Yes, sir,' replied the landlord. 'Make it in a minute.'

'Then you haven't got any ready?' said Yaji. 'That's unfortunate.'

'Ready in a minute, sir,' said the landlord. 'Please wait a moment.'

He seized some potatoes and began to cut them up without taking off the skins.

'Nabe, Nabe,' he called testily, 'what are you doing out there when I'm so busy? Come in, come in.'

A tousle-haired woman, with a baby on her back, came in at the back-door dragging her straw sandals along the ground and grumbling.

'I've only been having a bit of a chat,' she said. 'What a grumbler you are.'

'Who's a grumbler?' said the landlord. 'Here, get the things out for two guests. Look at your apron dragging on the floor.'

'What did you do with the chopsticks that were washed?' asked the woman.

'How do I know?' said the landlord. 'There we are. Now just hand me the chopsticks.'

'Do you mean these?'

'No, no. How do you think I'm going to pound potatoes with chopsticks? It's the pestle I want. Don't go to sleep. That ain't the tray. I told you to bring it here. What a fool the woman is!'

He seized the pestle and began to pound the potatoes in the mortar.

'You've got the pestle upside down,' said the woman.

'It don't matter. You look after your own business. There, the seaweed's burning.'

'What a fuss you make,' said his wife. 'You're just like a squalling brat.'

'Here, take hold of the mortar,' said her husband. 'Don't hold it like that. I never saw such a gawk.'

'And I never saw such a fool,' replied his wife.

'What, you scold!' cried the landlord, and he brought the pestle down with a whack on her head.

'You beast,' yelled the woman, and she took the mortar and threw it at her husband, spilling all the potato stew on the ground.

This made the landlord still more angry, and giving a yell he was going to strike her again with the pestle when he slipped on the potato stew and fell to the ground.

'Do you think I'm going to give in to such a fellow as you?' cried the wife, and she was just going to grab hold of him when she too slipped on the stew and fell.

Then the good lady opposite came running over.

'Aren't you ashamed of yourselves,' she cried, 'quarrelling like this? Behave yourselves.'

But when she began scolding them both she too slipped on the stew and went over. There they were, all three, slipping about and getting their clothes all covered with the stew. It was a terrible scene.

'This isn't any use,' said Yaji. 'We'd better get out.'

'What a terrible couple!' said Kita. . . .

The famous Sea of Totomi was calm and there was no wind to stir the pine-trees along the roads. The travellers were polite, the postboys' songs enjoyable; the carriers had no disputes, and the ferrymen did not charge more than their proper fares. The blind could walk alone, women go without protectors, and even the children who had stolen from their homes to go on pilgrimages were free from any danger of meeting robbers. Such was the Golden Age for which they had to be thankful. Wandering to all points of the compass and gathering everywhere indescribable pleasure, these two, Yajirobei and Kitahachi, unable to cross the River Oi, had to put up at Okabe. . . .

They paid for the food and started off and soon reached Fujieda, where at the entrance to the town they met an old man with a bundle on his back who was riding on a very restive horse. Just as he was passing the horse came into collision with Kita, sending him sprawling into a puddle. This made Kita very angry and he jumped up and seized hold of the old man.

'Here, old chap, haven't you got any eyes?' he cried. 'Can't you see where you're going? You'd better take something for it.'

'Dear me!' said the old man. 'I'm very sorry.'

'Very sorry? I should say you were. But that won't do. You may think you've got hold of something easy, but I tell you I've got a glare like a gold dolphin if I'm put to it. I'm the sort of man who's bathed in cold water ever since he was born.'

'Well, if you're used to bathing in cold water it's all right,' said the old man. 'But I'm afraid that wasn't water you fell into; it was horse's stale.'

'Eh?' said Kita. 'Horse's stale? What did you want to knock me down into that for?'

'The horse began to kick when I didn't expect it,' said the old man, 'and unfortunately it ran into you. It couldn't be helped, so you must really excuse me.'

'Excuse you?' said Kita. 'Not I. I wouldn't care if you were the boss of Mount Oe come with his big rod, or Sekison with his lantern, bearing a face like that of a bear crawling in the gutter. I'm the sort of fellow that wouldn't be afraid if Hainai of Kume were to enter my house.'

'You say such terrible things I don't understand what you are talking about,' said the old man. 'I come from Nagata, I do, and my family has always been headmen of the village. At New Year's time, too, when the village offers congratulations to the lord of the manor, I always have an upper seat. You must treat me with more respect.'

'None of your insolence,' said Kita, 'or I'll break your head.'

'Eh, eh!' said the old man. 'Haven't you got any brains? Don't you know I'm under the protection of Kwojin? Don't chatter so much.'

'Get out, you old shyster!' said Kita. He was going to strike the old man when Yaji intervened and separated them.

'You must forgive him, Kita,' he said. 'Here, gaffer, you shouldn't be so obstinate when you know it was your own fault. Go on and don't let us have any more of it.' Yaji soothed Kita while the old man went on grumbling to himself and with his face drawn with anger.

Laughing they crossed the river to Seto, where in front of a teahouse at the end of the town they came again upon the old countryman taking a rest. Immediately he saw them he started to call to them.

'Here, here,' he cried. 'Excuse my rudeness just now. I had taken a cup too much and I'm afraid I made some foolish remarks. Kindly forgive me. Won't you take a parting cup with me? Do come in.'

'We've had a drink already,' said Yaji.

'Dear me!' said the old man. 'I did so want you to have one with me. Do just have one. Here, landlord, bring out some good sakè.'

'Thanks for your kindness,' said Kita, 'but we can't stop. Come on, Yaji.'

'Dear, dear!' said the old man. 'You're such a hasty fellow. Do just come in for a moment.'

The old man caught hold of their hands and drew them in, and as their mouths were watering for the sakè, they made no resistance.

'Let's have a cup, Kita,' said Yaji, 'although it's a shame to make the old gaffer pay.'

'Not at all, not at all,' said the old man. 'Here, landlord, bring out plenty to eat. But I say, it's too exposed here. Let's go into a back room.'

'This way,' said the maid, and she took the sakè bottle and cups and led them round by the garden to a room at the back, where they sat on the verandah to save the trouble of taking off their sandals.

'Here, gaffer, you have the first cup,' said Yaji, offering it to the old man.

'Ah,' said the old man, 'let's try it. That's good. I'll offer the cup to the young man.'

'I'd rather have something to eat,' said Kita. 'I'm hungry.'

'What?' said the old man. 'Hungry? Then you'd better have some rice. That'll soon make you feel better.'

'I'll try a cup of sakè all the same,' said Kita. 'Ah, that's good. What's the soup? Boiled sardines? I suppose we shall have pumpkin soup after this, or roasted yams.'

'What stuff you talk!' said Yaji. 'Look at these shrimps. When they jump they look like the angels painted on the ceilings of the temples.'

'Ah, that's like in Bungo-bushi,' said Kita, and he began to chant. 'Ha-ha-ha! Here, gaffer, let me give you one.'

'No, no, let me pour for you,' said the old man. 'They'll bring something to eat directly. Here, waitress, waitress, I've been clapping my hands enough to break my wrists. Why don't you bring the things I ordered?'

'Coming, your honour,' said the girl, and at last the food was brought in.

'Oh, it's come at last, has it?' said the old man. 'What's in that box? Eggs?'

'That's why they were so long in coming,' said Yaji. 'They were waiting till the eggs were laid.'

'Then they're sure to be fresh,' said Kita. 'Excellent!'

'Please drink hearty,' said the old man. 'You know you saved my life back there by forgiving me so readily. I was so excited I didn't know what I was talking about.'

'No, no, it was I who got excited,' said Kita. 'I shouldn't have said what I did. Forgive me!'

'The gaffer's so good-natured,' said Yaji. 'As for this chap he's always ready for an excuse to eat and drink.'

As the old man was paying for the feast Yaji and Kita went on flattering him up to the skies, while all sorts of good things were brought from the kitchen. When the rice

PROVERBS

Some worms eat the smartweed; others do not.

Counting the skins before one has caught any badgers.

A lantern on a moonlight night.

The fish one has failed to land is always big.

Betters have their betters.

Inferiors have their inferiors.

The reverse side has also its reverse side.

Telling a lie is sometimes expedient.

Even a misfortune may prove useful in three years.

See a woman at night, from a distance, or under an umbrella.

Virtue carries a lean purse.

A bad daughter-in-law is worse than a thousand devils.

It is usually the wickedest man who knows the nearest path to the shrine.

came, Yaji and Kita, although they felt a little ashamed of taking advantage of the old man's kindness, made a good meal.

By-and-by the old man went out to do something.

'I say, Yaji,' said Kita, 'you owe all this to me. It's because I stood up to the old man that he's given us all this.'

'Get out,' said Yaji. 'You're not the only one. Let's have another drink while he's away.'

'I'm going to drink out of this teacup,' said Kita. Then he began to sing:

'Oh it's come! Yes, it's come!
Oh it's come, come, come!
Won't you have another cup with me
When it's come, come, come.'

Yaji also joined in.

'Oh, she's very like a log
That's been cut upon the hill,
But still she is my wife,
So I really love her still.

What fun we're having. By the way, where's the old fool gone?'

'He's a long time about it, isn't he? said Kita. 'I say waitress, that old chap who was here, where's he gone?'

'He went out at the front,' said the girl.

'Eh?' said Yaji. 'What's that for? Strange!'

They waited and waited for the old man but he never came back again. They looked everywhere for him but he was nowhere to be found.

'I say, waitress,' called Kita. 'Did that old man pay the bill before he went?'

'No, it's not paid yet,' said the girl.

'Oh, oh!' groaned Yaji.

'The old fool's trying to play a game on us,' said Kita. 'I'll lay him out.'

He jumped up and rushed out, but it was like chasing a cloud. As the old man lived in the district he knew all the lanes and bypaths, and had got away quickly without anybody seeing him. Kita came back disappointed.

'I can't find him, Yaji,' he said. 'He's done us.'

'It can't be helped,' said Yaji. 'We've got to pay up. The old devil's had his revenge.'

'Yes, but why should we bear all the cost?' said Kita. 'Botheration! And we were just getting a bit jolly too! It's all off now.'

'Like that dog of Jiro and Taro,' said Yaji.

'It's not a joking matter,' said Kita. 'Here, how much is it?'

'Ay, ay,' said the landlord. 'It's nine hundred and fifty coppers.'

'We've been cheated,' said Kita, 'but I suppose we've got to pay. The more I think about it the more annoyed I get.'

'He was a smart old chap,' said Yaji, 'and he played a clever trick on us!'

'Eh! It makes one angry to have one's eye plucked out like that,' said Kita.

But while reviling the old man Kita could not help laughing at the cleverness of his revenge. . . .

'By the way,' said Yaji to the maid, 'the guests in the back room are women, aren't they? Who are they?'

'They're witches,' said the maid.

'What, witches?' said Kita. 'That's interesting. Let's call up somebody.'

'It's too late, isn't it?' said Yaji. 'They won't come after four o'clock.'

'It's only a little past two,' said the maid.

'Well, just ask them,' said Yaji. 'I'd like to have a talk with my dead wife.'

'Fancy wanting to do that!' said Kita.

'I'll ask them afterwards,' said the maid.

So when the meal was finished she went into the next room to ask the witches. They agreed, and Yaji and Kita were conducted into their room. There the witches produced the usual box and arranged it, while the maid, who knew what was wanted, drew some water and brought it in.

Yaji, with his mind fixed on his departed wife, poured some water over the anise leaves and the younger witch began to invoke the gods.

'First of all,' she chanted, 'I reverently call upon Bonten and Taishaku and the four gods of Heaven, and in the underworld the great Emma and the five attendants who wait on him. Of our country's gods I invoke the Seven Gods of Heaven and the Five Gods of Earth, and of the gods of Ise, Amaterasu Omikami, and the forty descendants of the Outer Shrine and the eight descendants of the Inner Shrine. I invoke the God of Rain of Rain, the God of Wind, the God of the Moon and the God of the Sun, the God of the North Shrine of the Benku Mirror, and the spirit of the great Sun Goddess of Ama-no-Iwato, and Kokuzo, the God of Ten Thousand Good Fortunes of Asama-ga-dake, and the others in the sixty provinces of Japan, and also in the country of the gods, at the Great Shrine of Izumo. By the ninety-eight thousand gods of the country and the thirteen thousand Buddhas of the holy places, through the fearful road of the underworld I come. Ah, horror! The spirits of his ancestors crowd upon me, each couple as inseparable as the bow and the arrow. The skies may change and the waters may change, but the bow is unchangeable. One shot from it sends an echo through all the holy places of the temples. Ah! Ah! Oh, joyful sight! Well have you summoned me. I had for bedfellow a warrior famous with the bow, but alas! averse to a pure diet, in life he devoured fish even to the bones, and now, in punishment, is changed into a devil in the shape of an ox, his duty being to keep the gates of Hell, from which he has no release. Thus have I come alone.'

'Who are you?' asked Yaji. 'I don't understand what it's all about.'

'I have come for the sake of him who offered me water, the mirror of my body, my child-treasure.'

'Mirror of the body?' said Kita. 'I'll tell you what, Yaji, it's your mother.'

'My mother, eh?' said Yaji. 'I don't want to have anything to say to her.'

'Has the mirror of my body nothing to say to me?' continued the witch. 'To me, your bedfellow, whom you have thus without shame summoned from the depths? Ah, what agony I went through when I was married to you—time and again suffering the pangs of hunger and shivering with cold in the winter. Ah, hateful! Hateful!'

'Forgive me,' said Yaji. 'At that time my fortunes were low. How pitiful your lot that you should have been brought to the grave with care and hardships.'

'Halloa, Yaji,' said Kita. 'Are you crying? Ha-ha-ha! Even devils have tears.'

'I shall never forget it,' the witch went on. 'When you were ill you gave your sickness to me. Our only child, who had to carry on our name, grew weak and thin because there was no rice to fill his empty stomach. Every day the duns were knocking at the door and the rent remained unpaid. Yet I did not complain,—not even when I slipped in the dogs' dirt in the lane.'

'Don't talk of it,' said Yaji. 'You'll break my heart.'

'And then, when through my labours I had saved enough money to buy a kimono, I had to pawn it for your sake and never saw it again. Never again did it come back to me from the pawnbroker's.'

'At the same time you must remember what a pleasant place you are in now,' said Yaji, 'while I have to worry along down here.'

'What? What is there pleasant about it? It is true that by the help of your friends you erected a stone over my grave, but you never go near it, and you never contribute to the temple to get the priests to say prayers for my soul. I am nothing to you. The stone over my grave has been taken away and put into the wall, where all the dogs come and make water against it. Not a drop of water is ever placed on my grave. Truly in death we suffer all sorts of troubles.'

'True, true,' said Yaji.

'But while you thus treat me with neglect,' the witch went on, 'lying in my grave I think of nobody but you and long for the time when you will join me in the underworld. Shall I come to meet you?'

'No, no, don't do that,' said Yaji. 'It's really too far for you.'

'Well then, I have one request to make.'

'Yes, yes. What is it?'

'Give this witch plenty of money.'

'Of course, of course.'

'How sad the parting!' cried the witch. 'I have yet much to tell you, countless questions to ask you, but the messenger of Hell recalls me.'

Then recovering from her trance, the witch twanged her bow.

'Thank you very much,' said Yaji. He took out some money and wrapped it in paper and gave it to her.

'Ha-ha!' laughed Kita. 'Now all your hidden shames are revealed to the world. Ha-ha-ha! But I say, Yaji, you look very downcast. What do you say to a drink?'

Yaji agreed and clapping his hands ordered the maid to bring some sakè.

'How far have you come today?' asked the witch.

'We came from Okabe,' answered Yaji.

'How quick you are,' said the witch.

'Oh, that's nothing,' said Yaji. 'We can walk as fast as Idaten. If we're put to it we can walk thirty-five miles a day.'

'But then we shouldn't be fit for anything for ten days after,' put in Kita.

While they were talking the sakè was brought in.

'Won't you have a little?' said Yaji to the young witch.

'I never touch a drop,' she answered.

'Will your companion have any?' asked Yaji.

'Mother, Mother! Come here,' called the young witch.

'Oh, it's your mother, is it?' said Kita. 'I must take care what I say in front of her. But come, do have some.'

Soon they began to drink and enjoy themselves, the cup passing from hand to hand very quickly. Strangely enough, however, the witches, however much they drank, never seemed to be any the worse for it, while Yaji and Kita got so drunk they could not speak plainly. After making all sorts of jokes, which it would be too tedious to repeat, Kita at last in a drunken voice said, 'I say, mother, won't you lend me your daughter for the night?'

'No, no, she's going to lend her to me,' said Yaji.

'What an idea!' cried Kita. 'You'd better try and be good tonight. Haven't you any pity for your dead wife who spends her time in thinking of you and hoping you will join her quickly? Didn't she say she'd come and meet you after a bit?'

'Here, don't talk about that,' said Yaji. 'What should I do if she did come to meet me?'

'Then you had better be good,' said Kita. 'Now, old lady, what do you think?'

Kita here gave the young witch a loving caress, but she pushed him off and ran away, saying, 'Be quiet.'

'If my daughter doesn't want to,' said the mother, 'what about me?'

'Well, if it comes to that I don't care who it is,' said Kita, who was lost in a drunken dream.

While they were talking the supper was brought in and there was a good deal of joking too tedious to repeat, and finally Yaji and Kita, the effects of the sakè having already passed off, went back into their own room, where, as soon as it was dark, they went to bed. In the next room also the witches were apparently going to bed, worn out by their travels.

'That young witch is sleeping on this side, I know,' said Kita in a low voice. 'I'll creep in to her after a bit. Yaji, you'd better go to sleep.'

'Get out,' said Yaji. 'I'm going to be the one to get her.'

'Isn't he bold?' said Yaji. 'It would make a cat laugh.'

Thus talking they crept into bed and fell asleep. It was already about nine o'clock, and the night watchman's rattle, as he went round the inn, echoed through the pillows of the travellers. In the kitchen the sound of the preparations for the next morning's meal had died away, and all that could be heard was the barking of the dogs. It was just when night was at its darkest and eeriest hour that Kitahachi judged it the right time to creep out of bed and peep into the next room. The night-light had gone out, and he felt his way in very softly and crept into the bed where he thought the young witch was sleeping. To his surprise the witch, without saying anything, caught hold of his hand and pulled him in. Delighted with his reception, Kitahachi sank down under the coverlet with her arm for a pillow and soon realized his desire, after which they both fell asleep quite unconscious of their surroundings.

Yajirobei, who was thus left sleeping alone, soon opened his eyes. 'I wonder what time it is,' he muttered. 'I must go to the closet. It's so dark I can't see the way.'

Thus pretending that he was going to the closet he crept into the next room, quite unconscious of the fact that Kitahachi was already in there. Feeling about he came to the side of the bed where Kita was lying, and thinking in the darkness that it was the young witch's lips from which moans were coming, he put his lips to those of Kitahachi and took a bite.

'Oh! Oh!' yelled Kitahachi.

'Halloa! Is that you, Kitahachi?' said Yaji.

'Oh, it's Yaji, is it?' said Kita. 'Ugh! Ugh! How beastly!' and he began spitting.

At the sound of their voices the witch into whose bed Kita had crept woke up.

'What are you doing!' she said. 'Don't make such a noise. You'll wake my daughter up.' This was another surprise for Kita, for it was the old witch's voice. Cursing himself for his stupidity he got out of the bed and crept away softly into the next room. Yaji was going to do the same when the old witch caught hold of him.

'You mustn't make a fool of an old woman by running away,' she said.

'No, no,' stuttered Yaji. 'You've made a mistake. It wasn't me.'

'You mustn't try to deceive me,' said the old woman. 'I don't make a regular business of this, but when I meet a traveller on the road and sleep with him I like to get a little just to help me along. It's a shame to make a fool of me by running away. There, just go to sleep in my bosom till dawn.'

'What a nuisance you are,' said Yaji. 'Here, Kitahachi, Kitahachi.'

'Take care,' said the old woman. 'You mustn't call so loud.'

'But I don't know anything about it,' said Yaji. 'It's that chap Kitahachi that's got me into all this mess.'

Thus saying Yaji struggled out of her grasp, only to be caught again and thrown down. But at last, after a good deal of kicking, he managed to get away into the next room, where he repeated to himself,

'By stealth I entered, witch's love to earn,
But which was witch I could not well discern.'

Dawn seemed to come in no time, and awakened by the bustle of the travellers preparing for the road and the neighing of the horses, Yaji and Kita rubbed their travel-wearied eyes, got their breakfast, and forthwith set out, amused by the old witch's angry looks. Passing through Furumiya and Honda-no-Hachiman, they came to Shuto-no-Hata, which means mother-in-law's field, and to Yome-ga-Ta, which means bride's rice-field. Then said Yaji,

'The dried-up mother-in-law is cast aside
And turns again into the juicy bride.'

From there they reached the River Shoi, where the rain of the previous day having been heavy and the bridge presumably having been swept away, travellers were taking off their pants and pulling up their clothes to ford the river. Yaji and Kita were just about to follow their example when two blind men, going up to the capital and in doubt whether they could walk across the stream, accosted them.

'Can you tell me,' said one of them whose name was Inuichi, 'whether the water is only knee-deep?'

'Yes, yes,' said Kita, 'but the current's rather fast, so it's a little dangerous. Mind how you go.'

'Yes,' said the blind man, 'I can tell by the sound that it's running fast.'

He took a stone and threw it in. 'It seems shallow here,' he said. 'Here, Saruichi,' he called to the other blind man. 'We needn't both of us take off our leggings. You're younger than I. Take me across on your back.'

'Ha-ha-ha!' laughed Saruichi. 'None of your tricks. We'll play for it, and the one who loses will have to carry the other across. What do you say?'

'All right,' said Inuichi. 'Come along. Three times, you know.'

'Ryangosai! Ryangosai!' cried Saruichi, as they waved their right hands, while with their left hands they felt what each other was doing.

'I've won, I've won,' said Inuichi.

'What a shame!' said Saruichi. 'Well, tie my bundle up with yours and put them on your back. Are you all right? Come along then.'

He turned round for the other to get on his back, when Yaji, seeing his chance, stepped forward and got on instead. Saruichi, who thought he had Inuichi on his back, stepped into the water and was soon across. Inuichi, who had in the meantime been waiting on the other side, here began to call out.

'Saru, Saru,' he cried. 'What are you doing? Why don't you carry me across the river quick?'

Hearing Inuichi calling to him from the other side of the river, Saruichi began to get angry.

'None of your jokes,' he cried. 'Didn't I carry you across the river just now, and there you are on the other side again? Who are you fooling?'

'Don't talk nonsense,' said Inuichi. 'You went across alone. No cheating.'

'It's you that are cheating,' retorted Saruichi.

'You shouldn't talk like that to your elder,' replied Inuichi. 'Come and carry me across at once.'

Inuichi was beginning to show the whites of his eyes, so Saruichi, seeing that there was nothing to be done but to go back again, crossed the river once more.

'There, there,' he said. 'Get on my back.'

He turned round, and Kita, rejoicing at his luck, jumped on and Saruichi set out once more to cross the river. Inuichi now began to get very angry.

'Saruichi,' he cried. 'Where are you?'

Hearing this Saruichi stopped in the middle of the river. 'Halloa!' he cried. 'Who's this I've got on my back?'

Thereupon he promptly dropped Kita into the river.

'Help! Help!' cried Kita, and as he was being carried away by the current he began waving his arms and legs about till Yaji jumped in and pulled him out, wet to the skin.

'Look what that blind beggar's done to me,' moaned Kita.

'Well, take off your kimono and wring it out,' said Yaji.

'It was your fault,' continued Kita. 'If you hadn't got him to carry you across I shouldn't have tried it myself.'

'Ha-ha-ha!' laughed Yaji. 'What a shame to drop you in the river like that!'

Thus enjoying the joke Yaji made a little poem on it:

> 'Fooling the blind he had a little spill,
> The current was swift, the punishment swifter still.'

'I don't want to listen to your jokes,' said Kita. 'Shut up! Oh-h, it's cold.'

He shivered as he tried to wring the water out of his kimono.

Just then the blind men, who had at last got across the river, passed them.

'You can't wear that wet kimono,' said Yaji. 'You'd better get another out. We'll get it dried when we get to a fire.'

'I shall catch cold,' said Kita. 'What a shame!'

Grumbling and sneezing he got out another kimono, and having hung the wet one over his arm they went on.

Soon they got to Kakegawa, where at the last teahouse the girls were calling out, 'Stop here and eat. Try our fish-soup. Try our boiled cuttlefish. Walk in, walk in.'

Then there were the baggage-carriers singing their songs:—

> 'Blow! Blow! Blow! Blow! Blow!
> Heave her up! Heave her up! On you go.
> Light as a feather,—it's feathers you know.
> Light as feathers. Do you think they know?
> No! No!
> Do you think they know?'

'Hin, hin,' whinnied the horses.

'Look, Kita,' said Yaji. 'There are those two blind men in that teahouse.'

'That's good,' said Kita. 'I'm going to have my revenge on them for throwing me into the river.'

They went into the teahouse and Kita sat down by the side of the blind men.

'Shall I bring you a meal?' asked the maid.

'No, no, we're bursting already,' replied Yaji.

The two blind men went on drinking their sakè, quite unconscious of their presence.

'We've drunk all the sakè,' said Inuichi. 'Let's have some more.'

'So we have,' said Saruichi. 'Here, landlord, landlord, bring a little more drink.'

'Coming, sir,' cried the maid.

'By the way,' said Inuichi, 'I wonder what became of that rascal you threw in the river.'

'Oh, him,' said Saruichi, laughing contemptuously. 'Let's wet the other eye.'

He filled the cup and after taking a sip put it down by his side, when Kitahachi, softly stretching out his hand, took up the cup, drank off the contents and put it back where it was before.

'He was a rogue,' continued Saruichi. 'Got on my back as bold as brass, he did, but it was quite a different thing when he got into the water. Did you hear him calling "Help! Help!"? He was in a terrible fright. He's one of those chaps who go about bamboozling people. Probably he's a pickpocket!'

'That's about it,' said Inuichi. 'You can depend upon it he can't be up to any good. He's the sort of chap that would come to a place like this and go off without paying. Let's have another drink.'

'Oh, ah!' said Saruichi, 'I'd forgotten about the drink.'

He felt for the cup and was going to drink when he found that there was nothing in it.

'That's funny,' he said. 'I must have spilled it.' He felt about again. 'It's strange,' he said. 'However, let's fill it again.'

He filled it up again, took a sip and put it down. Immediately Kitahachi again reached for the cup, drank the contents and put it back.

'It would be funny if those chaps were to come in here,' said Inuichi.

'Not they,' said Saruichi. 'They're probably wandering about down there wringing out their clothes and trying to dry them. They're both stupid rascals.'

Feeling for the cup he took it up, only to find that again there was nothing in it.

'Now, how's that?' he said.

'What's the matter?' asked Inuichi. 'Spilled it again? How careless you are.'

'No, I didn't spill it,' said Saruichi. 'There's something very strange about this.'

'That's what you always say,' said Inuichi. 'I believe you drank it yourself.'

While they were disputing Kita got hold of the sakè bottle and filled his teacup twice, afterwards softly putting the bottle back where it was before.

'Here,' said Inuichi, 'you give me the cup.'

He snatched it from Saruichi and picked up the bottle to fill it.

'Hullo! he cried. 'Why, you've drunk it all.'

'Nonsense!' said Saruichi. 'What are you talking about?'

'Well, the bottle's empty.'

'Then it was never full,' said Saruichi. 'Here, landlord,' he called, 'do you think we are fools because we are blind? We've only had two sips out of this bottle of sakè and it's empty. What do you mean by it?'

'It was full when I gave it you,' said the landlord. 'Perhaps you've spilled it.'

'Spilled it, indeed!' said Saruichi. 'You dealers are all the same. At any rate we won't pay for it.'

Thus he began to get very angry. Now there happened to be a little girl loitering at the door of the teahouse and she had seen all that had happened.

'That man there,' she said, pointing to Kita, 'took the blind man's sakè and poured it into his teacup.'

'What's the child talking about?' said Kita. 'I'm drinking tea.' He quickly drank up all the sakè left in his teacup.

'You smell of sakè,' said the landlord, 'and your face is red. Perhaps you've drunk the gentlemen's sakè.'

'What?' cried Kita. 'You say the same? It's outrageous. My face is red because I'm drunk with tea. Persons who get drunk on sakè get tongue-tied, and in the same way persons who get drunk on tea, say "tea, tea, tea" all the time. That's why tea's so. Ha-ha-ha!'

'No, no,' said Saruichi. 'You don't fob us off in that way. What the child says is true. This man has drunk my saké on the sly and he's got to pay for it.'

'You're tea-tea-told you, only you will tea-tea-talk so much.'

'What's the good of playing the fool that way?' said Inuichi. 'You thought nobody would see you, but the child is a witness.'

'There's a certain proof, landlord,' said Saruichi. 'Smell his teacup and see whether it smells of sakè.'

Kitahachi, feeling that he was caught, tried to hide his tea-cup, but the landlord seized it and smelled it.

'It does, it does,' he cried, 'and it's sticky with it too. There can be no mistake, you drank it and you must pay for it.'

'I won't pay for the sakè because I didn't drink it,' said Kita, who saw that he was in a corner, 'but I'll pay anything you like for the tea. How much is it?'

'Very well, then, pay for the tea,' said the landlord. 'You've had two bottles of tea. That will be sixty-four coppers.'

'What?' cried Kita. 'For two bottles of tea? It's outrageous.'

'Here, we've had enough of this,' intervened Yaji. 'Pay up. You're always getting into trouble. Better pay up before anything happens.' He gave Kita a warning look, and there being nothing else to do Kita paid the money.

'Really,' said Saruichi, 'these people are outrageous. Probably they are the same people who played the trick on us at the river. To drink another person's sakè on the sly. It's robbery.'

'What, you call us robbers, you blind beggar?' cried Kita flying into a passion.

'We're in the wrong,' interposed Yaji. 'You must forgive him. When he gets drunk with tea there's no holding him. I'll tea-tea-take him away.'

He dragged Kita away and made him walk fast till they had left the stage far behind.

'Ha-ha-ha!' laughed Yaji. 'You're the biggest fool I've ever met.' . . .

The nuns passed and re-passed them. One of them was about twenty-two or -three and the other was considerably older. They had with them a little girl of about eleven or twelve. At last the younger nun stopped Kita. 'Could you give me a light?' she asked.

'Certainly, certainly,' said Kita. 'I'll strike a light for you in a minute.' He pulled out his flint and commenced striking.

'There you are,' he said. 'By the way, where are you going?'

'We're going as far as Nagoya,' said the girl.

'I should like to stop with you tonight,' said Kita. 'Come as far as Akasaka. Let's go together.'

'Thank you,' said the woman. 'Could you give me some tobacco? I've forgotten to buy any.'

'Pull out your tobacco pouch,' said Kita. 'I'll give you all I've got.'

'I'm afraid you'll want some yourself,' said the girl.

'No, no, that's all right,' replied Kita. 'By the way, I'm astonished at a beautiful girl like you shaving her head. It seems such a shame.'

'Why, nobody cares if I cut my hair off,' said the girl.

'I do,' said Kita. 'I care very much. Won't you care for me?'

'Ho-ho-ho!' laughed the girl.

'I wish we could stop together,' added Kita. 'I say, Yaji,' he called, 'shall we stop at the next stage?'

'What a fool you are,' scolded Yaji. 'I wish we had never met these nuns.'

They passed Hiuchizaka and reached Nikenchaya, when the nuns turned off into a side road.

'Here,' called Kita. 'Where are you going? That's not the way.'

'Goodbye,' said the nun. 'We've got to leave you here.' They went along a field path while Kita looked after them very disappointed.

'Ha-ha-ha!' laughed Yaji. 'You're in bad luck to-day.'

'It's a shame,' groaned Kita. . . .

Yaji and Kita were greatly amused at this talk, and after passing and repassing the pilgrims several times, Yaji at last spoke to them.

'Where are you gentlemen bound for?' he asked.

'Oh, we're going to Ise,' said Yoshitsune.

'I heard you just now calling each other Yoshitsune and Benkei and so on,' said Yaji. 'What's the reason of that?'

'It must have sounded strange to you,' said Yoshitsune. 'I'll tell you. Just before we left our village there was a festival and we acted in the piece called "The Thousand Cherry-trees," and as we all took part, and one was Yoshitsune and another Benkei and so on, we got into the habit of calling each other by those names and even now continue it.'

'I see,' said Yaji. 'Then I suppose you took the part of Yoshitsune?'

'Yes,' said Yoshitsune. 'Before that we had some players down from Edo who acted "Tenjinsama" and what do you think happened? I'll tell you. There's a bad man in the play named "Shihei" or "Gohei" or something like that, who caused Tenjinsama to be banished because he said he had spoken disrespectfully of the Emperor, and there he was in his palanquin, going into banishment, and all the people coming out to see him, and all the old women and the young women weeping and wailing. It was like the passing of an Imperial Abbot. And all the people in the theatre were throwing rice and money on to the stage because they felt so sorry for him. Then a horsebroker in the audience named Yogoza, a man of no account, ran up on the stage and shouted, "This play is no good. Why should Tenjinsama be banished to an island? That noble who appeared before, who looked like Emma at the Choraku temple, he is the bad man. Tenjinsama isn't guilty." ' . . .

Soon the maid came in and asked whether she should spread the beds.

'You might as well,' said Yaji.

'Is the marriage ceremony over?' asked Kita. 'I suppose the bride is very beautiful.'

'Yes,' said the maid. 'The bridegroom's a handsome fellow and the bride's very beautiful too. Unfortunately they have to sleep in the next room, where everybody will be able to hear their love-talk.'

'What a nuisance!' said Yaji.

'Awful!' said Kita.

'Good rest,' said the maid.

She went off, leaving them to get into bed, and soon they heard the sound of the door being opened in the next room. Apparently the bride and bridegroom were going to bed. Then they heard whispers and other movements, from which they judged it was not the first time that the couple had tasted the delights of love. The sounds kept Yaji and Kita from going to sleep.

'This is awful,' said Yaji.

'We've come to the wrong inn again,' said Kita. 'They don't mind us. How loving she is, the little beast.'

'They've stopped talking,' said Yaji. 'Now's the time.' He crawled softly out of bed and listened to what they were doing. Then he stood up and peeped through the cracks in the sliding door. Kita also crawled out of bed.

'I say, Yaji,' he whispered. 'Is the bride beautiful? Just let me have a peep!'

'Don't make a noise,' said Yaji. 'It's the critical moment.'

'Eh?' said Kita. 'Just let me look. Move away a little.'

But Yaji was peeping through the crack like a man in a dream, and what with Kita shoving him and his own obstinacy, they managed between them to push the sliding door out of its grooves, and it fell suddenly forward into the next room with Yaji and Kita on top of it. This startled the newly married couple.

'Oh, oh!' shouted the bridegroom. 'What's that? The door's fallen out of its grooves.' Jumping up he overturned the lamp and plunged the room into darkness. Yaji had already fled back into his own room and jumped into bed, but Kita was not quite so quick and got caught by the bridegroom.

'Excuse me,' said Kita. 'I was going out to do something and mistook the door of my room. Really the maid is very careless putting the lamp in the middle of the floor. I'm sorry you tripped over it. But I really must go if you'd just leave loose of me.'

'Such outrageous conduct!' said the bridegroom. 'Everything's covered with oil. Here, San, San, get up.'

The maid came out of the kitchen with a lamp and put things to rights, and Kita, looking very foolish, put the door in its grooves again and went very dejectedly to bed. Then as the night deepened all was still in the inn save only for the snores of the travellers. . . .

Ten thousand cocks were crowing and horses neighing bravely when Yaji and Kita woke up next morning. They ate their breakfast and quickly left Akasaka behind them, but just outside the town they caught up with three travellers who were going in the same direction. Apparently they were from Edo and, by their manner of speaking, three braves.

'I say,' said one, 'wasn't it funny last night?'

'What, about those fellows in the back room?' asked another. 'They were a couple of fools. Because there was a wedding at the inn they got envious, and in peeping through the cracks of the door they got so excited that they knocked the door over. They were the laughing stock of the place.'

'And the way they apologised to the bridegroom,' said the third man. 'I wasn't able to sleep for all the row they made.'

'And one of the rascals called the landlord earlier in the evening and asked him if the inn was a graveyard. He must have been cracked.'

It appeared from their talk that these men must have stopped at the same inn as Yaji and Kita. Yaji grew hot as he heard their talk, and quickening his step he caught them up.

'Look here, you three,' he said. 'I've been silent up to now, but I'd like to know why you call me a rascal.'

'It hasn't anything to do with you,' said the first man. 'We were talking about our own affairs.'

'Your own affairs, indeed,' said Yaji. 'Weren't you jawing about what happened at the inn? The person who made the door fall down, you said, was a rascal. That's me.'

'Oh, you're the rascal, are you?' replied the brave.

'Yes, I'm the rascal,' said Yaji.

'Ha-ha-ha!' laughed the brave. 'Well, if you're the rascal that's why we called you a rascal. Ain't that all right?"

'Look here, I won't stand any of your jokes,' said Yaji.

'Oh, go and eat dung,' said the brave.

'Eat dung?' said Yaji. 'That's easy. I'll eat it if you get it,' for he was so angry that he didn't know what he was saying.

The traveller picked up a piece of dung on his stick and held it out to Yaji. 'There it is,' he cried. 'Eat it, eat it.'

'No, no,' said Yaji. 'I don't like it.'

'Don't like it?' said the brave. 'But you must like it.'

Then the three men surrounded Yaji to make him eat it by force. Kita, who had been looking on amused, now intervened.

'Let him go,' he pleaded. 'It's much the same as if he'd eaten it, isn't it?'

'Ha-ha-ha!' laughed the three braves. 'Well, we'll let him off at that.' With that they went off. . . .

He went round to the back and did his business and looking about him afterwards, saw that a store-room had been turned into a house and that there was a girl of eighteen or nineteen alone there. Her hair was rather disordered, but she was a very pretty girl and she was alone.

Kitahachi, with his usual impudence, walked in smiling. 'Sorry to trouble you,' he said, 'but could you let me have some water to rinse my hands.'

While he was rinsing his hands the girl kept on giggling. 'What are you laughing at?' asked Kita. 'Do you live here alone? Isn't it dangerous?'

He looked around and saw nobody but the girl. Thereupon he seated himself and pulled out his pipe and tobacco. 'What are you laughing at?' he asked again. 'Is there anything to laugh at? Well, then, come and laugh here.'

He caught hold of her and pulled her down beside him, the girl making no objection, and Kita was just congratulating himself on his good fortune when a little boy came running by and saw them.

'Eh!' he shouted. 'Here's a man making love to the mad girl.'

Bursting into laughter the boy ran off. The startled Kita also wanted to run away, but the girl held him and would not let him go.

'Eh, young fellow,' she said, 'you're not going yet.'

But Kita was by this time rather frightened and he struggled so hard that he was able to break loose just as the girl's old father came on the scene.

'What are you doing with that young girl?' asked the old man.

'I'm not doing anything,' replied Kita.

'Then why did you come here?' asked the old man.

'I went to relieve myself and then I asked her for some water to rinse my hands,' said Kita.

'No, no, no,' said the old man. 'This girl is mad, and it is quite plain you came here with a bad intention.'

'How absurd!' said Kita.

'You can't deceive me,' went on the old man. 'You knew this girl was mad and so you came here to make a fool of her. I can't accept your excuses. It is unpardonable.' The old man spoke in a loud voice and was evidently intent on making a scene.

In the meanwhile Yaji, after waiting some time in the teahouse in front for Kita to return, had come round to the back and had, indeed, been secretly watching the scene for some time, much to his own amusement. Now he thought it was time that he showed himself, so he came slowly forward.

'Excuse me,' he said. 'I'm in charge of this man and I happened to hear what had taken place. I may tell you that this chap's a bit off his head, as you can see by his looks. Please pardon him. Eh, you rascal! You give me a lot of trouble, don't you? Just look at his face. See for yourself the restless look in his eye. Isn't that enough to show his condition? Your lunatic is a woman, so you can manage her, but this looney gives me all sorts of trouble.'

'No, no, it can't be,' said the old man. 'Is he really mad?'

'Look at his expression,' replied Yaji. 'You can see his condition at once.'

'What?' said Kita. 'I mad? How absurd. —That is . . . Well . . . It's falling, falling, falling! There, there! The flowers are blooming and falling, blooming and falling. Oh, the poor things cannot sleep. Ah, ah, there's my wife. No, she's not a good wife. Halloa! Halloa! Oh, oh, oh!'

'That's the way he goes on,' said Yaji. 'Look at his eyes. You can see he's a love-maniac. That's why he gets so excited when he sees a woman. He's quite lost to shame and reason. He's my younger brother. I never thought such a fate would overtake him.'

'You can talk of your affliction,' said the old man, 'but I have mine also. This girl that you see so afflicted is my only daughter. She's given me great trouble.'

'I expect so,' replied Yaji. 'Now then, you rascal, what are you giggling at? Well, gaffer, we must be going now. Sorry to have disturbed you.'

'Won't you have a drop of tea before you go?' asked the old man.

'No thank you,' said Yaji. 'We must really be going. Now then, looney, come along.'

Thus keeping up a ceaseless chatter Yaji settled the matter and led Kita away. It was not until they had quite escaped from observation that they burst into laughter. . . .

Passing on they came to Imamura, where an old woman in a teahouse pressed them to come and try the sugar rice-cakes for which the place is famous.

'How much each are those rice-cakes?' asked Kita.

'They're three coppers each,' said the old woman's husband.

'That's cheap,' said Kita. 'And how much are these with beans on?'

'They're three coppers also,' said the old man.

'They're dear for three coppers,' said Kita. 'I'll tell you what. Make these two coppers each and in return I'll give you four coppers for those round ones.'

'This is a strange sort of fellow,' thought the shopkeeper, 'but at any rate I shan't lose by it. Very well, your honour,' he said aloud, 'take what you like.'

Kita took two coppers out of his purse. 'I meant to have bought one of the round ones,' he said, 'but I've only got two coppers so I'll have to have one with beans on.'

He caught up the cake and walked off munching it.

'Ha-ha-ha!' laughed Yaji. 'Bravo, Kita! You did astonish that shopkeeper.'

'Ah, he'll know better next time,' said Kita.

'You are a rascal really,' exclaimed Yaji. 'I couldn't do a thing like that. Ha-ha-ha!' . . .

Then the boat started with all the travellers feeling very adventurous, and the wind being favourable they sped over the waves like an arrow. The sea was calm and all the passengers were in great spirits, talking enough to dislocate their jaws and laughing so shrilly that it almost seemed as if they were quarrelling with each other. Yaji went to sleep, and was only awakened by a number of trading boats which came up to them.

'Buy some sakè,' cried the men in the boats. 'Try our broiled eels. How about some dumplings? Try our pickles.'

'I've had a good sleep,' said Yaji. 'What a distance we've come. But I must relieve myself.'

He took the bamboo tube which the landlord had given him for the purpose, but as the tube was exactly like a fire-blower and had a hole at each end, as fast as he made water into it at one end it came out at the other into the boat. Soon the passengers began to be astonished at the water in the boat.

'What's this?' they cried. 'Everything's covered with water. Where's it coming from? Somebody must have upset a teapot. Dear, dear! My tobacco and paper have got all wet. What a nuisance! Why, surely somebody's been making water.'

Their cries threw Yaji into confusion and he hurriedly hid the piece of bamboo.

'What have you been doing, Yaji?' said Kita. 'If you want to make water you should go to the side of the boat so that it will fall into the water. You've made the boat all wet inside. How dirty!'

'I was going to empty it into the water afterwards,' explained Yaji.

'How disgusting!' said the passengers. 'Everything smells horribly. Here, boatman, haven't you got any more mats?'

'What's that?' said the boatman. 'Somebody been making water? He's defiled the patron god of the boat. Be quick and dry it up.'

'You haven't got any common sense,' said Kita.

'Look out, it's running out of the bamboo still,' cried the boatman. 'Throw it away.'

'No, no, no,' said Yaji. 'I'll put it up here. We can use it as a fire-blower afterwards.'

'What, when you've made it all dirty?' said Kita. 'Who would use it as a fire-blower now? Be quick and dry up the mess. How slow you are!'

Yaji took no notice of Kita's teasing, but undid his loin-cloth and mopped up the mess, while Kita turned the mats over and put things straight.

'There,' he said, 'that's all right now. You can all come and sit down.'

'I hope you'll excuse me,' said Yaji dejectedly. 'I'm afraid I've disturbed you all.'

The passengers laughed sarcastically but said nothing, and soon the boat arrived at the shore at Kuwana.

'Here we are, here we are,' they all cried. 'The boat's got here safely in spite of its being defiled. Thank goodness for that.'

So they all went on shore and indulged in sakè in honour of their safe arrival. . . .

Continuing their journey the two travellers soon arrived at Oiwake, which is famous for its cakes.

'Try our hot cakes,' called the girls at the teahouses. 'Come in and rest. Try our rice-cake stew.'

'That girl to the right is not bad-looking,' said Kita.

'Quite attractive,' said Yaji.

They went in and sat down. 'Will you have some tea?' asked the maid.

'Yes, and we'll try some of your cakes,' said Yaji.

The maid went away and soon came back with a tray. There was another traveller sitting in the teahouse, a man who was apparently a pilgrim to the Kompira shrines. He was wearing a short white coat over a heavy, wadded garment.

'Let's have some more cakes,' said Yaji. 'I feel as if I could eat them for ever.'

'That's only your talk,' said Kita.

'You gentlemen are from Edo, I suppose,' said the pilgrim, who was eating rice-cake broth.

'Yes,' said Kita.

'Ah!' said the pilgrim. 'When I was in Edo I ate twenty-eight cakes at the Torikai of Izumi. Very extraordinary!'

'The Torikai?' said Yaji. 'Why, that's quite close to my place. We used to eat fifty or sixty every day for tea.'

'You must have been remarkably fond of them,' said the pilgrim. 'I myself am fond of rice-cakes. As you see I have eaten five platefuls of this rice-cake broth without choking myself.'

'I've eaten fourteen or fifteen of these cakes,' said Yaji, 'and you see I'm still alive. Indeed, I feel as if I hadn't had enough.'

'They're so sickly,' said the pilgrim, 'I don't suppose you could eat any more. Fourteen or fifteen must be about all you can eat.'

'Oh no,' said Yaji. 'I could easily eat some more.'

'You only say that,' said the pilgrim. 'You know you couldn't eat any more.'

'Couldn't eat any more,' cried Yaji. 'If it wasn't that I didn't want to waste my money I'd eat a lot more. If anybody likes to feed me I'll go on eating with pleasure.'

'How interesting!' said the pilgrim. 'I hope you won't mind my offering to pay for those if you eat them.'

'Of course I can,' said Yaji.

'It will be your loss if you fail,' said the pilgrim.

'Of course, of course,' said Yaji. He began to eat with great confidence and got through ten of them. Then he began to feel uneasy, but nevertheless he was not going to let himself be beaten by the pilgrim, and he forced himself to eat the remainder.

'Wonderful! Wonderful!' said the pilgrim. 'I could never do that.'

'Have a try,' said Yaji. 'I could eat any amount of these small ones.'

'I don't think I could really,' said the pilgrim. 'But still I don't like to give in. I'll eat ten of them just to see.'

'What, only ten?' said Yaji. 'Eat twenty. Look here, if you eat them all up and don't leave one, in return I'll pay for the cakes and contribute a hundred coppers towards your expenses.'

'Thank you,' said the pilgrim. 'I'll trust in heaven and have a try.'

He seemed rather afraid to begin, but at last he started and munched steadily through ten of them. He made a wry face over the remaining ten, but finally managed to eat them all up.

Yaji was astonished. 'Wonderful, wonderful!' he said.

'As we agreed,' said the pilgrim, 'may I ask you to pay for the cakes and to make an offering of a hundred coppers?'

'All right,' said Yaji, 'but it's so wonderful that if you eat twenty more I'll contribute three hundred coppers, but if you fail you must give me two hundred coppers. How's that?'

'Fine, fine!' said the pilgrim. 'I'll try even if I burst myself.'

'We'll put up the cash,' said Yaji. 'Just put up two hundred coppers.'

He himself put out three hundred coppers, thinking that he would get back the hundred coppers that he had lost and interest on it into the bargain. He'll never be able to eat twenty more, he thought as he ordered the cakes. But this time the pilgrim, without any demur, gulped down the twenty cakes very quickly, and pocketed the three hundred coppers.

'Thank you very much,' said the pilgrim. 'Just pay for the cakes as well, will you? I didn't think I should have such a feast. Ha-ha-ha! Don't disturb yourselves for me,' and he slung his bag on his back and went off without even troubling to look behind him. Yaji was dumbfounded.

'That's a good 'un, laughed Kita. 'I thought it would turn out like that.'

'It's just my luck,' groaned Yaji. 'I thought I should get that hundred coppers back, but instead of that I've lost some more. What a nuisance!'

Just then a kago came along. 'Won't your honour take a ride?' asked the carriers.

'I'm not worrying about a kago,' said Yaji. 'I'm worrying about the three hundred coppers I lost seeing who could eat most cakes.'

'Aha, that would be the pilgrim we passed just now,' said one of the carriers. 'That fellow's always up to those tricks. He's Kamashichi of Otsu, a well known juggler. The other day he had a try who could eat most rice cakes and made out he'd eaten seventy-eight. He gets people to bet that he can't eat so many cakes and then pretends to eat a lot, but all the time he's putting them up his sleeve. You honour's been tricked. Ha-ha-ha!' . . .

Just as he was going to blow, however, he trod on a dog that was sleeping in front of the stall, making it howl.

'Get out, you cur,' said Yaji, and he struck at the dog with the blowpipe, whereupon the dog bit him. It was now Yaji's turn to howl, and he was running after the dog when he slipped and fell. Just where he fell was a tobacco pouch lying on the ground.

'I shan't lose by falling,' he said. 'Here's a tobacco pouch.'

He was just about to pick it up when a little boy on the other side of the road drew it away with a string he had fastened to it.

'Well, I'm blowed!' said Yaji. 'What a sell!'

'Fool, fool!' screamed the small boy and went off laughing.

'That's a good trick,' said Kita. 'Come on.'

They paid the blowpipe man and were going along again when they saw a tobacco-pipe lying by the side of the road.

'Ain't you going to pick that up, Yaji?' asked Kita.

'No, no,' said Yaji. 'I'm not to be caught twice. Let that old chap following us pick it up.' They went past it and then turned round just in time to see the old man pick it up, shove it in his bosom, and walk off quickly.

'Well I never!' said Yaji. 'It wasn't a sell after all.'

'That makes you feel bad, doesn't it?' laughed Kita. . . .

'Look, Kita,' said Yaji. 'How beautiful the girls all look.'

'They're Kyoto people,' said Gomajiru. 'But although they all look so grand they don't waste their money.'

Just then one of them stopped Gomajiru and asked him for a light.

'Take one from here,' said Gomajiru, and he held out the pipe which he was smoking. The Kyoto man put his pipe to it and sucked.

'Can't you get it?' asked Gomajiru. Still the stranger went on sucking without saying a word.

'What's this?' said Gomajiru. 'Why, you haven't got any tobacco in your pipe. I've heard of this before. You pretend you want a light, and all the time you go on smoking other people's tobacco. That's enough, that's enough. There,' he added, turning to Yaji. 'That's how stingy the Kyoto people are. Ha-ha-ha! Would you oblige me with another pinch of your tobacco.'

'Well, I don't know about Kyoto people being stingy,' said Yaji, 'but I notice you're very fond of smoking my tobacco.'

'I didn't bring my tobacco pouch with me,' said Gomajiru.

'Did you forget it when you came out?' asked Yaji.

'No, no, I didn't forget it,' said Gomajiru. 'The fact is I haven't got a pouch, the reason being that I'm such an inveterate smoker that I found I was spending too much money on tobacco. So I gave up carrying a pouch and only carry a pipe.'

'Is that so that you can smoke other people's tobacco?' asked Yaji.

'Yes, certainly,' said Gomajiru.

'So while you call Kyoto people stingy, you're stingy yourself.'

'Ha-ha-ha!' laughed Gomajiru. 'That's so, that's so. But hadn't we better walk a little faster, as it's getting late.' . . .

They were shown into a back room and treated with great respect, evidently because Yaji had told a lie about his name. Both he and Kitahachi thought it all very amusing, and after taking a bath they put themselves at their ease. . . .

By this time all the poets in the neighbourhood had begun to assemble at the door. 'Excuse us,' they cried.

'Dear me!' said Gomajiru. 'Is that you, Master Baldpate? Please all come this way.'

'Are you Jippensha Ikku?' said the first to enter. 'This is the first time I have had the honour of meeting you. I am Awfully Funnyman. The gentleman next to me is

Master Gaptooth, then comes Master Snottyface, and the one farthest away is Master Scratchy. Please give us all the honour of your acquaintance.'

'By the way, master,' said Gomajiru, 'if it is not troubling you too much, would you be so kind as to write one of your poems on a fan or a scroll?' He brought out a fan and a scroll as he said this.

Yaji was greatly perplexed as to what he should do. Should he carry out his joke boldly? But then he had no poems of his own and he couldn't think of one on the spur of the moment. He decided that he would write a poem by somebody else, and he wrote one.

'Thank you, thank you,' said Gomajiru. 'The poem reads:

Where can I hear the cuckoo sing?
Far from the wine-shop's roistering;
Far from the cook-shop's guzzling throng,
There can you hear the cuckoo's song.

'Dear me!' said Gomajiru. 'I seem to have heard that poem before.' Then he read another:

'Would you know of lovers' sorrow?
Ring the dawn bell once again;
For it brings the fatal morrow
Tells them they must part in pain.

'But isn't this poem by Senshuan?' asked Gomajiru.

'What are you talking about?' said Yaji. 'That's one of my best poems. It's a very well known poem in Edo. Everyone knows it.'

'Yes, but when I was up in Edo last year,' said Gomajiru, 'I saw Sandara and Shakuyakutei Ushi and others, and I brought back that very poem and pasted it on the screen behind you. It is in the poet's own handwriting.'

Yaji turned round and saw on the screen the very poem that he had written.

'My master's very careless,' put in Kita, 'and can't tell the difference between his own poems and those of others. Look here, Yaji—I mean master—write one of the poems you made up on the road.'

Yaji, though he was rather out of countenance, put his usual bold face on it and commenced to write another poem, one of those he had made up on the road.

Meanwhile Kita, who had nothing to do, fixed his eyes upon a screen.

'Aha!' he said. 'That's a picture of Koikawa Harumachi. What's that phrase [san] written above it?'

'That's a poem [shi],' said Gomajiru.

'And that poem [shi] above the god of good luck,' asked Kita, 'who did that?'

'No, that's a religious maxim [go] written by the priest Takuan,' said Gomajiru.

'What a chap this is,' thought Kita. 'When I say it's san [three] he says it's shi [four], and when I say it's shi [four] he says it's go [five]. Whatever I say he always goes one more. I'll catch him yet.'

'I say,' he said aloud, after he had looked round, 'that written on top of that hanging scroll,—I suppose that's roku [six].'

'I don't know whether it's six or what it is,' said Gomajiru. 'It was taken as a pledge [shichi=seven].'

Just then the maidservant came in. 'A letter has come from Master Higetsuru,' she said.

'Dear me!' said Gomajiru. 'I wonder what it is about.' He opened it and read it aloud:—'This is to inform you that Jippensha Ikku has just arrived at my house from Edo and has brought letters of introduction from his friends at Nagoya. I hasten to inform you at once of the news and shall later take the liberty of accompanying him to your house. This in the meantime.'

'What can be the meaning of this?' said Gomajiru. 'I can't understand it at all. You hear what my friend says, master. It seems that this man is taking your name. Luckily he will soon be here and you will be able to confront him. Don't you think we should have some fun with him?'

'I never heard of such impudence,' said Yaji. 'But still I don't think I'd care to meet him.'

'Why, why?' asked Gomajiru.

'Well, just a minute ago,' said Yaji, 'I felt a touch of my old complaint, the colic. If it hadn't been for that I should have shown him up. It's a great nuisance.'

This unexpected coincidence made Yaji feel very miserable, and his behaviour increased the suspicions of the landlord and his guests that he was trying to deceive them. They now began to press him with questions.

'Look here, master,' said Master Funnyman, 'this is a very strange thing that's happened. Even if you don't feel well I think you certainly ought to meet the false Jippensha.'

'Don't ask me, don't ask me,' said Yaji.

'By the way, master,' said Master Snottyface, 'where is your house in Edo?'

'Let's see,' said Yaji. 'Where is it? Is it in Toba, or Fushimi, or Yodotake?'

'Oh yes,' said Master Scratchy, 'you cross the ferry at Yamazaki and ask for Master Yoichibei. Get out. Ha-ha-ha!'

'But I see you have written on your hat Yajirobei, Hatcho-bori, Kanda, Edo,' said Gomajiru. 'Who is this Yajirobei?'

PROVERBS

If you pray to a Buddha, pray to one only.

Avoid three things—a snake, a smooth-tongued man, and a wanton woman.

If a man steals gold he's put in prison; if he steals a land he's made king.

When all men praised the peacock for his beautiful tail, the birds cried out with one consent, "Look at his legs! And what a voice!"

Never trust a woman, even if she has borne you seven children.

The laden almond tree by the wayside is sure to be bitter.

The reason why parents love the younger children best is because they have now so little hope that the elder will do well.

The sparrow flying in the rear of the hawk thinks the hawk is fleeing.

The heaviest rains fall on the leaky house.

Every man carries a parasite somewhere.

One dog yelping at nothing will set ten thousand straining at their collars.

'Aha!' said Yaji. 'Where have I heard that name before? Oh yes, of course. My real name is Yajirobei.'

'Oh, you're one of the Yajirobeis that go round begging with the dolls, I suppose,' said Gomajiru.

'That's it, that's it,' said Yaji.

'Well, Master Yajirobei,' said Funnyman, 'shall I bring the false Ikku?'

'No, no,' said Yaji. 'No, no. I'm just going.'

'Why, what do you think the time is?' said Gomajiru. 'It's ten o'clock.'

'Maybe, maybe,' said Yaji. 'It's my colic. If I sit like this it gets worse and worse. When I get out in the cool night air and walk a bit it soon gets better.'

'So you're going to start now,' said Gomajiru. 'Well, I'm agreeable. At any rate you can't stop here,—taking other persons' names like that and deceiving everybody. Get out.'

'How have I been deceiving you?' asked Yaji.

'How have you deceived us? Didn't the real Jippensha bring letters from his friends at Nagoya?' said Gomajiru. 'There's no getting over that.'

'I thought they were cheats from the first,' said another. 'Get out before we throw you out.'

'Throw us out?' said Yaji. 'Don't be ridiculous.'

'Look here, Yaji,' said Kita. 'Don't let's have a row. We're in the wrong. Let's go somewhere else and stop, even at a cheap lodging house. We're very sorry if we've done anything wrong.'

Kita thus went on repeating apologies to the landlord, who was half angry and half amused.

While they were getting ready to start, all the people in the house came to see them off and jeered and laughed and clapped their hands. Yaji, with a very angry face and a dignified air, walked out followed by Kita. . . .

'Where are my chopsticks?' asked Kita.

'They're lying on the tray before you,' said Yaji. 'What a chap you are!'

'Please give 'em to me,' said Kita. 'I can't bend my head to look down.'

'What's the matter?' asked Yaji. 'Halloa, your face is funny. Your eyes are pulled up so that you look just like a fox.'

'It's that barber,' groaned Kita. 'He did my queue up so tight. It's so painful that when I bend my neck it feels as if all my hair was being pulled out by the roots.'

'You're spilling all your soup,' said the Kyoto man. 'Look, you've put your soup on top of your rice. There you've spilled it. Haven't you any manners?'

'Wipe it up, Yaji, will you?' said Kita.

'What a bother you are,' said Yaji. 'What did you want to have your queue tied up so tightly for? You should have had it done loose. I expect you annoyed the barber.'

'That's it,' said the countryman. 'That's why he did it up so tight.'

'I can't even talk,' groaned Kita. 'Ain't there anything to be done, Yaji?'

'I'll make it looser for you,' said Yaji, and he gave Kita's queue a good hard pull.

'Ow! Ow!' yelled Kita. 'What are you doing?'

'That feels better, doesn't it?' said Yaji.

'Ah, I can bend my neck a little,' said Kita. 'What an unfortunate chap I am.'

Supper being over, the dishes were removed and they began talking about how they should amuse themselves.

'Let's go to Furuichi tonight,' suggested the Kyoto man.

'Well, it seems rather bad to go there before we've been round the temples,' said Yaji, 'but we might as well enjoy ourselves as not.'

'Come on,' said the Kyoto man. 'I've spent thousands there year after year so they'll be quite willing to let me be responsible. Come on, let's go at once.'

'I wish I'd had my hair dressed too,' said Yaji.

'Landlord, landlord,' called the Kyoto man. 'Just come here a minute.'

'Ay, ay,' answered the landlord. 'Did you call me?'

'The gentlemen from Edo wish to go mountain climbing.'

In the vulgar language of the place, going to see the courtesans is called climbing the mountain. . . .

Yaji got up to go in spite of all the apologies of the waitress, and broke away from her when she tried to detain him by force. Just then the courtesan named Hatsue, who had been selected for him, came running in.

'What's the matter?' she asked.

'I'm not going to be stopped,' said Yaji. 'Let go, let go.'

'Is it because you don't like me that you want to go?' asked the girl.

'No, no, it's not that,' said Yaji. 'Let go, let go!'

'No, no, no,' said Hatsue, and while he was trying to get away from her she caught hold of his cloak and pulled it off.

'Here, what are you doing with my cloak?' cried Yaji. 'Let go, let go.'

Then she took away his purse and his tobacco pouch, all the time scolding him for being so obstinate. As he still persisted in saying that he would go, she then caught hold of his girdle and undid it and began to take off his kimono. As Yaji had only got a dirty loin-cloth on underneath he did not like to have himself exposed and felt greatly embarrassed.

'Here, here,' he cried, catching hold of his kimono with both hands, 'forgive me, forgive me.'

'You'll stop here then?' asked Hatsue.

'Yes, yes,' said Yaji.

'Take pity on him, Hatsue,' said the waitress.

'There, there,' said the landlord of the Fujiya, 'everything's all right now. Come along.'

He took hold of Yaji's hand and made him sit down again. The dispute being thus over, the waitress cleared up the room, and having pulled the drunken Kyoto man to his feet she led him and Kita away to other rooms, leaving Yaji to follow.

Yaji, who was very vain of his personal appearance, was anxious lest anybody should see his dirty loin-cloth, so while he was going along he took it off and flung it through the lattice of a window out in the garden. He looked around as he did so to see if anybody had observed him, and nobody being in sight, he followed the waitress with his peace of mind restored.

As it was now late the singing in the back room was hushed and the only sound to be heard was the snoring of the travellers. But soon the four o'clock bell rang, and then followed the crowing of ten thousand cocks, while through the window of the dawn came the dim light of day. Rubbing their eyes the travellers arose.

'Come along,' said the Kyoto man. 'Let's get up. It's time to start.'

'Come on, Yaji,' called Kita. 'The sun's risen. Let's go.'

Going into the room where Yaji was sleeping they woke him up from a deep sleep.

'I did sleep well,' he said.

'Won't you stay another night?' asked the girl.

'Never, never,' said Yaji. 'Let's go.'

After they had made their preparations to start all the girls came out to bid them farewell, and one of them happened to peep out through the lattice window.

'Halloa!' she said. 'Look there. There's a napkin hanging to the pine tree.'

'Let me look, said Hatsue. 'So there is. Whose is it?'

'That's funny,' said Yaji. 'It reminds one of the feather-robe pine tree, eh? The tree with a loin-cloth is funnier still.'

'Isn't that yours, Yaji?' asked Kita.

"So it is,' said Hatsue. 'Isn't it your loin-cloth?'

She looked at Yaji and laughed, but Yaji, although he was secretly amused that the loin-cloth he had flung out of the window should have caught on to the pine tree, put on an innocent face.

'Nonsense!' he said. 'What should I be doing with a dirty loin-cloth like that?'

'Yes, but when I pulled off your kimono last night,' said Hatsue, 'you had a loin-cloth on just like that.'

'That he had,' said the Kyoto man.

'It's all nonsense,' said Yaji. "I don't like cotton loin-cloths. I always wear silk.'

'Ho-ho-ho!' laughed Hatsue. 'It's not true. It's his.'

'I know it quite well,' said Kita. 'That's it. If it's a lie show us the one you have on. I believe you're like the spearmen of a daimyo's procession, with nothing on.'

'Ha-ha-ha!' laughed Hatsue. 'Here, gardener,' she called through the lattice. 'That loin-cloth belongs to a guest. Just get it for him will you?'

The gardener picked it off the tree with a bamboo and thrust it through the lattice. 'There it is,' he said.

'Oh, how it smells!' said Hatsue.

'There you are, Yaji.' said Kita, laughing. 'Take it.'

'What spiteful things you say,' replied Yaji. 'I tell you it's not mine.'

'Well, show us the one you've got on, then,' said Kita. He seized hold of Yaji's girdle to undo it, but Yaji broke away and fled down the passage to the amusement of them all.

It was thus that they left the house.

'Botheration!' said Yaji. 'You put me to shame, Kita.'

'Well, a loin-cloth in a pine tree is rather a curious thing,' was Kita's reply. . . .

Their hurried preparations finished, they returned to Furuichi, where the keepers of the stalls and sideshows were calling to the people to come in, and there they saw

Sugi and Tama who allow people to throw coppers at their faces while they play on the samisen and sing a song which nobody understands.

'I'll see if I can't hit that girl on her dimple,' said Yaji.

He took two or three coppers and threw them, but each time the girl bobbed her head to one side so that he missed.

'Let me have a try,' said Kita. He threw, but he also missed.

'You'll never be able to hit her,' said the Kyoto man.

'You see this time,' said Yaji. Then he threw, but missed again.

'I've thrown a whole string of coppers and not hit her once,' said Kita. 'There must be a way of doing it. I'm going to hit her ugly mug somehow.'

He picked up a pebble and threw it, but the girl caught it in her mouth and spat it out, so that it hit Yaji on the face and made him yell.

'Ha-ha-ha!' laughed Kita. 'That was a good one.' . . .

Afterwards they went round the Shinji Shrine, the Hoken Shrine and many others, till, when they were climbing up to the Ama-no-Iwato, Yaji, for some reason, began to suffer from a stomachache. Quickly reaching the top they rested for a time, while Yaji took some pills they had with them. The pain did not abate, however, so they returned quickly to Hirokoji to look for an inn. While they were wandering about there the landlord of an inn addressed them.

'Won't you stop here for the night, gentlemen?' he asked.

'Well,' said Kita, 'my companion's taken rather sick so I think we had better.'

'Please come in,' said the landlord, and he called to the maid to show them in.

'You look very bad, Yaji,' said Kita. 'This must be a punishment on you for something you've done.'

'I don't remember doing anything bad,' said Yaji. 'It must have been the rice this morning.'

'You must have been eating something you're not accustomed to,' said the landlord.

'You haven't got any pluck,' said Kita.

He assisted Yaji into a room and the landlord brought in their baggage.

'It seems rather serious,' he said. 'Have you tried any medicine? As it happens my wife has just sent for the doctor, as she is expecting a baby. She's been feeling unwell from yesterday, so I've just called him. Would you like to see him too?'

'Yes,' said Yaji, 'if you don't mind calling him.'

'Certainly, certainly,' said the landlord, and he went off to the kitchen.

Meanwhile Yaji got worse.

'How would it do to take something?' said Kita. 'Some hot water, or tea, or sakè?'

'Don't talk nonsense,' said Yaji. 'How my stomach's rumbling! Where's the closet, Kita? Just ask.'

'Where have you put it?' said Kita. 'Perhaps it's up your sleeve.'

'Don't talk like a fool,' said Yaji. 'Fancy having the closet up your sleeve! I want you to look where it is.'

'I see,' replied Kita. 'Well, I'll have a look. Oh, there it is, fallen down in front of the verandah.'

'What are you jawing about!' groaned Yaji. 'Ugh, how it hurts!' He got up slowly and went off to do his business. Then a girl came from the kitchen and announced that the doctor had arrived.

'Show him in,' said Kita.

The doctor was evidently only the doctor's assistant, not the doctor himself. He was dressed in a dark brown cotton kimono with a crest and a black silk cloak.

'What unseasonable weather we're having,' he said. 'Let me feel your pulse.'

He seated himself beside Kita and began to feel his pulse.

'It isn't me that's sick,' said Kita.

'We can tell whether a person is ill or not,' said the doctor, 'by comparing their pulse with that of a healthy person. Just let me see.'

He felt Kita's pulse for some time very gravely.

'No, no,' he said at last. 'There's nothing the matter with you.'

'No,' said Kita.

'How is your appetite?' asked the doctor.

'Well, this morning I had three goes of rice and three bowls of soup.'

'Yes, yes,' said the doctor. 'I thought so. And you couldn't eat any more?'

'No,' said Kita.

'I thought I was right,' said the doctor. 'I thought from your pulse there was nothing wrong with you.'

'Yes, 'said Kita.

'I'm right, ain't I? said the doctor. 'The first thing in medicine is to feel the pulse. You needn't be anxious. Well, I must be going now.'

'Please look at the patient before you go,' said Kita.

'Oh yes,' said the doctor. 'That's right. I always forget to feel the patient's pulse when I am called in. It's a bad habit of mine. It's really not necessary but I may as well see him. Where is the patient?'

'He's just gone to the closet,' said Kita. 'Here, Yaji, Yaji. The doctor's come. Come out quick.'

'I can't come out,' said Yaji from inside the closet. 'Please tell the doctor to come here.'

'Nonsense!' said Kita. 'Who ever heard of such a thing? What a rude thing to say!'

'Well, I'll come out then,' said Yaji. He came out slowly and the doctor felt his pulse as if it was a matter of life and death.

'Aha!' he said. 'You're suffering from dizziness. Your confinement must be close at hand.'

'I don't remember becoming pregnant,' said Yaji.

'Isn't it pregnancy?' asked the doctor. 'How strange! That's the fault of my master. He sent a man to call me from the Igagoya in Hirokoji and told me that a patient was going to be confined and that probably she was suffering from dizziness and I must give her some medicine. Aren't you the patient?'

'I see, I see,' said Kita. 'There is a case of that here. But this gentleman is not suffering from it.'

'Dear me!' said the doctor. 'That's my mistake. But if you would suffer from the same complaint then I could administer the same medicine. That would save a lot of trouble.'

'That's so,' said Kita. 'Yaji, you'd better do as the doctor tells you and feel dizzy.'

'What are you talking about?' said Yaji. 'Men don't get dizzy.'

'Well, well,' said the doctor, 'perhaps it would be better for you to have another kind of illness. That will give me more practice. What do you say you're suffering from?'

'I've been suffering from grinding pains in the stomach for some time,' said Yaji.

'Probably only inside the stomach,' said the doctor.

'Yes, only in my stomach as you say,' replied Yaji. 'Not outside.'

'Ah, I thought so, I thought so,' said the doctor. 'Here,'—he called to the maid—'tell my man to bring my medicine-box in, will you?'

The maid went out but soon returned to say that she could not see the doctor's man.

'No wonder you couldn't see him,' said the doctor. 'I didn't bring him. I brought the chest in myself.' He opened a cloth he had brought and took out his medicine-chest.

'What a duck of a spoon you've got,' said the maid as she looked in the chest.

'That's because he's a quack doctor,' said Kita. 'Ducks always quack. But why have you got pictures on the medicines instead of names? What's the reason of that?'

'Ahem!' said the doctor. 'That's rather an embarrassing question, but I may tell you that from the time I was born I have never received any instruction in letters.'

'Then you can't read?' asked Kita.

'No,' said the doctor, 'I can't read at all. So I have the names of the medicines done in pictures.'

'That's interesting,' said Kita. 'What does that picture of the Dojo temple stand for?'

'That stands for cinnamon,' said the doctor.

'And this picture of Emma stands for rhubarb, I suppose. What's the meaning of the dog on fire?'

'That's dried orange peel.'

'And that picture of the woman in childbirth and somebody making water by her?'

'That's jasmine root, of course.'

'And that seal with the hair on it?'

'That's lizard tail.'

'And the devil breaking wind?'

'That's aegle.'

'Ha-ha-ha!' laughed Kita. 'How funny! But what about the medicine?'

'You must boil the medicine as usual,' said the doctor, 'and add a slice of ginger to it.'

'Wouldn't horseradish do?' suggested Kita.

'Don't be a fool,' said Yaji.

Just then they heard sounds from the kitchen as of people rushing about and the voice of the landlord calling, 'Here, Nabe, Nabe, send someone for the midwife. Here, heat some water, quick, quick. Have you got some hayame?'

In the midst of all these noises Yaji went on groaning.

'How is it, Yaji?' asked Kita.

'This won't do,' said the doctor. 'You mustn't come near the patient.'

As he drove Kita away there came from the kitchen the old midwife that had been summoned for the landlord's wife. The maid, all in a fluster, dragged her to where Yaji lay groaning under the bedding.

'Eh?' said the old woman. 'You mustn't give way. Sit up, sit up.' She dragged Yaji and in so doing accidentally scratched his face and made him yell. 'You must be patient,' she went on. "Here, where's the mat? Somebody bring the mat."

'Oh, oh, oh!' groaned Yaji.

'There, there,' said the old woman. This midwife was in fact a little blind and moreover so agitated that she had mistaken Yaji for a woman in labour. She now began to hold him up.

'Here', she called. 'Somebody come and help me. Quick, quick.'

Kita, who was enjoying the old woman's mistake, kept a straight face and began to help her hold Yaji up.

'What are you doing, Kita?' said Yaji. 'Oh, how it hurts.'

'You mustn't be so timid,' said the old woman. 'You must try and bear it.'

'How do you think I'm going to bear it?' said Yaji.' 'I'm off to the closet. Let go.'

'No, no,' said the old woman. 'You mustn't move.'

'But if I don't it will all come out here,' said Yaji.

'Well, let it,' said the midwife. 'There, there, its head's coming out.'

'Oh, oh!' yelled Yaji. 'That's not a child. Let go. Oh, oh, oh!'

He began to struggle, and as the old woman held him tight, he finally lost his temper and gave her a box on the ear. This astonished the old woman, but she still kept her arms locked round him, as she thought the patient was delirious.

Meanwhile from the kitchen came the cry of a newly born infant. Apparently the goodwife of the house had given birth to the child.

'There,' said the midwife. 'It's born. Why, it isn't here. Where can it be?'

The midwife letting go of him to look for the baby, Yaji immediately rushed away to the closet, while the landlord came out of the kitchen.

'Here, granny, granny,' he cried. 'I sent for you a long time ago. The baby's born now. Quick, quick.'

He dragged the old woman off into the kitchen, where could be heard cries of, 'What a fine boy! The finest boy ever born in the three countries. Congratulations! Congratulations!'

At receiving these congratulations the landlord was all over smiles. 'I'm sorry you've been disturbed,' he apologised to the guests. 'Happily my wife's had an easy birth.'

Just then Yaji came out of the closet. 'Congratulations,' he said. 'I also have had an easy delivery. I feel as if I had never had anything the matter with me at all.'

'You are also to be congratulated,' said the landlord.

Then sakè was served in honour of the event and there was great talking and laughing over the midwife's mistake. . . .

By this time the boat had passed Yodo.

'By the way, Kita,' said Yaji, 'I forgot to relieve myself before I got on the boat. You know I get so nervous in a boat that it always makes me feel that way. What a nuisance it is! Here, boatman. Just put in to the shore for a minute.'

'Do you want to land?' asked the boatman.

'I want to relieve myself,' said Yaji.

'Lean over the side of the boat and do it,' said the boatman.

'That would be all right if I could, but I can't,' said Yaji.

Seated next to them was a party of two, consisting of an old man and a young boy. The old man had been talking to Yaji and Kita earlier in the evening, but was now lying down covered with a quilt.

'Excuse me,' he said, 'but if you want to relieve yourself there's a pot over there. Here, Chomatsu. Wake up. He's too sleepy. You'll find it just over there. Please take it.'

'Thank you very much' said Yaji. He searched about in the dark and behind a brazier he found a teapot of a kind hardly ever seen in Edo. Yaji thought it must be the pot the old man meant and pulled it out.

'Here it is,' he said. 'It's the usual kind, I see.'

In reality it seemed to him a strange-looking pot. He thought at first the handle must be the mouth, but he found there was no hole. Then he thought it must have a stopper in, and stuck his finger in to see. He was in such a hurry to relieve himself that he kept twisting the teapot about in all directions till at last the lid fell off. 'Oh, there's a hole here,' he thought, and he did it in the top.

'Thank you very much,' he said to the old man, and put the teapot back where he he had found it.

'It's very cold,' said the old man. 'Chomatsu, get up and make a little fire. We'll warm some sakè. Can't you open your eyes? Wake up, wake up.'

The old man got up himself at last and raked together the fire in the brazier. Then he lit a small lantern, hung it on the gunwale and took up the teapot.

'What's this in the teapot?' he said. 'Oh, yes, we were going to make some tea and filled it with water.' With that he threw the contents of the teapot into the river and having put some sakè in it put it on the brazier to warm.

'Won't you Edo gentlemen have some sakè?' he asked.

'I shall be delighted,' said Kita.

'It's warm now,' said the old man. He brought out some comestibles and poured out some sakè into a cup.

'It's nice and hot,' he said, 'but it has a funny smell. Seems as if the sakè had gone bad. But it can't be that. Just try a cup.'

He handed the cup to Kita who drank it off at a gulp. It seemed to him to have a very strange salty taste and made him feel sick, but he said, 'Thank you.'

'Won't your friend have some?' said the old man.

'Here, Yaji,' said Kita, and he handed him the cup.

Yaji, who had been looking on, felt sure that the pot in which they had warmed the sakè was the one into which he had relieved himself, and he noted their grimaces after they had drunk. The situation seemed to him very funny, but he concealed his amusement, and when Kita handed him the sakè cup declined to have any.

'I don't know how it is,' he said, 'but I don't feel like drinking sakè tonight. But let me pass the cup to you.'

'Won't you have some?' the old man said.

'Why, he bathes in it usually,' said Kita. 'Won't you really have some, Yaji? Generally the very mention of sakè makes your mouth water. It's very strange.'

'Aha!' said the old man. 'I understand. Your friend mistook the pot in the dark and did it in here. I thought it tasted like that. We can't drink it now.'

'I never dreamt of it,' said Kita. 'When we were crossing the Kuwana ferry he made a mess in the boat and caused no end of a row, but I didn't think he would be as careless as this. Ugh! How dirty!'

'That's why the teapot was full when I took it up,' said the old man. 'I thought this lad had filled it with water and I emptied it into the river, but I must have left some in.'

'What a horrible thing,' said Kita. 'I feel sick.'

'So do I,' said the old man. 'Ugh! Ugh!'

'I'm really very sorry,' said Yaji. 'Shall I give you some medicine? Though I don't know what sort of medicine would be good for it. Has anybody got any pills for this complaint?' he asked the other passengers.

'No, no,' said the passengers. 'We haven't got any medicine that would be good for that!

'What a nuisance!' said Yaji.

'Just lift up the cover a little, Yaji,' said Kita.

'What for?'

'I want to do something.'

'Do something?'

'Yes, with my mouth.'

'Then you'd better go to the side of the boat and stick your head over. I'll hold on to you. How do you feel now? Is there some more? It's a pity there's no dog in the river.'

'What do you want a dog for?'

'Why if there was a dog I could call, "Shirokoi! Shirokoi!"'

'Don't be a fool! Ugh!'

'Chomatsu,' said the old man. 'Just rub my back. Ugh! Ugh!'

Soon the old man ceased to feel sick and washed his mouth with the river water.

'How's the other gentleman?' he asked.

'Well, I feel a little better now,' said Kita. He washed out his mouth also and sat with a very sad face. Yaji continued to conceal his mirth at the incident and the old man took him for a very good-natured person and did not get angry with him. . . .

They parted the sunblinds and went into a small teahouse.

'I see they've got some sweet sakè,' said Yaji. 'Here, granny, give us a cupful.'

'Ay, ay,' said the old woman. 'I'll draw you some in a minute.'

'Seems as if the old woman had fallen in love with you, Yaji,' said Kita. 'She keeps looking at you all the time in such a queer way.'

'Don't be a fool,' said Yaji. 'Here, old woman, hurry up.'

'Ay, ay' said the old woman. 'In a minute.'

Every time the old woman looked at Yaji her tears began to fall.

'What's the matter with your eyes, old lady? asked Yaji. 'Are they bad?'

'It makes me feel sad every time I look at you,' said the old woman.

'Why's that?' asked Yaji.

'Wai-wai,' sobbed the old woman.

'That's strange,' said Kita. 'What makes you feel so sad?'

'I lost my only son the other day,' said the old woman, 'and he was just like that gentleman,—just like him.'

'Was he like me?' said Yaji. 'Then he must have been very good looking. What a pity he died!'

'He'd got a hoarse voice just like you,' said the old woman, 'and his face was pock-marked and black like yours, and he had a turn-up nose just like yours, and his eyes were crooked like yours.'

'Well, he seems to have had all my bad points,' said Yaji.

'He couldn't have had any of the good ones,' said Kita, 'because there ain't any.'

'Not only that but he was bald just like you,' went on the old woman, 'with such a little queue. Oh, he was just like you.'

'When you've finished taking stock of my face, perhaps you'll let us have that sakè,' said Yaji.

'Oh dear, I forgot all about it,' said the old woman, and she brought out two cups and filled them with the sakè.

'It's very weak,' said Kita when he'd tasted it.

'That's because it made me so sad to look at the gentleman that my tears fell into it,' said the old woman.

'What?' said Yaji. 'It ain't only tears. Seems to me as if your nose ran into it too.'

'Well, to tell you the truth,' said the old woman, 'it ran from my nose and my mouth too.'

'Oh, how nasty!' said Kita. 'I can't drink any more.'

'I've drunk all mine,' said Yaji. 'How horrid! Come on, let's go.'

'How much is it?' asked Kita.

'That'll be six coppers,' said the old woman.

'You don't charge for the snot I suppose,' said Kita, and he went out spitting. . . .

In the Great Hall of the Hokwo Temple the principal image is a carving of Rushana in a sitting position. It is six jo and three shaku high. The Hall, which faces the west, is twenty-seven ken from east to west and from south to north forty-five ken.

'It's much finer than I thought,' said Yaji. 'Look at his great palms, the size of a room.'

'And he's got whatyoumaycallems as big as a badger,' said Kita.

'What improper things you say,' said Yaji. 'A man could walk up his nostrils with his hat on.'

'If he sneezed he'd get blown out pretty quick,' said Kita.

'Don't talk foolishness,' said Yaji. 'Let's go round to the back and see what's there. Halloa, there's a window at the back.'

'That's where he breathes,' said Kita.

'He's not a whale,' said Yaji.

'I say,' said Kita. 'Look at those holes in the beams.'

'So there are,' said Yaji. 'That's strange.'

At the bottom of the beams supporting the roof were cut holes just large enough to allow a person to wriggle through, and the country visitors were amusing themselves by getting through the holes. Kita also got through.

'That's interesting,' said Kita. 'I can get through, but I don't think you could, Yaji. You're too fat.'

'What are you talking about?' said Yaji, and pushing Kita out of the way, he went down on all fours and wriggled halfway into the hole. Then he found that he couldn't get any further and tried to get back, but the hilt of his dirk caught sideways in the hole and hurt him unbearably.

'Oh, oh!' he groaned, red in the face. 'What an awful thing I've done.'

'What's the matter?' said Kita. 'Can't you get out?'

'Here, just pull my hands,' said Yaji.

'Ha-ha-ha!' laughed Kita. 'What fun!' and he caught hold of Yaji's hands and gave them a good pull.

'Oh! oh!' said Yaji. 'That hurts.'

'What a weakling you are,' said Kita. 'Have a little patience.'

'Try pulling me by the legs,' suggested Yaji.

'All right,' said Kita, and he went round to the other side and caught hold of Yaji's legs. 'Ya-en-sa! Ya-en-sa!' he cried as he pulled.

'Oh! Oh! That hurts more,' groaned Yaji.

'Have a little patience and bear it,' cried Kita. 'You've come out quite a lot. Ya-en-sa! Ya-en-sa!'

'Wait a bit, wait a bit,' said Yaji. 'You'll pull my legs off. It's better from the other end.'

Accordingly Kita went round to the other side and began to pull his arms.

'Ya-en-sa! Ya-en-sa!' he cried. 'You've come out quite a lot.'

'Oh! Oh!' yelled Yaji. 'I can't stand it, Kita. Just go round to the other side and pull like you did before.'

'How you change your mind!' said Kita, and he went round to the other side and caught hold of his legs again.

'Ya-en-sa! Ya-en-sa!' he cried.

'Wait, wait,' said Yaji. 'It's better when you pull my arms after all.'

'If I go on pulling you first at one end and then at the other,' said Kita, 'we'll go on all day. Wait a bit. I've got an idea.' He called to some pilgrims who were standing by.

'Just come here a minute, will you?' he said. 'If you pull in front I'll go and pull behind.'

'Don't be a fool,' said Yaji. 'How are you going to get me out by pulling at both ends?'

'Well, we can't get you out pulling first at one and end then at the other,' said Kita.

'If we pulled at both ends,' said one of the pilgrims, 'we'd stretch you a bit and you'd come out easily.'

'I know what to do,' said Kita. 'We'll go and buy a bottle of vinegar for you to drink, Yaji.'

'What's the good of that?' asked Yaji.

'Why, you know vinegar makes you thin,' said Kita.

'Ha-ha-ha!' laughed the pilgrims. 'But we haven't time for that. What we'd better do is to get a hammer and hit him on the head, so as to drive him out.'

'I never thought of that,' said Kita, 'That's a good idea. But don't you think we might hurt him?'

'Then I don't see how we're going to get him out,' said the pilgrim.

Here a countryman joined in.

'I'm from a far province,' he said, 'but I don't like to see the gentleman in such a fix.'

'Well, if you can suggest anything,' said Kita, 'let's hear it.'

'Well, I think if we were to cut his leg and rub some hot pepper in he'd get such a shock that he'd get out by himself.'

'That's like the girl and the snake,' said Kita. 'It's a good idea.'

'What I think,' said another pilgrim, 'is that you want to make his bones soft. Then we could pull him out. What we ought to do is to get some quicklime and sprinkle it on him.'

'Ah,' said the countryman, 'and you might get him a coffin at the same time. If we break his arms and legs we could probably get him in.'

'What foolishness you're talking!' groaned Yaji. 'What's the use of saying such silly things? Can't you help me, Kita?'

'Wait a minute,' said Kita. 'Ah, I see. The scabbard of your dirk has got caught crossways,' and he put in his hand and felt about till at last he managed to take off the dirk.

'Ah, that feels easier,' said Yaji.

'There,' said Kita. 'Now if you'll all push in front I'll pull his legs from behind. Ya-en-sa! Ya-en-sa!'

'He's coming. He's coming,' said the pilgrim. 'Just a little more. Shove up.'

'Oh, oh!' groaned Yaji.

'Ha-ha-ha!' laughed Kita. 'What a joke!'

'Oh, oh! It hurts,' groaned Yaji.

'Can't be helped,' said Kita. 'En-ya-en-ya! There you are,' and he pulled Yaji out on to the floor.

'Thank you, thank you,' panted Yaji, wiping his face. 'Thank you all. Now I know that it hurts the person being born more than it hurts the person bearing. My bones did crack when I was coming out. And look at my kimono how torn it is.' . . .

Soon they came to the Kiyomizu Temple, in the main hall of which stands the Eleven-faced Thousand-handed Kwannon. Yaji and Kita rested here a while and then wandered round the precincts till they came to where an old priest, standing by a table on an elevated piece of ground, was calling to the crowd of pilgrims.

'A picture of the holy Kwannon of this temple may be obtained here,' he cried. 'Try its wonderful virtues. It makes the blind to talk and the dumb to hear. The cripples who have walked all the way here are able to walk all the way home again. Those who worship it just once, even though they are strong and healthy, enter Paradise immediately. The devout who desire salvation should not leave without receiving one of these pictures. Offerings may be made to any amount. Are there no believers here?'

'What a chattering old priest,' said Kita. 'By the way, Yaji, I've heard a story about people jumping off from this place.'

'From ancient times,' said the priest, 'those who have made a vow to Buddha have jumped from here in perfect safety.'

'They'd be smashed to pieces if they did,' said Yaji.

'Do they ever do it now?' asked Kita.

'Yes,' said the priest. 'Even naturally timid people have been known to come and jump off here. There was a young girl jumped off here the other day.'

'What happened to her?' asked Kita.

'She jumped and fell,' said the priest.

'Yes, but what happened after she fell?' asked Kita.

'What an inquisitive person you are,' said the priest. 'Well, as she was full of sin, the Buddha, for punishment, made her turn up her eyes.'

'Didn't her nose turn up too?' asked Kita.

'Well, she hadn't got any nose when she started,' replied the priest.

'Did she lose her senses?' asked Kita.

'Yes, she became unconscious,' answered the priest.

'And what happened then?' asked Kita.

'What a persistent fellow you are,' said the priest. 'What do you want to know all this for?'

'It's a bad habit of mine,' said Kita. 'I'm never satisfied till I hear everything to the end.'

'Well, I'll tell you,' said the priest. 'When the girl got to the ground she went mad.'

'Dear me,' said Kita. 'And what did she do then?'

'She began reciting the million prayers,' said the priest.

'And then what?' asked Kita.

'She struck the bell.'

'And what then?'

'Namu Amida Butsu.'

'And after that?'

'Namu Amida Butsu.'

'And what came next?'

'Namu Amida Butsu.'

'Yes, yes, yes, but what came after the prayers?'

'Well, you must wait till she's finished. She's got to say it a million times.'

'What?' cried Kita. 'Have I got to wait till she's done reciting the prayer a million times? How awful!'

'Well, you said you liked to hear about everything to the end,' said the priest, 'so if you have patience you'll know. If you get tired of waiting you might help her say the prayers.'

'Ah, that would be interesting,' said Kita. 'You help too, Yaji. Namu Amida Butsu. Namu Amida Butsu.'

'You must strike the bell too,' said the priest. He struck the bell loudly while he recited the prayer. 'Namu Amida Butsu. (Chan-chan.) Namu Amida Butsu. (Chan-chan.)'

'This is quite amusing,' said Kita.

'Here, just hold the bell a minute. I've got to go somewhere,' said the priest.

He thrust the bell into Kita's hand and went off. Kita took the bell and went on praying, 'Namu Amida Butsu. Namu Amida Butsu. (Chan-chan. Chiki-chan-chan. Chiki-chan-chan.)'

'You don't strike the bell properly,' said Yaji. 'Give it here.'

'What?' said Kita. 'Don't I do it properly?'

He began striking the bell so loudly and making such a row that a priest came out of the temple and fell into a terrible passion when he saw what was going on.

'Here,' he cried. 'What are you doing at that holy shrine? Don't you know any better than to behave in that uncouth manner in a sacred place?'

'The priest in charge went away,' said Kita, 'so we thought we'd just keep things going.'

'Don't make any of your silly jokes here,' said the priest. 'Where do you think you are?'

'This is Kiyomizu, Atsumori's burial place, ain't it?' said Kita.

'You must be mad,' said the priest.

'Yes, that's why we're saying the million prayers,' replied Kita.

'Nonsense,' said the priest. 'Go away at once. This is a holy place of prayer.'

The priest got so angry and spoke in such a loud voice that many more priests came running out of the temple, and as they looked very threatening Yaji and Kita slunk down the hill.

'That comes of being too clever with the bell,' said Kita.

It was now four o'clock and the two thought they had better set off for Sanjo to look for an inn for the night. As they were going along they saw a man coming from the opposite direction carrying a tub and some radishes.

'Radish stale,' he kept calling out. 'Radish stale.'

'Well, I've heard of pumpkins playing the flute, but never of radishes relieving themselves,' said Kita.

'I suppose he wants to exchange the radishes for the stale,' said Yaji.

'Here you are,' cried the man. 'Big radish stale.'

As he was going along calling, two men, apparently lower retainers of some sort, came up and began to bargain with the man.

'Here', cried one of them. 'We'll give you our stale for three radishes.'

'Well, just come down here and show me how much you've got,' said the man.

He led them down a side road, and Yaji and Kita, anxious to see what they were going to do, followed after.

'There, do it here,' said the man, putting the tub down.

After they had done it the man tilted the tub on one side to see how much there was. 'Is that all?' he asked.

'I broke wind at the end,' said one of the retainer, 'so there can't be any more.'

'That's no good,' said the man. 'Just shake yourselves and try again.'

'We're not keeping any back,' said the retainer. 'There's nothing left.'

'Then I can't give you three radishes.' said the man. 'Take two.'

'Yes,' said the other retainer, 'I know it's only a little, but it's very good. Other people only live on rice and tea, but we live on nothing but meat.'

'Yes, but there's nothing of it,' said the man.

'Well, don't make such a fuss,' said the retainer. 'Take it home and mix some water with it and it will make quite a lot. Give us the three radishes.'

'You say nothing but "give, give," ' said the man, 'but I want something in return. Go and drink some tea, and see if you can't do some more.'

They were going on disputing, when Kitahachi, who had been enjoying the joke, spoke to the retainers.

'Excuse me,' he said, 'but fortunately I want to relieve myself, and if it's not being too rude I'll let you have it. If you add mine to yours he'll let you have three radishes.'

'Thank you very much for your kind offer,' said one of the retainers, 'but I'm afraid we are trespassing on your goodness too much.'

'Not at all,' said Kita. 'I haven't very much to offer, but if the little I have is of any service to you . . .'

'Well, we'll accept your offer then,' said the retainer.

The tub was brought and put before Kita.

'No, no,' he said. 'Put it further away. My distance is a couple of yards.'

'That's wonderful,' said the man with the radishes. 'You can't be a native of this place. Theirs is so thin it's no use.'

'I've always been a great man at that sort of thing ever since I was born,' said Kita. 'I'm the sort of man that has to carry a tub around with him.'

'How lucky you are!' said one of the retainers.

'Well then, just put the tub on your shoulder and I'll go with you,' said the scavenger.

'Well, I'm not quite so frequent as that,' said Kita.

'You've got a friend with you, I see,' said the man. 'Doesn't he want to do something?'

'No, thank you,' said Yaji. 'I'm the sort of man that does four to eight gallons at a time without any difficulty, but lately I haven't been able to do any at all, which gives me much trouble.'

'There's a way to cure that,' said the man.

'How's that?' asked Yaji.

'Well, you know, if sakè won't run well from the bung of a sakè tub they bore a hole in the top of the tub and then it comes out very fast. If yours won't come out all you have to do is to bore a hole in your forehead and it'll come out all right then.'

'Ha-ha-ha!' laughed Kita. 'That's a good one. But it's getting late. Let's go.' . . .

The maid went and brought in another dish.

'How much is that dish?' asked Yaji.

'That's two momme five bun,' said the maid.

'Dear, dear,' said Kita.

'I'll get them,' said Yaji. 'I know a plan that will teach them not to be greedy.'

Of everything the maid brought in he asked the price, and when they had eaten everything up he called for the bill.

The maid brought in the bill and handed it to Yaji.

'Let's see, let's see,' said Yaji. 'Kita, look what they make the total!'

'Oh, oh!' cried Kita. 'Twelve momme five bun. What a price! Make 'em cut it down.'

'No, no, it's cheap,' said Yaji. 'There, bring me the change. Now then Kita, we've got something to carry. We'll take all these things with us.'

He took all the bowls and dishes, wiped them with paper, and began to wrap them up.

'What's that for?' asked Kita.

'We'll take 'em all away with us,' said Yaji.

'Oh, no,' said the maid. 'Dear, dear, what shall I do?'

'I asked you how much this bowl was,' said Yaji, 'and you told me it was five bun, didn't you? Then I asked you how much this dish was and you said it was two momme five bun, and the vegetable bowl was three momme. Isn't that right? And the plate three momme five bun, didn't you say? Altogether twelve momme five bun. I've paid you for them so there's no excuse.'

'Ho-ho-ho!' laughed the maid. 'How funny you are.'

'There's no ho-ho-ho about it at all,' said Yaji. 'I'm going to take them with me.'

He went on wrapping up the plates and dishes with quite a serious air, much to the dismay of the maid.

'I was telling you the price of the food not of the dishes,' she explained.

'If I'd been asking about the price of the food,' said Yaji, 'I'd have asked you how much the food in the dish was. But I didn't. I asked you how much the dish was and you said two momme five bun, didn't you?'

'Yes,' said the maid, 'but then I thought . . . Oh dear, what shall I do?'

'There's nothing to dispute about,' said Yaji.

Then a man in an apron came in from the kitchen and inquired the particulars.

'You're quite right,' he said to Yaji. 'Please take the dishes—as you have paid for them, but you haven't yet paid me for what you have eaten.'

'I see, I see,' said Yaji. 'What we have eaten won't be very dear. How much will it be?'

'That will be seventy-eight momme five bun,' said the man.

'Eh?' said Yaji. 'What a price! Do you think I'm blind? Why it's only worth about five or six hundred coppers. What a terrible price to ask.'

'Not at all,' said the man. 'All the food is brought from Osaka on foot and it costs a lot to bring it.'

'That may be all right for the fish,' said Yaji, 'but the vegetables can't be so dear. How much was that dish of greens?'

'That's seven momme five bun,' said the man.

'What? Seven momme five bun?' cried Yaji. 'You're too greedy for anything. It's only worth three or four coppers.'

'That may be what you think,' said the man, 'but the greens are a special production of Kyoto and I always pick them over very carefully and throw away the parts eaten by caterpillars, and select the best. And I always sift the dung out of them too.'

'Nonsense!' said Yaji. 'Whoever heard of such a thing? I'll only pay you two shu for what we've eaten.'

'No, no,' said the man. 'That won't do. If you think it's dear please return the things you've bought.'

Yaji now saw that he was beaten at his own game of quibbling.

'Here, Yaji,' said Kita. 'Don't let's bother about it any more.'

'You may make as many excuses as you like,' said Yaji, 'but I tell you the bill's unreasonable. I'll forgive you this time, but just you remember in future,' and with a glare at the landlord he walked out.

'Good-bye,' said the maid. 'Please come again soon.'

'Oh, suck it,' said Yaji. 'Ha-ha-ha!'

They left the precincts of the temple and went quickly in the direction of Sanjo to find an inn for the night, catching up as they did so with a number of women who were selling firewood, ladders, pestles, mallets, and other things, all of which they carried on their heads.

'Don't you want a ladder or a pestle?' they asked.

'Look how it makes them wag their tails,' said Yaji. 'Ha-ha-ha!'

'Won't you buy some firewood?' asked another woman.

'Ain't they strong,' said Kita, 'to be able to carry the things on their heads.'

Soon they came to a river bed, where all the women put down their burdens and sat down to have a smoke.

'That's what you might expect in Kyoto,' said Yaji. 'They ain't bad looking. I'll chaff 'em a bit.'

'You'll get into trouble again,' warned Kita.

'Nonsense,' said Yaji, 'it's you who do that.'

He took out his pipe and drew near to the women.

'Sorry to trouble you but could you let me have a light?' he said. 'By the way, how do you manage to carry those things on your heads? Ain't they heavy?'

'Ay, ay,' said one of the women.

'I used to go about with a stone weighing twenty or thirty kwamme on my head,' said Kita, 'and think nothing of it.'

'You must have been a miller's man,' said one of the women.

'You be quiet,' said Yaji.

'Won't you buy this pestle, gentlemen,' said another of the women.

'What, a pestle?' said Yaji. 'I would like to, but this one is too thin. I've got one as big as a log. Besides, I like a square one.'

'Ho-h-h!' laughed the woman. 'If you had a square pestle you'd want a square mortar.'

PROVERBS

Getting money is like digging with a needle; spending it like water soaking into sand.

Even the street-dog knows the house of a poor man.

Those discontented with their fate will accuse even the sun of partiality.

Even Fuji is without beauty to one who is hungry and cold.

What's an inch in the eye of a man is a foot in the eye of his master.

Deceive, but don't insult, the rich and powerful.

The life of man is like a long journey with a heavy load on the back.

At the first cup man drinks wine, at the second wine drinks wine, at the third wine drinks man.

When puss mourns for the mouse do not take her seriously.

Even the Emperor has straw-sandaled relations.

'Of course, of course,' said Yaji. 'At my place we make bean sauce in a store house.'

'What a smart gentleman he is!' said the woman. 'If you don't like the pestle, won't you buy a ladder?'

'Ha-ha-ha!' laughed Yaji. 'Fancy me buying a ladder. How much is it?'

'I haven't been able to sell much to-day,' said the woman, 'so I'll let you have it cheap for six hundred coppers.'

'I'll take it if you let me have it for two hundred coppers,' said Yaji.

'Don't make fun of us,' said the woman. 'Won't you give a little more?'

'No, no,' said Yaji.

'Won't you make it five hundred?' said the woman.

'No, no,' said Yaji.

'Well, I should get scolded if I took it home,' said the woman. 'I'll let you have it for two hundred.'

'What?' said Yaji. 'You'll sell it so cheap? What a silly thing to do!'

'It is cheap,' said the woman.

'However cheap it is, what should I do with a ladder?' said Yaji. 'I haven't got a place to put it.'

'That doesn't matter,' said the woman. 'Here, catch hold of it.'

'You must excuse me,' said Yaji. 'The truth is we're only travellers and I'm going to Sanjo to look for an inn. I can't carry a ladder about with me.'

'Well, what did you want to make a bid for it then if you didn't want it?' asked the woman.

'I oughtn't to have done it,' said Yaji. 'If it was something I could put in my sleeve or my bosom I wouldn't mind buying it whether I wanted it or not. But a ladder! It's dreadful.'

'You shouldn't come and make fun of people when they're trying to do a bit of business,' said the woman. 'I won't be played with. Here, take the ladder.'

Then four or five women surrounded Yaji and began scolding at the tops of their voices, while a curious crowd collected. Yaji, in the middle, was unable to escape, and although he made all sorts of excuses, they would not listen to him, and as they were women he could not very well get up a fight with them. In the end he was forced to pay the two hundred coppers and shoulder the ladder, whereupon the crowd dispersed laughing.

'Making me look like a fool!' groaned Yaji. 'Just catch hold of the other end, Kita.'

'Not I,' said Kita. 'You can carry it.'

'I've got caught again,' said Yaji. 'Botheration!' . . .

Laughing over the incident they tumbled into bed and the Tamba man was soon fast asleep and snoring. The other two lay talking for some time longer. They could hear the sound of dogs barking in the fields at the back of the inn and the noise of someone splitting bamboo. Then the drum beat for the hour of midnight.

'What's that rustling sound, Yaji?' asked Kita, lifting his head.

'I couldn't sleep,' said Yaji, 'and I was tumbling about when I found this.'

From the bedclothes he pulled out a small chip box.

'Why, isn't that the box the old chap brought out before?' said Kita. 'The one with the sugar candy in, I mean.'

'Don't speak so loud,' said Yaji. 'It must have dropped out of his wicker-basket. I've had my eye on it for a long time.'

'Let's have a bit,' suggested Kita.

'Wait a minute,' said Yaji. The lantern was so far away he could not see very well, but he took the lid off and put some of the contents into his mouth. 'It's hard,' he said.

'Let's see,' said Kita, snatching the box away. He also put some in his mouth and chewed it.

'Whatever is it?' he said. 'It's like ashes.'

'It's not sugar candy,' said Yaji. 'What a strong smell it has.'

Then he began to feel rather sick and to retch, whereupon the Tamba man opened his eyes at the noise and jumped up astounded when he saw what they were doing.

'What are you doing?' he cried. 'What are you eating my wife for?'

'What do you mean by your wife?' asked Yaji.

'What do I mean?' exclaimed the Tamba man. 'It's sacrilege. That is my dear wife. Look on the lid of the box.'

Yaji jumped up and went over to the lantern with the box. There he saw written on the lid 'Shugetsu Myokwo Shinnyo.'

'Then the box contains the ashes of your wife?' he asked.

'What? The ashes?' cried Kita. 'This is dreadful. That's why I feel so queer.'

'You may feel bad but I feel worse,' said the man. 'I'm carrying those remains from my village to Mount Koya. It's desecration for you to eat it. You can't be real men. You must be devils or beasts. Whatever shall I do? Whatever shall I do?'

Here he hid his face in his sleeve and began to cry.

'What a terrible thing!' said Yaji, although he was secretly rather amused. 'When you opened your wicker-basket it fell out and got tumbled about without anybody knowing what it was. That was your fault. My fault was in mistaking it for sugar candy. So, as there were faults on both sides there's nothing to quarrel about.'

'No, no,' cried the Tamba man. 'Put it back as it was before. Put it back.'

Thereupon he began to wail and cry again, till Kitahachi managed to soothe him with many excuses and he became appeased. . . .

As the lottery had been drawn the numbers of the winners were being written up one by one in front of the temple, and they saw that the number of the first prize was eighty-eight.

'Oh, oh!' groaned Yaji. 'I'm going to turn priest. My luck's out entirely.'

'Ha-ha-ha!' laughed Kita. 'Don't let your spirits go down. I'm going to get that hundred gold pieces, and I don't mind letting you have four or five out of them. Look at this.'

He pulled out of his bosom the ticket that Yaji had thrown away and held it up before him.

'What?' exclaimed Yaji. 'Did you pick it up? Well done, well done. Hand it over.'

'Oh no,' said Kita. 'None of that. You threw it away and I picked it up, so it's mine now.'

'No, no,' said Yaji. 'I saw it first and picked it up and so it's mine by right although you did pick it up again.'

'Yes, but didn't you throw it away?' said Kita.

'That doesn't matter,' said Yaji. 'You just pass it over.'

He tried to snatch it away from Kita, but Kita held it fast. Then Saheiji intervened.

'Be quiet,' he said. 'If you talk so loud the man who dropped it will hear you and he'll want it back. Let me settle the matter for you. As you've both picked it up, what you must do is to halve the prize, and while you're about it you might give me a share.'

'Of course, I'm quite willing to do that,' said Kita. 'But we'd better enjoy the good things while we have them. We ought to get the money at once. Where do they pay?'

'Over there,' said Saheiji, 'where that man's sitting.'

They went over to the lottery office, but there they saw a notice that owing to the confusion the winner in the lottery would not be paid till the next day. Thus seeing that there was nothing to be got that day, they continued their round of the shrines.

'Suppose the chap that lost the ticket goes and gets the money,' said Kita.

'Oh, don't worry about that,' said Saheiji. 'They won't pay the money till they get the ticket back, no matter how many witnesses he has.'

'Hooray!' cried Yaji. 'I feel quite happy now.'

'We'll get the hundred gold pieces tomorrow,' said Kita. 'It seems a long time to wait.'

'What's a long time?' asked Yaji. 'Ain't we going to get it all right?'

Thus rejoicing over their luck, they forthwith entered a teahouse and called for some sakè in honour of the event. . . .

After a hasty breakfast they put on the hired clothes they had worn the night before and set off hurriedly for the temple, where they soon found the place where the prizes in the lottery were to be distributed.

'Here's the place,' said Kita. 'Go in, Yaji.'

'You go first,' said Yaji.

'What are you bashful about?' said Kita, and he went in.

'Excuse me,' he said. 'I've won the first prize in yesterday's lottery. Will you please pay me?'

The man in the room came hurriedly forward. 'Dear me,' he said. 'Please come in.'

He led them into the hall, where he left them for a time. Soon he returned.

'We'll pay you the money,' he said. 'Please come this way.'

He led them into a large room at the back where they all sat down. The room was a very fine one, with a magnificent alcove and shelves, and not a crack or a stain to mar it. Soon a handsome boy of about thirteen or fourteen, dressed in black silk, came in with tea and a tobacco-box, and afterwards returned with a sakè bottle and some cups and some soup.

'I'll let you have the money directly,' said the priest, 'but just have a glass of sakè first, won't you?'

'Thank you, thank you,' said Yaji. 'It's really very good of you,' and he giggled with pleasure.

'What's there to giggle about?' asked Kita. 'You needn't make a fuss about it but just take what's given you.'

'You were very lucky to win the first prize,' said the priest. 'Allow me to drink a cup of sakè with you in congratulation.'

'Delighted with the honour,' said Yaji.

'The honour is mine,' said the priest.

'Thank you for your hospitality,' said Kita, and he began gulping down the sakè.

When you want to grow corn and reap the grain you have to prepare the ground, and so the priests gave the two as much sakè as they wanted and put all sorts of appetising dishes before them. As the priests all took turns in drinking with them they were half drunk when at last the sakè was removed and the dinner was brought in.

'Dear me,' said Kita. 'This is beyond our expectations.'

'Please don't put yourselves out for us,' said Yaji. 'Ha-ha-ha! It's so amusing I can't help laughing.'

When they had eaten as much as they could the dishes were removed and a person who seemed to be the chief priest of the temple came in, accompanied by two or three other priests bearing trays on which the gold pieces were piled up. At sight of them Yaji and Kita felt a thrill of rapture and could hardly refrain from laughing for joy.

'I am the head of this temple,' said the chief priest. 'Allow me to offer you my greetings and congratulate you on your good fortune.'

'Ay, ay,' said Yaji.

'Shall I present you with the money?' asked the chief priest.

'Yes, yes,' said Kita.

'But first I have a request to make,' said the chief priest. 'As you will have seen, this temple is in a great state of dilapidation, and as the lottery is arranged for the benefit of the temple we always make a request to the winner for a contribution of ten pieces out of every hundred. Will you be willing to make this donation?'

'Ay, ay,' said Yaji.

'I have another request to make,' said the priest. 'It's a thing that is always done, and that is to make donation of five pieces to the manager of the lottery. Will you be willing to do that?'

'Ay, ay, ay,' said Kita.

'There is one thing more,' said the priest, 'and that is that you buy a ticket for the next lottery.'

'Ay, ay, ay,' said Yaji.

'Then I'll deduct twenty pieces from the hundred and hand you the remainder,' said the priest. 'Will that be correct?'

'Yes, yes,' said Yaji. 'Whatever you like.'

'Then if you'll hand me the ticket,' said the priest, 'I'll give you the money.'

'Here it is,' said Kita, and he pulled the ticket out of his bosom.

The priest took it and looked at it with a surprised air. 'Is this the only ticket you have?' he asked.

'Yes, that's all,' said Kita.

'Then there has been a mistake,' said the priest.

'What's the mistake?' said Kita. 'Isn't the winning number eighty-eight?'

'Yes, certainly,' said the priest; 'number eighty-eight.'

'Then what mistake can there be?' asked Kita.

'This is not the right ticket,' said the priest. 'The mark on it is wrong. All the tickets issued by this temple have a special mark on them. The winning ticket was 88 ne. This one you have is marked 88 i.'

All the tickets were marked on the back with one of the twelve signs of the zodiac, so that there were twelve tickets each bearing the same number but with a different zodiacal sign. Kita had known nothing about this and had paid no attention to the mark. That was how the mistake had come about. At once all their hopes were dashed to the ground and they sat there crushed with despair.

'Then it ain't any good, ain't it?' said Kita. 'What shall we do, Yaji?'

'Oh, oh!' groaned Yaji! 'I can't bear it. Really I . . .'

'Don't cry,' said Kita. 'It makes you look such a fool.'

'It was very foolish of you not to examine the ticket,' said another priest, 'excessively stupid.'

'They're frauds,' said the chief priest. 'You'd better be off.'

'Get out,' cried all the priests.

'All right, all right,' said Yaji. 'We've had a good feed anyhow, although it wasn't what we came for. I think you might as well give us the money. A mark or two on the ticket don't make much difference.'

'Don't talk nonsense,' said the priest. 'You're a couple of rascals.'

'Everybody makes mistakes,' said Kita. 'Don't talk so foolishly.'

'If you get cheeky I'll knock you down,' said another priest.

Here Saheiji intervened.

'We're in the wrong,' he said. 'I'm sorry you've entertained us for nothing, but it can't be helped now. Come on, Yaji, we'd better be going. What's the matter with you? Can't you stand up?'

'Oh, oh!' groaned Yaji. 'Just lift me up behind.'

'What's the matter with you?' asked Saheiji.

'I've lost the use of my legs,' said Yaji. 'Oh!'

'What a faint-hearted chap you are,' said Kita. 'Come on, stand up.'

'Don't pull me like that,' said Yaji. 'Oh, oh!'

They pulled him up at last and he staggered along. No one went to the door to see them off. Only the carriers gathered there jeered at them. . . .

'I suppose the mark on the ticket was wrong,' said the clerk laughing.

'Yes,' said Saheiji. 'We'll have to be careful about that older one. He's clean lost heart. Don't lose sight of him, even when he goes to the closet. I shouldn't be surprised if he hanged himself.'

'That won't do,' said the clerk. 'You must get him out of the inn as soon as possible.' . . .

Separating from Saheiji the two went on, conversing as they went, till they came to a place where another road turned off and they felt doubtful which road to take. An old scavenger was going on in front, with two buckets slung across his shoulders, so they called to him, 'Which is the way to Tennoji?'

'I'm going there,' said the scavenger. 'Ye'd better follow me.'

'I'd rather not,' said Kita. 'What a stink!' He began to lag behind, but the scavenger turned round.

'I live near Tennoji,' he said, 'and I'll take you right there. Come along. Come along. Where d'you come from?'

'We're Edo folk,' said Yaji.

'Aha!' said the scavenger. 'Edo's a fine place. What do they give for two buckets of it up there?'

'I don't know,' said Yaji.

'I say, Yaji,' said Kita, pulling his sleeve, 'let's fall back a bit.' To let the old man get well ahead Kita relieved himself.

'What a nuisance he is!' said Yaji. 'He expected me to know the price of that filth. He's an idiot.'

Thinking the old man must have got a long distance ahead they walked on briskly, when they again came upon the old man waiting for them.

'Eh,' said Kita. 'How annoying! There's that old man waiting for us.'

'Come on! Come on!' cried the old man. 'You know you don't know the road. I saw one of ye just now doing something for himself. All ye Edo folk are wasteful like that. What a pity! How many times a day do ye gentlemen do it?'

'Well sometimes we do it three times a day, and other times we do it four or five,' said Yaji. 'It's not fixed.'

'Does it come out thick or thin?' asked the old man.

'You want to know all sorts of things, don't you?' said Yaji. "I'm no good, but this other fellow is like a waterfall.'

'I wish I'd known before,' said the old man. 'It's all wasted now.'

'Get on a bit faster, Kita,' scolded Yaji. 'What are you doing?'

But Kita secretly tweaked Yaji by the sleeve. 'Look inside his bucket,' said Kita. 'You can see the head of a gold hairpin.'

While Yaji went on talking to the old man, Kita behind picked up two pieces of bamboo and using them as pinchers tried to pick the hairpin out of the bucket. Just then, however, the old man shifted the buckets to the other shoulder and the pieces of bamboo were knocked out of Kita's hand and a splash of the contents of the buckets fell on his clothes. With an exclamation of disgust Kita rubbed it off with a piece of paper, while the old man, who in changing had shifted the back bucket to the front, discovered the hairpin.

'What's this?' he asked. He caught hold of the head of the pin and pulled it out and found it was apparently a valuable pin.

'I suppose it must have fallen in the privy,' said the old man. 'It'll be a fine present for my grand-daughter. I'm going on in front. Come along after me.'

He went off briskly without troubling any more about them. . . .

'You'll have to become a resident of Osaka,' he said.

'It would be all right if I had any occupation,' said Kita. 'But I can't earn my living, so it's all the same where we go.'

'Well, I've found something,' said Kawashiro. 'I've found something that one of you can do.'

'What's that?' asked Yaji.

'It's a position as man-mistress,' said the landlord. 'What do you say to that?'

'Really?' said Yaji. 'That would just suit me,' and he grinned with pleasure and began to look his old self again.

'Excuse me,' said Kita, thrusting himself forward. 'Don't you think I'd do better for the position?'

'Ha-ha-ha!' laughed Yaji. 'You wouldn't do at all. But look here, you'll excuse me asking—I've known you such a short time—but does she really want me? Is there no mistake? If it's true, of course . . . '

'No, no, I swear there's no mistake about it,' said Kawashiro. 'Moreover the widow's very beautiful, only twenty-three or twenty-four years old. Quite well off, too. I'm very friendly with her head clerk. I saw him just now and had a talk with him about it. He says she spends all her money buying actors, and that it would be better for her to have a respectable man-mistress upon whom she could rely. I shall be glad to recommend you. Would you like to see her?'

'What for?' said Kita. 'It wouldn't matter to him if her eyes were crooked and her nose gone. He'd have her all the same.'

'She's in the next room with her head clerk,' said Kawashiro. 'I'll just go and inquire.'

Kawashiro jumped up with great readiness and went into the next room.

'I'm going through with this, Kita,' said Yaji after the landlord had gone.

'How brave you are!' said Kita. 'Fancy you becoming a man-mistress with that face. Have you ever looked at yourself in the glass?'

'Nonsense!' said Yaji. 'It doesn't matter about a man's looks. I'm better looking than you anyhow.'

'Better looking, indeed!' said Kita. 'What do you say, Saheiji? If you were a woman which would you fall in love with, Yaji or me?'

'I'd rather not fall in love with either of you,' said Saheiji, laughing. 'But when a person's in love they always think they're better looking than other people."

'We'll call it equal for looks, then,' said Kita, 'but I think I ought to get her as I am the younger.'

'You must give way to your seniors,' said Yaji.

'I'll tell you what,' said Saheiji. 'You'd better draw lots. I'll hold the spills and whoever draws the long one shall have her.'

'All right,' said Kita. 'Oh, great god of Sumiyoshi,' he prayed, 'grant unto me that I may draw the long one.'

'There,' said Saheiji. 'Now draw."

'I've got the long one,' cried Yaji. 'I've won.'

In the midst of Yaji's rejoicing Kawashiro came back. 'It's all right,' he said. 'I've just been consulting with her head clerk. She'll make you an allowance of as much as you like and pay for all the burdock and eggs you can eat, besides providing you with silk clothes all the year round. But you'll have to take Sanzo and Koshiyoshi pills.'

'In Edo, at the Santokyoden,' said Yaji, 'they have some pills called Tokusho, and without joking they give you enormous energy. I'll get some of those and take them.'

'That's a good idea,' said Kawashiro. 'By the way, she's coming here.'

'What, here?' cried Yaji. 'Now? How awful! In my present condition too. I say, Saheiji, is there a hairdresser in the neighbourhood?'

'Get out,' said Kita. 'You can't make a crow white even if you wash it for a year, and you can't alter a man's disposition, either. You can't follow a trade with your eyes shut, so to speak. If she sees you she's bound to call it off.'

'There's a fine-looking woman coming out of that room over there,' said Saheiji.

'That's her, that's her,' said Kawashiro. 'She's probably coming here.'

'How awful,' said Yaji, and he hurriedly arranged his collar and put on a solemn look.

The widow was a fine-looking woman, with a skin as white as snow and an attractive manner. She was accompanied by her head clerk. Kawashiro rose to greet her.

'This is a pleasure,' he said. 'Please come in.'

'Excuse me,' said the widow, and she tittered as she entered.

'Good day to all,' said the head clerk. 'They're all ladies in the other room and I had nobody to drink with. Luckily Kawashiro came in and invited us to join you.'

'Sit down, sit down,' said Kawashiro. 'Excuse my boldness, but let me press you to have a cup of sakè.'

He handed a sakè cup to the widow, who took it with a smile.

'I've already drunk too much,' she said, 'so I'll only take a drop.'

She drank a little and then held out the cup to Kawashiro.

'Won't you drink with me in return?' she asked.

'I've been drinking a lot already,' said Kawashiro. 'Won't you offer it to somebody else?'

'Then if you don't mind,' said the widow, and she held out the cup to Yaji.

Yaji, who had been sitting as one in a dream, lost in contemplation of the widow's beauty, woke to life with a start on finding himself thus addressed.

'Yes, yes,' he said, all in a flurry, and he seized hold of what he thought was a sakè cup.

'Here, what are you doing?' said Saheiji. 'That's not a sakè cup you're holding. It's the tobacco-box.'

'Ah, so it is,' said Yaji. 'Ten thousand excuses. Kita, pour for me.'

'It's none of my businesss,' said Kita sulkily. 'Pour for yourself.'

'What an unmannerly chap he is!' said Yaji.

The waitress filled his cup and he tossed it off. Then he offered the cup to the head clerk.

'No, no,' said the head clerk. 'You're an expert at drinking I can see. Have another on top of it.'

'Well,' said Yaji, 'usually when I drink sakè I get whiter and whiter till I'm as white as silk. But to-day, somehow, it's made me go all red.'

'Allow me to offer a drink to your companion,' said the widow.

'Yes, yes,' said Yaji. 'Here, Kitahachi, the lady wants to offer you a drink.'

'Mind your own business,' said Kita.

'Ha-ha-ha!' laughed Yaji. 'Let me offer you one instead,' he said to the widow. The widow took the cup with a smirk and drank.

'Dear me,' said Kawashiro. 'You two passing the sakè cup to each other makes it look just like a wedding.'

'He-he-he!' tittered the widow. 'How funny!'

'Ha-ha-ha!' laughed Yaji in turn.

'Don't laugh so loud,' said Kita. 'You're laughing right into the food.'

'Never mind,' said Yaji. 'You be quiet. I can never do anything to please this chap,' he went on. 'If I just sing a bit of a song to the guitar and get all the girls praising me and saying how clever I am, he gets so jealous I don't know what to do.'

'Dear me,' said the widow. 'What a funny gentleman you are really.'

At this Yaji's heart bounded in his bosom, for he thought he had captured her and that all his bad luck had vanished. Then the widow's maid came in.

'Excuse me for interrupting you,' she said, 'but I thought you would like to know that Master Arakichi has come and is waiting for you in the other room.'

'Has Arakichi come?' cried the widow. 'Thank you, thank you. Excuse me everybody. Good-bye,' and she bowed hastily to them and hurried off, followed by her head clerk.

Yaji was overwhelmed with astonishment. 'What's the matter?' he asked. 'Who's this Arakichi?'

'That's Saburo Arakichi,' said Kawashiro. 'He's all the craze,—young and good-looking,—the leading actor in Osaka.'

'Ah, that's why she rushed off in such a hurry,' said Yaji. 'Looks to me as if she was in love with him.'

'It does look that way,' admitted Kawashiro.

'Well, you mustn't let your courage go down, Yaji,' said Saheiji.

'Ha-ha-ha!' laughed Kita. 'What a joke! I say, Yaji, when we were coming along I saw a barber's shop just near here. You'd better go and get your head shaved.'

'You're always envious,' grumbled Yaji.

While Yaji was grumbling to himself the head clerk came back.

'You see what anxiety she gives me, Master Kawashiro,' he said. 'She's got a passion for that Arakichi and they's going off somewhere by boat together. I've got to walk. I always get the worst of it. So all our talk comes to nothing. Well, I must leave you now. Excuse me everybody.'

He hurried off into the garden, where they saw the widow starting off with Arakichi and a maid, talking and laughing and looking very delighted.

'That chap Arakichi is a fine-looking fellow,' said Saheiji.

'What's there fine-looking about him?' said Yaji. 'Look at his sickly look. Seems as if he'd never been out in the sun.'

'You may say what you like,' said the waitress, 'but if he isn't a fine-looking man I never saw one. Why, there isn't a woman in Osaka that isn't in love with him.'

'Look there, Yaji,' said Kita. 'She's whispering something in his ear and pointing over here and laughing. She's probably talking about you.'

'Botheration!' said Yaji. 'Well, Master Kawashiro, it's very regrettable, very.'

Meanwhile the widow went away talking and laughing without paying the least attention to any of them, and this made Yaji feel so unhappy that he spoke of going back to the inn.

'I've got a good idea,' said Kawashiro. 'I've got a boat waiting. Let's go in it and interrupt their love making.'

'That's a good idea,' said Yaji. 'Come on. Let's go.'

'Wait a bit,' said Saheiji. 'It's beginning to rain.'

'It doesn't matter if it rains cats and dogs,' said Yaji. 'Come along.'

He jumped up and was going out, when all at once there was a tremendous peal of thunder right over his head,—goro-goro-goro.

'It's useless, it's useless,' they all cried, and Yaji ran back, almost stunned by the noise.

Now the rain began to come down in torrents, the lightning flashed and the thunder roared, and the people rushed about the house, pulling out the shutters to keep out the rain. All the women in the house came into the room, frightened out of their wits.

'That's finished you off,' said Kita. 'Wouldn't you like to be Arakichi now? They're in the boat, both wet through, and the widow's telling him how frightened she is and clinging to him.'

'Yes,' said Kawashiro. 'She was in love with him before, but after this storm she'll never let him go.'

'That's so,' said Kita. 'She'll never be able to say no, eh, Yaji?'

'Don't talk to me,' said Yaji. 'I'm praying.'

'There's another flash,' said Saheiji, and the thunder went goro-goro-goro.

'Oh, I'm so frightened,' said Kita, and he threw himself into Yaji's arms pretending that he was the widow. Yaji went flying.

'Oh, oh, oh!' he groaned. 'What did you want to do that for? Oh, oh, oh!'

'Where does it hurt?' asked Kita.

'It's the devil's nose in the wrapper,' said Yaji. 'Oh, it does hurt.'

'Ha-ha-ha!' laughed Kita. 'That's it, is it?'

'The rain's beginning to stop,' said Saheiji. 'Shall we go in the boat now?'

'Come on,' said Yaji. 'Come on quickly.'

He jumped up impatiently, but just as he got to the door there was a great flash of lightning and such a rattle of thunder over his head—goro-goro-goro-goro—that he fell down with a shriek.

'Oh, oh!' he groaned, his face wrinkled in pain.

'What have you done now?' asked Saheiji.

'What have I done now!' said Yaji. 'I've broken it. I've broken it.'

'What have you broken?' asked Kita.

'When it went pss-bang just now,' said Yaji, 'I got such an alarm that I slipped and fell on the bridge of the devil's nose. Oh! it does hurt.'

He kept hold of the devil's nose as he spoke whereupon they all burst into laughter.

In a little time the rain stopped, the thunder got further and further away and the sky began to clear.

'Come, it's getting fine now,' said Kawashiro. 'Let's have another cup before we go.'

So some more sakè was brought in and they each drank their fill to the accompaniment of many jests and much laughter.

Afterwards Kawashiro took Yajirobei and Kitahachi back to his inn and there they stayed a long time till they had seen all the sights of the city. Then, both of them being stout-hearted Edo folk, able to bear all kinds of hardships and pass them off with a jest, they determined to set forth on their travels again. The landlord, impressed by their courage, presented them with new clothes and money for their travelling expenses, and thus they started off in search of new adventures.

I Am a Cat (extracts)

Soseki Natsume (1867–1916) / Katsue Shibata and Motonari Kai

Soseki Natsume was born in Tokyo and educated at Tokyo Imperial University (now Tokyo University). He taught English in Japan before spending several years in London. After his return to Japan he taught at his alma mater, then worked for the newspaper Tokyo Asahi Shimbun.

Among younger Japanese his most popular work is his first novel, Botchan, *the story of a naïve but aggressive young man who goes to teach in a provincial high school; he is both pathetic and funny, ridiculous and sympathetic. Other readers appreciate most* I Am a Cat, *which was published in 1907 and immediately made Natsume famous.*

I am a cat but as yet I have no name.

I haven't the faintest idea of where I was born. The first thing I do remember is that I was crying, "Meow, meow," somewhere in a gloomy damp place. It was there that I met a human being for the first time in my life. Though I found this all out at a later date, I learned that this human being was called a Student, one of the most ferocious of the human race. I also understand that these Students sometimes catch us, cook us and then take to eating us. But at that time, I did not have the slightest idea of all this so I wasn't frightened a bit. When this Student placed me on the palm of his hand and lifted me up lightly, I only had the feeling of floating around. After a while, I got used to this position and looked around. This was probably the first time I had a good look at a so-called "human being." What impressed me as being most strange still remains deeply imbedded in my mind: the face which should have been covered with hair was a slippery thing similar to what I now know to be a teakettle. I have since come across many other cats but none of them are such freaks. Moreover, the center of the Student's face protruded to a great extent, and from the two holes located there, he would often emit smoke. I was extremely annoyed by being choked by this. That this was what they term as tobacco, I came to know only recently.

I was snuggled up comfortably in the palm of this Student's hand when after a while, I started to travel around at a terrific speed. I was unable to find out if the Student was moving or if it was just myself that was in motion, but in any case I became terribly dizzy and a little sick. Just as I was thinking that I couldn't last much longer at this rate, I heard a thud and saw sparks. I remember everything up till that moment but think as hard as I can, I can't recall what took place immediately after this. . . .

When the maid was about to throw me out for the last time, the master of the house made his appearance and asked what all the row was about. The maid turned to him with me hanging limp from her hand, and told him that she had repeatedly tried throwing this stray cat out but that it always kept sneaking into the kitchen again—and that she didn't like it at all. The master, twisting his moustache, looked at me for a while and then told the maid to let me in. He then left the room. I took it that the master was a man of few words. The maid, still mad at me, threw me down on the kitchen floor. In such a way, I was able to establish this place as my home. . . .

I felt somewhat sorry for him so, with the thought of trying to liven him up a little, I said, "But when it comes to rats, I hardly believe they would have a chance against you. Being such a famous rat catcher, you probably eat nothing else and that's why you're so plump and glossy, I'm sure."

I had said this to get him into a better mood but actually it had the contrary effect. He let a big sigh escape and replied, 'When you come to think of it, it's not all fun. Rats are interesting but, you know, there's nobody as crafty as humans in this world. They take all the rats I catch over to the police box. The policeman there doesn't know who actually catches them, so he hands my master five sen per head. Because of me, my master has made a neat profit of one yen and fifty sen, but yet he doesn't give me any decent food. Do you know what humans are? Well, I'll tell you. They're men, yes, but thieves at heart." . . .

My master usually wears the same expression on his face but that doesn't mean he is not interested when it comes to women. Once he happened to read a foreign novel and the hero was a bachelor who seduced almost every woman in the book. It was written in a satirical vein but my master praised it and announced that this was real life. But why a man who takes such an interest in sex should remain oyster-like was something which I, as a cat, cannot fathom. Some people might claim that it is because of some frustrated love, while others would suggest that it is because of his weak stomach. Still others might believe that it is because he does not have much money and, on top of that, is so cowardly. Whatever the reason, he is not a person likely to become famous in the history of the Meiji era, so perhaps it doesn't make any difference. . . .

I find that there is nothing as hard as trying to understand the psychology of male humans. For instance, I can't often tell whether my master is mad or joyful, or if he is trying to find consolation by reading philosophers. I am generally at a total loss to tell whether he is coolly laughing at the world, or if he is mad at something not worth being mad about; or whether he wants to be considered as a member of society or to isolate himself in another world.

Such matters are quite simple with us cats. When we are hungry we eat, when we want to sleep we do so; when we get mad we get as angry as we can; and when we cry, we do our best to make as much noise as possible. In the first place, we don't keep such senseless and meaningless things as diaries. There's no need. A person, like my master, who has two sides to his personality probably keeps a diary in order to express the feelings he cannot express to others. But with us cats, everything we do is known. There is no need to go to the trouble of jotting down what we already know. Instead of keeping a diary, I much prefer to take a nap on the veranda. The diary continued: . . .

The other day someone told me that if I stopped eating breakfast, I could soon cure my stomach. I gave up my morning meal for several days but the only thing that happened was that my stomach emitted gurgling sounds.

Then another person told me to stop eating pickled vegetables. According to his theory, all stomach disorders come from eating pickles. My chopsticks avoided the pickles on the table for about a week but then finding no change in my condition, I began eating them again.

According to still another person, massage is the only way to cure weak stomachs, but not in the ordinary way. He suggested that I try the Minagawa school of massaging, a very old method. If I tried this once or twice, I would be completely cured—that was what he told me. Sokken Yasui, a scholar of Confucianism, favored this method of massage and it is said that Ryuma Sakamoto, a famous swordsman, also received this treatment. Therefore, I wasted no time in going to Kami-Negishi. . . .

Suddenly the rickshawman's wife was heard again: "Hey, Nishikawa. I've got an order for you. Go and get me a pound of beef, and get it quick. Do you hear? A pound of beef, and it has to be tender. Do you understand?" The voice ordering a pound of beef shattered the stillness of the whole area.

Kuro planted his four feet firmly on the ground and sneered, "Huh, just listen to that old hag. She wants to let all the neighbors know that she's ordering beef. She only gets to eat it once a year or so. What a person!" . . .

"Then he roughly called the waiter and ordered two servings of tochimenbo. When the waiter asked if he meant fried mincemeat, Meitei became extremely serious and corrected the waiter. He repeated that it was tochimenbo and not mincemeat that he wanted."

"So. Well, just what is this tochimenbo? Does it really exist?"

"Though I thought it all strange at first, Meitei seemed very composed. Moreover, he understands many Western customs. I still believed that he had been abroad, so I chimed in and told the waiter that we wanted tochimenbo, even without knowing what it was."

"And what did the waiter do?"

"Thinking of it now, it was very comical. He stood there for a while and then told us that he was sorry but the tochimenbo was all sold out. He said that he could bring two servings of fried mincemeat, however. Meitei seemed extremely peeved and said it wasn't worthwhile coming to this restaurant any more. He asked the waiter whether there was any way at all possible for us to have tochimembo served, and he tipped him twenty sen. The waiter immediately changed his attitude and said that he'd go and ask the chef if something could be arranged."

"It seems as if Meitei wanted this tochimenbo very badly."

"Presently the waiter reappeared and apologetically asked if we could wait. He said it would take quite a while to prepare what we had ordered. Meitei said that as we had plenty of time, being New Year's, we were willing to wait. He then took out a cigar and serenely began puffing on it. Having nothing else to do, I took out a newspaper and commenced reading. The waiter then returned to the kitchen."

"Going to a lot of trouble, wasn't it?" My master moved his seat closer and looked as intent as when he reads about the Russo-Japanese War.

"The waiter again reappeared and said that the ingredients for tochimenbo had become extremely scarce and that none could be purchased at the Kameya or at the Jugoban House in Yokohama so that they would not be able to serve tochimembo for some time hereafter. He explained all this with a very long face. Meitei looked at me and repeatedly said that it was extremely discouraging because we had come here with the sole intention of eating tochimenbo. I couldn't just sit there without saying anything so I also added that it was very regrettable."

"I should think so," agreed my master. As for myself, I couldn't find any reason why my master should agree.

"The waiter expressed deep regret but said that in case they were able to get the ingredients, he would want us to come again. Meitei then asked the waiter what materials they used in preparing tochimenbo. The waiter just gave a giggle for an answer. Meitei, in order to make sure, asked him if they used a bunch of Japanese Haijin [haiku poets] to which the waiter replied that they were indispensable. So Meitei replied that now he understood why they could not be purchased in Yokohama nowadays."

"Ha, ha, ha! So that's the joke! That's a good one!" My master laughed so violently that I almost fell off his lap. Heedless of my plight, he kept on laughing. He discovered that he wasn't the only one who was caught in a joke like that of Andrea del Sarto. This made the story doubly enjoyable.

"Then the two of us stepped outside and Meitei said, 'How about that? Clever, wasn't it? Don't you think it was genius to order tochimenbo?' "[1] . . .

"Mi-ke would have nothing to regret as for her funeral. We had the priest come to offer prayers for her, and he even changed her name according to religious rites."

"Yes, ma'am, that's true. She's a very lucky cat. The only thing that I have to complain about is that the priest's prayers were too short and too simple."

"Yes, they were short and simple. I asked Priest Gekkei-ji about it and he said he had recited the part which was most significant and that ought to be sufficient to get a cat to paradise." . . .

"But, you know, ma'am," he suddenly boomed, as if he had hit upon a good idea, "it is only because he buys books and keeps piling them up that people call him a scholar." . . .

"He's eccentric. But you must remember that all scholars are eccentric." . . .

I noticed that when the owner of the sharp voice came into the room her crepe kimono was dragging on the floor because it was so long. She wore two coats, one over the other, and looked somewhat over forty years of age. She wore her hair high over her brow. It stood up, like some kind of a dike construction, and this gave the effect of doubling the length of her face. Her eyes had a slant similar to that of the slope leading from Hongo to Yushima. The eyes looked out of straight slits, thinner than the eyes of a whale. The nose was extraordinary! It seemed as if she had stolen somebody else's and had placed it in the middle of her own face. It was like a large stone lantern in a little garden. It completely dominated the face and did not seem to be at home at all. Besides, the nose was hooked, like the beak of an eagle. It had evidently commenced to grow straight out but then, thinking that this might be going too far, it had become more modest and began to droop. Finally it ended up by hanging down to tickle the

1. Tochimenbo is actually the name of a haiku poet.

lips. It was such a phenomenon that it made one believe that the nose, not the mouth, was doing the talking. In order to show my respect to this wonder, I shall, hereafter, call its proud owner Hanako, "Mrs. Nose." . . .

I know that I am a perfect cat. At the same time, I also realize that I am more intellectually developed than a third-year student of a junior high school. But, unfortunately, the construction of my throat is that of all cats and I cannot speak the language of humans. . . .

The feeling of curiosity is not limited only to humans; even we cats are full of psychological whims and we wish they were respected more. After the third time, an act becomes a habit, a necessity in our daily lives. There is no difference in this respect between humans and cats. You might wonder why I went to the Kaneda estate so often. Very well—but before giving you an explanation, I would like to ask a question myself. Why is it that you humans like to inhale cigarette smoke through your mouth and exhale it through your nostrils? Cigarette smoke does not fill the stomach, nor does it act in any way as medicine for the blood; yet humans insist on smoking. You who smoke don't have to criticize my sneaking into the Kaneda estate because, to me, such trips act in the same way as cigarette smoking does to humans. . . .

The cigarette slowly burned and the ashes, about an inch long, fell onto the blanket. My master, without noticing this, kept staring at the smoke which rose and vanished in the air. The smoke floated in the spring breeze in slow waves and a moving circle of smoke was drawn towards the dark hair of the Mrs. But I should have mentioned the Mrs. before.

She was seated on the floor, her posterior facing my master. You say that's impolite? Well, there's really nothing wrong about that. Courtesy depends on the parties concerned. My master's chin calmly pointed at the large and sublime rear end. There was nothing discourteous about it whatsoever. The couple, after their first year of married life, did away with any pretense of etiquette—in other words, they are a super-married couple.

As the day was fine, the Mrs., with her rear end facing my master, had just washed her long tresses with a substance like glue mixed in raw egg. She had her hair flowing down over her shoulders, as if showing it off, and was sewing a child's dress silently. She had brought her sewing box to the veranda and, sitting on a crepe silk cushion, was drying her hair in the sun. Her posterior just happened to be facing my master. Or perhaps my master had turned so that he would be facing the rear end. As I said before, the cigarette smoke rose and mingled with the black locks of freshly washed hair. This produced a halo. My master gazed at it, lost in thought. But smoke does not stay at one definite place forever. The nature of smoke is to rise higher and higher so after my master had studied the intermingling of the smoke with his wife's hair, his eyes followed it higher and higher. My master's gaze started from the location of the Mrs.'s hips and then gradually went up her back, and then from her shoulders to the back of her neck.

Once when his stare reached the head, he let out a sudden yell of surprise. He noticed that the Mrs., with whom he had promised mutual fidelity till death, had, right in the middle of her head, a large round bald spot! The naked shape, reflecting the soft spring light, shone brightly as if boasting of its existence. The eyes of my master, which had made this great discovery when least expected, showed great astonishment. Indifferent to the bright glare reflecting from the bald spot, he opened his eyes wide and concentrated on it in fascination. The naked patch first reminded my master of an old-fashioned saucer for candles placed in the family altar. My master belongs to the Shinshu sect of Buddhism whose custom it is to spend more than one can afford on family altars.

When my master was still a child, he had seen a small dirty shrine covered with thick gold leaf in a warehouse. He had noticed a brass saucer hanging inside and also that it reflected a dull light. Memories of the saucer suddenly came back to him when he saw the bald spot on his wife's head, or so it seemed. But soon his reverie was shattered.

All at once, it reminded him of the pigeons around the Goddess Kwannon at Asakusa. It would seem that his wife's baldness and the pigeons of Kwannon could have little connection, yet for my master, there was an intimate association between the two. During his childhood, he would often buy some peas to feed the pigeons whenever he went to Asakusa. A saucer of peas cost only three rin. All the saucers were made of red clay. Now, the size of the saucer and its color were exactly the same as the bald patch on his wife's head.

"It sure looks like one of those saucers," mumbled my master. Therefore the Mrs. asked, without looking back, "What does?"

"Do you know that you have a bald spot on your head?"

"Yes," sighed the Mrs. without stopping her work. It seemed she wasn't embarrassed in the least at having her baldness discovered. She is a model wife!

"Did you have it before we married, or did it happen afterwards?" asked my master. Although he didn't say it, he was thinking that if she had had it before they were married, he had been deceived.

"I don't know when it began. It doesn't make any difference anyway, does it?" Her logic sounded convincing.

"What do you mean 'it doesn't make any difference'? It's your own head," barked my master, somewhat irritated.

"That's right. It's my own head, so it doesn't make any difference," she replied. But she seemed to have become more self-conscious of the spot. She placed her right hand on it and caressed it. "Why, it's getting bigger! I didn't know it was this size." Considering her tone, she seemed to acknowledge the fact that the bald spot was larger than it should have been at her age.

"When a woman wears her hair in a marumage style,[1] the part in the center is so strained that all of us get bald there," she said, now on the defensive.

"If all women got bald so early in life, no women over forty would have hair. It must be some kind of a disease and it might be contagious. You'd better go to Dr. Amaki and have him look it over," suggested my master, feeling his own head.

"You say such things about me, but just look at yourself—you have white hairs

1. The marumage coiffure is worn only by married women.

in your nostrils. If baldness is catching, white nostril hairs might be contagious, too." The Mrs. was somewhat grumbling now.

"There's no harm in having white hairs in the nostrils because you can't see them. But when it comes to a bald spot on top of your head—especially the head of a young woman—it's not nice to look at. It's abnormal."

"All right! If I'm abnormal, why did you marry me? You married me because you loved me, and now you say I'm abnormal."

"That's because I didn't know. I didn't know about it until today. Why didn't you show this to me before we were married?"

"Nonsense! There's no country in the world where a girl must show her head before getting married."

"I'll drop the subject of the bald spot. But you're shorter than average. It's unsightly."

"You knew that I was short when you married me, didn't you?"

"Sure, I knew it. I knew that you were short but I thought you'd grow taller."

"Do you think that a person grows after the age of twenty? You certainly like to make fun of me!" She put down her sewing and twisted her body to face my master. Her countenance now showed that, depending on his reply, she might really get worked up.

"There's no law that says you can't grow after the age of twenty. I thought that after marrying you, if I fed you good nutritious food, you'd grow a bit taller." My master was explaining this very seriously. This queer reasoning was interrupted, however, by the bell at the front door. This was followed by a voice asking for entrance. Suzuki had finally reached the house with grass on the roof, the house of Mr. Kushami, the forlorn teacher.

Mrs., postponing the quarrel to some later date, hurriedly picked up her sewing box and dress, and ran into the tearoom. My master then rolled up the gray blanket and threw it into the study. Upon looking at the calling card the maid had brought, my master gave a slightly surprised look but asked the guest to be shown into the room. He then went into the toilet so suddenly I can find no reason. And why he went there with the calling card of Tojuro Suzuki is another thing I am at a loss to explain. In any case, it must have been an annoying surprise that compelled my master to go to that evil-smelling place.

The maid took out a printed cotton cushion, placed it in front of the alcove, and ushered the guest in. Suzuki took a look around the room after the maid left. A scroll written by Mokuan, a well-known master penman, was hanging in the alcove. It was an imitation but read: "Flowers in bloom. Spring has come to all countries." There was also an arrangement of pre-seasonal cherry blossoms in a cheap pottery vase made in Kyoto. After inspecting these items by turn, Suzuki's gaze fell on the cushion the maid had brought for him. He found a cat serenely sitting on it. There is no need to mention that the cat was me—The Cat—and nobody else!

The moment Suzuki saw me there, he felt a slight annoyance and it showed a little on his face. He knew that the cushion had been placed there for him but, before he could sit down, he found a strange animal curled on it. This was the first episode of that day to put Suzuki off balance. Even if the cushion had been left as the maid had placed it, Suzuki would have sat on the hard straw mats anyway, showing his modesty until my master came and urged him to use the cushion. But what had already occupied the cushion that he would eventually use? He might have offered his cushion to another person, but a cat! This was disgusting. That a mere cat was on his cushion gave him even more displeasure. This was the second thing that put Suzuki off balance.

Last, but not least, he found the attitude of the cat itself an irritation. The animal did not show any sign of pity at all for the guest. Though it had no right to be on the cushion in the first place, it assumed a haughty attitude. It looked up at Suzuki with wide round belligerent eyes, as if asking what right the man had to invade this home. This was the third factor that put Suzuki off balance. Of course he could have grabbed me by the neck and pulled me off the cushion but no! Suzuki just looked down at me. A dignified man would not be afraid of a cat. The reason Suzuki did nothing to satisfy his rage was simply because he wanted, as a man, to show more self-respect. Or so I believe. When it comes to using force, a child three feet tall is free to do what he likes with me. But this was Tojuro Suzuki, the right-hand man of Kaneda. He would not stoop to touch the cat, the Supreme God that had established itself in the middle of the two-foot-square cushion! Even though nobody was looking, it would have been beneath his dignity to fight with a cat over a cushion. It wouldn't be manly to fight. It was comilac. In order to avert dishonor, he had to experience the discomfort of the floor. But the more he endured it, the more he hated the cat. Occasionally, Suzuki would look at me and make a face. I, on the other hand, felt great pleasure in seeing him complain. Trying to ignore the ridiculousness of the situation, I attempted to maintain an unconcerned air. . . .

'Ha, ha, ha! It's good to be a teacher. Wish I had become one."

"Be one and you'll want to quit after three days."

"I wonder. It looks like a nice job. You have no worries, you have plenty of time, you can continue to study what you like, and—well it must be good. Being a businessman isn't all bad but in my position, it's rotten. If you're going to be a happy businessman, you have to be the top man. If you're down the ladder, you have to say things you don't feel and drink sakè with clients even when you don't want to. It's all very foolish."

PROVERBS

When you buy a vase cheap look for the flaw, and when a man offers favors search for his purpose.

The tongue of woman is her sword, which never rusts.

A satiated mouth soon forgets the benefactor.

Cold tea and cold rice are bearable; but cold looks and cold words are unendurable.

Learning without wisdom is a load of books on an ass's back.

What is quickly learnt is soon forgotten.

Even the frog's croak in the well is music to its mate.

It only takes a little twig to poke out the eye.

Better to be proficient in one art than an amateur in a hundred.

"I have never liked businessmen. They'd do anything for money. In the olden days they were looked down on, and rightly so." My master, with a businessman sitting right before him, was being indiscreet.

"You can't say that they're all bad, but it is true that some of them are lacking in taste. In any case, a person has to resolve to die rich in order to be successful. Money is important. I've just come from the home of a businessman and he told me that in order to make money, you have to use three techniques—forget obligations, forget sentiment, and forget shame. Don't you think that's interesting? Ha, ha, ha!" . . .

If I wrote down everything that happened during a twenty-four-hour period in full detail, it would take at least another twenty-four hours to read it. The new style of writing, originated by Shiki Masaoka, which describes minute observations in prose form, is a feat which a cat can by no means perform. Though my master may spend twelve active hours each day I do not possess the ability or the perseverance to introduce all of his eccentricities to others. Though regrettable, it cannot be helped. Rest, even for a cat, is necessary. . . .

I've heard much about cats who are unable to sleep. According to my understanding, we often go out at night, especially in the spring, in search of romance. As for myself, however, I do not seem to be much affected by the changing of seasons. Love is a universal motivation. All creatures, from Jupiter in Heaven to the lowly earthworm and cricket, indulge in it. It is therefore reasonable to believe that we cats often enjoy the pursuit of love. I myself used to think about Mikeko a great deal. It was rumored that even Tomiko had fallen in love with Kangetsu. I have no intention of scorning those cats who go mad because of this torment in the spring, a season worth a thousand gold pieces; but try as I might, I myself just cannot get into the mood. At the moment, my only desire was for rest. I was so sleepy that I couldn't even think about love, so I stretched myself out at the foot of the children's bedding and slept to my heart's content. . . .

It is usually believed that God is omniscient and omnipotent. The God of the Christians, until the twentieth century, seemed especially omniscient and omnipotent. But He possessed an omniscience and omnipotence which the ordinary person generally interprets as dullness and ignorance. This is clearly a paradox. That I am the one to refute this paradox for the first time gives me a feeling of vanity and also of not being a cat at all. Therefore I would like to warn haughty men that cats do not like to be made fun of.

God made all creation so man must also be a creation of God. This, it seems, is stated in a book they call the Bible. Now, in regard to human beings, they pride themselves in knowing what has happened during the past several thousand years. Though they hold God in deep wonder, it is a fact that they also seem to possess the tendency of recognizing Him as Omniscient and Omnipotent. This is not beside the question because in this crowded world, there is not one person who has exactly the same face as another. It's true that the faces of most humans are composed of the same ingredients and the size of each part is almost the same. In other words, it may be stated that the makings of the face are all the same but that the effect is never identical.

It's amazing that so many different faces can be made with such simple materials. You cannot but wonder at the Creator's great technique. So many different faces could never be made unless a large creative imagination were responsible. A painter, during his lifetime, could complete only about twelve or thirteen different masterpieces. When we consider this, the skill of the Creator, who alone undertook the task of making human beings, is a greater wonder than words can express. Such inventiveness cannot be seen in human society so it must be considered omnipotential.

Perhaps for this reason, man seems to fear God. And when considered from man's point of view, it is naturally something to be feared. But when considered from a cat's point of view, this same variety might possibly be interpreted as proof of God's incompetence. Though you might not dismiss Him as completely incompetent, it can be concluded, I'm pretty sure, that He is really not much better qualified than man.

God, as we have seen, made all people with different faces. But did he, in the first place, have this planned? How can we be sure He had not tried to make all faces the same? If so, he failed miserably and therefore brought about the present confusion. You might still argue that the creation of so many different faces is proof of God's great success, but it could also stand as proof of his failure. You may call God omnipotent if you wish but that is hardly a reason for me to consider Him as anything but incompetent.

Man's eyes are placed side by side on the front of his face so, unfortunately, he cannot look both to the left and the right at the same time. Only half an object comes into view. Much is occurring around him day and night that he remains unaware of. By not being favored by God, humans have no way of finding out much that goes on even in their own community. . . .

Therefore if God could have made each human face so much alike that it would be impossible to tell them apart—faces as identical as mass-produced masks—it would prove his omnipotence much better. His making each face so differently is merely instrumental, therefore, to prove his incompetence.

Now I forgot why I entered into such a discourse. You'll have to forgive me but, as you know, humans also forget so this happening to a cat is understandable. . . .

The policeman, without laughing, continued, "Then you'll have to submit a report—not a report—an accusation in writing, stating that a thief entered your home after removing the door from such-and-such a place after you had locked your house and had gone to bed on such-and-such a date and that you had been robbed of so many items of the below-listed articles. It's better not to address the report to anyone in particular."

"Do we have to list each individual item?"

"Make it out in list form stating so many haori coats were stolen valued at so much, et cetera. No, there's no need for me to go inside the house now. The things have been stolen already, haven't they?" Then the policeman calmly left.

My master got out his brush and inkstone and placed them in the middle of the room. Afterwards he called his wife and grumbled as if he were picking a fight, "I'm going to start writing the accusation now so tell me one by one which articles were stolen. I'm ready so go ahead."

"Why! You don't have to be so belligerent with me. Who'd want to tell you anything when you give orders like that." The Mrs. then sat down squarely in front of him. She had tied her kimono closed with a length of string.

"Look at yourself! You almost look like a prostitute of a post town. Why aren't you wearing an obi?"

"If you object so much to how I look why don't you buy me an obi? Not even a prostitute of a post town could wear an obi if the only one she had were stolen."

"Did the thief take your obi? That's terrible! All right, I'll begin with your obi. What kind was it?"

"What do you mean, 'What kind'? I only had one. It was a double black obi made of satin and silk crepe."

"One double black obi of satin and silk crepe. Now, about how much did it cost?"

"About six yen."

"How is it you had such an expensive obi? You'll have to buy a new one but don't pay more than one yen fifty sen."

"Where do you think you can buy an obi at that price? You're awful! You don't care how your wife is dressed—all you can think of is yourself, isn't that so?"

"Forget it. What's next?"

"A woolen haori coat. My Aunt Kono gave it to me as a keepsake. It's different from the ones you see nowadays."

"I don't have to know all that. How much?"

"Fifteen yen."

"You had a coat worth fifteen yen?"

"Why worry? You didn't buy it."

"What's next?"

"A pair of black stockings."

"Yours?"

"No. They were yours. Twenty-seven sen."

"Next?"

"A box of yams."

"Did he steal the yams, too? Wonder if he's going to eat them cold or heat them first."

"I don't know what he's going to do. Why don't you ask him?"

"How much were they?"

"I don't know the price of yams."

"All right, I'll put them down as twelve yen and fifty sen."

"Don't be absurd! They couldn't have cost twelve yen fifty sen, even if they were from Karatsu."

"But you said you didn't know how much they were."

"I don't know. I don't know, but twelve yen fifty sen is absurd."

"You don't know but yet you say that twelve yen and fifty sen is absurd. That doesn't make sense. That's the reason I call you Otanchin Paleologus."

Perhaps I had better let you readers in on this. "Otanchin" means a stupid person and the word is ordinarily used by adults as an abusive term. My master, however, added the family name of Constantin Paleologus, the last emperor of the Eastern Roman Empire, so the Mrs. would not be able to understand.

"What was that?"

"I said Otanchin Paleologus."

"What do you mean by Otanchin Paleologus?"

"What's next? I haven't heard any of my things mentioned yet."

"Never mind about the list. Tell me what Otanchin Paleologus means."

"There's no meaning to it at all."

"What's wrong in telling me? You're making fun of me again, aren't you? You call me a lot of bad names just because I don't know English."

"Nonsense! Better get on with the list. I'll have to submit the accusation soon or else we won't be able to get our things back."

"We won't see those stolen articles for a long time. Oh, please tell me the meaning of Otanchin Paleologus."

"You're very insistent, aren't you? I tell you, there's no meaning."

"Well, if that's your attitude, there's nothing more for the list."

"Stubborn woman! Then do as you wish. We just won't work on the list any more."

"And I won't tell you what else was stolen. You're the one who should make out the accusation. You already know what was taken from me."

"All right then, I quit." Then my master stood up and entered his study. The Mrs. went into the sewing room and sat in front of her sewing box. Both sat in silence for about ten minutes staring at the shoji paper sliding door separating them. . . .

It is said that a priest by the name of Dharma sat in religious meditation until his legs rotted. Even if a vine had crept through a crack in the wall and encircled his eyes and mouth, he would not have moved. But he was not asleep, nor was he dead. Within his mind, he was always active; he was thinking about some secret principles of the Zen doctrine, perhaps about why there is no difference between a saint and a mediocrity. . . .

I understand that Japan has been fighting a big war with Russia for some time. As I am a Japanese cat, I am, of course, on the side of Japan. If I could do so, I'd have organized a Mixed Cat Corps to go and scratch some of the Russians. . . .

Now, when you don't know what to do and cannot think of any good plan to solve a problem, the best thing to do is to pretend that such a problem will not occur. Just forget it. That's the quickest solution of all. For instance, take a look at what happens every day in the world. It would be impossible to say that the bride of today will not die tomorrow. But the bridegroom thinks about nothing except his present happiness—"We will live as long as an olive tree and we will be bound together everlastingly in bliss"—and shows no worry at all. That he does not worry is not because there is nothing to worry about—no! It is only because worrying does not solve the problem.

As for me, I had no way of knowing definitely that the rats would not charge from three directions simultaneously, but to think that this would not happen was extremely convenient and gave me a feeling of security. Security and contentment are necessities for the happiness of all creatures. I, too, needed security and contentment, so I decided that a charge from all three directions would not occur.

Even so, I couldn't help worrying about which would be the best of my three strategic plans. My strategy was ready to meet the charge from the closet, from the washroom and from the sink. But I was greatly at a loss as to which of these plans I should choose. Admiral Togo himself must have also worried about whether the Baltic Fleet would pass the Strait of Tsushima, the Strait of Tsugaru or the Strait of Soya. I can now easily understand how he must have felt. Not only was I like Admiral Togo, but I felt my anxieties were also the same as his. . . .

Then the cup used for gargling clinked against the metal basin. The enemy was behind me now. Just as I turned around, a big rat about five inches long dropped a bag of tooth powder and disappeared under the flooring. I tried to catch it but when I jumped down, it was nowhere to be seen. It was much harder to grab hold of a rat than I had thought. I wondered whether I really had a priori the ability to catch rats.

When I crossed to the bath, the enemy popped out from the closet; and when I was on guard by the closet, another would jump out from the sink. I stationed myself in the middle of the kitchen, but then they all became wildly active every place else. Should I consider them intelligent or cowardly? They did not prove themselves sporting enough, in any case, to be played with by a gentleman. I lunged around the kitchen this way and that, about fifteen times, doing my best to engage them in combat. But alas! I did not succeed in catching even one of them. Though regrettable, in dealing with such small adversaries, even Admiral Togo would have had no method.

At first, I had had courage—a gallant and spirit-stirring feeling—but now I found this game troublesome and foolish. Moreover, I was getting somewhat sleepy. I sat down right in the middle of the kitchen to take a long rest. Though I didn't move, I sat glaring all around me so the enemy, terrified of my great size, could do but little damage. My enemies proved themselves, contrary to my belief, cowards. My dreams of winning honor in battle disappeared and left me only with detestation for the rats. With this feeling of detestation, my enthusiasm disappeared; and I felt exhausted. I became indifferent to the rats and began to slumber. Even among enemies, one must rest.

Through the transom above the door, a handful of cherry petals were again blown in by the strong wind and they swirled around me. Then from a hole in the closet, a rat came charging out. Although I had time to escape the attack, it came toward me at full speed and bit my left ear. Just then another dark shadow came around to the rear and suddenly began to gnaw at my tail. This all happened in a flash. Mechanically, without thinking at all, I leaped up, and with all my strength I tried to shake these monsters off. The rat with his teeth in my ear lost his balance and hung limp across my face. The tip of its tail felt as soft as a rubber tube. Taking a strong hold of this tail, only thinking about ridding myself of these pests, I shook myself to the left and right. The body of my assailant hit an old newspaper that had been pasted on the wall and bounced back on the floor. Its tail was still between my front teeth. Without giving the rat a chance to recover, I pounced on it but it was like a rubber ball. It darted away right in front of my nose and then sat on its haunches on the edge of a shelf. It looked down at me while I could only look up at it from the floor. The shelf must have been about five feet tall. Between us, the moonlight cast its beams along the floor like a white obi.

After gathering strength, I jumped high into the air. I was able to grab hold of the shelf with my forepaws but my hind legs could only tread air. Moreover, the rat that had attached itself to my tail wouldn't let go. I was in danger! I tried to get a better grip on the shelf but when I moved my paws, the weight on my tail pulled me down. My claws scratched noisily along the shelf.

Knowing that I couldn't go on like this, I made a swing with my left paw to get a stronger grip but missed the shelf so I was now hanging only by my right paw. My body began to swing back and forth. The monster on the shelf had stayed still until now, watching and waiting the outcome. Suddenly, however, it aimed at my forehead and charged at me like a rock thrown from the shelf. I lost my hold and all three bodies, as if one, fell vertically, cutting through the moonbeams. The earthenware mortar, the pail and the empty jam can that were on the shelf fell too and clattered on the pot for live charcoal. All this took place in the dead of night so the racket we made was enough to freeze the blood.

"Thief, thief!" screamed my master hoarsely as he came rushing out from the bedroom. A lamp was hanging from his left hand and the cane was in his right. From his sleepy eyes shone a brightness that was appropriate in such a case. I myself quickly curled up beside my abalone shell and the two monsters disappeared into the closet. My master, feeling somewhat awkward, shouted in anger, "Who's there? Who's making all this noise?" There was no one to hear him.

The moon slanted farther west and the shaft of light that fell across the kitchen became narrower and narrower. . . .

It is difficult even for a cat to endure the heat. There's a story about an Englishman by the name of Sidney Smith who once said he would like to take off his skin and flesh, and become just bones to keep cool. I wasn't exactly asking to become just bones, but at least I would have liked to take this grayish spotted fur coat of mine off in order to have it washed, or to leave it in a pawnshop for a while. We cats might look as if we were enjoying our frugal life, wearing the same face throughout the year and wearing the same clothes spring, summer, autumn and winter. But just the same, cats do feel the heat and the cold. It is not that I don't like to take showers—no!—but it's extremely inconvenient to dry this fur of mine once it becomes wet. That is why I endure smelling sweaty. And that is also the reason I have never been honored with a bath all through these years! I wish I could use a fan in the summer but, unfortunately, I am not able to grip one so this is out of the question. . . .

Then there are those who cut their hair short on top, and long on the sides. They look as if their round heads had been put into a square frame, much like a hedge of small cryptomeria trees trimmed square by a gardener. There are also the half-inch, one-third-inch and the close-cropped styles. As such people grow older and balder, all this might end up in their having a minus-half-inch or a minus-one-third-inch style—a new mode. But in any case, I don't know what humans are trying to do with their sorry selves by devoting so much time to fashion.

They're extravagant in other ways, too. They only use two of their four feet, for example. They'd be able to walk quicker if all four were used, but they only let the remaining two hang awkwardly, like a couple of dried codfish. Isn't that foolish?

Because of such time-consuming customs, it seems that humans have much more free time than we cats do. Cats don't go around inventing such schemes or pretending to enjoy them. But perhaps the funniest human custom is that whenever people get together, they commence telling each other how busy they are. Indeed most of them actually look as if they really were busy. They make such a fuss that you'd think they are killing themselves with overwork.

Some humans express the wish to be as easy-going as I am. But if they want to be easy-going, all they have to do is to try—that's all. Nobody asked them to be so fussy. Inventing so many needless customs is like building a big fire and then complaining of the heat.

If the day ever comes that we cats begin to trim our hair in twenty different styles, then we won't be as easy-going as we are now. If you wish to be more carefree, simply practice being like me—wear a fur coat during the summer. But, I must confess, it's somewhat hot. Actually, it is a little too hot. . . .

"By the way, what's the title of your thesis?"

"It's called 'The Effects of Ultra-Violet Rays on the Electro-Movement Action of the Frog's Eyeball'." . . .

"Poetic styles have greatly changed in the last ten years so you have nothing to compare this with. You can't understand modern poems by reading them lying down or while waiting for a streetcar. Even the writer himself has a difficult time answering questions about his own compositions. They're written only when the poet feels inspired, so even the poet himself has little responsibility for the outcome. Notes and explanations are later attempted by critics but that's no concern of the poet.

"The other day, a friend of mine, Soseki by name, wrote a short story entitled 'One Night.' Everyone found it vague; there didn't seem to be any point to the plot. When I last met him, I asked about the parts I did not understand. He insisted that he himself didn't know either. This might be characteristic of all poets." . . .

Man was made to be slow right from the very beginning. That's why humans have only recently commenced to understand the virtues of exercise and the advantages of sea bathing. They seem to think they have made a great discovery. In regard to such matters, I knew about these benefits almost as soon as I was born.

When considering the medicinal value of sea water, it can be easily recognized simply by visiting the seashore. I don't know exactly how many fish there are in that wide span of water but, in any case, no fish ever becomes sick enough to go and see the doctor. They're all there, swimming about in the best of health. When fish are sick, their movements become impeded; and when they die, they float. That's why we Japanese term fish that have died as floating or, in other words, as having risen. As for birds, they're considered as falling or fallen; but for humans, they only pass away or simply croak.

Ask any person who has crossed the Indian Ocean if he has ever seen a dead fish. He would be sure to give you a negative answer—and no wonder. Nobody has ever seen a fish breathing its last (well, no—a fish could not be breathing its last so perhaps I'd better say gulping its last water) or seen one come floating to the surface. Considering the difficulty of finding even one poor fish that has risen, even after continuously searching by day and by night in the vast and boundless sea, we must arrive at the conclusion that fish are extraordinarily healthy and strong.

And why is it that fish are so healthy? The answer is so simple that even humans should easily guess—that is, if people weren't so human. The reason for such health in fish lies in the fact that they continuously gulp water and bathe themselves in the sea. Obviously, bathing is of great importance to fish. And if it is so advantageous for fish, it must also be of great importance to humans as well.

You can laugh and point out that this theory is not new at all. It is true that in 1750 Dr. Richard Russell claimed that if a person took a dip in the ocean at Brighton, it would cure him of four hundred and four illnesses instanteously. His claim, however, proved greatly exaggerated. . . .

In the same way, it is not necessarily wise to always present Shakespeare's plays only as Shakespeare originally wrote them. At times, it might be a good idea to watch Hamlet while standing on our heads. Perhaps we would learn to criticize it better and there would be more progress in the literary world. . . .

Fortunately, I have been given those sharp implements called claws so I can climb trees, one way or the other. But frankly speaking, it's not as easy as it may look and, besides, cicadas can fly. Different from mantises, once cicadas take wing, they make it impossible for me to follow. I often find myself in a sad plight, thinking that it would have been better if I hadn't bothered to climb the tree in the first place. Then, last but not least, there is the danger of being urinated on, and it almost seems that cicadas aim at my eyes. Of course, I understand their wanting to fly away, but I'd like to ask them not to make water when doing so. What is the psychological factor that affects a cicada's physiological organs and induces it to urinate when flying away? It is, most probably, caused by some pain. Or is it a way of gaining time, surprising its foes before its flight? If that is so, it would be the same as a squid which squirts black ink when in danger, or as a quick-tempered bully showing off his tattoos before coming to blows, or the same as my master who speaks in Latin when angered. This again, is another problem for researchers to deal with when studying the cicada. It might even win somebody a doctor's degree. But now let's get back to the main subject. . . .

Looking up from the foot of the fence, I saw the three crows still on their perch looking down at me with their beaks in a neat row.

The brutes! I glared at them but it did not have any effect. I bristled my back and snarled, but that didn't work either. Just as symbolical poems are not understood by laymen, neither were my gestures of anger understood by the crows—they showed no reaction. . . .

Then my master suddenly shouted, "Hey!"

Surprised, the Mrs. asked, "Yes?"

"Your 'yes'—is that an exclamation or an adverb? Which is it?"

"Well, I wonder—! But what difference does it make? Who cares?"

"It makes a great difference. This is the type of problem that continually occupies the authorities of the Japanese language."

"Do you mean to say that a 'meow' worries the authorities? What absurdity! Why, a cat's 'meow' isn't even Japanese at all!"

"That's why it's such a difficult problem. This is what you call comparative study."

"Is that so?" The Mrs. was wise through experience so she tried not to get herself involved in such a foolish discussion.

"And do you know which part of speech 'meow' is?" . . .

It's fun to tease humans. Even I, a cat, sometimes go around teasing little girls of the house. It must have also been fun for the refined students of the Descending Cloud Junior High School to tease a slow-witted person like Mr. Kushami.

When analyzing the psychology of teasing, there are two important factors. The first demands that the one being teased should not be indifferent; and the second is that the teaser should be bigger, either in strength or in number, than the teased. The other day, my master went to the zoo and saw something he admired very much. It seems he had seen a fight between a small dog and a camel. The little dog would run around the camel like a whirlwind, barking at it all the time, but the camel just stood there hunching the hump on its back. The little dog found that it was not causing any reaction so finally, disgusted, it gave up. My master laughed, saying that the camel was insensible, but this is a good illustration for the situation now at hand. No matter how good the teaser may be with his tricks, if the teased happens to be a camel, nothing happens. Yet if the animal being teased were a lion or a tiger, they'd be so strong that the joker wouldn't have a chance. He might even end up being torn to pieces for his trouble.

When a person is teased, he shows his teeth and gets mad. He may get angry but when he is harmless and you know you're safe, it's a lot of fun. There are various reasons why teasing is so fun. First, it's a good way to kill time, especially when you are so bored you feel like counting the hairs of your moustache. Long ago, there was a prisoner who was so bored he spent his days drawing triangles, one over the other, on the walls of his cell. There's nothing in the world that's worse than boredom; when there's nothing to stimulate you, it's pretty hard to enjoy living. Teasing is one amusement to create stimulation, but only when the other person can be made a little angry or irritated—otherwise it wouldn't be stimulating. Such amusement used to be most popular with the bored feudal lords who did not understand others. Today, teasing is especially enjoyable for the boys whose brains are so underdeveloped that they think about nothing but their own diversion, and who are at a loss how to use up their energy in other ways. Teasing is also an extremely simple method of trying to prove one's superiority. Killing, injuring, and imprisoning others are also methods employed for this object but such rash actions should only be taken when killing, injury, and imprisonment are the desired ends. Most people want to show their strength but, on the other hand, they are reluctant to cause physical harm. Teasing, therefore, is a most handy alternative. Actually, there is no rule which says that you must harm another person to prove that you are the greater. Though you might realize your own self-importance, the pleasure of this knowledge is only slight unless you can show off your superiority. Humans like to consider themselves as being self-reliant but only when other people are around to admire that self-reliance.

The people with the least amount of reasoning and those who most lack true self-reliance seem to be especially anxious to display their certificates of prowess. This can often be seen among judo enthusiasts. Many of them, still inexperienced in the sport, go around looking for someone even less skilled so they can throw him even once. Of course, there are many other reasons for a person wanting to prove himself but as it would take too long to explain, I won't discuss it here; but if you would like to hear my opinion, visit me someday with a box of dried bonito and I'll go into as much detail as you might want.

In taking the above into consideration, I believe the best way to get the most fun out of showing off one's superiority is to tease the monkeys in the Asakusa Zoo and—schoolteachers. I hope that no monkey will object to the comparison but, actually, they are in many ways similar to schoolteachers. As you know, the monkeys at Asakusa are in cages so even when they bare their teeth and shriek, there's no fear of getting scratched. Though a teacher is not in any cage, he is tied down by his meager salary so the students can tease him as much as they want. There's no fear that the teacher will resign or resort to physical violence because a person with enough courage to resign for this sole purpose would not have become a teacher in the first place. . . .

And so, as you see, there are many ways to bring the blood down but, unfortunately, no method has yet been found to make the blood rush to the brain. It is generally believed that a person loses more than he gains by becoming excited but there are cases that prove such hasty conclusions questionable. In some occupations, it is of great importance to get excited and to have the blood rush to the brain. Those who must take this into grave consideration are poets. It is just as essential for the blood to rush to the brain of a poet as coal is indispensable to a steamer; if the supply stopped for even one day, poets would become just ordinary individuals, doing nothing but eating.

Actually, frenzy is only another term for madness, but it doesn't sound any too good to say that a person can't do his work unless he goes crazy. By agreement, literary people call this madness "inspiration"—ah! inspiration!—as if it were of great beauty. This may deceive some people but it is still madness. Platon called this "divine" madness but, divine or not, the term still sounds to too many people like simply being crazy. So it is to their advantage to stick to calling it "inspiration"—a word that sounds to me like the name of some drug. Just as the base for ordinary boiled fish paste is the lowly yam, just as the image of the Goddess Kwannon is usually only a small decayed piece of wood two inches long, just as duck stew as served in most restaurants is really made from the flesh of crows, and just as the beef used in boarding-house sukiyaki is ordinarily horse meat—inspiration is nothing but temporary madness. The reason why most poets don't have to be locked up in the lunatic asylum in Sugamo is that their insanity is only temporary.

And it is quite difficult to attain this fleeting moment of insanity. It's comparatively simple for someone to be insane all his life; but God, who is good at creation, must have had a difficult time in making a man who would be insane only when he has a pen in his hand. For centuries, learned men have been racking their brains, trying to devise some method to induce blood to rush to the brain, besides bringing the circulation back to normal. There was once a man who ate twelve green persimmons every day in order to get inspiration. His theory was that by eating green persimmons, he would get constipated and this would cause the blood to rush to the brain. Another man would jump into an iron bathtub, heated from below, with a bottle of warm sakè. He believed that the blood would rush to the brain by drinking in a hot bath. According to this same man, even better results can be expected by taking a hot bath in port wine instead of water. Unfortunately he died before he had saved enough money to put this into practice. It is a pity.

Then there was a man who hit upon the idea that if he imitated men of old he would get some inspiration. This was an application of an older theory, that is, by imitating the attitude and action of a given person, one's mental state becomes similar to that person's. If you imitate a drunkard and talk nonsense as he does, for example, your mind eventually becomes like the drunk's; and if you sit in religious contemplation like a priest and endure the uncomfortable position until a stick of incense burns down, you will feel as if you were a priest yourself.

It has been said from times of old that a person becomes excited if he imitates the conduct of famous inspired writers. I understand that Victor Hugo used to lie on his back in a sailboat to receive inspiration; so if you should get on a boat and look at the azure sky, you're bound to become excited, too. Robert Louis Stevenson is said to have written his novels while lying on his belly; if you do the same, the blood is bound to rush to your head. There have been many persons who have tried to devise ways of pumping blood to the brain, but no one has yet felt completely satisfied with the results. It's unfortunate. But perhaps there will come a time when we can all feel inspired at will. I, for the sake of civilization, sincerely hope that this day will come soon. . . .

Some of you might believe that I am writing all this at random with my tongue in my cheek, but I am not a cat of such hasty judgment. There is a philosophy behind every word and every phrase; when words and phrases are joined together, the beginnings and ends correspond and reflect that philosophy. But if those same words and phrases were read only as nonsense, the philosophy would change until it would be more like preaching sermons.

Nobody, then, should be so insulting as to read while lying down or to read five lines all at once with the feet stretched out. When Liu Tsung-yuan read the works of Han T'ui-chih, a Chinese politician and a man of letters, he always made it a rule to wash his hands and to purify them in rose water first. In reading my work, however, I would only like to ask you to be enthusiastic enough to buy your own copies; do not borrow my books from your friends. . . .

Dr. Amaki was calm as usual and all smiles: "And what seems to be the trouble?" In almost all cases, doctors begin with "and what seems to be the trouble?" I for one would not have confidence in a doctor who didn't begin with "and what seems to be the trouble?" . . .

Even if his pockmarks render some merit, a thing that looks unclean is a thing unclean, any way you look at it. When my master became of age, he commenced to worry a great deal about his appearance and did everything possible to erase the unsightly scars. But they are different from the palanquin of the elderly Sohaku, and my master could not get rid of them. They will always remain distinctly on his face.

This seems to worry my master somewhat because every time he walks along a street, he counts the pockmarked people he sees. He jots down in his diary such details as how many he finds, whether they are men or women, and whether he sees them at the market in Ogawamachi or in Ueno Park. The other day, a friend who had gone abroad dropped in, and my master asked him if he had seen many Westerners with pockmarks. After thinking for some time, slanting his head to one side, the friend confessed, "Very few." My master asked again to make sure. "Very few? But there are some, aren't there?" Then the friend absent-mindedly replied, "Yes, but they're all beggars or hobos. I can't remember seeing any pockmarks on educated people." My master exclaimed, "Is that so? It seems to be a little different here in Japan, doesn't it?" . . .

By the way, some of my readers might not believe that my master ever combs his hair. It is true that he is lazy in doing most things, but the lazier he becomes, the more careful he is about combing his hair. Since I came to this house, I have never seen my master with a half-inch haircut, even in the hottest weather. He always has his hair cut to the length of two and a half inches. And not only does he part it on the left with great care, but he also flips up the ends of his hair on the right side to give a nonchalant effect. This, too, might be considered as the act of an insane person.

This elegant way of arranging his hair does not harmonize with my master's old desk at all, but as his vanity does not cause harm to others, nobody ever criticizes him for it. My master himself is extremely proud of his hair style but actually the reason he wears his hair long is this:

His pockmarks have not only invaded his face but have encroached upon his scalp. If he had a half-inch or a third-of-an-inch crop like most people, a lot of the marks would show. No matter how hard he would try to smooth down a short haircut, the uneven surface of his head would still be in sight. It might sound quite poetic, but I could liken it to a withered field with fireflies glowing here and there. But this might be disagreeable to the Mrs.

By wearing his hair long, there is no fear of the pockmarks being exposed—there is really no need to emphasize their presence. Perhaps my master would like his hair to grow down over his face so he could cover the scars there, too. My master believes that there is no need whatsoever to pay for a short haircut only to advertise that he has pockmarks all over his crown. This is the reason my master wears his hair long; and because he wears it long, he often combs it; and this is also the reason he often looks into the mirror. Therefore it seems strange that there is only one mirror in the whole house.

While my master was absorbed in pulling his moustache the many-cornered-faced Osan, the maid, came in from the kitchen, and held out some letters in her red hands. The mail had arrived. My master, still grasping his moustache with his right hand and holding the mirror in his left, turned his head around to face the intruder. The many-cornered Miss, seeing the moustache which usually droops down now straight up in the air, all of a sudden ran back into the kitchen and laughed herself out, supporting herself against the rice cooker.

My master did not seem bothered by this. He calmly put down the mirror and picked up one of the envelopes. The first was a printed letter, rather formal in style:

Dear Sir:

Allow us to offer our sincere best wishes for your happiness.

In reflecting on the past, we have enjoyed victory in every battle in the Russo-Japanese War. Our ever loyal officers and men are now returning amid shouts of "Banzai". The joy of our nation is overwhelming. When called to take up arms in this just battle, our brave troops offered their lives for their country with admirable spirit. They had to endure the discomforts of hot and cold climates for a long time in strange lands thousands of miles away. Their efforts can never be forgotten.

The victorious return of almost all of our troops will soon be completed. With this in view, it is our humble aim, as representatives of this district, to hold a celebration on the twenty-fifth of this month to pay homage to the officers and men from our district who fought in this war, and also to console the families of those who died in action.

In regard to this, we would like to have the kind support and cooperation of all concerned in order to make this occasion a success. Any donation on your part will be used to further this worthy cause.

Yours sincerely.

The letter was signed by a peer. My master, after having read it, folded it again, inserted it back into its envelope and then forgot all about it.

It is not often that my master does much donating. Once when there was a crop failure in the northeastern districts, he donated two or three yen, but later he would repeatedly complain that he had been deprived of a great deal of money because of the donation. Everyone knows that a donation is made willingly—it's not as if a person were being robbed by a thief. Therefore my master's saying that he had been deprived of money is not appropriate. In any case, my master is hardly the kind of person to donate anything so troops could be honored, not even when asked by a peer in a printed letter. Of course it might have turned out differently if the peer had come and vigorously negotiated, however, it is even more probable that my master would be thinking that he himself should be honored first at any function. Afterwards, he might welcome the troops—or anyone else. Now that he was constantly in want, however, he probably thought it would be wiser to have the peer arrange such matters all by himself.

My master picked up the second letter. It was also printed:

Now that we are having cool autumn weather, we sincerely hope that you are taking the best possible care of your health.

The construction of our new school building, as you most probably know, has at last entered the final stage. With great determination and perseverance while sustaining bitter hardships, we have been fortunate to acquire means of obtaining almost all the funds essential for this purpose. We are also fortunate to be able to announce that we have published a book, "Essentials of Sewing Techniques". This book is based on the principles and fundamentals of industrial art, acquired only after many years of research while experiencing untold-of difficulties.

It is my ardent wish that this book will be purchased by every household. It will certainly serve as a wonderful help to anyone interested in dressmaking. Besides, the small profit we can expect would help greatly to complete the school. We request your kind consideration and humbly ask you to obtain this book for your maid or some other interested person. Bowing nine times in humbly begging for your co-operation, I am,

Yours sincerely,
Shinsaku Nuida
Principal
Dai-Nippon Girls' Sewing High School
Postgraduate, Research Department

My master crumpled up this courteous letter and threw it carelessly into the wastepaper basket. It is a pity that Shinsaku's nine bows, along with his determination and perseverance, had gone to waste. . . .

Once my master pondered for a whole week on a question asked by a student: "Why, on a nasty day, do you say 'Good morning'?" It took him three days and nights to find out the meaning of "Columbus" in Japanese. Does the greatest hero in the world ever eat dried gourd shavings with vinegared bean paste? Can eating Korean ginseng bring about a revolution?—for such a man as my master, such puzzles are full of hidden significance.

My master, after having considered this difficult letter in the same way as he did the problem of "Good morning", seemed quite pleased with himself. He praised the letter exceedingly: "The meaning is deep. It must have been written by a person who has studied a lot of philosophy. A great view, indeed!" By this one statement, the stupidity of my master can be clearly proven. But there is at least one point which stands to reason; my master has the habit of praising anything he does not understand.

But this does not apply only to my master. In matters one doesn't understand, there are concealed bits of wisdom that one cannot mock; that which a person cannot fathom gives him a feeling of nobleness. That is why most people generally praise what they do not comprehend, and why scholars lecture on subjects they have mastered as if they didn't understand what they themselves were talking about. This can be seen every day in universities; when explained in such a way that the students can't understand it, the lecture is well spoken of. But when a lecture is given in clear terms, it is not considered intellectual.

That my master thought highly of this letter was not because he clearly understood the significance. And no wonder, since it had no significance at all. Consider the sea slugs appearing all of a sudden as did the excrement. The only reason my master praised this letter was because he could not understand it at all—like the Lavismists highly praising the Lao-tze, like the Confucians highly praising the Book of Morality, and like Zen priests highly praising the Reminiscences of Lin-chi. Of course they cannot admit that they do not understand these works, so they give the philosophies the interpretations that satisfy themselves and make believe they understand. To think highly of what is incomprehensible was fun even in the days of old. . . .

"You can't always tell who is fooling who. As for me, I hate people who say that they're like Zen priests or that they can foretell the future. Near my house, there's a temple called the Nanzo-in. The retired head priest there is about eighty years old. The other day, during a shower, lightning struck a pine tree in the garden of the temple right outside the old priest's window. Everyone told me how self-composed he was but when I asked the priest himself about the lightning, I found that he was stone deaf. So, you see, most phenomena can be explained in some logical way." . . .

I could hear Meitei talking away with two strangers, but presently he shouted, "Hey, Master of the house! Come here a moment. You're the only one that can handle this." My master resigned himself to duty and sluggishly stepped to the entrance, his hands still in his bosom. Meitei had a calling card in his hand, still talking with the two strangers in a crouching posture. His rear end was not in a very dignified position.

On the calling card was printed: "Torazo Yoshida, Police Detective, Metropolitan Police Board." There were two men in the vestibule. One was twenty-five or -six, high in stature and rather handsome, wearing a taffeta kimono. He stood there silently with his hands in his bosom, just like my master. I thought that I had seen that face before so I took a closer look. It really was a face I knew! He was the thief who had entered the house of my master and stole the yams! Aha! And now he was here again in broad daylight, and at the main entrance!

"This is a police detective. He has arrested this thief and now he wants you to go to headquarters."

Now that my master understood why the detective had come to his house, he lowered his head and bowed humbly. The thief was much better looking than the policeman so my master must have thought that he was the detective. It was to the thief, then, that my master bowed. The criminal must have been surprised but he couldn't very well say that he was a thief, so he just kept standing there without a word. He still had his hands inside his kimono. Since he was handcuffed, there was little else he could do with them.

For some strange reason, my master has a habit unbecoming a man of the present age; he feels it necessary to show gratitude to public officials and to the police. He believes that authority is to be greatly feared. Police officers are simply men paid by the public to work as watchmen, but my master cringes before them. The father of my master used to be the headman of a village on the outskirts of Tokyo, and he formed the habit of kowtowing to people in higher places. As a result of this, my master must also believe it necessary to humble himself before authority. It is extremely pitiful.

The detective must have thought it very funny for my master to bow to a thief and he couldn't help smile. "You're to come to the Nihon Zutsumi Branch Office Station at 9 A.M. tomorrow. What articles were stolen?"

"The stolen articles were—" began my master. But he had forgotten. All he remembered was the box of yams that Sampei Tatara had given him. The yams were of no importance at all, but it would be very embarrassing if he could not finish his sentence "The stolen articles were—." The articles had been taken from his own home and yet he could not answer. My master did not want to show how childish he really is so, making up his mind, he announced, "The stolen articles were—mmm—a box of yams."

The thief must have thought this extremely funny because he suddenly bent his head down and buried his chin inside the collar of his kimono. Meitei commenced laughing loudly. "You must regret the loss of those yams very much."

Only the police officer remained serious. "I don't think you can get your yams back, but most of the other things have been found. When you see them, you'll most probably remember. We will have to have a receipt for the stolen goods so don't forget to bring your personal seal. You must come before 9 A.M. It's the Nihon Zutsumi Police Branch which is within the jurisdiction of the Asakusa Police Station." After the policeman had finished this speech, he left. The thief followed him through the front door. As the prisoner couldn't take his hands out from his bosom, he had no way of closing the door so it was left open. Though humble before, my master seemed angry at this lack of courtesy because he slammed the door shut with a bang. . . .

"If I continue to compare myself with lunatics, maybe I'll go mad even sooner. My method is wrong. I worry about my sanity because I have been holding a lunatic as a model."

"Therefore, maybe I should try to reach the opposite conclusion by comparing myself to a normal person. How about beginning with Meitei's uncle in the frockcoat who came today? But that would involve the question 'Where must you place your mind?' No, Meitei's uncle is a little balmy himself. Then how about Kangetsu? He's grinding away at his glass balls from morning till night, hardly taking time out for lunch. He's a little crazy, too. Meitei? He considers it his God-sent duty to do nothing more than go gamboling about. He must be happy, but he's still a lunatic. How about the wife of Kaneda? That evil character of hers is completely opposed to common sense. She is certainly mad, without mistake! Then there's Kaneda himself. Though I haven't met him as yet, I know that he has found it possible to live with his wife in harmony. He must be an extraordinary person! But 'extraordinary' is just another word for insanity, so I must consider him along with the others. And then—oh, yes, there are those refined ruffians of the Descending Cloud Junior High School. They are still young but they will surely learn to surpass all the others in time.

"No, most people are more or less the same and this gives me unexpected hope. Society is a gathering of lunatics. Lunatics group together and fight among themselves—grabbing, pulling, plundering, and speaking ill of each other. Like microscopic cells they continue to survive—collapsing to rise, and rising to collapse. Is this, then, what we call society?

"Perhaps this is why we build insane asylums. We lock up those who cause trouble because they possess more understanding and have better reasoning powers than the rest of us. Are people in asylums sane and those outside the insane? As long as lunatics are considered different they will be locked up. But if those same people ever became organized and formed the majority of the population, they would no longer be thought of as being crazy. We often see examples of lunatics outside of the asylum who use their money and power to employ other lunatics to cause riots. Those are generally the men we consider as being great. It has become impossible to tell who is crazy and who is sane." . . .

Like on every morning, I heard the duster being swished around. The Mrs. had again begun her housecleaning. I wonder whether this chore is done for the sake of exercise or for play because the motions the Mrs. goes through, I must confess, are absolutely meaningless. The Mrs. seems to clean merely as a formality. She dusts the paper doors and briefly slides the broom over the straw mats, and that is the extent of her housecleaning. She does not seem to consider at all the cause and effect of her efforts. The places that are generally cleaned are always nice and neat, whereas the corners, where dust and dirt accumulate, are that way forever.

In ancient China, a sheep used to be sacrificed at a temple on the first day of every month but now the worshippers only go through the motions without killing an animal. Well, the housecleaning of the Mrs. is done in much the same way. It is only an empty formality. Yet she continues these rites every day. It is done so mechanically that the results are much the same as they must have been before the invention of the broom and the duster. . . .

Quite some time ago, a relative died and my master and his family took care of the house for a while afterwards. Later, when my master was able to find a home of his own, he possibly packed the brazier with his own household goods before moving.

There are many similar cases in the world today. It is said that bankers begin to think that the money they handle is really their own. Government officials are servants of the people so they are given some authority to carry out their jobs; but as they continue to work, they get to thinking that their authority is only to torment the people who gave them that authority in the first place. Therefore, with so many such people in this topsy-turvy world today, it would be quite improper to condemn my master as a criminal only because of the brazier. If you insist on calling my master a thief, then you may as well say that everyone else is a criminal, too.

At the table with my master was Boba, the little girl who had wiped her face with a mop that morning; Tonko the eldest daughter who went to the "paste made from tea" school; and Sunko, who had stuck her finger into the white face paint. They were already eating their breakfast. My master looked around impartially at his three daughters. Tonko's face has the shape of a steel sword guard. Sunko resembles her elder sister but looks more like a red lacquered tray made in the Loochoo Islands. Boba does not look at all like her sisters; her face is long. There are few faces that are not long but this child's was long horizontally. Although we know that fashions often change, a face that's long sidewise will not ever have much of a chance to become very fashionable.

Even though they are his children, my master is sometimes frightened of them. Like all children, they have to grow up. And grow they do—as fast as the bamboo shoots in the Zen temple nearby. Every time my master realizes how tall they have grown, it worries him deeply. It is as if he were being pursued from behind. Though my master is terribly absent-minded, he at least knows that his daughters are not boys. He knows, too, that there will come a time when he must see that they get married. He is at a loss what to do about them. Since he can never hope to take care of them properly, he should not have had children in the first place. But this is a common failing in humans. Humans are continually accumulating what they do not need and then pitying themselves for the burden. . . .

As might have been expected of an elder sister, Tonko exclaimed at Boba's dirty face after she had finished eating: "Boba! Your face is covered with rice!" First, Tonko picked off the rice which had clustered around Boba's nose. I thought she would throw these remains away, but to my surprise, she put them into her own mouth instead. Next she picked off the kernels on the cheeks. The other sister, Sunko, who until this time had been quietly gnawing on a pickled radish, scooped up a piece of sweet potato from her soup and suddenly threw it into her mouth. Now, as you all know, there are few things hotter than a sweet potato when cooked in soup. Even grown-ups, if they are not careful, sometimes blister their mouths with them. Sunko was now in a panic. With a cry, she spat the sweet potato out onto the table. Somehow two or three morsels came rolling right in front of Boba—and Boba is very fond of sweet potatoes. When she saw her favorite food right in front of her, she threw away her chopsticks, made a grab for the chunks of sweet potato and gobbled them up.

My master, who had witnessed everything without saying a word, was now picking his teeth. As for his children, his is a strictly "let-alone" policy. His three children, while still school girls in their sailorsuits, could run away from home with common-law husbands and my master would probably still look upon the situation without any comment.

My master does absolutely nothing. Yet, on the other hand, look at the people who are considered industrious. They lie, trick, bluff and intimidate others in order to get ahead. It seems they all believe it is the only way to act. Little junior high school boys see all this and follow the same course. It all makes me blush for shame. But I do not want to imply that these people are really good workers—no; they should be classified as sloppy. As I am a Japanese cat and patriotic, when seeing such people, I feel like scratching out their eyes. Each time the number of these incompetent egoists increases, my nation becomes that much weaker. A school with such students is an insult to all schools, and a nation harboring such citizens insults itself as a nation. We all recognize this to be an insult so it is hard to understand why there are so many of these people roaming about the country today. Perhaps the Japanese people don't have as

PROVERBS

He who gives away coals when it is snowing is a noble man—or a fool.

What has been the fashion once will come into fashion again.

No standing in the world without stooping.

Don't condemn till you've heard both sides of the case.

One cannot tell what passes through the heart of a man by the look on his face.

One half of the world spends its time in laughing at the other half, and all are fools.

A man's heart and the autumn sky are alike fickle.

All married women are not wives.

much pride as cats do. It is very unfortunate, indeed. I must confess that when I compare my master with such people, my master is the better human being. He is better because he is not ambitious, or efficient, or smart. . . .

"And he loves to contradict me. When I say right, he says left; and when I say left, he says right. Absolutely stubborn."

"Cross-grained, that's what he is. But that's Uncle's main pleasure. If you want him to do something, tell him not to. In that way you can make him do whatever you want. The other day I wanted a new umbrella. I kept telling Uncle that I didn't need one so he bought me one saying that there is no reason why I shouldn't have a new umbrella."

"Ho, ho, ho! That's wonderful! I'll do the same from now on."

"You won't get anything if you don't."

"Some time ago, an insurance salesman came and I certainly wish I could have tricked him into buying some. The salesman explained all the benefits that life insurance offers but he refused to buy. We don't have any money in the bank at all, so I naturally worry about the children. If he were insured, I would feel much more at ease."

"That's true. Something might happen." To talk so intimately about personal family matters does not become a girl of seventeen or eighteen.

"I listened to him talking to the saleman from the next room and it was really funny. He said that he recognized the value of insurance and insurance companies, but he stubbornly claimed that if a person were not destined to die, there was no need to buy insurance."

"Did Uncle say that?"

"Yes! The insurance man explained that life, though apparently long, is often cut surprisingly short. Then your uncle announced that he had decided not to die. Don't you think that unreasonable?"

"Even though he is determined, he'll have to die someday. I intended by all means to make high grades at school but I failed."

"That's what the insurance man said: life is something one cannot manage as one would prefer. He said that if a person could live as long as he wanted to, nobody would die."

"The insurance man was right."

"Of course, but my husband refused to be reasonable. He again proudly said that he would never die—that he was under pledge not to die."

"Queer, isn't it?"

"He certainly is. Your uncle insists that if he ever has enough money to pay for an insurance policy, he'll put the money in the bank instead."

"Has he ever saved any money?"

"Not in the least! He gives no thought of what might happen after he's dead."

"Then of course you're worried. I wonder why Uncle's that way. His friends who come here aren't that strange too, are they?"

"Absolutely not. Why, your uncle is without comparison." . . .

"Uncle, which do you dislike most, insurance or schoolgirls?"

"Who says I don't like insurance? Anyone who worries about the future should be insured. But schoolgirls are worse than useless."

"I don't mind being useless. By the way, do you have an insurance policy?"

"I'm thinking of being insured next month."

"Sure?"

"No mistake about it!"

"But why? Instead of buying insurance, it would be better to do something else with the money. Don't you think so, Auntie?" The Mrs. just smirked.

But my master suddenly became serious. "You probably think that you'll live one hundred or two hundred years. When you grow up you'll realize the necessity of insurance. I'm getting insured next month sure." . . .

Buemon, after having visited the home of his supervisor, must have learned a new truth about his fellowmen and, because of this discovery, he might learn to be all the more human in the future. He will become indifferent to the worries of others; he will laugh loudly when his friends are in trouble. And thus, future generations will be made up of such people as this Buemon, just as the world is already composed of such people as Mr. and Mrs. Kaneda. For his own sake, I prefer that Buemon learns to know himself as soon as possible so he can become a more ordinary person. If he does not learn, he will not be able to succeed in life like Mr. Kaneda has done. And if Buemon never learns to be indifferent to the suffering of others, he will be purged from the society of his fellow creatures and that would be worse than simply having to leave school. . . .

"As I lived in such a rural area, everybody in my home town was terribly Spartan. If anyone showed the least tendency towards the arts, they'd say that it was shameful; they would say that the students of other prefectures would laugh, so any artistic person was strictly disciplined. It was very troublesome." . . .

"When considering civilization today, I myself don't feel like living any more," complained my master.

"Go ahead and die if that's the case," Meitei promptly replied.

"I don't want to die, either." My master is insensibly stubborn.

"Nobody worries much when they are being born, but when they are about to die they take it hard," said Kangetsu, stating another truism.

"When you borrow money, you don't think much about it. But when you have to return it, you worry a lot. There are many similar examples." Meitei was very quick in giving such answers. . . .

"The only reasonable solution is in suicide. Someday everyone will leave the world simply by doing away with himself."

"The world will become quite insecure, won't it?"

"Probably. Henry Arthur Jones once wrote about a philosopher who strongly advocated suicide."

"And did he kill himself?"

"Unfortunately not. But in another thousand years, everybody will be committing suicide. In ten thousand years, people will talk about death in no other way than as self-destruction."

"That's going to be a terrible mess."

"Ways of committing suicide will be extensively studied and it will be considered a fine science. At the Descending Cloud Junior High School, they'll be teaching methods of suicide instead of holding classes in ethics."

"It's kind of fun to listen to this lecture on suicide. Meitei, did you hear Mr. Kushami's theory?"

"I heard it. I'd love to hear the teacher of ethics in the Descending Cloud tell his students that they should not adhere to the barbaric custom of public morality any more, but that, as future leaders, their first duty is to commit suicide. But the lesson could easily go one step further and make it lawful to kill others. That poor scholar Mr. Kushami, who lives near the Descending Cloud Junior High School, says he is tired of living so the students might consider it their duty to put him to death as quickly as possible. As we are now in a period of enlightenment, they mustn't be as cowardly as in the past and employ lances, halberds or missiles. By only speaking ironically, they could kill Mr. Kushami. It would be a charitable deed and, moreover, it would mean honor." . . .

"You know, for a businessman like me, common sense is absolutely essential. Sir, I've become rich in common sense nowadays. I'm greatly influenced by the people I meet every day."

"How do they influence you?"

"Cigarettes are also helpful. You can't cut much of a picture by smoking only cheap brands like Asahis and Shikishimas." Sampei then took out a gold-tipped cigarette of Egyptian make and commenced puffing on it.

"Can you really afford to be so extravagant?"

"No, but I will be able to be extravagant pretty soon. But for the moment I can impress a lot of important people by smoking imported cigarettes." . . .

I didn't really feel like drinking the beer any more but there is nothing like trying. When Sampei drank, he became red in the face and commenced to breathe heavily. Would a cat become gay by drinking beer, too? Well, I am bound to die sometime so it is best to do all things while still alive. After I'm dead, I don't want to feel regret so I made up my mind to drink some of it anyway.

I stuck my tongue out fast, and quickly lapped up some beer in one glass—and I was greatly surprised. I felt the tip of my tongue prickle as if needles were being stuck into it. I could not fathom for what freakish reason humans like to drink such bitter liquid. Any way you looked at it, beer and cats do not go hand in hand. It was terrible!

I retracted my tongue but then had a second thought. Humans often say that the best medicine is the most bitter to the taste. When they catch cold, I have often seen them take some obscure medicine while making a sour face. I was never sure whether they got well because of the medicine or in spite of it, but this was a good chance to find out. If my stomach became bitter after drinking the beer, that would be that. But if I became joyful, forgetting everything like Sampei, it would be an epoch-making discovery, and I'd tell all the cats in Japan about my experience. I felt I had to see what would happen so, leaving everything to fate, I stuck my tongue out again. It was difficult to drink with my eyes open so I shut them tight and began lapping up the beer again.

With great effort, I was finally able to drink a little more and then I felt a queer sensation. At first, my tongue burned and it seemed as if my cheeks were being pressed from outside. It was somewhat painful but, as I drank more, this feeling eased off. And when I had finished the glass, there was nothing painful about it any more. I knew it was safe now, so I drank the second glassful very easily. Then, just for good measure, I lapped up all the beer that had been spilled on the tray.

Then in order to find out how I felt, I stayed in a crouched position for a while. Gradually, my body became warm. My eyelids began to swell. My ears became hot. I suddenly wanted to sing. I felt like dancing to the old folksong E'en Though You Say 'Twas a Cat, 'Twas a Cat. I felt like telling my master, Meitei and Kokusen to go to hell. I wanted to scratch old man Kaneda; I wanted to bite off Mrs. Kaneda's nose; I wanted to do a lot of things. Finally, I wanted to stand up. And when I stood up I wanted to walk with a sway. Finding this great fun, I went outside. There I wanted to greet the moon good evening—"Hai! Konban-wa!" This was wonderful!

Realizing that this was what is called being gloriously drunk, I went aimlessly around as if taking a walk. Then again, it was as if I wasn't taking a walk. I took a few unsteady steps and became somewhat sleepy. I don't know myself whether I was sleeping or walking. I meant to keep my eyes open but they were extremely heavy. But I wasn't afraid of anything! I limply made one more step and then heard a splash.

Suddenly I was floating on some water. It was terribly disagreeable so I began to struggle but I could only claw at the water. I kicked with my hind feet and clawed with my forepaws. There was a grating sound. I had touched a solid object. My head only barely floated above the water but it was enough to see where I was. I had fallen into a clay rainbarrel. Now, this barrel had been filled with some water-shield plants during the summertime, but in early autumn, Kanko the crow came along and ate them all up. Afterwards he took a bath in the barrel. Since Kanko's first bath, much water had evaporated so the crow stopped coming. But I never dreamed that I would be taking a bath in the barrel instead of the crow.

The water in the barrel was about five inches below the rim. No matter how far I stretched my paws I could not reach the top. Nor did jumping do any good. If I did nothing, I would sink. When I struggled, my claws would scratch the sides of the barrel and I'd feel for a moment as if I were floating a little. But right away I'd sink again. Going under water was a terrible feeling so I'd begin clawing again. Presently my body began to tire. I became bewildered and my paws would not work the way I wanted them to. Finally I didn't know whether I was clawing to sink or if I was sinking to claw.

The reason I was undergoing such terrible torment was only because I had wanted to climb on top of the barrel. Of course I now know it was impossible. My paws are less than three inches long. If I could have floated on the water and stretched my front paws as far as possible, I would have still been about two inches away from the rim. Since my claws could not hook onto the rim of the barrel, it would have made no difference whether I clawed, or if I became bewildered, or whether I simply worked to death—I couldn't make it. Knowing that I couldn't get out but still trying, I was attempting the impossible. And when attempting the impossible, the anguish is horrible. What nonsense! I was only prolonging my agony.

"I'm going to quit. Don't care what happens now." I then let my front paws relax, and then my hind legs, my head and my tail. I didn't resist any more.

Gradually I felt uncommonly comfortable. Could this feeling of thankfulness be agony? Was I still in the water or in the middle of a room? But of course it didn't make much difference where I was, or what I was doing. The only thing that counted was that I felt comfortable. Then I could hardly even feel this comfort. I'll cut the sun and the moon down from the sky. I'll pulverize the heaven and the earth. I am entering the mysterious but wonderful realm of peace!

I die.
I die and receive peace.
Peace cannot be had without dying.
Save us, merciful Buddha!
Save us, merciful Buddha!
Gracious blessings,
Gracious blessings.

Kappa (extracts)

Ryunosuke Akutagawa (1892–1927) / Seiichiro Shiojiri

By the time he killed himself at the age of thirty-four Ryunosuke Akutagawa had published enough to fill ten volumes of miscellaneous writings. He had studied English literature at Tokyo Imperial University and was familiar with Western satire; his thesis was a study of William Morris. Qualities characteristic of his fiction are irony, use of the grotesque, a bitter whimsy. Many of his stories use historical material, handling it with twentieth-century frankness and sometimes bizarre detail. He was encouraged by Soseki Natsume to continue writing his unusual stories, of which "Rashomon" is best known in the West. Other stories are "The Nose," "Lice," "The Pipe," and "The Handkerchief."

Akutagawa belongs to no particular category of writers. He shaped his own style and imposed his individuality on modern literature. The grotesqueness of his art extended to his death: before drinking veronal he compiled a list of famous suicides and wrote out a philosophical defense for taking one's own life.

The kappa is an imaginary creature quite familiar in the folklore of Japan. In most versions it is a childlike being that lives in rivers and lakes. For a creature that does not exist, it has proved to be a remarkably popular model for Japanese artists, and Akutagawa himself drew pictures of kappas when he was an undergraduate.

This is a story Patient No. 23 of a lunatic asylum tells anybody he comes across. I think he is over thirty now, but he looks very young for his age. The joys and sorrows he had experienced before he went off his head—well, let them be buried in the past

He told his lengthy story to me and Dr. S——, head physician of the asylum, his hands clasped all the time round his knees, and his eyes looking now and then out of the iron bars of the window—outside of which was seen an oak tree, quite bare, without even a single dead leaf, spreading its branches against the sky darkened by snow-clouds. He made very few gestures, but when for instance he said he had been surprised, he suddenly threw his head back. . . .

I flatter myself that I have copied his narrative with tolerable accuracy. But if you are not satisfied with my notes, go and see him for yourselves at the S—— Lunatic Asylum in the village of —— just outside the city of Tokyo. Patient No. 23 will greet you with a deep bow, and motion you to a hard-seated chair. Then, with a gloomy smile, he will quietly repeat his story. And when he comes to the end of the story—I still remember the sudden change of expression on his face—he will spring to his feet and, brandishing his clenched fists, will roar at you:

"Get out, you scoundrel! You too are a stupid, jealous, obscene, brazen-faced, self-conceited, cruel, and cheeky beast, aren't you? Get out, you sneaking little scoundrel!" . . .

Before proceeding further, I think I must give you some idea of the animals called kappas. People still doubt whether they exist at all. But they do. There can be no doubt about it since I myself actually lived among them. They have a short-haired head and webbed hands and feet, like those pictured in the Suiko Koryaku (A Study of the Water-Tiger) and other books. Their average height is about three feet four inches. Their weight ranges from twenty to thirty pounds, according to Doctor Chack, though he says that there are some extraordinarily big ones who weigh more than fifty. The top of their heads is concave, forming an oval, dish-like hollow, and this dish seems to grow harder with years. For instance, old Bag's dish was quite different to the touch from young Chack's. But what is most remarkable about kappas is that unlike human beings they change color according to their surroundings. For instance, when they are in the grass they are just as green as the grass, and when they are on a rock they are just as grey as the rock. I think they have something in their skin tissue that chameleons have in theirs, for chameleons, you know, have the power of changing color. The discovery of this strange fact reminded me of a book of folklore which says that the kappas of western Japan are green and those of north-eastern districts red.

It seems that kappas have a very rich deposit of fat beneath their skin. They never clothe themselves in spite of the comparatively low temperature—about fifty degrees F.—of their underground country. Of course they wear spectacles, and carry cigarette cases and pocket-books and other things with them. But they get along very well without clothes or pockets, because, like kangaroos, they have a nice pouch on their bellies. One thing that struck me as being very funny was that they did not even wear a loin-cloth. I once asked Bag why they didn't. He went off into a fit of laughter, and with his body bent back, cackled and cackled away until he said:

"I should like to know what makes you cover yourself." . . .

Little by little I learned the everyday language of kappas, as well as their manners and customs. What puzzled me most was their topsy-turvy way of making fun of what we take seriously, and vice versa. Take for example "justice" and "humanity." They are very serious matters to us. But if you mention these things before kappas, they are sure to shake their sides with laughter. Perhaps it is because their idea of what is funny is entirely different from ours. I was once talking with Doctor Chack about birth control, when suddenly he burst out laughing, his mouth wide open, shaking himself so violently that he nearly dropped his pince-nez. I was naturally offended, and questioned harshly what made him laugh. Chack's answer was something like this—I am not quite sure about the details, because at that time I was not very familiar with the kappa language—but the gist of what he said was something like this:

"But it isn't fair for the parents to care only about their own convenience. It's too selfish, isn't it?"

From our human point of view, there is really nothing more funny than the way in which a kappa gives birth to a child. Shortly after that conversation about birth control, I went to Bag's house to see his wife in childbed. Kappas do the same thing as we do when they lie in. They get a doctor or a midwife to help them. But when at last the child is about to come out, the father puts his mouth at the . . . . of the mother as if he were on the telephone, asks in a loud voice:

"Do you wish to be born into this world? Think it over and give your answer."

Crouching on his knees, Bag repeated this question several times. Then he took a bottle of disinfectant from the table and rinsed out his mouth. The child in his wife's womb seemed to be somewhat constrained, for it replied in a very low voice:

"I don't wish to be born. In the first place, I don't like to inherit your blood. The insanity alone is horrible enough to think of. In the second place, I believe in the wickedness of living a kappa's life."

Bag looked embarrassed and scratched his head, while the midwife in attendance quickly inserted a big glass tube in the . . . . of Bag's wife and injected some liquid. She heaved a deep sigh of relief, and at the same time her belly, which had been so big, shrivelled up like a balloon emptied of its hydrogen gas.

As might be expected from the answer of that foetus, kappas can walk and talk as soon as they are born. Chack once told me that he knew a child-kappa who, on the twenty-sixth day after birth, gave a lecture on the existence of God, though he died in his second month. . . .

"Quax, Bag, quo quel quan?" (I say, Bag, what's the matter?)

Bag said nothing, but kept staring at me. Then he jumped to his feet, stuck out his tongue, and showed signs of springing upon me like a frog. I was frightened and rose stealthily from my seat and was just about to dash out of the room when, to my great joy, Doctor Chack came in.

"Hey, Bag, what are you doing?"

Chack glared at Bag through his pince-nez.

Bag looked creastfallen, and, raising his hand over and over again to his head apologetically, said:

"I'm sorry, sir. Awfully sorry. But it was really so amusing to see this gentleman scared that I couldn't help playing a little joke on him."

Then he turned to me and added, "I beg your pardon, sir." . . .

He believed that there was nothing so foolish as the life of ordinary kappas. Parents and children, husbands and wives, brothers and sisters, all derived their sole pleasure from tormenting each other. Especially, he said, the family system was absurd beyond all absurdities. . . .

In fact, love-making among kappas is quite different from ours. The moment a she-kappa comes upon a likable he-kappa, she takes any means whatever, fair or foul, to catch him. An artless girl-kappa simply runs and runs after the he-kappa. I myself once saw with my own eyes a she-kappa rushing like mad after a he-kappa. But it is not only the girl-kappa that gives the chase. She is often reinforced by her parents and brothers and sisters. Oh, how miserable the he-kappa is! For even if by good fortune he could escape from the she-kappa after running about a great deal, he would certainly be confined to bed for a few months at least. . . .

Somehow I liked Gael, president of the glass manufacturing company. Gael was one of the biggest capitalists. Probably no other kappa in the whole country had a bigger belly than his. How happy he looked in his easy chair with his litchi-like wife and cucumber-like children beside him! I often went with Judge Pep and Doctor Chack to dine with him, and used his letters of introduction to see various factories with which he or his friends were connected in some way or other. One of the most interesting was a book factory. A young kappa engineer conducted me over it, and showed me giant machines run by hydro-electric power. I was deeply impressed with the enormous progress the kappas had made in their mechanical industry. The engineer told me that the annual production of the factory amounted to seven million volumes. But what struck me with wonder was not the quantity of the output, but the remarkably simple process by which so many millions of books were produced. For in that country books are manufactured merely by throwing paper, ink and grey-colored powder into the funnel-shaped mouths of the machines. In less than five minutes these materials are poured out in torrents of books printed in quartos, octavos, etc. I asked what that grey-colored powder was. The kappa engineer, who was standing before the shiny black machines with an air of importance, replied indifferently:

"Oh, just rubbish—brains of asses dried and ground to powder. Current price is two or three sen per ton."

Of course book-making is not the only branch of industry where such miracles are accomplished. Picture manufacturing and music manufacturing are done by no less wonderful processes. In fact, according to Gael, an average of seven or eight hundred new machines are invented every month, and things are produced on a larger and larger scale with less and less labor. The result is forty or fifty thousand more kappas thrown out of work every month. But while in that country I did not even once come across the word "strike" in the newspapers which I used to read every morning. It struck me as being very strange, so that at one of the dinners at Gael's, to which I was invited together with Pep and Chack, I asked what the reason was.

"They are all eaten up," said Gael nonchalantly, a cigar between his lips.

I did not see what he meant by "eaten up." Chack, who was wearing pince-nez as usual, seemed to have perceived my bewilderment and explained:

"We kill all those workers and eat their flesh. Just look at this newspaper here. This month 64,769 workers have been dismissed, and the price of meat has dropped accordingly."

"Do they meekly consent to be killed?" I asked.

"It's no use making a fuss," said Pep, who sat frowning by a wild peach in a pot. "We've got the 'Workers Butchery Law.'"

I was disgusted, of course. But not only Gael the host but also Pep and Chack seemed to take it all for granted. Indeed, Chack even laughed and said in a mocking way:

"After all, the state is so good as to save them the trouble of starving to death or of committing suicide. Just a little poisonous gas, you see, and they are done for. So they don't suffer much pain."

"But how can you eat—"

"Oh, don't be silly. If Mag heard you, he would surely break out into roars of laughter. In your country some of the low-class girls become prostitutes, don't they? It is sentimentalism to be indignant over the custom of eating workers' flesh."

Gael, who had been listening to all this, took a plate of sandwiches from a table near at hand and offered it to me.

"Won't you have some?" he asked coolly. "This is the flesh of one of those workers."

I was so shocked and nauseated that I ran out of the drawing-room into the darkness of the night, with the laughter of Pep and Chack behind me. The sky was threatening. Not a single star was shining above the houses. And all the way home I kept on throwing up pale, whitish liquid, leaving it here and there on the dark road. . . .

"War? Did you ever wage war?"

"Why, yes. It may at any time break out again. As long as we have a neighboring country. . . ."

To tell the truth, it had never occurred to me that the kappas had a neighbor nation. Gael told me that the kappas always regarded the kawaosos (otters) as their potential enemy, and that the kawaosos maintained armaments no less powerful than those of the kappas.

"Before the war," Gael continued, "both countries were busy making military preparations and were jealously watching each other. The kawaosos were afraid of us, and we were no less afraid of them. And in that tense atmosphere, it happend one day that a kawaoso, who was staying in this country, paid a visit to a kappa and his wife. Now this she-kappa had secret designs to dispose of her husband. He was a regular rake. Besides, the insurance money on his life may have tempted her in some measure to commit the crime."

"Do you know them?" I asked.

"Not both. I only know the husband. My wife speaks of him as if he were a damned rascal. But I think that he is not so much a rascal as a maniac obsessed by the fear of being caught by she-kappas.—Well, the she-kappa put a dose of prussic potassium into her husband's cocoa cup, and gave it in mistake to the guest kawaoso, who of course died. And then—"

"And then the war?"

"Yes. For unluckily the kawaoso was a holder of an order."

"Who won the war?"

"The kappas, of course. As many as 369,500 brave kappas were killed in battle. But the losses were negligible compared with those of the enemy. Almost all the furs we have are kawaoso furs. I sent coal-cinders to the front during the war, besides manufacturing glass."

"Coal-cinders? What for?"

"Food, of course. Kappas eat anything when they are hungry."

"But—don't take it ill—but the poor kappas at the front— Well, it would cause scandal in my country."

"It does in this country too. But as I go about telling people about it, no one is scandalized. Mag the philosopher, you know, says, 'Confess thy misconducts of thine own accord, and they will all vanish.' —Moreover, my heart was burning with patriotism, as well as with the desire of making money." . . .

It was a rather cold afternoon. Having got tired of reading A Fool's Words, I left my little house to call on Mag the philosopher. When I came to a lonely street corner, I saw a thin mosquito-like kappa leaning absently against a wall. Who do you think it was? Well, it was that very kappa who had stolen my fountain pen some time before. I was glad I had got him at last, and called to a stout police-kappa who was just passing by:

"Will you just examine that kappa, please? He stole my fountain-pen about a month ago."

"Hey, look here," said the officer to the kappa, raising the club in his right hand. Police-kappas carry a yew club with them, instead of a sabre. I was afraid that the thief might run away, but he stepped towards the officer calm and composed, and stood before him with his arms folded, looking defiantly at him and at me. The police-kappa nonchalantly took a note-book out of his belly-pouch and asked:

"Your name?"

"Grook."

"Occupation?"

"A post-kappa, until a few days ago."

"Very well. Now, Grook, this gentleman says that you stole his fountain-pen?"

"Yes—about a month ago."

"What for?"

"I wanted to give it to my child as a plaything."

"And the child?"

Here the officer fixed a stern look on the kappa.

"He's been dead for a week now."

"Have you got the death certificate with you?"

Grook drew out a sheet of paper from his belly-pouch. The police-kappa just glanced over it, and with a grin tapped the kappa on the shoulder, saying:

"All right. Sorry to have troubled you."

I was dumbfounded and stared at the officer, while the thief walked off, grumbling. Then I collected myself and asked:

"Why don't you arrest that kappa?"

"He isn't guilty."

"But he actually stole my fountain-pen—"

"Yes, probably to give it to his child as a plaything. But the child is dead now. If you want to know more about it, please look into Article 1,285 of the Penal Code."

With these words the officer walked quickly away. I did not know what to do, so I hurried to Mag's house. . . .

I told him all about the fountain-pen affair and asked him what Article 1,285 of the Penal Code prescribed.

"Well, it runs: 'No criminal shall be punished after the circumstances that have compelled the same to commit the crime have ceased to exist.' By this provision, you see, that kappa who stole your fountain-pen for his child has been acquitted of the crime automatically, because he is no longer a father."

"It's ridiculous, I should think."

"Don't be silly. It is the identification of a kappa who was a father with a kappa who is a father that is ridiculous. By the way, the Japanese law regards the two as one and the same person, doesn't it? That is very funny in our eyes. Hu-hu-hu-hu!" . . .

But on asking his name I found that he was the very old kappa whom Bag had spoken of.

"But you look like a child—"

"You don't know anything about me yet. By some fortune or other, I was grey-haired when I came out of my mother's womb. I grew younger and younger, and now I am only a child as you see. But if you ask my age, well, may be I'm about one hundred and fifteen or sixteen, assuming that I was only sixty years old when I was born."

I looked round the room. There was something about the plain chairs and tables, it seemed to me, that suggested the purity and happiness of a saintly life.

"You are happier than any other kappa, I suppose?"

"Well, maybe I am. I was old in my youth, and am young in my old age. So I'm not so covetous as old kappas generally are, nor am I a slave to lust like young kappas. Anyway, my life has been at least peaceful, if not happy."

"I see. Surely that would bring one peace of mind."

"Not always. One cannot enjoy a peaceful life without health and wealth. Fortunately I've always been in good health, and inherited sufficient means to support

PROVERBS

There are some gods who abandon men; they are those gods who know men.	The pebble in the brook secretly thinks itself a precious stone.
When fortune comes to a house the devil accompanies it to the door.	One good deed is better than three days of fasting at a shrine.
A woman's tongue is only three inches long, but it can kill a man six feet high.	There are gods in everything—even in hell.
Applause is the beginning of abuse.	It's the poor who give alms to the poor.

myself all my life. But what has contributed most to my happiness is, I think, that by good fortune I was already an old kappa when I was born." . . .

Dr. S—— says that I am suffering from dementia praecox, but according to Chack the doctor-kappa I am quite all right. He says—an insulting remark, to be sure—but he says that it is you, and Dr. S——, and people like you, that are victims of dementia praecox. . . .

Last night again I had a chat in the moonlight with Gael, president of the glass manufacturing company, and Mag the philosopher. Besides, Graback the musician obliged me with a tune on the violin. Look at the bunch of black lilies on that desk over there. Graback brought them last night— [I looked back, but of course there was nothing to be seen on the desk.] And this book is a gift from Mag the philosopher who brought it all the way to me. Just read the first poem. Oh, I'm sorry. You don't understand the kappa language. Well, I'll read it for you in Japanese. This is a volume from Tock's complete works published recently—

[Patient No. 23 opened an old telephone directory, and began to read the following poem in a loud voice:]

> Among bamboos and flowering dates,
> Buddha's long been fast asleep.
>
> And with the withered wayside fig,
> Christ is also dead, it seems.
>
> But rest we must, actors all,
> Even right before the scenes.
>
> (And the back of the finely painted scenes
> Is with patches and patches of dirty canvas patched!)

But I am not so pessimistic as this poet. So long as my kappa friends come to see me now and then— Oh, I've omitted to tell you one thing. You remember my friend Judge Pep, don't you? That kappa went off his head altogether after he had been dismissed from office. I hear that he is now in a lunatic asylum in the country of kappas. I should like very much to go and see him, if Dr. S—— would permit me to do so. . . .

February 11, 1927

INDIA

ON INDIAN HUMOR

The traditional explanation for the absence of tragedy as an art form in India is metaphysical: "Since the law of *Karma* mechanically dispenses a kind of cosmic justice for every thought, word, and deed, no occurrence in human life can be considered as really tragic."[1] Of the nine major "sentiments" required for the classical Sanskrit play, Lal lists three related to humor or satire: *hasa,* laughter or comical joy, but not laughter involving cynicism or scorn; *krodha* or *raudra,* anger arising from the feeling of ill-treatment; *jugupsa* or *bibhatsa,* aversion or loathing. To a Western viewer the humor of Sanskrit plays seems quite subdued and, except in plays like *The Little Clay Cart* and *Ratnavali,* concentrated largely in the jester, who is usually a Brahman and resembles Shakespeare's wise clown.

It is not in its dramatic literature that Indian humor most successfully expresses itself but in narrative. Even in the very early epic the *Mahabharata* there are a few satiric epigrams, cynically warning against trusting anybody and accepting hypocrisy as an indispensable requirement for social advancement. The *Panchatantra* satirizes meretricious Brahmans and lustful women, the power of wealth and the duplicity of men. The folktales of India reveal a realistic acceptance of a world in which people are as materialistic, sensual, and vain as those portrayed in Western folktales.

It is in the popular tales that the real values of daily life are revealed and the illusion of spiritual dedication on the part of the masses is disproved. Describing Indian society during the early centuries of the Christian era, J. A. B. Van Buitenen writes: "Kautiliya maintains in his textbook that of the three principal goals of life—the pursuit of virtue, the pursuit of profit, and the pursuit of love—the second ranks highest."[2] And as one reads *Shankar's Weekly* today one cannot escape the feeling that to Indian satirists modern Indian civilization does not seem any more excessively spiritual than it was in classical times.

Like other people, Indians get pleasure from the feeling of superiority that a moment of "sudden glory" provides. The discomfiture of others is the most common source of this feeling, and their favorite jester, Tenali Rama, outwits dupes to please readers. He promises two guards half of what he gets if they let him into the palace; they share the beating he was supposed to be given. Tenali Rama also outwits the king by giving a cat hot milk, sells his horse for a penny to trick the priest who is entitled to the proceeds, and in several other incidents makes fools out of his antagonists. His method is not always gentle, as the decapitated astrologer and the hunchback whom an elephant tramples to death discover.

1. P. Lal, *Great Sanskrit Plays,* p. xv.
2. Van Buitenen, *Tales of Ancient India,* p. 5.

It may seem that a spiritually centered people should not indulge in practical jokes, but in "The Red Lotus of Chastity" the faithful wife tricks her would-be seducers by giving each a drugged drink, branding him with a dog's paw on the forehead, and having him thrown into a cesspool. Tenali Rama also delights in practical jokes, on one occasion tricking the king and chief priest into dressing up like women and trying to seduce each other. In another story a Brahman who had been mistreated by a procuress tricks her into stripping naked, shaving her head, painting one side black and the other red, and exhibiting herself on top of a pillar. A woman tricks her husband, who is spying under the bed, into believing that her adultery will save his life.

The objects of Indian satire turn out to be the same as those everywhere else. The greed of poor people leads to their insisting on being the heirs of a "rich" man; instead, they have to pay his debts. The brutality of war is contrasted with the wisdom of a king who orders one soldier a year to demonstrate the army's courage by killing himself. Authority is mocked in the *Panchatantra* when we find a policeman arranging a rendezvous with a prostitute, when the king of the frogs feeds plebeian frogs to a snake in exchange for pleasant rides, and when a princess takes a handsome stranger off the street right into her bed.

Women are attacked with almost sadistic intensity by both Buddhist and Hindu writers. Dandin tells stories of a courtesan who wins a bet by luring a famous ascetic into sexual humiliation and of a princess who betrays a loving husband for the love of an ugly cripple. And the author of the *Sukasaptati,* a collection of seventy tales narrated by an extremely articulate parrot, concocts the following list: "The arts of women are these: deceitful speech; craft; oaths; pretended emotions; pretended weeping; pretended laughter; meaningless expressions of pleasure and pain; asking questions with a deferential air; indifference; not distinguishing between good and evil; sidelong glances toward lovers; that is the list of accomplishments practiced by the ladies of the town."

Fools abound in Indian literature and are laughed at as heartily as in less spiritual countries: foolish peasants, gullible husbands, naïve Brahmans, stupid camels, and a jackal who follows a bull for years, waiting for his testicles to fall off. In Kashmir long ago appeared the fools who could not count their number correctly because the one doing the counting always forgot to include himself.

Nor are the familiar vices missing. Hypocrisy is demonstrated by the sons who have accepted the father's wealth, then mistreat him until they are tricked into thinking that he is rich again. The serving of luxurious foods to impress guests is criticized. The deceitfulness of men is abundantly apparent: when Tenali Rama pretends to have died, the king violates his oath and tries to take Rama's property. And religion comes in for its share of ridicule, in the form of imperfect behavior by priests and monks, who exhibit vanity, pomposity, and an unclerical interest in sex.

As for the methods used by Indian satirists and humorists, they are quite familiar to Western readers. The device of unexpected truth is common: the priest who has been punished for omitting his morning dip asks a friend how he can avoid getting caught. The friend replies, "Bathe." Tenali Rama suggests an effective way of persuading a philosopher that the world is not an illusion: stop feeding philosophers. And when the king threatens to punish him for diverting milk to his own family,

Tenali Rama says, "Kings should see that children have milk before cats are catered to."

Unexpected logic serves Indian writers well. Told by the angry king to choose the form of his death, Tenali Rama says, "I choose death by old age." In an ancient tale appears this bit of reasoning: "A true harlot is like a saintly hermit: whether youth, child, or old man, whether handsome or ugly, all are the same to her as to the hermit, and thus both obtain the greatest good." And the other popular devices, exaggeration and pretense, distortion and surprise, all appear in Indian literature.

Because of space limitations only a small amount of Indian humor and satire is anthologized here, with no plays included, although *The Little Clay Cart* and *Ratnavali* contain a number of comic scenes. A jester almost as popular in India as Tenali Rama is Birbal, whose escapades and tricks are similar to those traditionally ascribed to Western jesters. There is also satire in the poetry of the Urdu writer Sauda, the writings of Mirza Ghalib, and other works by Aubrey Menen and Narayan.

For scholars who believe that India is the source not only of many Western fables but also of many anecdotes and jokes, there is considerable evidence available in the oral folklore going back perhaps as far as three thousand years. When the king offers a precious jewel to the first man who can travel around his kingdom, a wit walks around the king and claims the reward. To an emperor's question, "What people have the biggest bellies?" the jester replies, "The landlords." A holy man, asked by the king what the essence of religion is, says, "You are sitting on your throne, and I am sitting on the ground, so how can I tell?" When a king, anticipating modern doctors, tells a man, "Even the donkey will have nothing to do with tobacco," the smoker replies, "Donkeys don't know how to enjoy themselves."

A fool asks, "Where did the dirt go when the canal was dug?" and his disgusted father-in-law tells him, "I ate half and your father ate half, having such a stupid son-in-law." A man bathing a rich man uses sand instead of sandalwood, saying, "Consider the sand of the Ganges to be sandalwood." When he asks for his fee, the rich man picks up a frog and gives it to him: "Know that the frog of the Ganges is a cow." In an early version of the Shylock trick, the buyer of an ox insists that the attached load of wood goes with the purchase. To get revenge, the cheated man disguises himself and sells the swindler another ox for "a handful of coppers"; the court allows him to claim the hand as well.

A one-eyed man comes to a merchant, tells him that the latter's father had taken his eye to sell, and demands his eye back or the money for it. The merchant asks for the remaining eye to take with him so he can identify the other eye among many.

In a story which appears in many Indian dialects, a man who is neglected at a banquet because of his poor clothes leaves, changes his clothes, and returns. This time he is treated with respect. "Feed my clothes," he says, "for it is they who are welcome."

A Himalayan story tells of the man who invited to a feast only those whose household had never been touched by death. No one came.

When a king asks an old man why he has been silent in his presence, the man says, "What do you do when in the company of a fool?"

The story about the blind men and the elephant has been traced back to the Ganges valley; in this version they conclude, respectively, that the elephant is like a log, a rope, a fan, and something without beginning or end.

Fool story: when a numbskull's beard is cut off, he does not know himself.

In a story anticipating Jacob's account of three wishes granted by a monkey, an Indian family is granted three wishes. The wife, having wished for beauty, elopes with a prince; the husband then wishes her into a pig; and the son has to use the third wish to restore her human form.

In a series of anecdotes illustrating remedies worse than the disease, a woman wishing to punish a cat fastens cotton to its tail and lights it; the whole village is burned down. Other fools burn houses, in one case to get rid of rats, in another insects. To punish his nagging wife by making her a widow, a man kills himself. And in a story long familiar to Western readers, a man's young wife pulls out all his gray hairs while his old wife pulls out all the black.

Among the fools of Indian folklore, the one who cut off the tree limb on which he was sitting appeared very early. And, in separate stories, foolish thieves get caught because they stop to admire beautiful objects before stealing them, or debate which object to take, or cook the stolen food and wake the household, or ask help from the owner, or beat a drum they find in the burglarized house.

The shepherd who cried "Wolf" too often is cited in a number of ancient Indian tales. So is the dog who can't make up his mind between two castles and so misses eating at both. While two excessively polite travelers argue over who should get aboard first, the train departs. While officials argue over whose duty it is to put out the fire, the whole town burns down. And stories of fools bewailing a calamity which has not occurred provide entertainment for several Indian provinces.

Other stories which will sound familiar to Western readers include that of the fool who, told to find a twenty-year-old man, brings two ten-year-old boys instead. When the last two cakes finally fill him up, the fool regrets that he had not eaten the last two first. And a Himalayan queen, long before Marie Antoinette, told that the peasants have no bread, suggests that they eat cake.

In stories involving somewhat faulty logic, a poor man decides that the idol in the temple is poorer than he is, since it is naked. A robbed man blames a thief for not warning him so that he could have witnesses to the theft. An innocent man is executed because his neck fits the noose. A scribe refuses to write a letter because he has a bad leg—he must deliver the letter in person since no one else can read it. A rooster believes that it is his crowing that makes the sun rise. And a servant sent to the doctor is frustrated: the doctor may not be in; if he is in, he may not give the medicine; he may give the medicine, but it may not prove helpful; if the medicine does help, still the man has to die someday and the medicine will not save him.

A man who had been told that the dead have cold feet gets frozen feet, lies down for dead. Indian storytellers have a number of variants of the tale of the student who tells a woman he comes from Paris; she mistakes it for Paradise, gives him money to take to her dead husband. Another fool—this time a physician—cauterizes a "sick" cart to keep it from creaking; the cart is burned up. A numbskull refuses to take six rupees for a piece of cloth; he has been told to sell it for four. A girl shortly to be married complains, "It was easy enough for you, Mother, to marry Father, but I am to marry a complete stranger."

More forerunners of familiar Western tales about fools: the dunce who had been warned, "Never show your head again," reappears with a large pot over his head. A man and wife make a wager, penalizing the one who speaks first; there are usually a number of indignities they endure before one finally breaks silence, including one variant in which they are carried to the funeral pyre before one gives in. To prove their equality, twelve fools sleep on the floor and put their feet on the one bed provided for the chief. A fool who has received a letter erroneously reporting his uncle's death believes the letter even when he sees the uncle alive. A coward boasts of what he would have done, once the danger is over. And a fool worries lest an earthquake make him fall against a knife blade.

There is no lack of cruelty in Indian folktales. Blind men are duped into fighting, while their money is stolen. A trickster who says, "I don't believe you have a gold coin," is handed money by four blind beggars, each thinking that a member of the group has spoken. A fool takes a threat to a child literally, cuts off the boy's ears. Several other dunces, told to shove the boy along if he is lazy about weeding, shove him with their weeding knives and kill him. Told to quiet a noisy patient, the numbskull does so—by killing him. And a foolish bridegroom, told that he should not let the paint wear off his bride's feet, carries her upside down across the river and drowns her.

Indian tales abound in ingenious twists. An importunate lover is imprisoned and starved, then given the choice of the lady or food; he chooses food. A woman deceives her lover by providing an inferior substitute. A girl tells her would-be seducer that she cannot comply until he has bathed; she prepares the bath herself and puts acid in it. And a princess convinces her abductor that he has to wait for her menstrual period to end—in twelve years.

In a series of clever seduction tales, a man tricks a woman by posing as her husband; a god seduces a mortal woman; a man poses as a saint to achieve his end; a devil comes to the rendezvous instead of the woman's lover; a hero who feigns death is seduced by divine maidens; an animal disguise tricks a woman into making love; and lovers gains access to women's rooms disguised as peddlers or madmen.

Nor was adultery ignored by Indian narrators. A woman in love with a doctor feigns illness, manages to obtain more than medical treatment. When a lover poses as a pregnant woman, the gullible husband sends his wife to act as midwife. One wife drugs her husband to sleep with her lover; another feigns need to use the toilet, goes out to meet her paramour. When a husband kills his wife's lover, the wife persuades him it was a thief.

Deception takes an earthy form. A man frightens away a bear by threatening to cleave its skull with his penis. The bear then meets a woman whom he tells about the man's threat. The woman shows him the cleft in her vulva as evidence of the cleaving she once got; it is not completely healed yet.

Hypocrites appear fairly often in Indian tales, sometimes as animals, sometimes as men. A fox lies to a wolf about the tiger, then lies to the tiger about the wolf. A stepmother weeps as she tells her departing husband that she will take good care of the stepchildren even though they beat her; actually, she does the beating. A rich man who pretends he enjoys good music arranges to be signaled when he is to applaud. A man who has found a lost jewel announces the fact, but so softly that no one can hear; he thus has a clear conscience. Another hypocrite will not share in a stolen chicken—he takes only the gravy. A man who breaks his vow and fails to give a coin to charity justifies his action—the coin was short weight. And a king sends his regrets to the family of the man whom he had had executed.

The imperfections of Western character seem adequately matched by Eastern defects. In Benares a man lets his legs burn in a fire rather than move them, and in a Bengali tale a man is burned to death because he is too lazy to put out a spark. A Himalayan boy, told to see whether it is raining, calls in his dog and feels its paws. And a lazy servant tells his master to cover his face; that will save the servant the trouble of putting out the lamp.

Vanity seems not to have been entirely eliminated by Hindu spirituality. In a race to town, an old woman defeats the fop who kept stopping to adjust his clothes. A man keeps using long words just to show off his education. A neglected wife who has been given a trifling gift boasts about it. And a coward who has given up his purse to a thief offers a lame excuse for his behavior. Nor is greed absent in Indian culture. A gluttonous wife eats up the entire meal while preparing it. The new son-in-law, offered a choice of dishes, eats all of them. A husband eats his wife's share of the food as well as his own. A greedy person gets his hand stuck in the food jar.

Among the misers in Indian folklore, one refuses to eat butter; he only looks at it and enjoys the thought of eating it. The wife of a stingy man prays that he may fall sick so that she can get better food. Another wife keeps half of the money she was supposed to have given to a shrine. A Kashmiri wood dealer prays for the raja's death so that he can sell sandalwood for the funeral pyre. A miser prays that he can enter heaven with his clothes on; he has sewn gold coins into the undergarments.

One begins to suspect that ingratitude is not completely unknown in India, judging from the folklore. Rescued animals regularly threaten, or eat up, their rescuers. Men saved by animals fail to reward their saviors, in spite of promises to do so. A man kills his rescuer to collect a reward; ungrateful brothers plot against the man who freed them. And a Brahman who was saved by a wild goose gives the bird to the king as a remedy against leprosy.

In other displays of human callousness, a faithful old bullock is deserted and left to die; a man overloads and starves his camel; thirsty people are refused permission to drink from a water tank. A common man, after speaking to the king, snubs his own family. An ass who had associated with a lion ignores other asses.

Western readers will find both the form and the object of this Himalayan anecdote familiar. A man says, "I saw a hundred wolves." "There weren't so many as that," he is told. "Well," he says, "then what made the noise in the bushes?" And as in Western folklore, Indians have a great many anecdotes whose humor depends on discomfiture or disability. When a pig licks a sleeping man's lips, the man thinks he is being kissed, and the audience laughs. There are many jokes at the expense of the deaf, the blind, hunchbacks, fat people, and poor singers.

Among the occupations ridiculed are those of tailors (thieves and cowards), scholars (impractical), and doctors. One doctor guarantees to stop palpitations of the heart; he does, but the patient stops breathing. Another doctor cures snakebites—by cutting off patients' heads. A third prescribes eyedrops for stomachache so that the patient can see what he is eating. And a doctor called to attend a sick man immediately gives orders for the funeral.

As in other cultures, Indians have anecdotes at the expense of minority groups living among them and the nationalities living near them, with Muslims often made the butts of the witticisms. There are also stories about liars, and the tall tale is appreciated. In one, a whole village is lifted; in another, an elephant is put in a man's pocket as a curiosity to show his friends. A man ties up seven hundred camels in a corner of his sheet, a child throws out an elephant's carcass, a man pulls three hundred carts of wood, and a beautiful girl holds a big elephant in each hand while she devours them. The exploits of hunters remind one of Münchhausen: a fruit tree grows from the head of a deer who had been shot with fruit-pits by a hunter who had no bullets. In an Assamese story a tiger lies in water with his mouth open while a cat drives the fish in. When tigers stand on each others' heads trying to reach a man in a tree, his tears form a stream. And in the Ganges valley there was a mosquito so big that he had a golden palace in his mouth.

FOLKTALES AND FABLES

Tales About Tenali Rama

translated by A. S. P. Ayyar

The people of South India consider Tenali Rama the greatest jester who ever lived. (In North India a wit named Birbal has that distinction, and every culture has its own favorite jokester who eventually is given credit for witticisms and practical jokes which other people perpetrated.) Tenali Rama was the royal jester at the court of Krishna Deva Raya, the emperor of Vijayanagar from 1509 to 1529. According to Indian tradition, Krishna Deva Raya was one of history's great rulers: a brave warrior who led his troops into battle, a respected scholar, a writer of dramas and philosophical treatises, a patron of music and painting and dancing, and an enlightened ruler of conflicting religious sects.

He would have needed a good sense of humor to put up with some of Rama's tricks. Granted that the purpose of a court fool is to distract the king from normal cares and to tell him in jest the unpleasant truths that no one else would dare tell him, still Tenali Rama seems to have pushed his luck often and was lucky to die in bed. Some of the pranks here ascribed to Tenali Rama are in other cultures credited to Till Eulenspiegel, Robin Goodfellow, and Nasrudin.

In retelling these stories about Tenali Rama, A. S. P. Ayyar has interpolated some of his own details, a temptation few raconteurs can resist. He has woven the stories together and added transitional passages that give continuity to the Tenali Rama tradition.

KALI BLESSES RAMA

Rama went to the temple and repeated the great prayer a thousand and eight times. At midnight, Kali came with her thousand faces, all showing terrible teeth dripping with the blood of the hosts of demons she had killed. She looked terrific and awe-inspiring.

But, instead of getting terrified at her fearful appearance, as all were wont to do, Rama laughed with real enjoyment. Kali looked at the bold and handsome youth, and demanded sternly why he was laughing.

He said, "O, it is nothing, Mother. When I get a cold, I find it almost impossible to look after my running nose, though I have but one. I was wondering how you would manage if you caught a cold, seeing that you have only two hands, like me, but a thousand noses which will all run at one and the same time."

Kali was struck by the broad humour, and laughed heartily. "You vikatakavi!"[1] said she.

"Ah, I like the title, Mother," said Rama. "Vi-ka-ta-ka-vi reads the same, read from either end! I could have desired for nothing better."

Kali was pleased with this, and showed him two gold bowls, held in her right and left hands, and said to him, "In the bowl in my right hand is the milk of learning. In the bowl in my left hand is the curd of wealth. Choose either, and you shall have it."

"Mother," asked Rama, "why is wealth a little sour?"

"Because the methods of acquiring it are none too sweet," said Kali.

"Mother, how can I choose without tasting them, and seeing which I like better?" asked Rama.

"All right. Taste a little from each bowl," said Kali.

But Ramalinga dipped his hands deep in both the bowls, scooped a good handful from each, and swallowed both the handfuls at a gulp, saying, "Mother, I want both. One without the other will make life uninteresting and miserable."

"You mischievous imp," said Kali, "you have disobeyed my orders, and taken both. You shall, therefore, be condemned for ever to be a vikatakavi, instead of being a kavi."[2]

"Mother," said Ramalinga, "don't be angry with me. Forgive me. If a mother will not forgive her son, who will? And, why are you carrying both the bowls, Mother? Is it not because both are deemed essential by you? Why do you object when I want to do what you are doing?"

"Well," said Kali, pleased by the remarks, "you shall be a kavi all right, and shall write a great poem on Siva, and another on Vishnu, but shall be known to your contemporaries, and to coming generations, more as a jester than as a poet. You are, indeed, a born jester. You will, with my blessings, be the greatest jester India has ever produced, and will shine at the court of one of her greatest kings, Krishna Deva Raya of Vijayanagar."

THE ROYAL JESTER

The next day, he repaired to the court. When he entered the great durbar-hall, people were having a grand debate on the reality of objective phenomena. One learned man was expounding the theory that the whole world was an illusion, and that nothing in all the phenomena perceived by our senses was real, and that our thought alone made us think that we were seeing things, hearing things, tasting things, smelling things, and touching things. "Really," he added, "we are doing no such thing at all, but are merely thinking that we are doing so."

All were perplexed at this exposition, which was contrary to experience but was supported by books and subtle arguments difficult to meet. Rama butted in at this stage, and asked the learned man, "Sir, is there really no difference about our eating a thing, and thinking that we are eating it?"

1. *Vikatakavi* means a clever buffoon, an intelligent ne'er-do-well.
2. *Kavi* is a poet pure and simple; *vikatakavi* is, of course, a perverted poet.

"None at all," was the reply.

"In that case," said Rama, to the assembled people, "it will be easy to test this learned man's theory. Let us all eat the rich feast, provided by this generous monarch, and let our friend think that he eats it and fill his belly!"

Everybody laughed at the discomfited Pandit. The king was so pleased at the joke that he gave Rama a purse of gold, and made him his court jester on the spot.

REVENGE

After some time at court, Tenali Rama felt an irresistible impulse to revenge himself on Tatachari for his failure to keep his promise and for his insulting behaviour when an interview was sought with him. He discovered that Tatachari was in the habit of going alone and bathing naked in a deep and lonely pool in the Tungabhadra, some three miles from the town, at about four in the morning, keeping all his clothes on the bank.

Rama went, one morning, and took and concealed all the clothes when the Rajaguru was unsuspectingly enjoying his bath. After finishing his bath, when he went to look for his clothes, Tatachari found them missing, and Tenali Rama standing near by.

"Ramalinga, where are my clothes?" asked he, highly embarrassed by his naked state.

"Oh, so, you have now recollected my name," said Rama.

"Give me my clothes!" said Tatachari.

"Your clothes! I never saw them," replied Rama. "And why should a Rajaguru bathe naked, instead of with his clothes on, as required by the sastras?"

After some argument, Tatachari said, in despair, "Ask what you want, and I shall do it. For God's sake give me my clothes. It is getting late for me to go to the palace."

Rama made Tatachari swear to carry him to the palace square on his shoulders. Seeing no remedy, Tatachari swore to that effect, and was given back his clothes.

After dressing himself, the Rajaguru returned to the town, carrying Tenali Rama on his shoulders. When the town was reached, a cheering crowd followed him, wondering at this strange phenomenon. The king heard the mob's shouts from the terrace of the palace, where he happened to be, saw the look of misery on his Rajaguru's face, and that of triumph on the jester's, and was indignant at the outrage on his chaplain. He called two members of his bodyguard, and said to them, "Go quickly to the palace square. You will see a man carrying another on his shoulders. Do not utter a word, or listen to any representations, but quickly push down the man on the shoulders, and give him some blows and kicks, and leave him there, and bring to me the man who is carrying him." Then he withdrew from the terrace, satisfied with the action taken.

But Rama had seen the king watching from the terrace, and calling the two soldiers. He guessed what the royal orders would be, and at once got down from the Rajaguru's shoulders, caught hold of his feet firmly, shed profuse tears, and begged his pardon for the outrage, and insisted on carrying him on his shoulders in token of his complete repentance. "Oh great soul," said he, "noble ones, like you, should forgive the thoughtless acts of fools like me."

The Rajaguru foolishly took this to be the result of true penitence and fear, and joyfully acceded to the jester's proposal, and seated himself with a haughty and satisfied air, on the jester's shoulders. When the jester had walked with his priestly burden for fifty yards, the two hefty men of the guard came on the scene. Without a word, they threw down the Rajaguru, and gave him some blows and kicks, and took the jester to the king.

Tatachari lay grovelling on the ground, wondering at their strange behaviour and cursing his own fate. He said to himself, "I took him to be an earth-worm. He has proved to be a scorpion, and has stung me. Ah me, this over-estimation of myself is the cause of my discomfiture."

HUNCHBACK WASHERMAN COMES TO GRIEF

But, the very next week, Rama came to trouble. He had heard of a wicked man dressed as a hermit who was in the habit of administering dhatura[1] to unsuspecting persons and of murdering them or making them go mad, at the instigation of their enemies, by worming himself into their confidence, as a helpless and stranded stranger seeking their hospitality for the night. One of his victims was wandering about the town as a violent maniac at that very time. Yet there was no evidence to book the cunning criminal, and so he was merrily pursuing his course. Rama went to him when he was on his rounds, and walked with him for some time, conversing on diverse matters, and quietly led him to his old victim, and put his hand in the maniac's. The maniac hurled the false hermit to the ground, caught hold of him by his long hair, and dashed his face against the hard earth, over and over again, till he died. This matter went before the king. He let off the mad man, as irresponsible, but sentenced Rama to be trampled to death by an elephant, as he was responsible for the hermit's death by acting through the maniac.

Two executioners took Rama to a lonely place that evening, at dusk, and buried him neck-deep, and then went to fetch the elephant, to do the trampling. No one was left with him, as they considered that he could not possibly escape. When he was left alone, a hunchback washerman passed that way and asked Rama why he was buried like that. "Oh," said Rama, "I had a hunchback twice the size of yours. I suffered from this for ten years. Everybody laughed and jeered at me, including my wife. Finally, a great sage came along, and asked me to lie buried at this holy spot neck-deep for one whole day, shutting my eyes firmly, and keeping perfectly silent, whatever happened, and promised that I would be all right. Please dig up the pit so that I may verify if I am all right now."

The washerman dug up the pit, and saw, to his astonishment, that there was not a trace of the hunchback on Rama. He begged to be buried in the same pit, saying, "For many years, I have been suffering from this cruel deformity without hearing of

1. A poison which brings about stupefaction, insanity, or death, according to the dose. It is prepared from the thorn-apple plant.

this simple remedy. They say well that everything has its time. Please bury me here, and take my bundle of clothes to my wife in Washerman Row, and ask her to come here tomorrow with my breakfast. Don't refuse me this favour, and don't tell her that I shall be rid of my hunchback by tomorrow. I want to give her a surprise."

"All right," said Rama. Then he buried the hunchback neck-deep in that pit, took his bundle, and went away, saying to him, "Close your eyes fast, and keep your mouth shut, whatever happens. If you don't do so, this remedy will fail, and the hump will become twice as big."

"Count on me to do it," said the hunchback. "I have suffered far too long to mind these necessary restrictions."

The king's men came after dark, with a state elephant, and had the unsuspecting hunchback, who kept absolutely quiet, trampled to death without ever dreaming that it was a different man.

They went and reported the execution to the king who was, by that time, sorry for the death sentence he had ordered in a hurry, since his spies had, on enquiry, discovered enough about the hermit to show what a bad fellow he was, and how the maniac had only, in fact, taken revenge for the misdeed which had brought about his madness. So he said to himself, "It is a great pity that poor Rama had to die for having the just punishment meted out to a villain whose activities my police officers could not discover and punish."

Just as he said this, Rama appeared before him and said, "Victory to the king!"

The king was astounded. When he heard the whole story, he laughed heartily, pardoned Rama, and ordered a good pension to be given to the washerman's widow.

"She gets a double relief," said Rama. "She gets rid of a hunchback husband, and also gets a pension for life."

GIFT OF BLOWS

Some days later, a famous singer and dancer from Kuchipudi in the Telugu country arrived at Vijayanagar, to exhibit his art. The king had a special performance arranged in the palace for the queens, and gave orders that Tenali Rama, who had by now become notorious for his pranks, should not be told about it. Rama, however, got news of the dance, and went there and wanted to get in. The sentry at the outer gate told him, "The king's orders are that you are not to be even told about this performance. So, I shall not let you in."

"But, there is no order of the king prohibiting my admission should I come to know about the dance myself. I tell you what. Let me in and I shall give you half of whatever I get," said the jester.

"All right," said the sentry, troubled by the legal point raised, and thinking of the handsome gifts sure to be secured by the jester. "Get in. Only don't forget to give me half of whatever you get."

Rama reached the inner gate. The sentry there too refused to let him pass. Rama told him how the outer sentry had let him in, and mentioned that he had promised to give him half of whatever he got, and added, "I shall give you the other half."

"All right," said the inner sentry, beaming. "Only, don't fail to do so," and let him in.

Rama went in. The Bhagavata man was dancing and singing about Krishna's boyhood theft of butter and the beatings he used to receive from the milkmaids. Rama took a stout wooden rod and gave a blow with it on the dancer's head. The dancer howled with pain. Rama jeered, "Krishna received many a blow from the milkmaids for his butter thefts and pranks and did not utter a single cry. So, you too should not utter a word of pain at such a trivial blow, so long as you act the part of Krishna."

The performer, however, continued to howl with pain.

The king was wroth at the jester's conduct, and called Kama Nayaka and said, "This fellow has been spoilt by receiving too many gifts from me. Now, he shall get something different. Give him two dozen stripes."

When Kama Nayaka approached Rama and asked him to follow him, for receiving the punishment, Rama said, "Sir, I need not come. I have already given away the gift now made to me."

"What!" asked the king. "Is there any fool in our kingdom who will take over this gift?"

"There are two such, close to, my lord," said Rama, "and they are guarding the outer and inner gates of this palace. They let me in only on my promising to give them half of whatever I got from you."

The king sent for and questioned the two sentries who had to admit the bargain. So, they were given a dozen stripes each by the police officers in attendance, and the amused king gave Rama a bag of gold, observing, "Your drama has been more entertaining that that of the dancer. It may be natural to steal butter, but I have never heard of a gift of blows till now."

CAT REFUSES MILK

Two months passed. The king heard of the increase of rats in the town, and resolved to have a thousand Persian cats reared, in order to combat the menace. He imported them and boarded them out to citizens who were also given a good cow each for feeding the animals the milk. Tenali Rama, of course, applied for, and got, a cow and a cat. The very first day, he put before the cat boiling milk. The poor thing eagerly lapped up the milk, and got so badly scalded that, from the next day onwards, it would run away even from cold milk. The jester used the entire milk got from the cow for himself, his wife, mother and son.

At the end of the quarter, the king held a review of all the cats. All of them were sleek and fat, with nice fur, but the jester's animal was miserable-looking, and was a veritable disgrace to the tribe. The king, in wrath, asked him, "Why did you not give it the milk of the cow?"

"Sire," replied the jester, "it will not touch milk."

"Not touch milk!" exclaimed the king. "Do you think that I will swallow such a fib?"

"It is no fib, sire; it is the honest truth," replied the jester.

"I shall give you a hundred gold coins if what you say is true, and a hundred stripes if what you say is false," said the king. The jester agreed.

A pail of milk was brought. The king took the cat in his own hand, and said, "Pussy, pussy, drink!" The cat, frightened at the sight of the dreaded liquid, wrenched itself free from the king's grasp, and frantically escaped, mewing piteously.

"I have won the hundred gold coins," said Tenali Rama.

"You have," said the king. "But, let me probe into this matter further." He had the cat caught and examined, and saw the terrible scar of the previous burning.

"Ah," said he, "you villain, you purposely gave this poor animal scalding milk in order to frighten it. Are you devoid of even common decency? Are you nnt ashamed of robbing a cat of its milk?"

"Sire," said the jester, "kings should see that children have milk before cats are catered to."

Krishna Deva Raya laughed and gave the jester his hundred gold coins, saying, "Let at least these prevent you from robbing the lower animals."

SAND EATEN WITH RELISH

A week after this, the king got some rare sugar of exquisite purity. He had it out for drying. When the jester went, and asked him what it was, he said, in joke, and in order to prevent his depredations on it, "It is a peculiar variety of sand." The jester kept quiet, as if he believed this. The king was amused, and went indoors, and told his queens how he had fooled Rama. The queens looked out and saw the jester and his son putting the sugar into their mouths in handfuls. They drew the attention of the king to this. In great anger, the king asked the jester, "What are you doing?"

"Our buffalo calf is dead. So, we are throwing this sand into our mouths, in sorrow," said the jester.

The king laughed, and saved what was left of the consignment.

FORM OF DEATH CHOSEN

Ismail Adil Shah, the Sultan of Bijapur, was terribly afraid that Krishna Deva Raya would attack and try to recover Raichur and Mudkal, which had formerly belonged to Vijayanagar. He had heard of the capture of the impregnable fortresses of Kondaveedu, Kondapalle, Udayagiri, Srirangapattinam, Umattur and Sivansamudram by the resourceful and fearless Raya and had come to the conclusion that the only way to save the two towns, and indeed Bijapur and Gulburga, was by treacherously assassinating him. By a huge reward, he persuaded Kanakaraju, a fellow-pupil of Tenali Rama and a man related to the uncle who had brought him up, to undertake this foul job. Kanakaraju went to Tenali Rama's house and was given a warm welcome by the unsuspecting jester who kept him in his house. One day, when Rama had gone out on some business, Kanakaraju sent word to the king, as if from Tenali Rama, that, if he went there urgently, he would have an experience of a lifetime. The unsuspecting king went there, unarmed, and was suddenly set upon by the ruffian, with a dagger. Fortunately, the king was able to catch the man's wrist firmly before the blow could be dealt, and, soon, the man was overpowered and killed on the spot by Kama Nayaka, the captain of the bodyguard.

Under the laws of the realm, anybody who harboured a man who made an attempt on the king's life had to be sentenced to death. Tenali was accordingly sentenced to death by a Special Tribunal presided over by the Prime Minister, Saluba Thimmaraju. Rama appealed piteously to the king for pardon.

Krishna Deva Raya said to him, "I cannot go against the laws of the realm and pardon you. How can you expect to be pardoned when you harboured that viper? I, however, allow you to choose the form of your death. Come along, choose!"

"I choose death by old age," said Tenali, to the astonishment of everyone.

The king laughed and said, "You have got off this time also."

KING AND QUEEN RECONCILED

One day, Tenali Rama received a message that Queen Tirumaladevi was in great distress, and wanted to see him urgently. He went to her, and learnt that the king was highly put out at her yawning when he was reading and explaining to her his play *Jambavati Kalyanam* and had left off visiting her for a number of days running.

She said to him, "It was no fault of mine. I couldn't help it. I apologised, but it had no effect. What shall I do?"

"Well. Yawning does not lend itself much to poetic treatment. But I shall adopt my own method and set this matter right soon. Don't worry," said Rama.

He went to the durbar hall where the king was discussing with his ministers the rice situation in the Ceded Districts.

"It is imperative to increase the rice production," said the king. "How can we do it? By the Raya channel, Nagalapuram tank, etc., we have done something, but that is not enough."

"Your Majesty," said Tenali Rama, producing a sample paddy seed, "if this seed is used, the yield will be three times the present one."

"Really?" said the king. "That will solve the problem nicely. Perhaps it requires a special soil or manure?"

"Oh, no," said Rama. "It only requires that it be sown, and the crop reared and reaped, by one who has never yawned, and never will."

"Fool!" said the king. "Can there be a single person in the whole world who has never yawned?"

"I forgot that. How silly of me!" said the jester. "It is a good thing that your Majesty has remembered it. I must go and tell Queen Tirumaladevi about this folly of mine."

"No. I shall go and tell her myself," said the king.

Everybody laughed.

The king went, after the durbar, and made up with the queen, and gave the jester a bag of gold. So did the grateful queen.

HEAD FOR TOE

Some days later, Rama was on a walk with the king. He inadvertently trod on some filth lying on the road margin. The small toe of his right foot was tainted with it. He at once ran and washed it clean, in a nearby channel, scrubbing it well with earth. When he returned to the king, the latter said to him, "However much you wash it, a portion of the filth will stick to your toe. The only way to get rid of it is to cut the little toe off."

"I have scrubbed the toe well with earth and washed it several times with water," said Rama.

"That would have only driven some of the filth in," said the king. "Don't enter my special room, with the lovely Persian carpets, with that horrible toe on."

"We don't wash ourselves any better," said Rama, "even when we answer our calls."

"That is our own filth. Another's filth can be got rid of only by the method I suggest," said the king.

"What if I convince your Majesty of the error of your opinion?" asked Rama.

"You are welcome to do so," said the king. "I don't think I shall ever change my opinion."

Rama stayed away from court for a few days. He had some excellent rose plants planted in a pit full of filth covered over lightly with turf. Then when the roses were in full bloom, he met the king, on his daily walk, and invited him to go and see his magnificent roses. The king unsuspectingly went with him. He was delighted with the flowers, and exclaimed, "Oh, what lovely roses.!" Being a lover of flowers, he went near them to inspect them at close range. The turf gave away, and he sank, up to his neck, in the warm filth of the pit.

"Wait a minute. I shall bring a sword, and cut off the polluted portion, neatly, at the neck," said Rama.

"What! Cut my head off?" asked the king, in surprise.

"What else can be done unless your Majesty revises your opinion, expressed to me the other day, and holds that my toe has been thoroughly cleansed by scrubbing with earth and water, and that, therefore, a similar treatment will cleanse your body, too," said Rama.

"I revise the opinion. Pull me up quick, before others see me," said the king frantically, and Rama pulled him out.

KING PAYS FOR CONTEMPT

One day, the king and jester went out riding. The king's horse, a fine Arab steed worth a thousand gold coins, galloped and trotted in right royal fashion, while the jester's horse, a miserable hack not worth fifty, jogged along painfully.

"What a worthless horse you have got!" said the king. "Can you do with it what my horse is capable of?"

"Why, I can do with it what you can never do with yours," said Rama.

"I bet a hundred gold coins you can't," said the king.

"I accept the bet," said Tenali Rama.

They were just then going along the newly constructed bridge over the Tungabhadra. The river was in floods, and the muddy waters, thirty feet deep, were swirling viciously. Tenali suddenly got down from his horse, and pushed the animal, over the edge, into the swirling waters below.

"Do it with yours. Let me see," said he.

The astonished king, unwilling to lose his fine horse, paid Tenali the hundred gold coins.

"Tell me," said he, "how you got this idea."

"I read in a Tamil book,[1] written by a sage, the other day, that the only advantage of your having a worthless fellow as a friend is that you will have no regrets when you lose him," said Tenali.

The king laughed heartily.

SEAT AT FIRE

The king was camping at Ramandrug, in the hills, near Nagalapuram. Rama went there on his horse in pouring rain and was drenched to the bone. When he reached the choultry assigned to the courtiers, shivering with cold and eager to warm himself, he found all the seats round the fire taken up already by the courtiers who were eating mutton chops from an enormous pile kept there.

He went up to them and said, "Can I have a few mutton chops to give my horse? He is starving."

"What! Will your horse eat mutton?" they asked in wonder.

"Go and see for yourselves," he said.

Half a dozen of them left at once with some mutton chops to see if the horse would eat them. Tenali took one of the vacant seats and sat coolly near the fire, and warmed himself thoroughly.

A few minutes later, the courtiers returned and said, "The horse does not eat the mutton chops however much we press them on it."

"Possibly, now that it finds its master warm and comfortable, it expects to get its usual grass and oats, and has given up the idea of taking to the desperate remedy of eating mutton chops," said Tenali, laughing.

BOASTERS SILENCED

One evening, at court, several nobles were boasting of their prowess in war.

"With a mere handful of my men, I attacked a whole battalion of the enemy, and forced them to retreat," said General Apadsahayan.

"I held a pass alone against fifty of the enemy's picked men," said Nagama Nayaka.

1. The *Kural*.

"I cut off the tail of the leading elephant of the foe," said Kondamaraju.

"What is all that beside what I did?" said Tenali. "I cut off the leg of the commander-in-chief of the enemy on the battlefield itself."

There was great sensation at this. When the listeners had recovered from it, Kondamaraju asked Tenali, "Why didn't you cut off his head?"

"Because some fellow had done it already before me," said Tenali, amidst loud laughter.

ASTROLOGER'S PROPHECY FALSIFIED

The Sultan of Bijapur heard of the death of Raja Sahib, and of the accelerated preparations made by the Vijayanagar emperor for an attack on Raichur. He got thoroughly alarmed and upset. He knew that he could not resist such a formidable attack by so skilful and determined a leader. So, he took to more fifth column tactics. He bribed the palace astrologer, by giving him a lakh of rupees, and asked him to prophesy the death of the king if he crossed the Tungabhadra within one year from that day.

The rascally astrologer made a prediction accordingly. The king laughed and said, "I don't believe I run any risk at all by an invasion now." But the nobles and generals said to him, "Your Majesty, the safety of crores of people depends on you, and you should not risk your precious life, at least for their sake. The lord of the eastern, western and southern oceans can afford to wait one more year. The Muslims are no problem for you, but the planets and stars are different. In avoiding one evil, care must be taken not to fall into another. Do nothing without regard to the consequences."

The queens too begged of the king not to start on any expedition against the Muslims that year. The king said to Tenali, "My heart is set on this expedition now. But I do not like to displease my queens and nobles."

"Every prediction is not to be believed," said Tenali.

"I wish some one could prove this astrologer's prediction to be wrong. I am prepared to give ten thousand gold coins to any one who can do it."

"I accept the offer. I would also require Your Majesty's pardon for any punishment I might inflict on the astrologer if I prove him to be uttering a lie in order to help the enemy," said Tenali.

"If it is a lie, he deserves immediate execution," said the king.

Tenali discussed the matter with his friend General Apadsahayan and evolved a plan.

The next day, Tenali asked the astrologer, in the king's presence, "Sir, are all your predictions correct?"

"Yes. What doubt is there?" replied the astrologer. "If any one proves one of them to be incorrect, I offer my life as forfeit."

"Our country is really fortunate, then, in having such a marvelous astrologer," said Tenali. "May I know what your present age is, sir, and how long you will live?"

"I am now forty-four. I have thirty years more to live. I shall die only when I am seventy-four, and not a second earlier," said the astrologer, proudly, with a joyous smile.

Out flashed the sword of Apadsahayan and the astrologer's head rolled helplessly on the ground. Tenali exclaimed, "What a beautiful head! Yet it is of no value as it is entirely without brains. His prophecy has been falsified and his life forfeited. Harm seek, harm find! He boasted that he could foretell the fortunes of others. How is it that he did not foresee his own?"

A search of the astrologer's house proved his traitorous correspondence with the enemy.

Everybody praised Tenali. The king paid him the promised ten thousand gold coins, and marched at once into the Bijapur territory. Raichur fell after a glorious victory. The victorious army marched on Bijapur and Gulburga, capturing those cities also. Then the king returned home in such triumph as no king of Vijayanagar had ever known. "And I owe this largely to Tenali," said he to his ministers and nobles, giving another huge purse to Rama.

VICARIOUS BRANDING

The Brahman priests of Vijayanagar were an avaricious lot, and sponged on the generous king too much. One day, Krishna Deva Raya consulted them as to what should be done to appease the spirit of his mother who had wanted a mango fruit on her death-bed, but had died before it could be brought. They told him, "Give a hundred and eight priests a gold mango each, and her manes will be satisfied. Whatever a dying person wanted, but could not be given, can be given to priests, and will certainly satisfy the departed soul." The pious king did as they desired, and the priests rejoiced at the triumph of their plans.

Tenali Rama was disgusted at this, and resolved to teach them a lesson. So, when Lakshmamma died, a month later, he invited them to his house, stating that he too had to satisfy his dead mother. The 108 priests assembled at his house, expecting costly presents of some kind, as he was reputed to be fabulously rich by this time, and was known to be lavish in his gifts. When they were all seated down, he had the doors closed, and asked his men to bring red-hot irons and brand them systematically.

There was a wild attempt to escape on their part. All rushed to the doors shrieking, but were caught hold of and given a branding each. News reached the king. He went there in person, and had the doors opened and the priests rescued. He angrily asked Tenali Rama why he had branded the priests.

PROVERBS

All counselors draw profit from
A king in worries pent,
And that is why they always wish
For him, embarrassment.—PANCHATANTRA

A man is quickly found, O King,
To say the sycophantic thing;
But one prepared to hear or speak
Unwelcome truth, is far to seek.
—PANCHATANTRA

Caress a rascal as you will,
He was and is a rascal still:
All salve- and sweating-treatments fail
To take the kink from doggy's tail.
—PANCHATANTRA

A friend in need is a friend indeed;
Although of different caste;
The whole world is your eager friend
So long as riches last.—PANCHATANTRA

The jester replied, "May it please Your Majesty! My mother died of acute rheumatism. Her last wish to me was to brand her, and relieve her pain. But, before the irons could be heated and brought, she died. As these reverend men told Your Majesty, the other day, that whatever a dying person wanted but could not be given in time could be given to them, and that this would be sure to satisfy the departed soul, I gave them the brandings I could not give my mother in time."

The king laughed and left. The Brahmans hung their heads and slunk away.

BARBER WANTS TO BECOME BRAHMAN

Krishna Deva Raya used to have his daily shave by dawn. One morning, he was not awake by dawn, owing to a late durbar the previous night. The royal barber went in time and found him sleeping. He thought it a pity to wake up the king, and was also quite confident that he could shave him even while asleep. So, he set to work, and finished his shaving, to his entire satisfaction, without waking [the king]. Then he went away.

The king woke up, an hour later, and was a bit vexed with himself for sleeping so late and for not having had his shave yet. He put his hand on his face, and was astonished to see that he had been shaved already. He was highly pleased with the skill of the barber who had done this without waking him up, and so sent for him and said to him, "I am very pleased with you for your remarkable performance. You may ask for any favour you like."

"Sire, I want to be made a Brahman," said the barber.

"Rather curious, this," said the king. "Why do you want this, and not money, or lands or jewels? It will be a difficult thing to persuade the Brahmans to take a barber into their fold."

"I don't think that it will be impossible, Sire, I have heard that the scriptures say that the path of the devotee lies along a razor's edge. Now, I am more familiar with the course of the razor's edge than any Brahman alive. And it has been my life's ambition to become a Brahman," said the barber.

"All right" said the king. "Since you are so keen about it, I must get it done."

He called the leading Brahman priests, and ordered them to convert the barber into a Brahman. They were astounded. They told him that it was against the scriptures and immemorial custom.

"I have given you hundreds of villages as gifts," said the king, "and am giving you so much cash and so many other presents. You must do this for me and enable me to grant his boon. I give you six months. If you do not do this, I shall resume the villages, and exile all of you."

The Brahmans were in a fix. They did not want to have their gifts resumed, and themselves exiled from the court of this great and generous monarch. But, on the other hand, it was out of the question to make this barber a Brahman. They thought that they could find a way out in six months.

Days passed. Only a day remained for the six months' period to run out. Yet, they had found no way out. In despair, they approached Tenali Rama, forgetting his having branded them, and said, "Oh Rama, you alone can help us. You alone can tackle the king, you alone can bell the cat. You must help us as a fellow-Brahman. We implore you in the name of Mother Kali."

Tenali Rama agreed, on hearing the holy name of Kali invoked. He said to them, "Do not worry. I can set the whole thing right in no time."

He went to a tank lying on the king's daily riding round, and began dipping a black dog in it, and taking it out. He repeated this process interminably. The dog barked, and yelped and howled, but he went on repeating his act. The king passed by, and noticed this. He alighted from his horse, and asked the jester, "Fool, what are you doing this for?"

"I want to make this black dog white," said Tenali Rama.

"But will a black dog ever become white? Stop these foolish and cruel dippings," said the king.

"Where is the impossibility of a black dog becoming white in the dominions of Your Majesty, seeing that a barber is going to become a Brahman tomorrow?" asked the jester.

The King saw the point, laughed heartily, sent for the barber on the spot, told him about the dog incident, gave him a bag of gold, and said to him, "You can no more become a Brahman, under the caste system, than this black dog can become white, under the colour system," and sent him away, convinced and happy. Tenali Rama of course left the dog, and went his way with another bag of gold which the king gifted to him.

PRIEST BALKED

The pup died in a day. Rama got a raging fever soon afterwards. A priest declared that Rama must do expiation for his sins, and especially for the sin of causing the poor pup's death, before he could get rid of the fever.

"What will it cost?" asked Rama.

"A hundred gold coins," said the priest.

"Where am I to get all that money from?" asked Rama.

"Why, you can sell your horse and give me the proceeds," said the priest.

So, finally, Rama agreed to sell his horse and give the priest whatever he sold it for. The priest joyfully performed several expiatory ceremonies and prayed for Rama's speedy recovery. Rama recovered completely in a few days.

Then the jester went to the market place along with the priest, with his horse and a basket. He offered his horse for sale for an anna, but said that whoever wanted to buy the horse had to buy the basket also which he priced at a hundred gold coins. A man purchased them both at once for the prices named, and the jester handed over to the priest one anna for all his trouble!

KING TESTED AND FOUND WANTING

One day, shortly after his return from Delhi, Rama wanted to test the king. He put on a most dejected and melancholy look.

"Why do you look so forlorn?" asked the king.

"A doctor, in whom I have great confidence, has told me that a mysterious disease has me in its grip, and that it will finish me off in ten more days. I am, therefore, dejected, and am thinking as to who will look after my poor wife and child after my death," said Rama.

"Don't worry," said the king. "These doctors' predictions never come true. Even if they do, I am here to protect your wife and son. Why do you worry?"

"They say, 'Put not your trust in princes'," said the jester.

"They say wrong with regard to some princes at any rate," said the king.

"I am grateful to Your Majesty," said Rama.

But, from the next day, Rama did not attend court and had it given out that he was laid up. On the tenth day, he had it given out that he was dead. He himself got into his big treasure chest, emptying it of its contents, and asked his wife to allow it to be taken away by the king's servants if they came.

News reached the king about the jester's death. The courtiers remarked on the fabulous wealth Rama must have left behind. "A great part of Your Majesty's treasures has been appropriated by that rogue, who was always knocking away purses of gold. Really, we think that Your Majesty ought to confiscate all that treasure, and give only a reasonable pension to the widow and son," said they.

The king, who was in great need of ready cash just then, fell in with the idea, and at once sent his men to fetch the treasure chest. They did so. The jester's wife had also given them the key, in a sealed cloth bag. The king took out the key, and eagerly opened the box, and, lo, the jester came out of it, crying out, "Put not your trust in princes!"

"So, you are not dead, after all," said the king.

"No. How can I afford to die, and leave my wife and son in such hands?" asked the jester.

Fables from the "Panchatantra"

translated by Arthur W. Ryder

Most Western beast-fables, including Aesop's, have been traced by scholars to Indian sources, the most famous of which is the Panchatantra *(Five Books). A king with three dull sons hires a wise Brahman to teach them how to get along in the world, and the device the Brahman uses is to tell the boys a series of fables, most of which feature animal characters, to illustrate the problems they may expect to face as they grow up. The animal characters in the* Panchatantra, *says Arthur W. Ryder in the introduction to his translation (p. 15), "present far more vividly and more urbanely than men could do, the view of life here recommended—a view shrewd, undeceived, and free of all sentimentality; a view that, piercing the humbug of every false ideal, reveals with incomparable wit the sources of lasting joys."*

When the Brahman accepts the king's offer to educate the princes, he offers a fairly unusual condition: "If I fail to render your sons, in six months' time, incomparable masters of the art of intelligent living, then His Majesty is at liberty to show me His Majestic bare bottom."

THE BHARUNDA BIRDS

By a certain lake lived birds called bharunda birds. They had one belly and two necks apiece.

While one of these birds was sauntering about, his first neck found some nectar. Then the second said, "Give me half." And when the first refused, the second neck angrily picked up poison somewhere and ate it. As they had one belly, they died.

THE GULLIBLE CARPENTER

There was once a carpenter in a certain village. His wife was a whore, and reputed to be such. So he, desiring to test her, thought: "How can I put her to the test? For the proverb says:

> Fire chills, rogues bless, and moonlight burns
> Before a wife to virtue turns.

Now I know from popular gossip that she is unfaithful. For the saying goes:

> All things that are not seen or heard
> In science or the Sacred Word,
> All things in interstellar space
> Are known among the populace."

After these reflections, he said to his wife: "Tomorrow morning, my dear, I am going to another village, where I shall be detained several days. Please put me up a nice lunch." And her heart quivered when she heard this; she eagerly dropped everything to make delicious dishes, almost pure butter and sugar. In fact, the old saw was justified:

> When lowering clouds
> Shut in the day,
> When streets are mired
> With sticky clay,
> When husband lingers
> Far away,
> The flirt becomes
> Supremely gay.

Now at dawn the carpenter rose and left his house. When she had made sure that he was gone, with laughing countenance she spent the dragging day in trying on all her best things. Then she called on an old lover and said: "My husband has gone to another village—the rascal! Please come to our house when the people are asleep." And he did so.

Now the carpenter spent the day in the forest, stole into his own house at twilight by a side entrance, and hid under the bed. At this juncture the other fellow arrived and got into bed. And when the carpenter saw him, his heart was stabbed by wrath, and he thought: "Shall I rise and smite him? Or shall I wait until they are asleep and kill them both without effort? Or again, shall I wait to see how she behaves, listen to what she says to him?" At this moment she softly locked the door and went to bed.

But as she did so, she stubbed her toe on the carpenter's body. And she thought: "It must be that carpenter—the rascal!—who is testing me. Well, I will give him a taste of woman's tricks."

While she was thinking, the fellow became insistent. But she clasped her hands and said: "Dear and honored sir, you must not touch me." And he said: "Well, well! For what purpose did you invite me?"

"Listen," said she. "I went this morning to Gauri's shrine to see the goddess. There all at once I heard a voice in the sky, saying: 'What am I to do, my daughter? You are devoted to me, yet in six months' time, by the decree of fate, you will be a widow.' Then I said: 'O blessed goddess, since you are aware of the calamity, you also know the remedy. Is there any means of making my husband live a hundred years?' And the goddess replied: 'Indeed there is—a remedy depending on you alone.' Of course I said: 'If it cost my life, pray tell me, and I will do it.' Then the goddess said: 'If you go to bed with another man, and embrace him, then the untimely death that threatens your husband will pass to him. And your husband will live another hundred years.' For this purpose I invited you. Now do what you had in mind. The words of a goddess must not be falsified—so much is certain." Then his face blossomed with noiseless laughter, and he did as she said.

Now the carpenter, fool that he was, felt his body thrill with joy on hearing her words, and he issued from under the bed, saying: "Bravo, faithful wife! Bravo, delight of the family! Because my heart was troubled by the gossip of evil creatures, I pretended a trip to another village in order to test you, and lay hidden under the bed. Come now, embrace me!"

With these words he embraced her and lifted her to his shoulder, then said to the fellow: "My dear and honored sir, you have come here because my good deeds earned this happiness. Through your favor I have won a full hundred years of life. You, too, must mount my shoulder."

So he forced the fellow, much against his will, to mount his shoulder, and then went dancing about to the doors of the houses of all his relatives.

THE FROGS THAT RODE SNAKEBACK

There was once an elderly black snake in a certain spot, and his name was Slow-Poison. He considered the situation from this point of view: "How in the world can I get along without overtaxing my energies?" And then he went to a pond containing many frogs, and behaved as if very dejected.

As he waited thus, a frog came to the edge of the water and asked: "Uncle, why don't you bustle about today for food as usual?"

"My dear friend," said Slow-Poison, "I am afflicted. Why would I wish for food?

For this evening, as I was bustling about for food, I saw a frog and made ready to catch him. But he saw me and, fearing death, he escaped among some Brahmans intent upon holy recitation, nor did I perceive which way he went. But in the water at the edge of the pond was the great toe of a Brahman boy, and stupidly deceived by its resemblance to a frog, I bit it, and the boy died immediately. Then the sorrowing father cursed me in these terms: 'Monster! Since you bit my harmless son, you shall for this sin become a vehicle for frogs, and shall subsist on whatever they choose to allow you.' Consequently, I have come here to serve as your vehicle."

Now the frog reported this to all the others. And every last one of them, in extreme delight, went and reported to the frog-king, whose name was Water-Foot. He in turn, accompanied by his counselors, rose hurriedly from the pond—for he thought it an extraordinary occurrence—and climbed upon Slow-Poison's hood. The others also, in order of age, climbed on his back. Yet others, finding no vacant spot, hopped along behind the snake. Now Slow-Poison, with an eye to making his living, showed them fancy turns in great variety. And Water-Foot, enjoying contact with his body, said to him:

"I'd rather ride Slow-Poison than
The finest horse I've seen,
Or elephant, or chariot,
Or man-borne palanquin."

The next day, Slow-Poison was wily enough to move very slowly. So Water-Foot said: "My dear Slow-Poison, why don't you carry us nicely, as you did before?"

And Slow-Poison said: "O King, I have no carrying power today because of lack of food." "My dear fellow," said the king, "eat the plebeian frogs."

When Slow-Poison heard this, he quivered with joy in every member and made haste to say: "Why, that is a part of the curse laid on me by the Brahman. For that reason I am greatly pleased at your command." So he ate frogs uninterruptedly, and in a very few days he grew strong. And with delight and inner laughter he said:

"The trick was good. All sorts of frogs
Within my power have passed.
The only question that remains,
Is: How long will they last?"

SMART THE JACKAL

In a part of a forest lived a lion named Thunder-Fang, in company with three counselors, a wolf, a jackal, and a camel, whose names were Meat-Face, Smart, and Spike-Ear. One day he fought with a furious elephant whose sharp-pointed tusk so tore his body that he withdrew from the world.

Then, suffering from a seven-day fast, his body lean with hunger, he said to his famished advisers: "Round up some creature in the forest, so that, even in my present condition, I may provide needed nourishment for you." The moment he issued his orders, they roamed the wood, but found nothing.

Thereupon Smart reflected: "If Spike-Ear here were killed, then we should all be nourished for a few days. However, the master is kept from killing him by friendly feeling. In spite of that, my wit will put the master in a frame of mind to kill him. For, indeed,

> All understanding may be won,
> All things be slain, and all be done,
> If mortals have sufficient wit;
> For me, I make good use of it."

After these reflections, he said to Spike-Ear: "Friend, Spike-Ear, the master lacks wholesome food, and is starving. If the master goes, our death is also a certain thing. So I have a suggestion for your benefit and the master's. Please pay attention." "My good fellow," said Spike-Ear, "make haste to inform me, so that I may unhesitatingly do as you say. Besides, one earns credit for a hundred good deeds by serving his master."

And Smart said: "My good fellow, give your own body at 100 per cent interest, so that you may receive a double body, and the master may prolong his life." On hearing this proposal, Spike-Ear said: "If that is possible, my friend, my body shall be so devoted. Tell the master that this thing should be done. I stipulate only that the Death-God be requested to guarantee the bargain."

Having made their decision, they all went to visit the lion, and Smart said: "O King, we did not find a thing today, and the blessed sun is already near his setting." On hearing this, the lion fell into deep despondency. Then Smart continued: "O King, our friend Spike-Ear makes this proposal: 'If you call upon the Death-God to guarantee the bargain, and if you render it back with 100 per cent of interest, then I will give my body.' " "My good fellow," answered the lion, "yours is a beautiful act. Let it be as you say." On the basis of this pact, Spike-Ear was struck down by the lion's paw, his body was torn by the wolf and the jackal, and he died.

Then Smart reflected: "How can I get him all to myself to eat?" With this thought in his mind, he noticed that the lion's body was smeared with blood, and he said: "Master, you must go to the river to bathe and worship the gods, while I stay here with Meat-Face to guard the food-supply." On hearing this, the lion went to the river.

When the lion was gone, Smart said to Meat-Face: "Friend Meat-Face, you are starving. You might eat some of this camel before the old master returns. I will make your apologies to the master." So Meat-Face took the hint, but had only taken a taste when Smart cried: "Drop it, Meat-Face. The master is coming."

Presently the lion returned, saw that the camel was minus a heart, and wrathfully roared: "Look here! Who turned this camel into leavings? I wish to kill him, too." Then Meat-Face peered into Smart's visage, as much as to say: "Come, now! Say something, so that he may calm down." But Smart laughed and said: "Come, come! You ate the camel's heart all by yourself. Why do you look at me?" And Meat-Face, hearing this, fled for his life, making for another country. But when the lion had pursued him a short distance, he turned back, thinking: "He, too, is unguipugnacious. I must not kill him."

At this moment, as fate would have it, there came that way a great camel caravan, heavily laden, making a tremendous jingling with the bells tied to the camels' necks.

And when the lion heard the jingle of the bells, loud even in the distance, he said to the jackal: "My good fellow, find out what this horrible noise may be."

On receiving this commission, Smart advanced a little in the forest, then darted back, and cried in great excitement: "Run, master! Run, if you can run!"

"My good fellow," said the lion, "why terrify me so? Tell me what it is." And Smart cried: "Master, the Death-God is coming, and he is in a rage against you because you brought untimely death upon his camel, and had him guarantee the bargain. He intends to make you pay a thousand fold for his camel. He has immense pride in his camels. He also plans to make inquiries about the father and grandfathers of that one. He is coming. He is near at hand."

When the lion heard this, he, too, abandoned the dead camel and scampered for dear life. Whereupon Smart ate the camel bit by bit, so that the meat lasted a long time.

THE UNTEACHABLE MONKEY

In a part of a forest was a troop of monkeys who found a firefly one winter evening when they were dreadfully depressed. On examining the insect, they believed it to be fire, so lifted it with care, covered it with dry grass and leaves, thrust forward their arms, sides, stomachs, and chests, scratched themselves, and enjoyed imagining that they were warm. One of the arboreal creatures in particular, being especially chilly, blew repeatedly and with concentrated attention on the firefly.

Thereupon a bird named Needle-Face, driven by hostile fate to her own destruction, flew down from her tree and said to the monkey: "My dear sir, do not put yourself to unnecessary trouble. This is not fire. This is a firefly." He, however, did not heed her warning but blew again, nor did he stop when she tried more than once to check him. To cut a long story short, when she vexed him by coming close and shouting in his ear, he seized her and dashed her on a rock, crushing face, eyes, head, and neck so that she died.

A REMEDY WORSE THAN THE DISEASE

A flock of herons once had their nests on a fig tree in a part of a forest. In a hole in the tree lived a black snake who made a practice of eating the heron chicks before their wings sprouted.

At last one heron, in utter woe at seeing the young ones eaten by a snake, went to the shore of the pond, shed a flood of tears, and stood with downcast face. And a crab who noticed him in this attitude, said: "Uncle, why are you so tearful today?" "My good friend," said the heron, "what am I to do? Fate is against me. My babies and the youngsters belonging to my relatives have been eaten by a snake that lives in a hole in the fig tree. Grieved at their grief, I weep. Tell me, is there any possible device for killing him?"

On hearing this, the crab reflected: "After all, he is a natural-born enemy of my race. I will give him such advice—a kind of true lie—that other herons may also perish. For the proverb says:

> Let your speech like butter be;
> Steel your heart remorselessly:
> Stir an enemy to action
> That destroys him with his faction."

And he said aloud: "Uncle, conditions being as they are, scatter bits of fish all the way from the mungoose burrow to the snake's hole. The mungoose will follow that trail and will destroy the villainous snake."

When this had been done, the mungoose followed the bits of fish, killed the villainous snake, and also ate at his leisure all the herons who made their home in the tree.

MISTER DULY

In a certain city lived a merchant named Ocean. His son picked up a book at a sale for a hundred rupees. In this book was the line: "What's duly his, a man receives."

Now Ocean saw it and asked his son: "My boy, what did you give for this book?" "A hundred rupees," said the son. "Simpleton!" said Ocean, "if you pay a hundred rupees for a book with one line of poetry written in it, how do you calculate to make money? From this day you are not at home in my house." After this wigging, he showed him the door.

This melancholy rebuff drove the young man to another country far away, where he came to a city and stopped there. After some days a native asked him: "Whence are you, sir? What might your name be?" And he replied: "What's duly his, a man receives."

To a second inquirer he gave the same reply. Then on all who questioned him, he bestowed his stereotyped answer. This is how he came by his nickname of Mister Duly.

Now a princess named Moonlight, who was in the first flush of youth and beauty, stood one day with a girl friend, looking out over the city. At that spot a prince, extraordinarily handsome and charming, chanced to come—it was fate's doing—within her range of vision. The moment she saw him, she was smitten by the arrows of Love, and said to her friend: "Dear girl, you must make an effort to bring us together this very day."

So the friend went straight to him and said: "Moonlight sent me to you. She sends you this message: 'The sight of you has reduced me to the last extremity of love. If you do not hasten to me, I shall die, nothing less.' "

On hearing this, he said: "If I cannot avoid the trip, please tell me how to get into the house." And the friend said: "When night comes, you must climb up a stout strap that will be hanging from an upper story of the palace." And he replied: "If you have it all settled, I will do my part." With this understanding the girl returned to Moonlight.

But when night came, the prince thought it over:

"A Brahman-slayer, so they say,
Is he who tries to house
With teacher's child, or wife of friend,
Or royal servant's spouse.

And again:

A deed that brings dishonor,
Whereby a man must fall,
That causes disadvantage,
Don't do it—that is all."

So after full reflection he did not go to her. But Mister Duly was roaming through the night and spied a strap hanging down the wall of a fine stucco house. Out of curiosity mingled with bravado he took hold and climbed.

Now the princess, being perfectly confident that he was the right man, treated him with high consideration, giving him a bath, a meal, a drink, fine garments, and the like. Then she went to bed with him, and her limbs thrilled with joy at touching him. But she said: "I fell in love with you at first sight, and have given you my person. I shall never have another husband, even mentally. Why don't you realize this and talk to me?" And he replied: "What's duly his, a man receives."

When she heard this, her heart stopped beating, and she sent him down the strap in a hurry. So he made for a tumble-down temple and went to sleep. Presently a policeman who had an appointment with a woman of easy virtue arrived there and found him asleep. As the policeman wished to hush the matter up, he said: "Who are you?" and the other answered: "What's duly his, a man receives."

When he heard this, the policeman said: "This temple is deserted. Go and sleep in my bed." And he agreed, but made a blunder, lying down in the wrong bed. In that bed lay the policeman's daughter, a big girl named Naughty, beautiful and young. She had made a date with a man she loved, and when she saw Mister Duly, she thought: "Here is my sweetheart." So, her blunder due to the pitchy darkness of the night, she rose, gave herself in marriage by the ceremony used in heaven, then lay with him in bed, her lotus-eyes and lily-face ablossom. But she said: "Even yet you do not talk nicely with me. Why not?" And he replied: "What's duly his, a man receives."

On hearing this, she thought: "This is what one gets for being careless." So she gave gave him a sorrowful scolding and sent him packing.

As he walked along a business street, there approached a bridegroom named Fine-Fame. He came from another district and marched with a great whanging of tom-toms. So Mister Duly joined the procession. Since the happy moment was near at hand, the bride, a merchant's daughter, was standing in the door of her father's house near the highway. She stood on a raised step under an awning provided for the occasion, and displayed her wedding finery.

At this moment an elephant reached the spot, running amuck. He had killed his driver, had got beyond control, and the crowd was in a hubbub, everyone scared out of his wits. When the bridegroom's parade caught a glimpse of him, they ran—the bridegroom, too—and started for the horizon.

In this crisis Mister Duly perceived the girl, all alone, her eyes dancing with terror, and with the words: "Don't worry. I will save you," manfully reassured her, put his right arm around her, and with enormous sangfroid gave the elephant a cruel scolding. And the elephant—it was fate's doing—actually went away.

Presently Fine-Fame appeared with friends and relatives, too late for the wedding; for another man was holding his bride's hand. At the sight of his rival, he said: "Come, father-in-law! This is hardly respectable. You promised your daughter to me, then gave her to another man." "Sir," said the father-in-law, "I was frightened by the elephant, and I ran too. I came back with you gentlemen, and do not know what has been going on."

Then he turned and questioned his daughter: "My darling girl, what you have done is scarcely the thing. Tell me what this business means." And she replied: "This man saved me from deadly peril. So long as I live, no man but him shall hold my hand."

When the story got abroad, dawn had come. And as a great crowd gathered in the early morning, the princess heard the story of events and came to the spot. The policeman's daughter also, hearing what passed from lip to lip, visited the place. And the king in turn, learning of the gathering of a great crowd, arrived in person, and said to Mister Duly: "Speak without apprehension. What sort of business is this?" And Mister Duly said: "What's duly his, a man receives." Then the princess remembered, and she said: "This law not even God can break." Then the policeman's daughter said: "My heart is not surprised, nor grieves." And hearing all this, the merchant's daughter said: "For what is mine, no strangers take."

Then the king promised immunity to one and all, arrived at the truth by piecing their narratives together, and ended by respectfully giving Mister Duly his own daughter, together with a thousand villages. Then he bethought himself that he had no son, so he anointed Mister Duly crown prince. And the crown prince, together with his family, lived happily; for means of enjoyment were provided in great variety.

HANG-BALL AND GREEDY

In a certain town lived a bull named Hang-Ball. From excess of male vigor he abandoned the herd, tore the river-banks with his horns, browsed at will on emerald-tipped grasses, and went wild in the forest.

In that forest lived a jackal named Greedy. One day he sprawled at ease with his wife on a sandy river-bank. At that moment the bull Hang-Ball came down to the same stretch of sand for a drink. And the she-jackal said to her husband when she saw the hanging testicles: "Look, my dear! See how two lumps of flesh hang from that bull. They will fall in a moment, or a few hours at most. So you must follow him, please."

"My dear," said the jackal, "nobody knows. Perhaps they will fall some day, perhaps not. Why send me on a fool's errand? I would rather stay here with you and eat the mice that come to water. They follow this trail. And if I should follow him, somebody else would come here and occupy the spot. Better not do it. You know the proverb:

If any leave a certain thing,
For things uncertain wandering,
The sure that was, is sure no more;
What is not sure, was lost before."

"Come," said she, "you are a coward, satisfied with any little thing. You are quite wrong. We always ought to be energetic, a man especially. There is a saying:

Depend on energetic might,
And banish indolence's blight,
Let enterprise and prudence kiss—
All luck is yours—it cannot miss.

And again:

Let none, content with fate's negation,
Sink into lazy self-prostration:
No oil of sesame, unless
The seeds of sesame you press.

And as for your saying: 'Perhaps they will fall, perhaps not,' that, too, is wrong. Remember the proverb:

Mere bulk is naught. The resolute
Have honor sure:
God brings the plover water. Who
Dare call him poor?

Besides, I am dreadfully tired of mouse-flesh, and these two lumps of meat are plainly on the point of falling. You must not refuse me."

So when he had listened to this, he left the spot where mice were to be caught and followed Hang-Ball. Well, there is wisdom in the saying:

Only while he does not hear
Woman's whisper in his ear,
Goading him against his will,
Is a man his master still.

And again:

In action, should-not is as should,
In motion, cannot is as can,
In eating, ought-not is as ought,
When woman's whispers drive a man.

So he spent much time wandering with his wife after the bull. But they did not fall. At last in the fifteenth year, in utter gloom he said to his wife:

"Loose they are, yet tight;
Fall, or stick, my dear?
I have watched them now
Till the fifteenth year.

Let us draw the conclusion that they will not fall in the future either, and return to the old mouse-trail."

THE BRAHMAN'S GOAT

In a certain town lived a Brahman named Friendly who had undertaken the labor of maintaining the sacred fire. One day in the month of February, when a gentle breeze was blowing, when the sky was veiled in clouds and a drizzling rain was falling, he went to another village to beg a victim for the sacrifice, and said to a certain man: "O sacrificer, I wish to make an offering on the approaching day of the new moon. Pray give me a victim." And the man gave him a plump goat, as prescribed in Scripture. This he put through its paces, found it sound, placed it on his shoulder, and started in haste for his own city.

Now on the road he was met by three rogues whose throats were pinched with hunger. These, spying the plump creature on his shoulder, whispered together: "Come now! If we could eat that creature, we should have the laugh on this sleety weather. Let us fool him, get the goat, and ward off the cold."

So the first of them changed his dress, issued from a by-path to meet the Brahman, and thus addressed that man of pious life: "O pious Brahman, why are you doing a thing so unconventional and so ridiculous? You are carrying an unclean animal, a dog, on your shoulder. Are you ignorant of the verse:

> The dog and the rooster,
> The hangman, the ass,
> The camel, defile you:
> Don't touch them, but pass?"

At that the Brahman was mastered by anger, and he said: "Are you blind, man, that you impute doghood to a goat?" "O Brahman," said the rogue, "do not be angry. Go whither you will."

But when he had traveled a little farther, the second rogue met him and said: "Alas, holy sir, alas! Even if this dead calf was a pet, still you should not put it on your shoulder. For the proverb says:

> Touch not unwisely man or beast
> That lifeless lie;
> Else, gifts of milk and lunar fast
> Must purify."

Then the Brahman spoke in anger: "Are you blind, man? You call a goat a calf." And the rogue said: "Holy sir, do not be angry. I spoke in ignorance. Do as you will."

But when he had walked only a little farther through the forest, the third rogue, changing his dress, met him and said: "Sir, this is most improper. You are carrying a donkey on your shoulder. Yet the proverb tells you:

> If you should touch an ass—be it
> In ignorance or not—

You needs must wash your clothes and bathe,
To cleanse the sinful spot.

Pray drop this thing, before another sees you."

So the Brahman concluded that it was a goblin in quadruped form, threw it on the ground, and made for home, terrified. Meanwhile, the three rogues met, caught the goat, and carried out their plan.

THE ASS IN THE TIGER-SKIN

There was once a laundryman named Clean-Cloth in a certain town. He had a single donkey who had grown very feeble from lack of fodder.

As the laundryman wandered in the forest, he saw a dead tiger, and he thought: "Ah, this is lucky. I will put this tiger-skin on the donkey and let him loose in the barley fields at night. For the farmers will think him a tiger and will not drive him out."

When this was done, the donkey ate barley to his heart's content. And at dawn the laundryman took him back to the barn. So as time passed, he grew plump. He could hardly squeeze into the stall.

But one day the donkey heard the bray of a she-donkey in the distance. At the mere sound he himself began to bray. Then the farmers perceived that he was a donkey in disguise, and killed him with blows from clubs and stones and arrows.

Kashmiri Tales

translated by J. Hinton Knowles

While he traveled in India as a missionary toward the end of the nineteenth century, the Reverend J. Hinton Knowles began collecting local legends and anecdotes. The following narratives come from his book Folk-Tales of Kashmir.

THE HUNGRY PEASANT

One morning a peasant started off for his work with ten chapatis, his day's allowance, tied up in his loin-cloth. He had not proceeded very far from the house when he felt very hungry, and therefore sat down to eat. One, two, three, four chapatis disappeared, but he was not satisfied. Four, five, six, seven, eight chapatis were eaten; still he was hungry. However, he rose up and walked on.

"What shall I do?" he thought. "I ought not to eat all these chapatis before commencing my work. If I do, what will there be left for the rest of the day? And yet my stomach is not full."

Such reasonings, however, proved in vain. Hunger got the better of the argument, and the peasant sat down again and finished off the other two chapatis, and then felt happy.

"Alas!" said he, "what a fool I was not to have eaten these last two chapatis first of all! There would then have been eight in my loin-cloth for the rest of the day. Now I shall perish from hunger."

The foolish fellow thought that the first eight chapatis had not in the least helped to satisfy his hunger.

COUNTING HEADS

Ten peasants were standing on the side of the road weeping. They thought that one of their number had been lost on the way, as each man had counted the company, and found them nine only.

"Ho, you! what is the matter?" asked a townsman passing by.

"Oh, sir," said the peasants, "we were ten men when we left the village, but now we are only nine."

The townsman saw at a glance what fools they were; each of them had omitted to count himself in the number. He therefore told them to take off their caps and place them on the ground. This they did, and counted ten of them, whereupon they supposed they were all there, and were comforted. But they could not tell how it was.

SECOND THOUGHTS

A peasant was constantly praying to God to give him a horse. One day, while out walking, he cried aloud, "O God, grant me a horse!" when a Pathan appeared riding on a mare, that gave birth to a foal just as it reached him. As the foal could not immediately follow its mother, the tyrannical Pathan forced the peasant to carry it along after him to his house. When he arrived at the place he was so tired with his load that he changed his mind, and cried, "O God, I thank Thee for answering my prayer by giving me this foal, but pardon me if I return it. I do not want a horse now." Thus saying, he threw down the beast on the ground and departed.

PROVERBS

A certain course for hell to steer,
Become a chaplain for a year;
Or try more expeditious ways—
Become an abbot for three days.
—PANCHATANTRA

The man has constant vigor? Dares
On others' backs to mount?
Speaks in a self-sufficient tone?
He has a bank account.—PANCHATANTRA

Proceed in pure straightforwardness
With Brahmans, with the gods no less,
With teachers, with yourself; but treat
All other creatures to deceit.—PANCHATANTRA

A hermit mastering his soul
May see life simple, see it whole;
Not those who thirst for carnal things,
Nor, most particularly, kings.
—PANCHATANTRA

Blind folly always has to pay
For giving property away.—PANCHATANTRA

OUTSMARTING HIMSELF

It was in the month of October, when a man from the villages came to the city to sell his cotton. It was his first visit. As he walked through the bazar he noticed the goldsmiths constantly putting gold ornaments into the fire, and then selling them directly afterwards. Thought he, "There must be some trick in this. I will do the same. Why should I wander all over the place to sell my cotton when I can thus command purchasers?" So he went to a blacksmith's shop and threw his basket of cotton into the furnace and then waited. Of course the cotton was destroyed.

MONEY MAKES MONEY

There is a saying in Srinagar City, "Rupees come to rupees," which is equivalent to the English, "Money makes money."

Once upon a time a stupid peasant heard this saying, and understanding it literally, went to a money-changer's shop, where he saw two or three piles of silver and copper, and put a rupee in one of the chinks of the wall, saying, "Come, come, rupees, to my rupee." In his excitement the foolish man put the rupee in so far that it tumbled down inside the shop, and was counted among the money-changer's money, whereupon he wept and went home.

Some time afterwards he met the person who had quoted the saying to him, and told him how he had proved the falsity of it.

"Not at all," said the man. "I spoke correctly. Your rupee went to the money-changer's rupees. They, being the more, had the greater power."

THE MAN FROM SHIRAZ

A long time ago a Shirazi visited Kashmir, and called on an old friend, and stayed with him for three days. This friend, who prided himself on his hospitality, prepared a great feast for his guest. During dinner he naturally looked for some expression of approval from him, and the Shirazi, seeing that he was expected to say something complimentary, after a little while remarked that the dinner was good, very good, but not for a moment to be compared with the feasts given in his country. Other conversation followed, and then the company dispersed.

The host, however, was so disappointed at the Shirazi friend's modified commendation of the dinner that he could not sleep. All through the long night he was endeavouring to smother his feelings, or planning for a still larger and more extravagant dinner on the morrow; and long before daylight he ran and called the cook, and gave him such an order, and explained everything so minutely to him, that his guest might at least say that the dinner was equal to the meals prepared in his country. If it was a success he promised to give the cook ten rupees bakhshish. But it was not a success. All the expense and all these preparations were again in vain. The feast was declared to be inferior to those in Shiraz. Not that it was owing to any fault of the cook. On the contrary, no feast could have been cooked or served up better than this one.

The Kashmiri, now suspecting that his cuisinier was not so skilful as he thought him to be, engaged another servant in his place, whom he ordered to prepare a still more elaborate meal for the following day, and promised the man twenty rupees if the dinner was thoroughly approved of by the guest. However, there came the same reply—"My dear friend, your feasts cannot match those which are served up in my country."

Some years elapsed, and the Kashmiri, being a traveller as well as his guest, found himself in the city of the Shirazi, and seeking out his old friend's house, called on him. He received a very hearty welcome, and was asked to tarry there for three days, with which he complied. After ablutions and a change of garments he sat down to smoke the pipe of friendship and peace, while dinner was being prepared. He waited with much expectation and curiosity to see what kind of a dinner it would be. "I shall now see," thought he, "in what respect these Shirazi feasts are superior to ours." At last dinner was served. Imagine the chagrin and surprise of the Kashmiri when he saw simply a large tray of boiled rice, dotted here and there with bits of vegetable, placed before him. At first he thought it must be a dream, and rubbed his eyes to make quite certain that he was awake. Still the same tray of rice and vegetables was before him. He rubbed his eyes again; he cracked his fingers; he stretched his legs. Still there was the same tray. There was no doubt about it. These rice and vegetables were all that his host had prepared for that evening's meal. Perhaps this meagre display was owing to the lateness of the hour of his call, and that on the morrow a grander dinner would be provided. The morrow came, and the third day, and still the same fare was provided. During the last meal the Kashmiri could not refrain from asking the reason of his friend's remark concerning the inferiority of Kashmiri to Shirazi feasts. The host replied, "Well, we here in Shiraz are very plain folk. We welcome you to our country and homely fare. You see us. You have dined with us. Yesterday, today, and for ever this is our manner of life. But the feast you provided in honour of my coming (I thank you for it) was special only for a day. Man could not always live at that rate; for the pocket of the host would soon be emptied and the stomach of the guest impaired—the result to both would be most unpleasant. Hence my remarks, of which I am quite certain you will perceive the truth."

HOW THE WICKED SONS WERE DUPED

A very wealthy old man, imagining that he was on the point of death, sent for his sons and divided his property among them. However, he did not die for several years afterwards; and miserable years many of them were. Besides the weariness of old age, the old fellow had to bear with much abuse and cruelty from his sons. Wretched, selfish ingrates! Previously they vied with one another in trying to please their father, hoping thus to receive more money, but now they had received their patrimony, they cared not how soon he left them—nay, the sooner the better, because he was only a needless trouble and expense. This, as we may suppose, was a great grief to the old man.

One day he met a friend and related to him all his troubles. The friend sympathised very much with him, and promised to think over the matter, and call in a little while and tell him what to do. He did so; in a few days he visited the old man and put down four bags full of stones and gravel before him.

"Look here, friend," said he. "Your sons will get to know of my coming here today, and will inquire about it. You must pretend that I came to discharge a long-standing debt with you, and that you are several thousands of rupees richer than you thought you were. Keep these bags in your own hands, and on no account let your sons get to them as long as you are alive. You will soon find them change their conduct towards you. Salam. I will come again soon to see how you were getting on."

When the young men got to hear of this further increase of wealth they began to be more attentive and pleasing to their father than ever before. And thus they continued to the day of the old man's demise, when the bags were opened, and found to contain only stones and gravel!

ANECDOTES

translated by A. S. P. Ayyar

JANAKI'S SILVER PLATE

In a Hindu family there were five daughters-in-law. Four of these were from poor families. But the fifth, Janaki, was the daughter of a judge and was made much of by the mother-in-law, the sister-in-law and the neighbours. One day, a rich lady visited the family. According to custom, the lady visitor has to be given betel and nuts, and the ladies of the family have to sit with her and chew. In the case of poor people the betel leaves, quick-lime, nuts and spices are brought on a wickerwork plate. The lower middle class use brass plates, and the upper middle class silver plates. The very rich use even gold plates.

That day, as soon as the lady visitor took her seat in the drawing room there was a wild search for Janaki's silver plate. The mother-in-law and the daughters-in-law ransacked every corner of the house, and yet it could not be found. Room after room was searched, but to no purpose. The maid servant was questioned but replied that she had not seen it. The visitor was left to herself while this vigorous search went on. At first, she mildly remonstrated with the mother-in-law that they need not bother about the silver plate since a brass plate was quite enough for her. But the proposal was turned down with a curt, 'What, bring betel on a brass plate to you! If you don't care for your dignity, we do,' and the old lady pronounced the word 'brass' in such a withering tone of contempt that if the poor metal had been present it would have wept for very shame. The visitor had perforce to keep silent for some time, but, after patiently waiting for fifteen minutes and yawning at least a dozen times, she went to the mother-in-law and said, 'It must have been misplaced somewhere. Why worry now? Bring the things on a brass plate and let us have a good chat.'

'But,' said the mother-in-law, 'suppose the plate has been stolen!' and a veritable look of horror came on her face.

'What fine flowers it had!' said the eldest daughter-in-law.

'And the dragons!' said the second, 'weren't they lovely?'

'Such a polished surface I have never seen,' said the third.

'It was a regular masterpiece,' said the fourth.

'It must have cost at least a hundred rupees,' said the mother-in-law.

'That is only to be expected, her father being a judge,' said the visitor.

Janaki said nothing, but the visitor thought it natural, for it was not for her to expatiate on her own plate. The fear of the loss of this precious plate made the visitor wait patiently for another fifteen minutes. Then being thoroughly bored by sitting alone, she again approached the mother-in-law and said, 'It must have got mixed up with your innumerable things. I don't believe anybody could have stolen it.'

'I too don't think so,' said the mother-in-law, 'we are careful here, and the maid servant is honest.'

'None would steal it, were it only for the fear of Janaki's father, the judge,' said Seetha, the first daughter-in-law and the person who had conducted the search most vigorously.

'Nobody has stolen it,' said Janaki.

'Then, for Heaven's sake, bring the things on a brass plate and let us chew and chat to our hearts' content,' said the visitor. 'Even if it has been stolen, her father can afford to give her another plate.'

The mother-in-law agreed now. The things were brought on a brass plate. The ladies chewed and chatted for two hours, and then the visitor departed leaving her hostesses in the best of spirits and hoping that the silver plate would be found soon.

The next week, Seetha, as the representative of her family, paid a return visit, the mother-in-law being unable to go and having deputed her for this purpose. The very first question the rich lady asked Seetha was whether Janaki's silver plate had been found.

'No,' replied Seetha, 'but we hope to get it in a month.'

'Why, was it stolen?' asked the lady sympathetically. 'Is it in some court now?'

'No,' replied Seetha.

'Then what became of it?' asked the lady in surprise.

'It never existed,' was the astounding reply.

'Then why did you all search for it so long and describe it so minutely? And how will you get it in a month?' asked the rich lady in bewilderment.

'We searched for it,' said Seetha, 'as it would not look nice if a daughter of a judge had not got a silver plate. And since the father had not yet had the generosity to give one we were forced by our mother-in-law to invent one. The prolonged search and the minute descriptions were intended to make you fully believe in its existence and to give Janaki's father an exact idea of the plate he was expected to give. Janaki has now made her father place an order for it. We shall get it in a month. Your visit has done the trick!'

MY ALL TO THE POOR

A big merchant in a famous seaport of a small Hindu kingdom in ancient days was on his deathbed. Several poor people had assembled in the compound of his house in the expectation of receiving small presents. The big merchant caused them all to be summoned to his bedside and said in a voice broken by tears and sobs, 'Friends, I have been a great sinner all my life. I forgot God and the poor. After deep deliberation I have resolved to give my all to the poor.' The atmosphere resounded with the shouts of joy of the assembled poor and the heart-rending cries of the merchant's four sons who had been disinherited by this declaration. The merchant asked his sons to cease weeping. 'Do not weep so bitterly. It is all for the best. My gift to the poor will never make your position worse in any respect. I began with nothing, but have lived all my life in luxury. So you also will do well to begin with clean slate,' said he.

The news of the legacy spread like wild fire in the town, and three thousand poor assembled and marched to the palace, and put in a petition to the king to recognize them as the sole heirs of the merchant. 'He has given us his all, and we want his all,' declared they. The sons protested, but their protests were overruled as the merchant had not ancestral property, and so his property, being self-acquired, could be disposed of in any way he liked. The king therefore passed a decree transferring all the assets and liabilities of the merchant to the three thousand poor in equal shares. There was wild rejoicing among those poverty-stricken creatures, and they blessed the merchant and prayed for his instant death and perpetual salvation.

Three hours after the decree was passed, the merchant died. When the king's officers looked up his accounts, it was found that he had left assets of Rs. 30,000 and debts amounting to Rs. 150,000. The creditors clamoured for full payment. The three thousand poor, the legates, began to melt away on hearing that the merchant's all meant net liabilities amounting to Rs. 120,000, but the king forced them all to take up the legacy. Each poor man was forced to pay up forty rupees to the creditors, or, if he had no money, to work for the creditors free till this debt of forty rupees was discharged. Too late, the unfortunate creatures realized the meaning of the words 'It is all for the best.'

MENTAL GYMNASTS

An Englishman asked an Indian friend, 'I say, what a waste of energy it is to talk about monism, dualism, qualified monism and what not, as you Indians do. Of what earthly use is it all?'

'Don't you admire the climbers of Everest?' asked the Indian.

'Ah,' said the Englishman, warming up, 'what doubt is there? What a grand spirit!'

'Well,' said the Indian, 'what a waste of energy, all this climbing up of hills and peaks in which you Europeans delight. Of what earthly use is it all? No crops grow on the tops of these peaks.'

'But it is the conquest of Nature by man,' replied the Englishman. 'Exactly,' said the Indian, 'so is the thing you object to in India. You are physical gymnasts. So you climb up peaks. We are mental gymnasts. So we climb up ideas.'

KESAVAN THE SIMPLE

A simple landlord, nicknamed Kesavan the Simple, lived in an interior village in Malabar. He had a servant called Rama. One morning, the servant did not turn up at the usual hour. A passerby told Kesavan that he had heard that either Rama or his brother had died the previous night. The next day, the servant turned up for his work.

Kesavan, in order to set his doubt at rest, asked him, "Rama, is it you or your brother who died?" . . .

One day, Kesavan wanted to give delicious milk porridge to some European friends. He had not entertained Europeans before. He had only a vague idea that everything had to be served to them in plates and crockery. So, he went to a shop in the nearest town, and inspected the crockery stock there. A chamber pot with lid fascinated him. He did not know its real use, and bought it for serving the porridge. He bought also a number of fine cups and saucers.

As soon as the guests were assembled, neat crockery cups and saucers, of Dresden china, were placed before them. But, they rose like one man, in disgust, and fled when they saw a big chamber pot being brought, and an attempt made to take out its contents for being served to them. Kesavan was scandalised at the abrupt departure of his guests, and learnt the reason for it only a few days later. He went and apologised to them all, saying, "Just as you never dreamt that I would use a pot like that for such a purpose I, too, never dreamt that you would use a pot like that for such a purpose."

THE KING'S REVIEW

It was a custom in an ancient Hindu kingdom that a king should on his coronation day review the army in order to find out whether it was keeping up its ancient courage and efficiency. Kirtivarman held the usual coronation day review in the way laid down by custom and precedent. He picked out a soldier at random and asked him to climb up a tree forty feet high and jump down. Without the slightest hesitation, the soldier did as he was ordered, and so met with instant death. The king gave a handsome pension to the deceased man's wife and relations for life, ordered for the dead soldier a cremation with full military honours, announced that the soldiers retained all their ancient courage and efficiency, and declared the review over. A foreign visitor was shocked at the seemingly cruel order of the king and told him that the whole thing was barbarous in the extreme. 'No,' replied Kirtivarman, 'this is not more barbarous than war in general. War implies implicit obedience to command, undaunted bravery, and readiness to die at a moment's notice. All these were tested now by selecting one man at random, and his relations are rewarded. Some kings indulge in bloody wars involving the loss of countless lives in order to keep their soldiers fit. I keep my soldiers fit by an occasional sacrifice of one life. So long as the demon of war remains, this is inevitable.'

THE UNFAILING DEVICE

Brahman priests must bathe before officiating at ceremonies. Sometimes, these ceremonies begin at 5 A.M., and in the rainy season to bathe before that hour is very trying. Padmanabh was a priest who did not like a cold plunge early in the morning. One day, in midwinter, he had to attend a ceremony at 5 A.M. It was bitter cold. So

Padmanabh just rubbed his body with a wet cloth instead of bathing by immersion, as required by the sastras, and, putting on his caste-mark, went to perform the ceremony. Some people had their suspicions about him and asked him whether he had bathed. 'I bathed ten minutes ago,' said Padmanabh. They felt his hair and found it dry. The lying priest was driven out, and another priest engaged.

Some days later, Padmanabh had an engagement in another house. This time he took greater precautions. He sprinkled water on his hair also and went to perform the ceremony. Again, some people suspected him and asked him whether he had bathed. 'Yes, see my hair,' said Padmanabh. Some urchins thrust their fingers under his hair and said, 'Look, the scalp is bone dry. He has merely sprinkled water on his hair.' Padmanabh was again driven out ignominiously, and another priest engaged. Poor Padmanabh unburdened his soul of his woes to a friend and said, 'What shall I do? Do what I will, I am found out. Is there any unfailing device which I can adopt?'

'Yes,' said the friend; 'bathe, then you will never be caught.'

THE SARDARS

[A community called sardars are often butts of humor.] Once two sardars went to Delhi at night. The moon was full. One said, "Hey, look at the sun." The other said, "That isn't the sun. It's the moon." They kept arguing until a third sardar came along. "What do you think it is?" they asked him. "The sun or the moon?" He replied, "Friends, I am new to this city, so I can't say anything."

POETRY

The Indian gift for acerbic wit and biting satire is seen in the following poems to extend unbroken from the time of the ancient Panchatantra *and* Jataka *(tales of former lives of the Buddha) down to the present. Professor Arthur W. Ryder's translation of verses from the* Panchatantra *exhibits his wit and skill as well as those of the original authors. He has not changed the content of the poems but has made even more satisfying their satiric commentary on such universal themes as greed, money, old age, and women by his felicitous transformation of the Sanskrit into pungent English. The* Jataka *poem translated by H. T. Francis is another treatment of a favorite subject, the evils of womankind.*

The contemporary verses, written in English, employ modern poetic techniques to comment on Indian subjects. G. S. Sharat Chandra teaches English literature in the United States, while M. P. Bhaskaran teaches English at an Indian university.

CONFLICTING INTERESTS

from "Panchatantra" / Arthur W. Ryder

Suppose he minds the king's affairs,
The common people hate him;
And if he plays the democrat,
The prince will execrate him.

So, since the struggling interests
Are wholly contradictory,
A manager is hard to find
Who gives them both the victory.

GREED

from "Panchatantra" / Arthur W. Ryder

Some eat the countries; these are kings;
The doctors, those whom sickness stings;
The merchants, those who buy their things;
And learned men, the fools.

The married are the clergy's meat;
The thieves devour the indiscreet;
The flirts their eager lovers eat;
  And Labor eats us all.

DOUBTS

from "Panchatantra" / Arthur W. Ryder

When a poem or daughter comes out,
The author is troubled with doubt,
  With a doubt that his questions betray;
Will she reach the right hands?
Will she please as she stands?
And what will the critics say?

WOMEN

from "Panchatantra" / Arthur W. Ryder

Learn science with the gods above
  Or imps in nether space,
Yet women's wit will rival it;
  How keep them in their place?

Behold the faults with women born:
Impurity, and heartless scorn,
Untruth, and folly, reckless heat,
Excessive greediness, deceit.

Be not enslaved by women's charm,
Nor wish them growth in power to harm:
Their slaves of manly feeling stripped,
Are tame, pet crows whose wings are clipped.

Honey in a woman's words,
  Poison in her breast:
So, although you taste her lip,
  Drub her on the chest.

This palace filled with vice, this field where sprouts
Suspicion's crop, this whirling pool of doubts,
This town of recklessness, sin's aggregate,
This house where frauds by hundreds lie in wait,
This basketful of riddling sham and quip

O'er guessing which our best and bravest trip,
This woman, this machine, this nectar-bane—
Who set it here, to make religion vain?

A bosom hard is praised, a forehead low,
A fickle glance, a mumbling speech and slow,
Thick hips, a heart that constant tremors move,
A natural twist in hair, and twists in love.
Their virtues are a pack of vices. Then
Let beasts adore the fawn-eyed things, not men.

For reasons good they laugh or weep;
They trust you not, your trust they keep;
These graveyard urns, oh, haunt them not!
Keep kin and conduct free from spot.

A wife forever nagging
  And falling in a rage,
Is not a wife, say sages,
  But premature old age.

Therefore with patient effort
  Avoid the very name
Of every earthly woman,
  If comfort be your aim.

For what she feels, she does not say;
She speaks and looks a different way;
Far from her looks her actions veer;
Oh, woman, woman! You are queer.

FOOLS

from "Panchatantra" / Arthur W. Ryder

A hundred counsels, when a life
  Obeys no rigid rule;
A hundred cogent arguments
  Are lost upon a fool.

Perfume offered to a corpse,
Lotus-planting dry,
Weeping in the wood, prolonged
Rain on alkali,
Taking kinks from doggy's tail,

Drawl in deafened ear,
Decking faces of the blind,
Sense for fools to hear.

Your heavy boastings startle, shock,
And make of you a laughingstock;
One marvels if the rabbit plants
A dung-pile like the elephant's.

OLD AGE

from "Panchatantra" / Arthur W. Ryder

Slow, tottering steps the strength exhaust;
The eye unsteady blinks;
From driveling mouth the teeth are lost;
The handsome figure shrinks;
The limbs are wrinkled; relatives
And wife contemptuous pass;
The son no further honor gives
To doddering age. Alas!

MONEY

from "Panachatantra" / Arthur W. Ryder

They may be honored gentlemen,
They may devoted be,
Yet servants leave a monarch who
Forgets the salary.

A king may scold
Yet servants hold,
If he but pay
Upon the day.

After money has departed,
If the wit is frail
Then, like rills in summer weather,
Undertakings fail.

Beggars have, no doubt, their virtues,
Yet they do not flash;
As the world has need of sunlight,
Virtues ask for cash.

Beggars-born less keenly suffer
  Than the men who crash
From a life of comfort to a
  Deficit of cash.

Like the flabby breasts of widows,
  Hopes and wishes rash
Helpless fall upon the bosom,
When there is no cash.

The sun that stuns the eyes that shun,
  In vain he strains to see;
The light so bright is wrapped in night
  By veils of poverty.

No poor man's evidence is heard,
Though logic link it word to word:
While wealthy babble passes muster
Though crammed with harshness, vice, and bluster.

The wealthy, though of meanest birth,
Are much respected on the earth;
The poor whose lineage is prized
Like clearest moonlight, are despised.

The wealthy are, however old,
Rejuvenated by their gold;
If money has departed, then,
The youngest lads are aged men.

Since brother, son, and wife, and friend
Desert when cash is at an end,
Returning when the cash rolls in,
'Tis cash that is our next of kin.

THE WICKED WOMAN (extracts)

from "Jataka" / H. T. Francis

Her husband's absence she approves nor grieves should he depart,
Nor at the sight of his return rejoices in her heart,
She ne'er at any time will say aught in her husband's praise,
Such are the signs that surely mark the wicked woman's ways.

Undisciplined, against her lord some mischief she will plot,
His interest neglects and does the thing that she ought not,

With face averted lies she down beside him, fully dressed,
By such like signs her wickedness is surely thus confessed.

Restless she turns from side to side nor lies one moment still,
Or heaves a long drawn sigh and groans, pretending she is ill,
As if at nature's call from bed she often times will rise,
By such like signs her wickedness a man may recognise.

Perverse in all her acts, she does the thing she should eschew,
And hearkens to the stranger's voice, her favours should he sue,
Her husband's wealth is freely spent some other love to gain,
By signs like these her wickedness to all is rendered plain.

The wealth that by her lord with toil was carefully amassed,
The gear so painfully heaped up, behold, she squanders fast,
With neighbours far too intimate the lady soon will grow,
And by such signs the wickedness of women one may know.

Stepping abroad, behold her how she walks about the streets,
And with the grossest disrespect her lord and master treats;
Nor of adultery stops short, corrupt in heart and mind—
By such like signs how wicked are all womenfolk we find.

Often she will at her own door all decency defy,
And shamelessly expose herself to any passing by,
The while with troubled heart she looks around on every side—
By such like signs the wickedness of women is described.

As groves are made of wood, as streams in curves and windings flow,
So, give them opportunity, all women wrong will go.

Yea, give them opportunity and secrecy withal,
And every single woman will from paths of virtue fall:
Thus will all women wantons prove, should time and place avail,
And e'en with humpback dwarf will sin, should other lovers fail.

Women that serve for man's delight let everyone distrust,
Fickle in heart they ever are and unrestrained in lust,
Ladies of pleasure fitly called, the basest of the base,
To all men such as common are as any bathing place.

[After telling of the sins of women in old-world stories, in yet another way, still speaking of their misdeeds, the Buddha said:]

Poor fickle creatures women are, ungrateful, treacherous they,
No man, if not possessed, would deign to credit aught they say.

Little reck they of duty's call or plea of gratitude,
Insensible to parent's love and ties of brotherhood,
Transgressing every law of right, they play a shameless part,
In all their acts obedient to the wish of their own heart.

However long they dwell with him, though kind and loving be,
Tender of heart and dear to them as life itself may be,
In times of trouble and distress, leave him they will and must,
I for my part in womenfolk can never put my trust.

How often is a woman's mind like shifty monkey's found,
Or like the shade cast by a tree on height or depth around,
How changeful, too, the purpose lodged within a woman's breast,
Like tire of wheel revolving swift without a pause or rest.

Whene'er with due reflection they look round and see their way
To captivate some man of wealth and make of him their prey,
Such simpletons with words so soft and smooth they captive lead,
E'en as Cambodian groom with herbs will catch the fiercest steed.

But if, when looking round with care, they fail to see their way
To get possession of his wealth and make of him a prey,
They drive him off, as one that now has reached the furthest shore,
And cut adrift the ferry boat he needeth nevermore.

Like fierce devouring flame they hold him fast in their embrace,
Or sweep off like stream in flood that hurries on apace;
They court the man they hate as much as one that they adore,
E'en as a ship that hugs alike the near and farther shore.

They not to one or two belong, like open stall are they,
One might as soon catch wind with net as women hold in sway.

Like river, road, or drinking shed, assembly hall or inn,
So free to all are womenfolk, no limits check their sin.
Fell as black serpent's head are they, as ravenous as a fire,
As kine the choicest herbage pick, they lovers rich desire.

From elephant, black serpent, and from flame that's fed on ghee,
From man besprinkled to be King, and women we should flee,
All these whoso is on his guard will treat as deadly foe,
Indeed their very nature it is very hard to know.

Women who very clever are or very fair to view,
And such as many men admire—all these one should eschew:

A neighbour's wife and one that seeks a man of wealth for mate,
Such kind of women, five in all, no man should cultivate.

[Then the narrative proceeds:]

On hearing him, Ananda, the Vulture King, said: "My friend, Kunala, I too by my own powers of knowledge will tell of women's faults." . . .

[And the Buddha proceeds to declare that, at the time he speaks of, Ananda "uttered these stanzas":]

Although a man with all this world contains of golden gear
Should her endow of womankind his heart may count most dear,
Yet, if occasion serves, she will dishonour him withal—
Beware lest thou into the hands of such vile wretches fall.

A manly vigour he may show, from worldly taint be free,
Her maiden wooer may perhaps winsome and loving be,
In times of trouble and distress leave him she will and must,
I for my part in womankind can never put my trust.

Let him not trust because he thinks 'she fancies me, I trow,'
Nor let him trust because her tears oft in his presence flow:
They court the man they hate as much as one that they adore,
Just as a ship that hugs alike the near and farther shore.

Trust not a litter strewn with leaves and branches long ago,
Trust not thy whilom friend, perchance now grown into a foe,
Trust not a King because thou think'st, 'My comrade once was he';
Trust not a woman though she has borne children ten to thee.

Women are pleasure-seekers all and unrestrained in lust,
Transgressors of the moral law; in such put not your trust.
A wife may feign unbounded love before her husband's face;
Distrust her: women common are as any landing-place.

Ready to mutilate or slay, from nothing do they shrink,
And after having cut his throat then e'en blood would drink:
Let no man fix his love on them, creatures of passion base,
Licentious and as common as some Ganges landing-place.

In speech they no distinction make betwixt the false and true,
As kine the choicest herbage pick, rich lovers they pursue.

One man they tempt with looks and smiles, another by their walk,
Some they attract by strange disguise, others by honeyed talk.

Dishonest, fierce and hard of heart, as sugar sweet their words,
Nothing there is they do not know to cheat their wedded lords.

Surely all womenfolk are vile, no limit bounds hteir shame,
Impassioned and audacious they, devouring as a flame.

'Tis not a case of love or hate with womenfolk we see,
It is for gold they hug a man, as parasites a tree.

A man may corpses burn or e'en dead flowers from temples rake,
Be groom of horse or elephant, or care of oxen take,
Yet women after such low castes will run for money's sake.

One nobly born they leave if poor, as 'twere a low outcast,
To such an one, like carrion vile, if rich, they hie them fast.

[After listening to what Ananda had to say on the vices of womenkind, Narada the ascetic is said by the Buddha to have at this point uttered the following stanza:]

Four things can never sated be—list well to these my words—
Ocean, Kings, Brahmins, Womankind, these four, O King of Birds.

All streams in earth that find their home will not the ocean fill,
Though all may with its waters mix, something is lacking still.

A Brahmin cons his Vedas and his legendary lore,
Yet still he sacred knowledge lacks and craves for more and more.

A king by conquest holds the world, its mountains, seas and all,
The endless treasures it contains his very own may call,
Yet sighs for worlds beyond the sea, for this he counts too small.

One woman may have husbands eight, complaisant to her will,
All heroes bold, well competent love's duties to fulfil;
Yet on a ninth her love she sets, for something lacks she still.

Women like flames devour their prey,
Women like floods sweep all away,
Women are pests, like thorns are they,
Women for gold oft go astray.

That man with net might catch the breeze,
Or single-handed bale out seas,
Clap with one hand, who once should dare,
His thoughts let range on woman fair.

With women, clever jades, Truth aye is found a rarity,
Their ways as much perplex as those of fishes in the sea.
Soft-speaking, ill to satisfy, as rivers hard to fill,
Down—down they sink: who women know should flee far from them still.

Seducing traitresses, they tempt the holiest to his fall,
Down—down they sink: who women know should flee afar from all.

And whomsoever they may serve for gold or for desire,
They burn him up as fuel burns cast in a blazing fire.

When Narada had set forth the vices of women, the Great Being once more by special instance illustrated their bad qualities.

ON THE WAY TO MOUNT KAILASH

G. S. Sharat Chandra (b. 1935)

All these sanyasis, naked to the loin,
Their ash smeared skin glowing,
Are not a sign of sacredness
But a farce,
Imbibing in senile and superstitious minds
That gods would be wrathful if the sanyasis
Are not cared for—
They are a hoax my Country,
They stand together in their plot
Against us who occasionally eat two meals.
They want to have one of them.

All these brazen cattle that roam our streets
In the guise of sacredness and eat our wheat
And go unpunished are the other sanyasis
That make a living while others starve.
They are not holy my Country,
But the crafty robbers of our sentiment.
Get rid of these beggars.
That would be more of an absolution
Than the blessing of our gods.

ABOUT TIME

G. S. Sharat Chandra

This is a song about a clock.
It is a noisy song about a clock
That stopped working with the small hand on IX and the big on II
Greenwich time.
The clock was manufactured by the people of the United Soviet Socialist Republic
But that has nothing to do with the song
Only with the clock.
I took it back to Honest Ed's who sold it for $1.99
And Ed referred me to the Department of Clocks, Watches & Bells
Where the salesman wrenched open its back and talked
About cheap clocks that would not stand up to time
And the failure of the Soviets to warranty goods delivered
And advised me to buy a new one rather than have
The Soviet clock fixed because it took parts made only in Japan
And he didn't have any.
I asked him for a good old Canadian clock
And he said there was no such thing and the so called Canadian clocks
Were actually assembled in Switzerland
And Swiss movement was expensive
And while we were thus chatting an alarm went clanging
Couple of birdies popped out of wall clocks and cuckooed
And it was one o'clock American Standard Time
By most of the ding-dongs and tick-tocks and the salesman went for lunch.
Care for a swap?

AT THE PUB

G. S. Sharat Chandra

the way
he sits talking about Zen
in his cool and detached style
downing scotch after scotch after scotch
without taking a leak
almost makes me believe
in the mystic orient.
but the fact
he hasn't been as far east as detroit
forces one to speculate
the fat old buzzard
is just putting it off
  for effect.

NEW YEAR RESOLUTION IN INDIA

M. P. Bhaskaran (20th century)

Mr. A. L. Srinivasan, member of the Central Board of Censors, told the Press Trust of India that "close proximity in love scenes would come in for a rigorous application of the censorship rules."

The Censors are worrying
Why after twenty years of independence
Our morals aren't rising
Appreciably. Poor, underfed, muddled,
Corrupt and at each other's throats we may be,
But throughout our long and glorious history
We've been chaste sexually.
We've led the world in hockey and prudery
And incompetence in high places.
Fret not, countrymen, over the loss of an Olympic crown
But rather strive every nerve to maintain
Our magnificent lead in celluloid virginity.
The Censors will see that lovers keep a proper distance
With not the ghost of a chance
Even to hold hands: let them sigh across the vast spaces
Our culture demands.
They'll approve of plots which put the boy in Bombay
And the girl in the Andaman islands,
And never the twain shall meet until their wedding day.
They'll go a step further, their smile broader
Across their smug and vacant faces, and even recommend
The film for an Akademi prize
If the producer would show the couple sleeping in different rooms
Throughout their blissful married lives.
And they're really hopeful, being what they are,
That in some future year
A genius will arise
Prophesied by astrologers and hailed by Parliament
Who will make a beautiful film with a Government grant
Explaining in psychedelic colour and stereophonic sound
That it is the stork
Brings the
Babies:
Our thirteen million babies
Each year.

HEAD-SHRINKING

Leonora (20th century)

"Ministers may have to consider appointing personal psychiatrists."—FATESINGRAO GAEKWAD, *Gujarat Health Minister*

According to the honourable gentleman's pleading
Ministers head-shrinking may be needing
(No alarm; that's slang for psycho-analysing),
But what he suggests isn't so surprising
For if we do some astute thinking
We'll realise Ministers really need head-shrinking,
For these ordinary guys when to office get wedded
Inexplicably become so swollen-headed!

STORIES AND SKETCHES

A Tale Told by the Buddha (extract)

from "Jataka" / John M. Senaveratna

The following tale is from the Jataka, *a Buddhist work containing 550 birth stories of the Buddha as narrated by himself. A typical Jataka story begins with an introduction that explains the particular circumstances in the Buddha's life which led him to tell this birth story in which he reveals an event in one of his previous existences as a Bodhisattva—that is, a being destined to attain Buddhahood. At the end of the story the Buddha identifies the characters who appeared in the story as animals or human beings. It often turns out that the most sympathetic character, whether animal or human, is actually the Buddha in a previous incarnation, and the villain often proves to be a traditional enemy of spirituality and goodness.*

In the days when Brahmadatta was King of Kasi and had a powerful army, he made war on the Kingdom of Kosala, put to death its King, and carried off his Chief Queen to Benares, and there made her his consort.

At the time of her capture, the Queen was pregnant, and in due time she gave birth to a daughter.

As the King of Kasi had no son or daughter of his own, the event gave him great pleasure, and he was minded to grant her any boon she cared to ask. On his intimation of this to her, she gladly accepted the offer, but deferred, for a later occasion, the choice of the boon she would ask for.

The King agreed. The young Princess was named Kanha.

The time came when she had grown up in stature and beauty, and one day her mother said to her:

"Kanha dear, when you were born, your father offered me a boon, the choice of which I put off for a later day. I am willing to leave it to you now to make the choice. What would you like to ask?"

Excess of passion broke through maidenly modesty and shame, and she said:

"The only thing lacking to me is a husband. Ask him to hold an assembly to enable me to choose one for myself."

The mother explained to the King that this was the boon she chose. And the King, anxious to please her and the daughter as well, had it proclaimed that an assembly would be held in order to select a suitable husband for the Princess.

On the day appointed for the assembly, a large number of men, arrayed in their best, thronged the palace yard. But Kanha, with a basket of flowers in her hand and looking down on the crowd from an upper window, found no one of them suit her fancy.

On that same day, however, there arrived in Benares the five sons of the famous King Pandu. The names of these were Ajjuna, Nakula, Bhimasena, Yudhitthila and Sahadeva.

After going through a course of instruction and training under a famous teacher of Takkasila, they had been touring various countries and cities in order to enlarge their education and experience, and, in the course of that tour, had arrived at Benares on that day.

They found the city in a turmoil, as it were, and inquiry as to the cause revealed what the commotion was about. Tempted to gain this new experience, they came to the Palace courtyard, all five of them, and stood in a row like so many gleaming statues of gold.

The moment Kanha's eyes fell upon them, she fell in love with all five of them, and, turning to her mother who stood by her, she said:

"Mother dear, I choose all five of these men."

The King, when apprised of Princess Kanha's choice, was naturally greatly annoyed. But, remembering his assent to any choice and disinclined to go behind his pledged word, he raised no objection.

He inquired who these five men were, what their parentage was. And on learning that they were the sons of King Pandu, he loaded them with honours and gave Princess Kanha to them as wife.

They took up residence in her seven-storied Palace, and, by the very favour of her passion, she soon won the hearts of them all.

Now, there was in the Palace a hump-backed cripple who served Princess Kanha as an attendant. And with this deformed cripple she soon became illicitly and sinfully intimate, sinning with him whenever the Princes happened to be out of the Palace.

In the flush of her passion for this monstrosity, she said to him one day:

"You are dearer to me than any other. I will kill these Princes and have your feet laved with the blood from their throats."

But when she was alone with the eldest of the royal brothers, what she would say to him was:

"You are dearer to me than any of your four brothers, so much so that I am willing to sacrifice everything, even my life, for your sake. When my father dies, it will be on you alone that I will bestow the kingdom."

And she said the same thing to each of the four others, when she was alone in the company of each.

The result was that all the five Royal brothers were greatly enamoured with her, each one counting on her professed love for him to mount the throne of Kasi in due course.

One day, however, Kanha fell sick, and all of them gathered together to minister to her. Of the five brothers, one sat at the head of the bed, chafing her head, and two on either side, each chafing a hand or leg. The hunchback sat at her feet.

To the eldest of the royal brothers, Ajjuna, who was chafing her head, she made a sign with her head, intending to emphasise, as it were, what she had already assured him of previously, namely:

"You are dearer to me than any of your four brothers. All my life I shall live only for you, and, when my father dies, it will be on you and no other that I will bestow the kingdom."

In this way she strengthened the measure of his love for her.

And, in the same way, and to the same effect, she made signs with hand or foot, to each of the other four Princes.

But to the hunchback, she made a sign with her tongue, intended to intimate to him:

"You are the only one that is dear to me. For your sake only shall I live."

Each one of them, remembering what she had said to him previously, understood the purport of the sign now made to him.

But, while the understanding of the rest of them went no further than realising, each for himself, the implication of the particular sign made to him by her, Prince Ajjuna, who had seen the motions of hand, foot and tongue, thought within himself:

"For me, as for the rest, these signs have a particular meaning, a special significance, for each. And since a sign was made to the hunchback himself, she must have been intimate with this man as well."

Prince Ajjuna beckoned to his brothers and took them outside.

"Did you," he asked them, "see the lady-who-has-five-husbands making a sign to me with her head?"

"We did," they replied.

"Do you know the meaning of it?"

"We do not," said they.

"The meaning of it," said Ajjuna, "was that she said she loved me more than she did any one of you, and that, at her father's death, she would bestow the kingdom on me. Now, I ask you: Do you know the purport, the significance, of the sign she gave each of you with hand or foot?"

"Yes, I know," said each one of them.

"Then you can see for yourself," said Ajjuna, "that the meaning, the purport, of the sign which she gave, not only to each of us but also with her tongue to the hunchback, signified the one and the same thing. As with ourselves, she has been intimate with the hunchback."

"Ridiculous! Impossible!" said the four brothers.

But Ajjuna forthwith had the hunchback brought out to them and questioned him threateningly.

The man related the full story of his amour with the Princess Kanha.

The story amazed them and left them disgusted, rooting out of their hearts whatever affection they had had for her. And in the bitterness of their feelings, they exclaimed:

"Truly, womankind is evil and profligate, lost to all virtue and decency, shameless in wickedness. In spite of having men like ourselves, of noble birth and good fortune, she misbehaves with a disgusting, repulsive monstrosity of a creature like this hunchback. Who that has a spark of wisdom can find any happiness in consorting with this woman, so perverse and so devoid of all shame as Kanha is?"

Condemning womenkind in these and similar terms, the five Princes decided for themselves that they had had enough of married life, and they wended their way into the Himalayan forests, there to abide as recluses for the rest of their lives.

Apaharavarman's Adventure (extract)

Dandin (6th cen.?) / Arthur W. Ryder

Very little is known about Dandin, the author of The Ten Princes, *from which the following two stories are taken. He is thought to have lived shortly before the seventh century A.D., when the actions in the book take place. A young Indian prince, Rajavahana, is brought up at court with nine young companions, all princes. When Rajavahana disappears in the jungle, his nine friends go out to search for him, and their individual adventures form the body of the book.*

Your Majesty, on the day when you plunged into Devils' Hole in order to serve a Brahman, and all your friends set out in search of you, I too roamed the earth. Now I learned from a certain group of gossipers that in the Anga country, on the bank of the Ganges outside the capital Champa, there lived a great sage named Marichi in whom potent austerities had begotten divine insight; and I traveled to that region, desirous of learning from him your whereabouts. In his hermitage I discovered under a baby mango a hermit pale with depression of spirit, from whom I received the attentions due a guest. Then after a moment's rest, I said: "Where is saintly Marichi? I desire to learn from him the route of a friend who had occasion to make a distant journey. The sage has an international reputation for miraculous powers of penetration."

With a deep-drawn, burning sigh he told his tale: "Such a sage there was in this hermitage. To him one day there came in deep dejection a member of the frail sisterhood, named Kamamanjari. She had fairly won her name as gem of the Anga capital, but her breasts were starred with teardrops and her disheveled hair swept the ground as she paid him homage. At the same moment a group of her relatives, headed by the mother, came running compassionately behind her and fell to the ground in a long line before the hermit. That merciful creature consoled them with his liquid tones and asked the courtezan the source of her distress; and she, with seeming shame, despondency, and dignity, replied: 'Holy sir, your servant is a vessel of tribulation in this life, yet, in hope of a blessed resurrection, takes refuge at your holy feet, known as a defense of the afflicted.'

"At this point the mother lifted her hands, touched the earth with hair dappled with grey, lifted her head, and spoke: 'Holy sir, this your maidservant acquaints you with my own wrongdoing. And this wrongdoing of mine lay in the performance of my obvious duty. For obvious duty is as follows for the mother of a fille de joie: care of her daughter's person from the hour of birth; nourishment by a diet so regulated as to develop stateliness, vigor, complexion, intelligence, while harmonizing the humors, gastric calefaction, and secretions; not permitting her to see too much even of her father after the fifth year; festive ritual on birthdays and holy days; instruction in the arts of flirtation, both major and minor; thorough training in dance, song, instrumental music, acting, painting, also judgment of foods, perfumes, flowers, not forgetting writing and graceful speech; a conversational acquaintance with grammar with logical inference and conclusion; profound skill in money-making, sport, and betting on cockfights or chess; assiduous use of go-betweens in the passages of coquetry;

display of numerous well-dressed attendants at religious or secular celebrations; careful selection of teachers to insure success at unpremeditated vocal and other exhibitions; advertising on a national scale by a staff of trained specialists; publicity for beauty-marks through astrologers and such; eulogistic mention in gatherings of men about town of her beauty, character, accomplishments, charm, and sweetness by hangers-on, gay dogs, buffoons, female religionists, and others; raising her price considerably when she has become an object of desire to young gentlemen; surrender to a lover of independent fortune, a philogynist or one intoxicated by seeing her charms, a gentleman eminent for rank, figure, youth, money, vigor, purity, generosity, cleverness, gallantry, art, character, and sweetness of disposition; delivery, with gracious exaggeration of value received, to one less affluent, but highly virtuous and cultivated (the alternative is levying on his natural guardians, after informal union with such a gentleman); collection of bad debts by vamping judge and jury; mothering a lover's daughter; abstraction by ingenious tricks of money left in an admirer's possession after payment for periodical pleasures; steady quarreling with a defaulter or miser; stimulation of the spirit of generosity in an overthrifty adorer by the incentive of jealousy; repulse of the impecunious by biting speeches, by public taunts, by cutting his daughters, and by other embarrassing habits, as well as by simple contempt; continued clinging to the open-handed, the chivalrous, the blameless, the wealthy, with full consideration of the interrelated chances of money and misery.

" 'Besides, a courtezan should show readiness indeed, but no devotion to a lover; and, even if fond of him, she should not disobey mother or grandmother. In spite of all, the girl disregards her God-given vocation and has spent a whole month of amusement—at her own expense!—with a Brahman youth, a fellow from nowhere whose face is his fortune. Her snippiness has offended several perfectly solvent admirers and has pauperized her own family. And when I scolded her and told her: "This is no kind of a scheme. This isn't pretty," she was angry and took to the woods. And if she is obstinate, this whole family will stay right here and starve to death. There is nothing else to do.' And the mother wept.

"Then the hermit spoke to the gay girl: 'My dear young woman, be assured that life in the forest is difficult. Its reward is either final salvation or a period in Paradise. Now of these the former is grounded in profound insight and is, as a rule, hardly attainable; while the latter is easy for anybody who fulfils the duties of his station. You had best resign your visionary ambition and abide by your mother's judgment.'

"But she impatiently rejected this sympathetic counsel, saying: 'If I find no refuge at your holy feet, may the god of fire provide a refuge for my misery.'

"So the hermit, after some reflection, said to the courtezan's mother: 'Go home for a time. Wait a few days, until this delicate creature, wonted to pleasant luxury, grows disgusted with the hardships of life in the forest and, with the aid of repeated homilies from me, returns to normalcy.' And her relatives withdrew, assenting.

"Now the courtezan grudged no devotion to the holy hermit. She wore a neat and simple costume; was not overattentive to ornament; watered the seedling trees; took pains to gather bunches of flowers for ceremonies of worship; made a pleasing variety of offerings; provided perfumes, garlands, incense, lamps, dance, song, and instrumental music in honor of Love's chastiser, Shiva; drew the hermit into corners to discuss the relations of the three things worth living for (virtue, money, and love); and discoursed decorously of the Supreme Being. In a surprisingly short time she had him in love.

"One day, seeing that he was secretly smitten, she said with a little smile: 'Why, the world is a fool even to consider money and love in comparison with virtue.' 'Tell me, my soul,' said Marichi, 'by what percentage you value virtue above money and love.' Thus encouraged, but slow and shy, she began:

" 'A poor, ignorant thing like me! Can I teach a holy hermit the bigness or littleness of virtue, money, and love? Still, your question is just one more kindness to a servant. So listen. Of course, without virtue there isn't any money or love. But virtue without those things gives us blissful felicity, and we can get it by simple introspection. It doesn't depend so much on external instruments, the way money and love do. And if nourished by seeing the real Truth, it isn't hurt if you pursue—just a little, you know—money and love. Or if it is, it is restored without much trouble and you win a special blessing by avoiding that sin in future. For example: Brahma pursued Tilottama, Shiva flirted with sixteen thousand girls, Prajapati offered love even to his own daughter, Indra was Ahalya's paramour, the moon-god fouled his teacher's bed, the sun-god debauched a mare, the wind-god seduced the wife of a monkey, Brihaspati ran after Utathya's wife, Parashara deflowered a fisherman's daughter, his son intrigued with a brother's wife, Atri had dealings with a doe. And when immortals do all those things, such devil's tricks don't injure their virtue, because they have the power of Truth. And when a soul is purified by virtue, dirt never sticks, any more than in the sky. So I feel that money and love don't touch even one per cent of virtue.'

"Having listened to this, the sage felt the tide of passion surge, and he said: 'My pet, you are truly wise: with those who have vision of the Truth, virtue is not shackled by the indulgence of sense. But from birth I have never studied the doctrine of money and love. I ought to learn their nature, attendant conditions, and reward.'

" 'Well,' said she, 'the nature of money is to be earned, multiplied, and saved; its attendant conditions are agriculture, cattle-raising, trade, peace, war, and so forth; its reward is charity to the deserving. Love's nature lies in an exquisite contact with ineffable joy in a man and a woman whose minds concentrate on sense-experience. Its attendant conditions are all that is blissful and blazing in this contact. And its reward is a manifest and self-communicated gladness, intensely delightful, arising from reciprocal tangency, sweet in memory, occasioning self-approbation, supreme. For love's sake, men—even men who live in the most sacred places—endure grievous martyrdoms, great sacrifices of money, terrible battles, sea-voyages, and other fearful dangers.'

"Hereupon, were it constraining destiny, or the woman's smartness, or his own dulness, he forgot his vows and yielded to her fascination. She put the poor booby in a carriage and carried him far away along the splendid public street to her own home in the city. And drums were beaten with the announcement: 'Tomorrow is Love's festival.'

"The next day, when the sage had been bathed and anointed, had assumed a pretty garland, had practiced lovers' manners and so turned his back on his true profession that he grieved if a moment passed without her, she took him along the gaudy public street to a holiday crowd in a wooded garden, where the king sat among hundreds of young ladies. And when the king said with a smile: 'My dear, be seated with His Holiness,' she made a fluttering curtsy, smiled, and sat down.

"Thereupon a most beautiful woman rose, lifted her joined hands, and curtsied to the king, saying: 'Your Majesty, she has won the bet. From this day I am her slave.' Then the crowd raised a racket rooted in wonder and delight. The king too was delighted and dismissed the courtezan with gracious gifts of precious stones in settings and a great train of attendants, while the most eminent ladies of her profession and the most prominent citizens gave her a multitudinous ovation.

"She, however, before going home, said to the sage: 'My duty to you, holy sir. You have put your servant under no transient obligation. You may now resume your vocation.' 'My darling,' he cried, pricked by love as by a knife-point, 'what does it mean? How can you be so cynical? What has become of your superlative fondness for me?'

" 'Holy sir,' she replied with a smile, 'you saw the girl who just confessed defeat before the royal retinue. She and I once had a tiff, and she said with a sneer: "You boast as if you had seduced Marichi." So I wagered my freedom and went into the business. And I won. Thank you so much.'

"Thus cast off, the poor innocent repented and listlessly returned to the woods. And I, dear sir, am the wretched man whom she treated so."

Mitragupta's Adventure (extract)

Dandin / Arthur W. Ryder

There is a country called Trigarta. In it lived three householders with much accumulated capital; they were brothers, and their names were Dhanaka, Dhanyaka, and Dhunyaka. During their lifetime Indra sent no rain for twelve years: the grain drooped; plants failed to seed; trees bore no fruit; the clouds were barren; rivers dwindled; swamps were mere mudholes; many springs went dry; bulbs, roots, and fruit grew scarce; story-telling declined; social pleasures fell into disuse; robber bands multiplied; anthropophagy appeared; human skulls, white as cranes, rolled underfoot; thirsty crows migrated in clouds; cities, villages, towns, and other settlements decayed.

When these householders had exhausted their store of grain, and had eaten in turn the goats and sheep, the drove of buffalo, the herd of cows, the maidservants, the manservants, the children, the eldest and the middle wife, they agreed to eat next day the youngest wife, Dhumini. But Dhunyaka, the youngest brother, unable to eat his darling, fled with her the same night. Carrying her when she grew weary, he plunged into a forest. Relieving her hunger and thirst with his own flesh and blood, he carried her, until in mid-journey he encountered a man writhing on the forest floor, with hands and feet and ears and nose cut off. This man too he charitably took on his shoulder, and in a forest nook abounding in bulbs, roots, and deer he laboriously thatched a hut of leaves, where he lived a long time. He treated the pitiful mutilations with oil of almonds and sesame, and shared his own meat and vegetables equally.

One day, when the wounds were healed and vigor had returned, when Dhunyaka had gone to hunt deer, Dhumini approached the man with sexual desire, and for all his upbraiding, forced him to satisfy her. When her husband returned and asked for water, she tossed him the bucket and rope, saying: "Draw your own drink; my head aches." Then, as he drew water from the well, she gave him a quick push from behind.

She put the cripple on her shoulder and wandered from land to land winning the name of a devoted wife and a variety of honors. Finally she settled down in immense affluence through the favor of His Majesty of Avanti. Presently she learned that her husband, accidentally discovered and rescued by thirsty merchants, was roaming Avanti, begging his bread. So Dhumini deposed that he was the wretch who had mutilated her lord, and had that saintly character condemned by the unwitting king to torture and death.

But when Dhunyaka was being led to execution, his arms bound behind his back—since a prolongation of life was predestined, he cheerfully said to the functionary: "If the beggar whom I am supposed to have mutilated is prepared to speak ill of me, my punishment is deserved." "No harm in trying," said the officer, summoned the cripple, and presented him. That upright fellow wept profusely, fell at the saintly feet, and gave a true relation of the man's charity and the woman's vile behavior. The king, enraged, disfigured the trollop's face and appointed her cook for the dogs, while Dhunyaka became the recipient of his favor. And that is why I say that woman's heart may be callous.

The Tale of Two Bawds

translated by J. A. B. Van Buitenen

Most of the stories in J. A. B. Van Buitenen's Tales of Ancient India, *three of which follow, were translated from material in two Indian collections which are themselves translations and adaptations of a lost original. One of his sources is* Oceans of the Rivers of the Great Romance, *composed in the twelfth century by a Kashmiri Brahman named Somadeva. The other is* Abbreviation in Verse of the Great Romance, *by the eighth-century writer Budhasvamin. Both books were adaptations of* The Great Romance, *by Gunadhya. The original was written not in Sanskrit but in a northwestern Indian dialect; Gunadhya was aiming at merchant readers rather than Brahmans. The ideals emphasized in the book, writes Van Buitenen, "are not the hermit's serenity or the warrior's triumph; they are, frankly and in a civilized way, the ideals of success and acquisition. The age in which Gunadhya wrote was indeed the most successful and the most acquisitive in the history of India. . . ." In northern India, with which most of the tales are concerned, this age extended from the first until the seventh century.*

There is in this country a great, wealthy city which is called Citraketu. In that place once lived a merchant, Ratnavarman, who possessed great riches. He was blessed with a son through the favor of Lord Siva, and hence he gave the boy the name Isvaravarman.[1]

When the eminent merchant, who had only this one son, saw that Isvara had finished his studies and was approaching manhood, he thought: "The Creator has made one creature which is immorality incarnate—in order to rob rich young men who are blinded by their virility—and harlot is its name. I shall entrust my son to a bawd so that he can learn the tricks of harlots and will never be taken in by them."

Having made up his mind, he went with his son Isvara to the house of a procuress called Yamajihva, Tongue-of-Death. He found the heavy-jowled, long-toothed, pug-nosed bawd engaged in teaching her daughter.

"Everybody has his price, daughter, and a prostitute more so. But no price is paid when she falls in love; therefore a harlot must guard against love. Passion is like the dusk: just as the twilight announces the fall of night, so passion is the harbinger of a courtesan's downfall. Like a well-trained actress a harlot must put up a false show. First she must seduce her man, then milk him of his money, and finally, when his money is gone, desert him. But when he has found new money, she receives him back. A true harlot is like a saintly hermit; whether youth, child, or old man, whether handsome or ugly, all are the same to her as to the hermit, and thus both obtain the greatest good."

Ratnavarman approached the bawd while she was instructing her daughter and, when he had been received with due honor, sat down with her.

"You must teach my son the arts of the harlot," he said, "until he is an expert. I shall give you a fee of one thousand pieces of silver." She agreed eagerly, and they struck the bargain. Ratnavarman paid out the silver, committed his son to her care, and went home.

Isvara pursued his studies in Yamajhva's house for one year, after which he returned to his father's house. He was sixteen years old.

"Money," he declared, "brings merit and love. Money brings honor. Money brings fame."

"So it does indeed," agreed his father and gave him a fortune of fifty million. The merchant's son took his fortune, and on an auspicious day he joined a caravan and departed for Sumatra to trade. He journeyed by land and eventually reached a city called Goldtown. The young man set up quarters in a grove just outside the city, where he had a bath, massaged his skin, and took his meal. Thereupon he entered the city and went to a temple to see a play. At the performance he saw a courtesan, Sundari, who gave a dance—she was a wave of the ocean of beauty swept up by the wind of elegance. As soon as he set eyes on her, his mind was so full of her that the procuress's lessons were piqued and withdrew.

He sent a friend to her after the dance to make a proposition. She agreed with a bow: "I am favored!" Isvara posted reliable watchmen in his quarters to guard his treasures and himself went to stay at Sundari's house. There the girl's mother, Makarakati, welcomed him with all the amenities of the house which were proper at that hour.

When evening fell, Sundari took him to her own room, where a bed was made up on

1. Isvara is one of Siva's names.

a couch overhung by a canopy aglitter with precious stones; and there he enjoyed the favors of the willing Sundari, who was as adept at the various postures of love as at those of the dance. The next day when the young man saw that she did not part from his side and showed herself passionately in love, he was unable to tear himself away. For these two days the merchant's son wanted to give Sundari two and a half million in gold, jewelry, and so forth; but she protested: "I have plenty of money, but I have never had a man like you. As long as I am with you, what do I care for gold?"

While Sundari remonstrated—with false pretenses—and refused to accept his gold, her mother Makarakati, whose only daughter she was, said, "All that we have is now his. What does it matter, then, if you take it and hold it in common?" Sundari finally allowed herself to be persuaded by her mother and accepted; and the naïve Isvara thought that she was genuinely in love with him. And so, seduced by her beauty, her songs and dances, the merchant spent two months with Sundari, meanwhile lavishing twenty million on her in gifts.

Then a friend of his, Arthadatta, came and spoke to him in private: "Is it possible, friend, that the lessons of the procuress, which you have done so much to master, have proved useless just when they mattered most, like a coward's swordsmanship? For you believe that that harlot's love is real! Is a mirage in the desert real? Let us go before all your money goes. Your father won't forgive you when he learns of this!"

"You are right," said Isvara. "Harlots are not to be trusted, but Sundari is different. Why, Arthadatta, when she does not see me for a moment, she is ready to kill herself! If we really have to go, you must tell her yourself."

With Isvara looking on, Arthadatta said to Sundari and her mother Makarakati: "Your love for Isvara is certainly unparalleled, but now he must continue on his journey to Sumatra to do his trading. He will make a fortune so that he can come back and live with you happily for the rest of his life. Let him go, my dear."

Sundari gazed at Isvara's face with tears in her eyes. "You know best," she said in a desperate voice. "Who am I to speak? Who dares trust another before he sees the end? But let it be enough what fate has disposed for me. . . . "

Her mother said reassuringly: "Don't be unhappy, my child. Control yourself. Your friend will surely come back; he won't desert you when his fortune is made." The daughter took hold of herself, and the two bawds plotted together. Then the mother secretly had a net fastened inside a certain well. Isvara's heart was swinging in doubt, and Sundari in her sorrow took very little food and drink. But she did not restrain her love in her songs, lute playing, and dances; and Isvara consoled her with all manner of affectionate gestures.

On the day set by his friend, Isvara left Sundari's house while the procuress spoke benedictions. With her mother, Sundari followed him in tears outside the city, as far as the well where the net had been fastened. And when he told Sundari to turn back and continued on his journey, she threw herself into the well, on top of the net. Her mother and the servants cried out piercingly, "O my daughter! O mistress!" The merchant's son immediately turned about-face, with his friend, and he was numbed when he learned that his love had thrown herself in the well. Makarakati, weeping plaintively over her daughter, had her trusted servants, who knew of the plot, descend into the well. As they climbed down the ropes, they shouted, "O blessing, she lives, she lives!" and they lifted Sundari out of the well. The rescued girl feigned death, but when she was told that her lover had come back, she cried out faintly. Isvara, completely reassured, took his beloved mistress and returned with his friend to her home. Certain in his mind that Sundari's love was genuine, he thought that having her was the greatest boon life could offer, and he gave up all plans for travel.

When he had settled down once more, his friend Arthadatta spoke again: "Have you taken leave of your senses? Don't trust Sundari's love just because she jumped in a well. The tricks of a bawd are as inscrutable as the machinations of fate. What are you going to tell your father when you have lost your entire fortune? Where else can you go now? Get out of here today, if you are still sound in mind!"

The merchant's son took a month in considering his friend's advice. By that time he had spent the remaining thirty million, and, when he was broke, Makarakati gave him the crescent[1] and threw him out.

Arthadatta and the other friends hurried back to Citraketu and reported to Isvara's father all that had happened. When Ratnavarman heard that, he was shocked, and the merchant prince went to Yamajihva the procuress.

"You have taken such a large fee, but you have failed to teach my son properly if Makarakati could plunder him so easily!" and he described his son's misadventures.

"Bring your son here," said the old bawd. "I shall see to it that he robs Makarakati of everything she possesses."

At the procuress' promise Ratnavarman sent his son's friend Arthadatta with a message and traveling funds to bring Isvara back. Arthadatta journeyed to Goldtown and gave Isvara his father's entire message. "My dear fellow," he continued, "you did not follow my advice, and now you see with your own eyes the dishonesty of the harlot. You gave fifty million and got the crescent in return. What man, if he is wise, expects oil in the sands and love in a whore? Or have you forgotten the nature of things? A man is clever, serene, and meritorious as long as he avoids falling into the snares of wanton women. Therefore you must now return to your father and cure the anger that consumes him!"

Arthadatta started out at once with Isvara to return him to his city, and, relieved, son returned to father. Ratnavarman loved his son so much that he treated him kindly. Forthwith he took him to Yamajihva the procuress; the woman interrogated him, and he relayed through Arthadatta all that had befallen him, the loss of his money, and Sundari's leap into the well.

"I am to blame," said Yamajihva. "I forgot to teach him that trick. Makarakati had fastened a net inside the well, and Sundari threw herself on the net inside the well so that she did not drown. But there is something that can be done." The procuress ordered her servant girls to bring her monkey in, a pet monkey called Ala.

While they were all looking on, she gave the monkey one thousand gold pieces; then she commanded, "Swallow!" and the trained animal swallowed the gold.

"Give him twenty pieces, son," she ordered, "give him sixty pieces, a hundred!" and every time the monkey produced the exact amount from the gold pieces which Yamajihva had told him to swallow.

Having demonstrated the monkey trick, Yamajihva said: "Take this little monkey, Isvaravarman, and return to Sundari's house as before. Feed the monkey every day in

1. The universal grip of bouncers; index finger and thumb are stretched to form a crescent, firmly planted on the victim's neck and followed through with a competent push.

secret as much money as you will need for your expenses and then ask him for it in public. When Sundari sees that, she will think Ala is the stone of wishes, and, if you insist, she will barter all she has to get her hands on that monkey. Take her money, give the monkey two days' expenses to swallow, and don't lose time getting away."

The procuress gave Isvara the moneky, and his father added twenty million. He set out again for Goldtown with the monkey and the money, and when he reached it, he sent a messenger to Sundari the courtesan to announce his arrival and entered her house. With passionate embraces, Sundari welcomed the young man like tenacity itself—whose entire substance is the means to succeed—and also his friend Arthadatta. Isvara assured her of his good fortune and at her house and in her presence told Arthadatta, "Go and fetch Ala." "Certainly!" said his friend and brought the monkey in. Isvara commanded the animal, which had already swallowed a thousand pieces of gold: "Ala, my boy, give me three hundred dinars for food and drink and another hundred for betel and dessert. And give mother Makarakati one hundred, and another hundred to the priests, and give the change of one thousand to Sundari."

At his master's command the monkey spat out the precise amount for these expenditures.

After Isvara, with this trick, had made Ala produce as much money as he needed for his expenses, Sundari took counsel with her mother. "Surely, this must be the stone of wishes which has been conjured in a monkey's body, if it can produce one thousand dinars every day," she said. "If he were to give us the monkey, we would have succeeded in all our designs!"

When the two women had secretly plotted together, Sundari begged Isvara as he was taking a rest after his meal, "If you really love me, you must give me Ala!"

Isvara laughed. "He is my father's entire fortune. It would not be right to give it away."

"I will give you fifty million for the monkey."

"If you offered me your entire fortune," said Isvara decisively, "and the whole city to boot, it still would not be right for me to give him to you. So what are a few millions?"

"I will give you all I own, but let me have that monkey! My mother will be furious with me," and she threw herself at his feet.

Arthadatta and the other friends said, "Give her the monkey and let it go." At last Isvara consented to sell him to her, and he spent the rest of the day with an overjoyed Sundari. The next morning, after he had made the monkey swallow two

PROVBRBS

Money gets you anything,
Gets it in a flash:
Therefore let the prudent get
Cash, cash, cash.—PANCHATANTRA

Give a woman food and dresses
(Chiefly when her trouble presses)
Give her gems and all things nice;
Do not ask for her advice.
—PANCHATANTRA

Where a woman, gambler, child,
As a guide is domiciled,
Death advances, stage by stage—
So declares the ancient sage.
—PANCHATANTRA

Only while he does not hear
Woman's whisper in his ear,
May a man a leader be,
Keeping due humility.—PANCHATANTRA

thousand pieces in secret, he turned him over to the prayerful harlot and received her entire fortune and her house in exchange. He left instantly and departed on business to Sumatra.

For two days the monkey Ala provided Sundari to her great joy with all the money she asked, one thousand gold pieces a day. The third day she asked again and again, but the monkey failed to produce any money, no matter how she coaxed him, and she struck Ala with her fist. The monkey jumped on her in a rage and rent her face and her mother's with his paws and teeth while they tried to beat the furious beast off. With the blood streaming down her face the mother clubbed the monkey furiously until he was dead. When the two woman saw that the monkey was dead and that all their fortune was lost, they were near to killing themselves.

The story went around, and the people jeered:

"Makarakati stole one merchant's money with a net,
But he made a monkey of her with a monkey pet."

Now that they had lost their money and their faces, Sundari and her mother could barely be prevented by their relatives from killing themselves. Shortly afterward Isvara returned from Sumatra, the Island of Gold, to his father's house in Citraketu with another fortune added to his own. And when Ratnavarman saw his son return with immense wealth, he honored the procuress Yamajihva with gifts and held a very large feast. Isvaravarman, having learned the matchless tricks of harlots, was forever cured of any affection for them; and he took a wife and stayed at home.

The Red Lotus of Chastity

translated by J. A. B. Van Buitenen

In this world is a famous port, Tamralipti, and there lived a rich merchant whose name was Dhanadatta. He had no sons, so he assembled many brahmins, prostrated himself before them, and requested: "See to it that I get a son!"

"That is not at all difficult," said the priests, "for the brahmins can bring about everything on earth by means of the scriptural sacrifices.

"For example," they continued, "long ago there was a king who had no sons, though he had one hundred and five women in his seraglio. He caused a special sacrifice for a son to be performed, and a son was born to him. The boy's name was Jantu, and in the eyes of all the king's wives he was the rising new moon. Once when he was crawling about on all fours, an ant bit him on the thigh, and the frightened child cried out. The incident caused a terrific disturbance in the seraglio, and the king himself lamented—'My son! O my son!'—like a commoner. After a while, when the ant had been removed and the child comforted, the king blamed his own anxiety on the fact that he had only one son.

" 'There must be a way to have more sons,' he thought, and in his grief he consulted the brahmins. They replied: 'Indeed, Your Majesty, there is one way by which you can have more sons. Kill the son you have and sacrifice all his flesh in the sacred fire. When the royal wives smell the burning flesh, they will all bear sons.' The king had everything done as they said and got as many sons as he had wives.

"Thus with the help of a sacrifice," concluded the brahmins, "we can bring you, too, a son."

So at the advice of the brahmins, merchant Dhanadatta settled on a stipend for their sacerdotal services, and the priests performed the sacrifice for him. Subsequently a son was born to the merchant. The boy, who was given the name Guhasena, grew up in due time, and his father Dhanadatta was seeking a wife for him. And the merchant voyaged with his son to the Archipelago to find a bride, though he pretended that it was just a business expedition. In the Archipelago he asked the daughter of a prominent merchant, Dharmagupta, a girl named Devasmita, On-Whom-the-Gods-Have-Smiled, in marriage for his son Guhasena. Dharamagupta, however, did not favor the alliance, for he loved his daughter very much and thought that Tamralipti was too far away. But Devasmita herself, as soon as she had set eyes on Guhasena, was so carried away by his qualities that she decided to desert her parents. Through a companion of hers she arranged a meeting with the man she loved and sailed off from the island at night with him and his father. On their arrival in Tamralipti they were married; and the hearts of husband and wife were caught in the noose of love.

Then father Dhanadatta died, and, urged by his relatives to continue his father's business, Guhasena made plans for a voyage to the island of Cathay. Devasmita, however, did not approve of his going, for she was a jealous wife and naturally suspected that he would love another woman. So with his relatives urging him on and his wife opposing Guhasena was caught in the middle and could not get on with his business.

Thereupon he went to a temple and took a vow of fasting. "Let God in this temple show me a way out," he thought. Devasmita came along, and she took the same vow. God Siva appeared to both of them in a dream. He gave them two red lotuses and spoke: "Each of you must keep this lotus in his hand. If one of you commits adultery while the other is far away, the lotus in the other's hand will wither away. So be it!" The couple woke up, and each saw in the other's hand the red lotus which was an image of the lover's heart.

So, carrying his lotus, Guhasena departed, and Devasmita stayed home watching hers. Presently Guhasena reached Cathay and went about his business, trading in precious stones. But the lotus he carried around in his hands aroused the curiosity of four merchant's sons who noticed that the flower never seemed to fade. They tricked him into accompanying them home and gave him quantities of mead to drink; when he was drunk, they asked him about the lotus, and he told them. Calculating that the merchant's trade in precious stones would take a long time to be completed, the mischievous merchant's sons plotted together, and, their curiosity aroused, all four set sail at once for Tamralipti, without telling anybody, to see if they could not undo the chastity of Guhasena's wife. Reconnoitering in Tamralipti, they sought out a wandering nun, Yogakarandika, who lived in a Buddhist monastery. They ingratiated themselves with her and proposed, "Reverend Madam, if you can bring about what we wish, we shall reward you richly."

"Of course, you boys want some girl in town," said the nun. "Tell me. I shall see to it. I have no desire for money, because I have a clever pupil named Siddhikari, and thanks to her I have amassed a great fortune."

"How is that? You have acquired great wealth through the favor of your pupil?" the merchant's sons asked.

"If you are curious to hear the story, my sons," said the nun, "I shall tell you. Listen.

"Some time ago a merchant came to town from the North. While he was staying here, my pupil, in disguise, contrived to get herself employed in his house as a maid of all work; and as soon as the merchant had come to trust her, she stole all the gold he had in his house and sneaked away at dawn. A drummer saw her leave town and, his suspicions aroused by her fast pace, started with his drum in his hand to pursue and rob her in turn. Siddhikari had reached the foot of a banyan tree when she saw the drummer approach, and the cunning girl called out to him in a miserable voice: 'I have quarreled with my husband, and now I have run away from home to kill myself. Could you fasten the noose for me, my friend?'

" 'If she is going to hang herself, then why should I kill the woman?' thought the drummer, and he tied a noose to the tree. He stepped on his drum, put his head through the noose, and said, 'This is the way to do it.' The same instant Siddhikari kicked the drum to pieces—and the drummer himself perished in the noose. But at that moment the merchant came looking for her, and from a distance he discerned the maid who had stolen his entire fortune. She saw him come, however, and immediately climbed up the tree and hid among the leaves. When the merchant came to the tree with his servants, he saw only the drummer dangling from the tree, for Siddhikari was nowhere in sight.

" 'Can she have climbed up the tree?' the merchant questioned, and immediately one of the servants went up.

" 'I have always loved you, and here you are, with me in a tree!' whispered Siddhikari. 'Darling, all the money is yours. Take me!' And she embraced him and kissed him on the mouth and bit the fool's tongue off with her teeth. Overcome with pain the servant tumbled out of the tree, spitting blood, and cried something unintelligible that sounded like 'la-la-la.' When he saw him, the merchant thought that the man was possessed by a ghost, and in terror he fled home with his servants. No less terrified, Siddhikari, my pupil, climbed down from the top of the tree and went home with all the money."

The nun's pupil entered just as her mistress finished, and the nun presented her to the merchant's sons.

"But now tell me the truth,' resumed the nun, "which woman do you want? I shall prepare her for you at once!"

"Her name is Devasmita," they replied, "Guhasena's wife. Bring her to bed with us!" The nun promised to do so and gave the young men lodging in her house.

The wandering nun ingratiated herself with the servants at Guhasena's house by giving them delicacies and so on, and thus she gained entrance to the house with her pupil. But when she came to the door of Devasmita's chambers, a dog which was kept on a chain at the door barked at her, though never before had the bitch been known to bark. Then Devasmita saw her, and wondering who the woman was that had come, she sent a servant girl to inquire and then herself conducted the nun into her chamber. When she was inside, the nun gave Devasmita her blessing, and after courteous amenities for which she found a pretext, the wicked woman said to the chaste wife: "I have always had a desire to see you, and today I saw you in a dream. That is why I have come to visit you. I see that you are separated from your husband, and my heart suffers for you; if youth and beauty are deprived of love's pleasures, they are fruitless."

With such talk the nun gained Devasmita's confidence, and after having chatted awhile she returned to her own home. The next day the nun took a piece of meat covered with sneezing powder and went to Devasmita's house. She gave the meat to the dog at the door, and the animal at once swallowed it. The sneezing powder caused the dog's eyes to run, and the animal sneezed incessantly. Then the nun entered Devasmita's apartment, and once she had settled down to her hostess' hospitality, the shrew began to weep. Pressed by Devasmita she said, as if with great reluctance: "Oh, my daughter, go and look outside at your dog; she is crying. Just now she recognized me from a former life when we knew each other, and she burst out in tears. Pity moved me to weep with her."

Devasmita looked outside the door and saw the dog which seemed to be weeping. "What miracle is this?" she wondered for the space of a moment. Then the nun said: "Daughter, in a former life both she and I were the wives of a brahmin. Our husband had to travel everywhere at the king's orders as his envoy, and while he was gone, I carried on with other men as I pleased, to avoid frustrating the senses and the elements. Our highest duty, you know, is to yield to the demands of sense and element. That is why I in this present life have the privilege of remembering past existences. But she in her ignorance guarded her chastity, and so she has been reborn a bitch, though she does remember her other life."

"What kind of moral duty is that?" thought Devasmita, who was clever enough. "This nun has some crooked scheme afoot!" Then she said: "Reverend Madam, how long I have been ignorant of my real duty! You must introduce me to some handsome man!"

"There are some merchant's sons from the Archipelago who are staying in town," said the nun. "I shall bring them to you if you want."

Overjoyed the nun went home. And Devasmita said secretly to her servant girls: "I am sure that some merchant's sons have seen the never-fading lotus which my husband carries in his hand, and out of curiosity they have asked him about it when he was drinking. Now the scoundrels have come here from their island to seduce me and have engaged that depraved nun as their go-between. Fetch me immediately some liquor loaded with Datura drug and go and have a dog's-paw branding iron made." The maids did as their mistress told them, and one of them, at Devasmita's instructions, dressed up as her mistress.

Meanwhile the nun selected one of the four merchant's sons, who each commanded to be taken first, and brought him, disguised as her own pupil, to Devasmita's house. There she bade him go inside and went away unobserved. The maid who posed as Devasmita gave the young merchant with all due courtesies the drugged liquor to drink, and the drink (as though it were his own depravity) robbed him of his senses. Then the girls stripped him of everything he wore and robed him monastically in air. Thereupon they branded the dog's-paw iron on his forehead, dragged him outside, and threw him in a cesspool. In the last hours of night he came to his senses and found himself sunk in the cesspool—the very image of the Avici hell which his own wickedness had brought on! He got up, and, fingering the mark on his forehead, he returned naked to the nun's house.

"I won't be the only ridiculous one!" he thought, and so he told his brothers in the morning that he had been robbed on his way back. Pretending a headache from his long night and deep drinking, he kept his marked forehead wrapped in a turban's cloth.

The second merchant's son who went to Devasmita's house that night was manhandled in the same way. He too came home naked and said that, despite leaving his jewelry at home, he had been stripped by robbers as he came back. And the next morning he too kept his head bandaged, supposedly because of a headache, to conceal the brand on his forehead. All four of them, though they dissimulated everything, were castigated, branded, plundered, and put to shame in the same fashion. Without disclosing to the nun how they had been maltreated ("Let the same thing happen to her!"), they departed.

The next day the nun, who thought that her plan had succeeded, went with her pupil to Devasmita's house. With a show of gratitude Devasmita courteously poured them drinks with Datura, and when the nun and her pupil has passed out, the chaste wife cut off their noses and ears and tossed them outside in a sewage pit.

But then Devasmita began to worry. "Might those merchant's sons now kill my husband in revenge?" She went to her mother-in-law and told her everything that had happened.

"Daughter," said her mother-in-law, "you have done well. But something bad may now happen to my son."

"Then I shall save him as Saktimati once saved her husband with her presence of mind!"

"And how did she save her husband?" asked her mother-in-law. "Tell me, my daughter."

"In my country," Devasmita began, "we have a great Yaksha who is famous under the name of Manibhadra. He is very powerful, and our ancestors have built him a temple in our town. My countrymen come to this temple, each with his own presents, to offer them to Manibhadra in order to gain whatever it is they wish. There is a custom that any man who is found in this temple at night with another man's wife is kept with the woman in the sanctum of Manibhadra for the rest of the night, and the next morning they are brought to court, where they will confess their behavior and be thrown in jail.

"One night a merchant named Samudradatta was caught in the act with another man's wife by one of the temple guards. The guard led the merchant away with the woman and threw them into the sanctum of the temple where they were securely chained. After a while the merchant's faithful wife, Saktimati, who was very ingenious, got to know what had happened. Immediately she took an offering for puja worship and, disguised, went out into the night to the temple, full of self-confidence and chaperoned by her confidantes. When she came to the temple, the puja priest, greedy for the stipend she offered him, opened the gates for her, after informing the captain of the guard. Inside the temple she found her husband who was caught with the woman. She dressed the woman up to pass for herself and told her to get out.

The woman went out into the night in her disguise, and Saktimati herself stayed in the sanctum with her husband. When in the morning the king's magistrates came to examine them, they all saw that the merchant had only his wife with him. The king, on learning the fact, punished the captain of the guard and released the merchant from the temple as from the yawning mouth of death.

"So did Saktimati save her husband that time with her wits," concluded Devasmita, and the virtuous wife added in confidence to her mother-in-law, "I shall go and save my husband with a trick, as she did."

Then Devasmita and her maids disguised themselves as merchants, boarded a ship on the pretext of business, and departed for Cathay where her husband was staying. And on her arrival she saw her husband Guhasena—reassurance incarnate!—in the midst of traders. Guhasena saw her too, from a distance, and drank deep of the male image of his beloved wife. He wondered what such a delicate person could have to do with the merchant's profession.

Devasmita went to the local king and announced: "I have a message. Assemble all your people." Curious, the king summoned all citizens and asked Devasmita, who still wore her merchant's disguise, "What is your message?"

"Among these people here," said Devasmita, "are four runaway slaves of mine. May it please Your Majesty to surrender them."

"All the people of this town are assembled here," replied the king. "Look them over, and when you recognize your slaves, take them back."

Thereupon she arrested on their own threshold the four merchant's sons, whom she had manhandled before. They still wore her mark on their foreheads.

"But these are the sons of a caravan trader," protested the merchants who were present. "How can they be your slaves?"

"If you do not believe me," she retorted, "have a look at their foreheads. I have branded them with a dog's paw."

"So we shall," they said. They unwound the turbans of the four men, and they all saw the dog's paw on their foreheads. The merchant's guild was ashamed, and the king surprised.

"What is behind this?" the king asked, questioning Devasmita in person, and she told the story, and they all burst out laughing.

PROVERBS

Women seek for selfish treasures,
Think of nothing but their pleasures,
Even children by them reckoned
To their selfish comfort second.
—PANCHATANTRA

All advice you may discard
From a barber, child, or bard,
Monk or hermit or musician,
Or a man of base condition.
—PANCHATANTRA

A hundred's mine? A thousand, please.
Thousand? A lakh would give me ease.
A kingdom's power would satisfy
The lakh-lord. Kings would own
the sky.—PANCHATANTRA

The hair grows old with aging years:
The teeth grow old, the eyes and ears,
But while the aging seasons speed,
One thing is young forever—greed.
—PANCHATANTRA

Fire chills, rogues bless, and moonlight
burns
Before a wife to virtue turns.
—PANCHATANTRA

"By rights they are your slaves, my lady," said the king, whereupon the other merchants paid the king a fine and the virtuous woman a large ransom to free the four from bondage. Honored by all upright people, Devasmita, with the ransom she had received and the husband she had rejoined, returned to their city Tamralipti and never again was she separated from the husband she loved.

Mahosadha's Judgment

translated by J. A. B. Van Buitenen

A woman took her baby boy to the pond of the learned Mahosadha to give him a bath. When she had bathed the child, she laid him on her clothes on the bank and wiped his face; then she went into the pond to take a bath herself.

That very instant a ghoul saw the child. Wishing to devour him, the ghoul changed herself into a woman and said, "That is a beautiful boy, my friend. Is he yours?"

"Yes," the mother answered.

"I want to give him suck."

"Do so."

The ghoul picked the child up, played with him for a little while, and then started running away with him. The other woman saw her. She ran too and took her child back, saying, "Where are you going with my son?"

"Why do you take my child away from me?" asked the ghoul. "He is my son!"

While they were quarreling, they passed the gate of Mahosadha's house. The man heard them quarrel and called to them. "What is this?" he asked and heard what the quarrel was about. He saw by the redness and unblinking steadiness of her eyes that one of the women was a ghoul. Yet he said, "You shall abide by my judgment."

"We shall abide," the women replied.

Whereupon he drew a line on the ground, placed the child on the line, and told the ghoul to hold the hands and the mother to hold the feet. "Both of you," he said, "try pulling the child to your side. He is the son of the one who can pull him to her side."

They both started to pull. As the child was being pulled, it felt pain and began crying. The mother, as though her heart had broken, let go of her son and stood weeping.

The learned man asked the crowd, "Is it the mother's heart that softens for her child, or a strange woman's heart?"

"The mother's heart, learned one."

"Is the mother she who has kept hold of the child or she who released him?"

"She who released him, learned one."

"Surely you know who the child-snatcher is?"

"We do not know, learned one."

"She is a ghoul. She seized the child to devour him."

"How do you know, learned one?"

"From the unwavering steadiness and redness of her eyes, from the absence of her shadow, and from her urgency and ruthlessness."

Then he interrogated her. "Who are you?"

"I am a ghoul, my lord."

"Why did you seize this child?"

"To devour it, my lord."

"Blind fool, you became a ghoul because of the evil you had done in a former life. Now you do evil again. Indeed, you are a blind fool." Thus he admonished her and made her firm in the five principles and dismissed her.

The mother of the child praised the learned Mahosadha, saying, "Live long, O lord," took her child, and departed.

My Grandmother and the Dirty English (extract)

Aubrey Menen (b. 1912)

Born and educated in England, having an English mother, nurtured in Western culture, Aubrey Menen is certainly not a representative Indian writer. But he has observed India with a detachment that few other Indians have been able to achieve, and he is unquestionably the wittiest Indian writing in the English language.

In Menen's writing there are qualities reminiscent of Bernard Shaw and Evelyn Waugh, the humor of unexpected logic and the delight of shocking truth, the sophistication of understatement and the charm of whimsy, the rare pleasure of clever dialogue by unsanctimonious adults. Menen has never been as much appreciated by Western readers as he deserves to be.

My grandmother, like Michelangelo, had *terribilita.* She had a driving will; she would not be balked and whatever she did was designed to strike the spectator with awe. She was also something of a stick. She rarely spoke to anyone who was not of her own social station and she received them formally: that is to say, with her breasts completely bare. Even in her time women were growing lax about this custom in Malabar. But my grandmother insisted on it. She thought that married women who wore blouses and pretty saris were Jezebels; in her view, a wife who dressed herself above her waist could only be aiming at adultery.

When I was twelve she demanded that I be brought and shown to her. I was incontinently taken half across the earth, from London to South beyond the town of Calicut. My mother came with me.

The last part of the journey was made by dugout canoe (there being no railways and no good roads near our family estate) and in this we were poled on a moonlit night up the Ponnani River. The river was lined with palm trees and crocodiles.

My mother taking fright of these beasts, I sang to keep them away from the boat. I sang a song I had been taught at school called "Drake's Drum." This had been written in the reign of Queen Victoria and told how, if the Spaniards should embark on the unlikely project of attacking nineteenth century England, Drake would come back to life and drum them up the Channel "as he drummed them long ago." I had been taught many songs of similar sentiments but this was the noisiest. I sang it with a will because my young heart (especially in such very foreign parts) glowed with the sentiment. The crocodiles yawned and, like the Spaniards in the Victorian age, showed no signs of attacking.

This singing marked a stage in my life. Shortly afterwards I lost my innocence. My grandmother took me in hand and I never thought the English were perfect again.

When our boat journey was done, servants with flaming torches led us along narrow paths between tall trees, and finally conducted us to a house. This was (my father said) not my ancestral roof.

When my grandmother had heard that my mother intended to make the visit as well as myself, she had given orders for a special house to be put in repair for my mother's accommodation. It was on the furthest confines of the family property. This was her solution of a difficult problem. My mother was ritually unclean, and therefore whenever she entered my family house, she would defile it. The house would have to be purified and so would every caste Hindu in it. It followed logically that if my mother stayed in the house, it would be permanently in a state of defilement and permanently in a state of being ritually cleaned. Since this ceremony involved drums and conch shells, my mother's visit foreshadowed a prolonged uproar. All this was avoided by my grandmother's decision to put her up in a separate building.

I cannot say that my grandmother was ever rude to my mother. She never referred to her by name but always as 'the Englishwoman.' This was not necessarily an insulting expression, but my mother had Irish blood and what with this, and the house, and some other pin-pricks, her temper rose. She ordered a quantity of medical stores from Calicut, and when they arrived she set up a free dispensary on the verandah, to which the peasants flocked. It was an admirably devised answer. My grandmother had shut the door in my mother's face: she now had the galling experience of seeing my mother industriously cleaning up the doorstep. As my mother well knew, each drop of iodine that she dispensed stung not only the grateful patient, but also my grandmother's conscience.

My grandmother brooded on this for a while and then sent my mother a bag of golden sovereigns. My mother, taking this to be a bribe at the worst, or at the best, a tip, sent it back. But she was wrong. It was a peace offering. It was sent again next day, accompanied by the family goldsmith who sat, slept and ate on the verandah for one week while he made the sovereigns (with tweezers and a charcoal fire) into a great gold collar which my mother still, on occasions, wears.

When, fourteen years before my trip, my father had written from England to say that he was getting married to a white woman, my grandmother had been far from giving the union her blessing. But it would be wrong to say that she had objected to it. If an American boy of twenty-two wrote home from foreign parts to say that he had taken to cannibalism, his parents would not object. They would be so revolted that a mere objection would never meet the case. So with my grandmother.

She had never met the English but she knew all about them. She knew they were tall, fair, given to strong drink, good soldiers and that they had conquered her native country. She also knew that they were incurably dirty in their personal habits. She respected them but wished they would keep their distance. It was very much the way that a Roman matron looked upon the Goths.

My eldest uncle had been to England for two years and he spoke up for the English. He said that while the Hindus were undoubtedly the most civilised race on earth and had been civilised a thousand years before the English, nevertheless, the English were now the masters of the Hindus. My grandmother's reply to this was that the English were masters of the Hindus only because 'nobody would listen to us.' By this she meant that our family along with others of the same caste had strongly objected to Vasco da Gama being allowed to land in Calicut. They had, in fact, done their best to get him and his sailors massacred. But the country was not behind them and he escaped. Everything, my grandmother argued (and not without some reason) had started with that.

But her chief complaint was that the English were so dirty, and this was rather a poser for my uncle. When my grandmother asked if, like decent people, they took a minimum of two baths a day, my uncle, who could not lie to his mother without commiting a disgraceful sin, said that, well no: but a few took one bath and that the habit was spreading. He could go no further than that. But he added that my grandmother should remember that England had a cold climate. This she loyally did, and when she discussed the matter with me, she was able to treat the matter lightly, as one does the disgusting but rational liking of the Eskimos for eating blubber.

As for the question of eating, she did not have the expected prejudices. She did not think it strange that the English ate ham and beef. The outcaste hill-tribes (called Todas) who made the family straw mats and cleaned the latrines, ate anything. She was not disturbed either, about their religion, because my uncle assured her that they had practically none. Their manners, however, she abominated. If she did not mind them eating meat, she considered their way of eating it beyond the pale of decent society. In my family home, each person eats his meal separately, preferably in a secluded corner. The thought that English people could sit opposite each other and watch each other thrust food into their mouths, masticate, and swallow it, made her wonder if there was anything that human beings would not do, when left to their own devices.

She was not surprised to hear, after this, that in England a woman could have more than one husband, particularly (and this was the crowning paradox) if she had been a widow. To the day of her death my grandmother could never understand how people could call themselves civilised and yet allow widows to marry again. For her the very foundation-stone of society was that a child should have one father, and obey him. Nobody ever dared her wrath sufficiently to explain the position of women in English society. She was intensely proud of the standards of her house and she permitted no lewd talk to defile them — certainly never in her presence.

With this background, then, my grandmother's peace offering of a bag of sovereigns was a considerable victory for my mother, particularly since the gold collar which the goldsmith had been told to make from them was the characteristic jewellery of a Malabar bride.

The way was now open for me. I could go and see her. I had waited about three weeks.

The things my grandmother told me were a puzzle at the time. But I have come to understand them better. Much as she looked down on the English, I think that had she met some of them, had she overcome her well-bred fastidiousness and actually mixed with them, she would have found she and they had much in common. Her riding passion, like theirs, was racial pride. She believed—and this made her character—that she belonged to the cleverest family of the cleverest people on earth. According to Lord Russell, this was also the firm faith of Mrs. Beatrice Webb, who used to repeat it to herself in moments when, otherwise, she might have felt inferior, such as when she made her entry into a distinguished party. Though my grandmother never went to parties I'm sure that she, too, repeated the formula as a stiffener of her already formidable morale.

She felt that she was born of a superior race and she had all the marks of it. For instance, she deplored the plumbing of every other nation but her own. She would often say to me, through my uncle:

"Never take a bath in one of those contraptions in which you sit in dirty water like a buffalo. Always bathe in running water. If you have servants to pour it over you, that's best. But otherwise you must stand under a tap or pour the water over yourself. A really nice person does not even glance at his own bath water much less sit in it." Here she would laugh to herself, while my uncle translated; not an unkind laugh, but a pitying one, as she thought of the backwardness of the white man's bathroom.

Fakirs—Then and Now (extracts)

Aubrey Menen

It should be explained at once that a fakir is as normal a figure in the public life of India as a Senator is in America. He is as easy to meet and when met is not looked upon as being any more bizarre.

Like the Senator, he is a member of an envied profession; but he is perhaps regarded with more affection. To the common man of India a fakir is an escape from the dull round of seed-time and harvest, death and procreation. They are his headline personalities, and just as the Western man follows the fortunes of some tennis player or boxer, or indeed any athlete who can hit a man or a ball harder than anyone else so the man-in-the-village-street follows the exploits of Ramakrishnan who buries himself alive for a month, Mahadev who swings from a pole supported by nothing more than a hook through his chin, or Gurushankar who once sat still for twenty-three years.

But all fakirs are not gymnosophists, just as all idols in the West are not men of muscle. Without drawing the comparison too fine one might say that there are fakirs who are the equivalent of motion picture celebrities: people who possess some knack of charm or attraction, such as the well-known fakir who is ninety years old and has never washed.

In all religions there are saints who live uncomfortable lives and saints who are jolly. The public likes both sorts and so they do in India. There are fakirs, for example, who have pictures painted on one foot to show that they have never set it on the ground. On the other hand, there are fakirs who are merely quiet old gentlemen who tell their beads. Both may be equally revered. Indeed both may be equally holy: saintliness is the most chancy of professions.

But this is changing and very fast. Even as I write it may no longer be true. When India was a subject land, the fakirs went quietly about the country, sticking pins in themselves or chanting prayers, and minding their own business. No sooner was the first all-Indian Government installed in New Delhi than a patriotic section of the fakir's profession came to the city of Bombay and staged a week's demonstration on the beach. While the gymnosophists performed unheard-of austerities, others burned unparalleled quantities of melted butter upon an inferno of sacrificial fires. They were persuading the gods to make peace between the nations. In interviews with the Press, they declared that India, for millennia the most civilised nation on earth, was now free, and she had a duty to lead mankind to a better world. . . .

I was very struck by this. I wished to know more but the crowd round the beach numbered half a million persons and I could not even see the ceremonies, much less study this new example of national pride.

But after the peacemakers had gone, I went on a journey into the country and there I discovered a temple area in which I could meet fakirs not only at my leisure but at theirs. This temple area was principally a large square swimming pool (called a 'tank') with steps leading into the water and a paved walk on all four sides. Lining the outer edge of the paved walk were various small temples, cheek by jowl. At the entrance to this sacred enclosure was a small plot of ground with some trees—for holy men who preferred to sit under trees—and here fakirs would meet.

Since all this may seem strange to a Western reader, I shall describe what I found with due attention to atmosphere and detail. I shall introduce him to three fakirs—the first two will demonstrate what they were; the last will serve to show what many of them have become.

My first acquaintance was Pandit Mahadev, an educated and polite man of some fifty years, smeared with cow dung ash and sporting a large white moustache. He habitually sat under the first tree on one's left as one entered the enclosure.

For my initial visits I did no more than salute him, and then made my way to some temple or other where I paid a priest to hammer on a bell. He was always busy cooking something in a pot over a small fire.

On my third visit he read my palm in a desultory fashion and then said, "You are a . . ." He paused and I said:

"A writer."

"So I thought," he said. "You are at the moment engaged on a work about . . ."

"Holy men," I said.

"As anyone can see from your palm," he went on.

Easy relations having been thus established between us I was able to ask him many questions. He readily answered them, and in the course of several more visits we became old friends.

I asked him one day about the food in his perennially boiling pot:

"Is all your food given to you?" I asked. He nodded, and I commented at such a convenient method of keeping house.

"It is really nothing so very extraordinary," said the Guru. "Elsewhere in the world professors and learned men are paid salaries with which they buy food. Here we make matters a little more simple. That is really all there is to it."

I asked him further:

"Do you teach? Do you give lectures to the people who buy you this food?"

At this point his little pot began to splutter and the Pandit gave it his attention. He said to me, in a kindly but preoccupied fashion:

"If you go over to the white stone you're bound to find somebody putting down an offering. They'll tell you all about it."

He poked around in the pot and blew up his little fire in an irritated manner. I judged it best to follow his advice and leave him to his cooking for a while. On the edge of the clearing round the tree was a stone about three feet high that had been whitewashed. A tall peasant with a handsome but vacant face was laying out fruit on its top. I went over to him and he gave me a deep salute. I returned this clumsily.

"These are for the Pandit?" I said.

"Yes, if he'll take them."

"Do you want him to pray for you?"

The tall peasant straightened himself up and looked more handsome and more vacant than ever.

"Pray, sahib? Pray? Why should I want him to pray for me?"

"Isn't that why you give him the fruit?"

"Oh, no." He paused. He looked across to where the Pandit squatted over his pot. The peasant lowered his voice. "All I want is to stop him cursing me. He's the cleverest devil in the whole Tank. Has he told you what he was before he came here? He was a vakil."

This meant that the Pandit had been a lawyer.

"And he was making enough money at it to buy up our whole village. He saved three men from hanging and jailed I don't know how many. Oh, he's clever all right. No beating him."

"Still, why should he curse you?"

"Why not?" said the peasant. "Why should a clever chap like that wish any good to an ordinary plain fool peasant like me?" Then, sketching a salute, he went away.

When I returned to the tree the Pandit was blowing mightily at his fire and he did not break the rhythm of his puffs while saying:

"Ah (phooh-huh!), there you are (phooh-huh!). That surprised you (hoooohf!), I'll bet."

"He said he was afraid you'd curse him."

"So I would (phoof!) I daresay, if I knew (pooff!) how to do it. There, it's going nicely at last."

He sat back, his cheeks pink with blowing, and he grinned at me.

"What did he say about me?"

"He said you were a clever devil."

"So I am."

"He said you were a vakil."

"So I was."

"Why did you give it up?"

"Well, now, have I given it up? That's the question. When I was a lawyer, young fellows like that one who got into trouble used to pay me thousands of rupees to defend them. You see I had a reputation of not doing it unless I was paid a fat fee. The gallows is as good a machine as the rack to threaten a man with."

"And you had that on your conscience, so you gave it all up?" I suggested.

"My conscience? Well, now, I wonder. People say that great criminal lawyers—I was called that y'know—they say that great criminal lawyers haven't got a conscience. I don't think that's quite true. I certainly had a conscience and I used to examine it very strictly. But whatever the charge I brought against it, I was such a good lawyer I could always secure an acquittal. And I'm afraid it's much the same with most members of my profession. The reason for my giving up the bar and doing this"—and he indicated his ash-marks—"was quite different. Almost commonplace, you might say, at least for India. My young brother fell very ill and I made a vow that if he got well again I would make a pilgrimage as a mendicant to Benares. My father had done it. He left home with one rupee, got safely to Benares and returned by train, first class, paying his fare with the money he'd got out of people on his way. And so I did it too, because my brother recovered. I set out for Benares with one rupee and I got here without any undue difficulty. That was about ten years ago."

"And you didn't go any further?"

"No."

"Why?"

He lowered his head, studied the ground, and stayed in this posture for some considerable time, deep in thought. Finally he raised his face to mine and beaming, said:

"I liked the life."

It will be seen that the Pandit was the old-style simple type of fakir. But he was not at all famous. Of the simple, but famous, Big Tim was a good instance. I do not know his proper name because I could never properly catch all its syllables and I never saw it written down in English. It ended in the syllable Tim. So much as I could catch. And Tim was undeniably big. He was introduced to me by my friend the Pandit after the Pandit had entertained me one day to a breakfast of bananas and some soured milk which I drank from a gleaming brass pot. When I had finished he took me for a walk round the 'Tank.'

We had gone scarcely ten yards along the East side when we came across Big Tim leaning his great length against one of the pillars that are slotted for oil-lamps, and which make a pyramid of fire on the festival of Divali. Big Tim was wearing a loose robe that fell to his ankles. It opened to show his chest, rather like a bathing wrap—he was in fact thinking of taking a ceremonial dip—and I could see that he was of a mountainous build.

The Pandit went up to him and looked absurdly small. He told Big Tim who I was and he told me Big Tim's name. Big Tim moved his position very slightly and turned his enormous oval head in my direction. He smiled in a serious way. On being first introduced to an elephant only the most collected person thinks of patting its trunk. As for me, I was thoroughly put out and pushed my right hand forward in the English fashion, although I should have remembered to fold my hands in front of my face. Big Tim put out his own right hand, seized mine and held it in his own, where it lay entrapped like a mouse in some flesh-eating tropical plant. As is so often the way with large men when embarrassed, he simpered.

"Big Tim," said the Pandit (although he used, of course, his proper name), "is just the man I wanted you to meet. He is one of our most famous men. He is perhaps the best-known naked fakir in India."

"Oh yes?" I said.

"You understand what I mean? He goes stark naked." Big Tim, still holding my hand was looking from one of us to the other in an uncomprehending manner and the Pandit said to him in one of the easier common languages of India:

"I was just explaining to the gentleman here that you go naked."

Big Tim said in the same lingua franca, and to me:

"But only in public."

"Oh, of course," I said, and we all sat down on the top step of the 'Tank.'

Two or three devotees were taking their morning bath in a very pretty fashion. They walked slowly down the steps into the water which rose slowly to their waists (since the steps continued well beneath the water). They then, all together, scooped some water into their cupped hands and flung it forwards, saying prayers. Next they moved down two or three more steps, clearing away the lotus-leaves that lay on the surface of the water by swinging their hands and their bodies in wide arcs from left to right and back again. All this looked very fine in the morning sun. When the water was up to their necks, they raised their arms into the air and sang a hymn. . . .

The Pandit asked Big Tim to explain to me exactly what he did and Big Tim tried. But he was hamstrung in his attempts at the outset because he could not honestly see that there was anything to explain. To put one's self in Big Tim's position one must imagine oneself as slow in speech, not given to conversation, and having to explain to a Matabele why one wears a collar and tie.

"There are a lot of us," he said, "who don't wear any clothes. I mean I'm not the only one."

And when he saw from the Pandit's expression that this was scarcely good enough he struggled a step further.

"It's been going on a long time," he said apologetically.

"About three thousand years," the Pandit intervened impatiently, "but this gentleman wants to know what you do. He has an enquiring mind and he wants to find out all he can about his fatherland." He added here an admirably brief summary of my background. "So you can see, we ought to help him all we can, if only so that he can correct all those silly notions about us. I've told him a lot but I am really only on the fringe of things. Now you are a real fakir. So be a good chap," (or 'be a fine fellow' or 'be a stalwart,' if you prefer it; I am trying to translate his vernacular with English vernacular) "be a good chap and tell him what you do."

Big Tim nodded slowly and several times. Then swaying his body towards me like a falling tower he said:

"Well you see, I go naked."

I nodded.

"I don't say I like going naked. Then again, I don't say I don't like it." He stopped. "You follow me?" he enquired anxiously.

"You mean you don't really care one way or another," I said.

"That's it," he said. "That's just it," and he gazed at me for a moment clearly admiring my quickness of wit. "It's the women who like it."

"Oh," I said. "Oh, yes, of course."

Here the Pandit took over the explanation as it had been obvious that he wanted to do from the very moment it began.

"You mustn't be misled by Big Tim's simple way of putting things. Big Tim is a simple thinker: and after all, why not? His is a very simple way of life. In fact it is difficult to think of one more simple. All he does is to take off his clothes and walk in a procession. Of course there are prayers and so forth, but we all say prayers and it comes as a second nature in time, like breathing. As for the women, well, Big Tim's reputation is made entirely by them, as you will understand when I describe the procession to you which I shall do straight away if Big Tim wouldn't mind stepping in if I get any of the details wrong."

The processions, he explained, take place several times a year and all over the country. There is no fixed calendar (here Big Tim said that he didn't know about a calendar but they always had a procession after the rains) and the ceremony took place virtually when enough naked fakirs were gathered together to make a passable display.

They would then meet at an early hour in some temple precincts or the borders of a 'Tank' such as the one we were in, and they would say some prayers. They then took off their clothes and formed a procession. Should the fancy take any of them to do so they might twine flowers in their hair. But this was usually considered proper only for the younger fakirs. The elder ones—and there were naked fakirs of eighty and ninety who had been processioning all their lives—put on a little ashes and cow-dung and nothing more.

Attendants, clothed, would blow on conch-shells and beat gongs. The devotees would strike up an anthem and the whole procession would wind out of the temple into the public streets.

These would be lined with spectators, among them many women. The men in the watching crowd would regard the spectacle purely as an entertainment, though they would not, whatever the temptation, be irreverent. Those of the women who were barren or desired a child would watch the procession with passionate intensity. It was a fertility rite.

Later, when the procession had got back to the temple, the women would come to some secluded grove nearby and the fakirs would sit round in state, reading (if they could read), muttering prayers or telling their large carved wooden beads. The unfertile women would then touch their organs of generation and go away in the belief that their ritual act had given them the fecundity they sought.

The virtue thus transferred could, in theory, flow from any naked devotee, however old. There was (so the Pandit said) some feeling that the rite was more refined if the women selected a venerable and bearded fakirs. The essence of the thing was the worship of the god. Everything else was only an outward show and symbol of the inner piety.

But human nature being what it is the outward show and symbol often had more importance in people's eyes than the theological background. Old men were sought out for the blessings: the younger ones for their virility. As these latter moved about the country their reputation would precede them: and it was a fact (so I was assured) that the god did grant fertility to those who favoured his disciples.

The younger men with big reputations were surrounded by flattery and applause, and the more greedy among them could demand and get food and money and even (so illogical is the pious mind) sumptuous clothing. Some of them grew vain under all this attention and put on the airs of prima donnas. Others, like Big Tim, remained modest. Big Tim's reputation as a miracle worker, nevertheless, stood as high as anyone's, and in certain areas where he had been particularly efficacious, it stood above all his rivals. The processions in which he took part were extremely elaborate. Old men were proud to be seen in them, and younger aspirants felt that it was a step in their career. When these had all defiled in front of the eager spectators, singing and chanting, Big Tim's appearance at the tail of the procession, walking alone with a clear space all round was, the Pandit assured me, something of a coup de theatre. . . .

My first conversation with Big Tim had to be cut short for I had other business, but I spoke with him on very many other occasions and he became quite a friend. He had a simple kindliness that was very attractive. I asked him a good many questions. One of the things I was most curious to know was whether the processions and their subsequent ritual ever led to any scandals.

Big Tim, when his tongue was a little loosened by familiarity with me, answered me very equably. He was always even-tempered with me, and I think he was much the same with everybody else. It came from the fact that he had quite made up his mind that he had everything he needed in life.

"Oh yes," he said. "There are scandals. Quite a lot."

There was nobody in the 'Tank' on this particular morning and Big Tim was skimming flat stones across the water. It was a game he was fond of and it was a complicated form of 'Ducks and Drakes.' Not only did one have to make one's stone hop three times, but one of the hops had to be over a specified clump of lotus plants. The challenger skimmed and straddled a particular bunch with four stones one after the other; the other player had to take in that bunch in his own throws.

"Some of our people," said Big Tim, filling in his usual long pauses with throws, "do—well—just what you'd—think—and"—he paused for a long while during which he made a beautiful cast—"they don't wait for the god to take action but do it themselves. Get's us all—a bad—name."

He challenged me to throw stones. I tried, and failed to hop the lotus bunch. He said:

"Well, I've been doing this a lot longer than you have, so you mustn't be disappointed. I can't—think—why they do it."

"You mean—why they go with the women?"

"Yes," said Big Tim, with little frowns of bewilderment. "I don't see it myself, women never did interest me very much."

"No?"

"No. We take a vow of chastity—" he stopped.

"Go on."

"You won't be interested."

"Oh yes I will be."

"It's not interesting really. All I wanted to say was that—I find—the vow—easy to keep. Those other fellows seem to want to make life a lot more difficult than it need be. Shabash!" he said, congratulating me on a lucky throw and thus ending what must have seemed, to him, a lengthy oration. . . .

Not all the fakirs had Big Tim's pellucid character. The longer I knew Big Tim the more I liked him. But some of the others were different and after meeting them, I avoided their company.

There was one such man called Ramchandra. He had held his right arm above his head for twenty years, and he now could not get it down again, even if he wanted to. But he did not want to get it down because he maintained that he was holding up the prestige of his country and the universe. I did not like Ramchandra at all.

NOVELS

Swami and Ftiends (extracts)

R. K. Narayan (b. 1906)

The prolific Narayan is considered India's best living novelist. Unlike Aubrey Menen, he sets all of his scenes in India and fills them, almost without exception, with Indian characters. The imaginary town of Malgudi is the locale for several of his books, in which he recreates the Indian scene with consummate technical skill, absolute knowledge of the social structure, and delightful wit.
Narayan is a devout Hindu, an advocate of traditional Indian values, and an admirer of Graham Greene. His satire varies from the gentle depiction of children's affectations, as in Swami and Friends, *to sophisticated commentary on academic pretentions in* The English Teacher. *Portions of both are included here. Perhaps his best-known novel in America is* The Guide.

The Scripture period was the last in the morning. It was not such a dull hour after all. There were moments in it that brought stirring pictures before one: the Red Sea cleaving and making way for the Israelites; the physical feats of Samson; Jesus rising from the grave; and so on. The only trouble was that the Scripture master, Mr. Ebenezar, was a fanatic.

'Oh, wretched idiots!' the teacher said, clenching his fists. 'Why do you worship dirty, lifeless, wooden idols and stone images? Can they talk? No. Can they see? No. Can they bless you? No. Can they take you to Heaven? No. Why? Because they have no life. What did your Gods do when Mohammed of Gazni smashed them to pieces, trod upon them, and constructed out of them steps for his lavatory? If these idols had life, why did they not parry Mohammed's onslaughts?'

He then turned to Christianity. 'Now see our Lord Jesus. He could cure the sick, relieve the poor, and take us to Heaven. He was a real God. Trust him and he will take you to Heaven; the kingdom of Heaven is within us.' Tears rolled down Ebenezar's cheeks when he pictured Jesus before him. Next moment his face became purple with rage as he thought of Sri Krishna: 'Did our Jesus go gadding about with dancing girls like your Krishna? Did our Jesus go about stealing butter like that arch-scoundrel Krishna? Did our Jesus practise dark tricks on those around him?'

He paused for breath. The teacher was intolerable today. Swaminathan's blood boiled. He got up and asked, 'If he did not, why was he crucified?' The teacher told him that he might come to him at the end of the period and learn it in private. Emboldened by this mild reply, Swaminathan put to him another question. 'If he was a God, why did he eat flesh and fish and drink wine?' As a brahmin boy it was inconceivable to him that a God should be a non-vegetarian. In answer to this, Ebenezar left his seat, advanced slowly towards Swaminathan and tried to wrench his left ear off. . . .

Next day Swaminathan was at school early. There was still half an hour before the bell. He usually spent such an interval in running round the school or in playing the Digging Game under the huge Tamarind tree. But today he sat apart, sunk in thought. He had a thick letter in his pocket. He felt guilty when he touched its edge with his fingers.

He called himself an utter idiot for having told his father about Ebenezar the night before during the meal.

As soon as the bell rang, he walked into the Head Master's room and handed him a letter. The Head Master's face became serious when he read:

Sir,

I beg to inform you that my son Swaminathan of the First Form, A section, was assaulted by his Scripture Master yesterday in a fanatical rage. I hear that he is always most insulting and provoking in his references to the Hindu religion. It is bound to have a bad effect upon the boys. This is not the place for me to dwell upon the necessity for toleration in these matters.

I am also informed that when my son got up to have a few doubts cleared, he was roughly handled by the same teacher. His ears were still red when he came home last evening.

The one conclusion that I can come to is that you do not want non-Christian boys in your school. If it is so, you may kindly inform us as we are quite willing to withdraw our boys and send them elsewhere. I may remind you that Albert Mission School is not the only school that this town, Malgudi, possesses. I hope you will be kind enough to inquire into the matter and favour me with a reply. If not, I regret to inform you, I shall be constrained to draw the attention of higher authorities to these Un-christian practices.

I have the honour to be,

Sir,

Your most obedient servant,

W. T. Srinivasan

In the ill-ventilated dark passage between the front hall and the dining-room, Swaminathan's grandmother lived with all her belongings, which consisted of an elaborate bed made of five carpets, three bed sheets, and five pillows, a square box made of jute fibre, and a small wooden box containing copper coins, cardamoms, cloves, and areca-nut.

After the night meal, with his head on his granny's lap, nestling close to her, Swaminathan felt very snug and safe in the faint atmosphere of cardamom and cloves.

'Oh, granny! he cried ecstatically, 'you don't know what a great fellow Rajam is.' He told her the story of the first enmity between Rajam and Mani and the subsequent friendship.

'You know, he has a real police dress,' said Swaminathan.

'Is it? What does he want a police dress for?' asked granny.

'His father is the Police Superintendent. He is the master of every policeman here.' Granny was impressed. She said that it must be a tremendous office indeed. She then recounted the days when her husband, Swaminathan's grandfather, was a powerful Sub-Magistrate, in which office he made the police force tremble before him, and the fiercest dacoits of the place flee. Swaminathan waited impatiently for her to finish the story. But she went on, rambled, confused, mixed up various incidents that took place at different times.

'That will do, granny,' he said ungraciously. 'Let me tell you something about Rajam. Do you know how many marks he gets in Arithmetic?'

'He gets all the marks, does he, child?' asked granny.

'No, silly. He gets ninety marks out of one hundred.'

'Good, but you must also try and get marks like him. . . . You know, Swami, your grandfather used to frighten the examiners with his answers sometimes. When he answered a question, he did it in a tenth of the time that others took to do it. And then, his answers would be so powerful that his teachers would give him two hundred marks sometimes . . . When he passed his F. A. he got such a big medal! I wore it as a pendant for years till— When did I remove it? Yes, when your aunt was born. . . . No, it wasn't your aunt . . . It was when your father was born. . . . I remember on the tenth day of confinement . . . No, no. I was right. It was when your aunt was born. Where is that medal now? I gave it away to your aunt—and she melted it and made four bangles out of it. The fool! And such flimsy bangles too! I have always maintained that she is the worst fool in our family. . . .'

'Oh, enough, granny! You go on bothering about old unnecessary stories. Won't you listen to Rajam?'

'Yes, dear, yes.'

'Granny, when Rajam was a small boy, he killed a tiger.'

'Indeed! The brave little boy!'

'You are saying it just to please me. You don't believe it.'

Swaminathan started the story enthusiastically: Rajam's father was camping in a forest. He had his son with him. Two tigers came upon them suddenly, one knocking down the father from behind. The other began chasing Rajam, who took shelter

PROVERBS

The village says "go"; the cemetery says "come."

The desires of the poor spring up just to be destroyed.

An old woman makes a chaste wife.

The cake in the oven is yours; the cake in the tray is mine.

Make peace with the powerful, war with the equal; and make quick raids against the timid.

Rare is the man who practices the virtue he preaches.

Does it matter a bit if you drink milk in a dream out of a pottery cup or a golden vessel?

Everything is created with a companion that will destroy it.

In a quarrel between bulls, it's the calf's leg that gets broken.

Everyone claims relationship to the rich.

behind a bush and shot it dead with his gun. 'Granny, are you asleep?' Swaminathan asked at the end of the story.

'No, dear, I am listening.'

'Let me see. How many tigers came upon how many?'

'About two tigers on Rajam,' said granny.

Swaminathan became indignant at his grandmother's inaccuracy. 'Here I am going hoarse telling you important things and you fall asleep and imagine all sorts of nonsense. I am not going to tell you anything more. I know why you are so indifferent. You hate Rajam.'

'No, no, he is a lovely little boy,' granny said with conviction, though she had never seen Rajam. Swaminathan was pleased. Next moment a new doubt assailed him. 'Granny, probably you don't believe the tiger incident.'

'Oh, I believe every word of it,' granny said soothingly. Swaminathan was pleased, but added as a warning: 'He would shoot anyone that called him a liar.'

Granny expressed her approval of this attitude and then begged leave to start the story of Harichandra, who, just to be true to his word, lost his throne, wife, and child, and got them all back in the end. She was half-way through it when Swaminathan's rhythmic snoring punctuated her narration, and she lay down to sleep. . . .

He went home, flung his coat and cap and books on the table, gulped down the cold coffee that was waiting for him, and sat on the pyol, vacantly gazing into the dark intricacies of the gutter that adorned Vinayaka Mudali Street. A dark volume of water was rushing along. Odd pieces of paper, leaves, and sticks floated by. A small piece of tin was gently skimming along. Swaminathan had an impulse to plunge his hand in and pick it up. But he let it go. His mind was inert. He watched the shining bit float away. It was now at the end of the compound wall; now it had passed under the tree. Swaminathan was slightly irritated when a brick obstructed the progress of the tin. He said that the brick must either move along or stand aside without interfering with the traffic. The piece of tin released itself and dashed along furiously, disappeared round a bend at the end of the street. Swaminathan ran in, got a sheet of paper, and made a boat. He saw a small ant moving abont aimlessly. He carefully caught it, placed it in the boat, and lowered the boat into the stream. He watched in rapture its quick motion. He held his breath when the boat with its cargo neared a danger zone formed by stuck-up bits of straw and other odds and ends. The boat made a beautiful swerve to the right and avoided destruction. It went on and on. It neared a fatal spot where the waters were swirling round and round in eddies. Swaminathan was certain that his boat was nearing its last moment. He had no doubt that it was going to be drawn right to the bottom of the circling eddies. The boat whirled madly round, shaking and swaying and quivering. But providentially a fresh supply of water from the kitchen in the neighbour's house pushed it from behind out of danger. But it rushed on at a fearful speed, and Swaminathan felt that it was going to turn turtle. Presently it calmed, and resumed a normal speed. But when it passed under a tree, a thick dry leaf fell down and upset it.

Swaminathan ran frantically to the spot to see if he could save at least the ant. The boat and its cargo were wrecked beyond recovery. He took a pinch of earth, uttered a prayer for the soul of the ant, and dropped it into the gutter. . . .

Swaminathan went to his grandmother. 'Granny,' he said, 'I have talked to you about Rajam, haven't I?'

'Yes. That boy who is very strong but never passes his examination.'

'No. No. That is Mani.'

'Oh, now I remember, it is a boy who is called the Gram or something, that witty little boy.'

Swaminathan made a gesture of despair. "Look here granny, you are again mistaking the Pea for him. I mean Rajam, who has killed tigers, whose father is the Police Superintendent, and who is great.'

'Oh,' granny cried, 'that boy, is he coming here? I am so glad.'

'H'm. . . . But I have got to tell you—'

'Will you bring him to me? I want to see him.'

'Let us see,' Swaminathan said vaguely. 'I can't promise. But I have got to tell you, when he is with me, you must not call me or come to my room.'

'Why so?' asked granny.

'The fact is—you are, well you are too old,' said Swaminathan with brutal candour. Granny accepted her lot cheerfully.

That he must give his friend something very nice to eat, haunted his mind. He went to his mother, who was squatting before a cutter with a bundle of plantain leaves beside her. He sat before her, nervously crushing a piece of leaf this way and that, and tearing it to minute bits.

'Don't throw all those bits on the floor. I simply can't sweep the floor any more,' she said.

'Mother, what are you preparing for the afternoon tiffin?'

'Time enough to think of it,' said mother.

'You had better prepare something fine and sweet. Rajam is coming this afternoon. Don't make the sort of coffee that you usually give me. It must be very good and hot.' He remembered how in Rajam's house everything was brought to the room by the cook. 'Mother, would you mind if I don't come here for coffee and tiffin? Can you send it to my room?' He turned to the cook and said: 'Look here, you can't come to my room in that dhoti. You will have to wear a clean, white dhoti and shirt.' After a while he said: 'Mother, can you ask father to lend me his room for just an hour or two?' She said that she could not as she was very busy. Why could he himself not go and ask?

'Oh, he will give more readily if you ask,' said Swaminathan.

He went to his father and said: 'Father, I want to ask you something.' Father looked up from the papers over which he was bent.

'Father, I want your room.'

'What for?'

'I have to receive a friend,' Swaminathan replied.

'You have your own room,' father said.

'I can't show it to Rajam.'

'Who is this Rajam, such a big man?'

'He is the Police Superintendent's son. He is—he is not ordinary.'

'I see. Oh! Yes, you can have my room, but be sure not to mess up the things on the table.'

'Oh, I will be very careful. You are a nice father, father.'

Father guffawed and said: 'Now run in, boy, and sit at your books.' . . .

Rajam's visit went off much more smoothly thau Swaminathan had anticipated. Father had left his room open; mother had prepared some marvel with wheat, plum, and sugar. Coffee was really good. Granny had kept her promise and did not show her senile self to Rajam. Swaminathan was only sorry that the cook did not change his dhoti.

Swaminathan seated Rajam in his father's revolving chair. It was nearly three hours since he had come. They had talked out all subjects—Mani, Ebenezar, trains, tiger-hunting, police, and ghosts.

'Which is your room?' Rajam asked.

Swaminathan replied with a grave face: 'This is my room, why?'

Rajam took time to swallow this. 'Do you read such books?' he asked, eyeing the big gilt-edged law books on the table. Swaminathan was embarrassed.

Rajam made matters worse with another question. "But where are your books?'

Swaminathan made desperate attempts to change the topic: 'You have seen my grandmother, Rajam?'

'No. Will you show her to me? I should love to see her,' replied Rajam.

'Wait a minute then,' said Swaminathan and ran out. He had one last hope that his granny might be asleep. It was infinitely safer to show one's friends a sleeping granny.

He saw her sitting on her bed complacently. He was disappointed. He stood staring at her, lost in thought.

'What is it, boy?' granny asked, 'Do you want anything?'

'No. Aren't you asleep? Granny,' he said a few minutes later, 'I have brought Rajam to see you.'

'Have you?' cried granny, 'Come nearer, Rajam. I can't see your face well. You know I am old and blind.'

Swaminathan was furious and muttered under his breath that his granny had no business to talk all this drivel to Rajam.

Rajam sat on her bed. Granny stroked his hair and said that he had fine soft hair, though it was really short and prickly. Granny asked what his mother's name was, and how many children she had. She then asked if she had many jewels. Rajam replied that his mother had a black trunk filled with jewels, and a green one containing gold and silver vessels. Rajam then described to her Madras, its lighthouse, its sea, its trams and buses, and its cinemas. Every item made granny gasp with wonder. . . .

Swaminathan sat in his father's room in a chair, with a slate in his hand and pencil ready. Father held the arithmetic book open and dictated: ' "Rama has ten mangoes with which he wants to earn fifteen annas. Krishna wants only four mangoes. How much will Krishna have to pay?" '

Swaminathan gazed and gazed at this sum, and every time he read it, it seemed to acquire a new meaning. He had the feeling of having stepped into a fearful maze. . . .

His mouth began to water at the thought of mangoes. He wondered what made Rama fix fifteen annas for ten mangoes. What kind of a man was Rama? Probably he was like Sankar. Somehow one couldn't help feeling that he must have been like Sankar, with his ten mangoes and his iron determination to get fifteen annas. If Rama was like Sankar, Krishna must have been like the Pea. Here Swaminathan felt an unaccountable sympathy for Krishna.

'Have you done the sum?' father asked, looking over the newspaper he was reading.

'Father, will you tell me if the mangoes were ripe?'

Father regarded him for a while and smothering a smile remarked: 'Do the sum first. I will tell you whether the fruits were ripe or not, afterwards.'

Swaminathan felt utterly helpless. If only father would tell him whether Rama was trying to sell ripe fruits or unripe ones! Of what avail would it be to tell him afterwards? He felt strongly that the answer to this question contained the key to the whole problem. It would be scandalous to expect fifteen annas for ten unripe mangoes. But even if he did, it wouldn't be unlike Rama, whom Swaminathan was steadily beginning to hate and invest with the darkest qualities.

'Father, I cannot do the sum,' Swaminathan said, pushing away the slate.

'What is the matter with you? You can't solve a simple problem in Simple Proportion?'

'We are not taught this kind of thing in our school.'

'Get the slate here. I will make you give the answer now.' Swaminathan waited with interest for the miracle to happen. Father studied the sum for a second and asked: 'What is the price of ten mangoes?'

Swaminathan looked over the sum to find out which part of the sum contained an answer to this question. 'I don't know.'

'You seem to be an extraordinary idiot. Now read the sum. Come on. How much does Rama expect for ten mangoes?'

'Fifteen annas of course,' Swaminathan thought, but how could that be its price, just price? It was very well for Rama to expect it in his avarice. But was it the right price? And then there was the obscure point whether the mangoes were ripe or not. If they were ripe, fifteen annas might not be an improbable price. If only he could get more light on this point!

'How much does Rama want for his mangoes?'

'Fifteen annas,' replied Swaminathan without conviction.

'Very good. How many mangoes does Krishna want?'

'Four.'

'What is the price of four?'

Father seemed to delight in torturing him. How could he know? How could he know what that fool Krishna would pay?

'Look here, boy. I have half a mind to thrash you. What have you in your head? Ten mangoes cost fifteen annas. What is the price of one? Come on. If you don't say it—' His hand took Swaminathan's ear and gently twisted it. Swaminathan could not open his mouth because he could not decide whether the solution lay in the realm of addition, subtraction, multiplication, or division. The longer he hesitated, the more violent the twist was becoming. In the end when father was waiting with a scowl for an answer, he received only a squeal from his son. 'I am not going to leave you till you tell me how much a single mango costs at fifteen annas for ten.' What was the matter with father? Swaminathan kept blinking. Where was the urgency to know its price?

Anyway, if father wanted so badly to know, instead of harassing him, let him go to the market and find it out. The whole brood of Ramas and Krishnas, with their endless transactions with odd quantities of mangoes and fractions of money, were getting disgusting. . . .

The Head Master entered the class with a slightly flushed face and a hard ominous look in his eyes. Swaminathan wished that he had been anywhere but there at that moment. The Head Master surveyed the class for a few minutes and asked, 'Are you not ashamed to come and sit there after what you did yesterday?' Just as a special honour to them, he read out the names of a dozen or so that had attended the class. After that he read out the names of those that had kept away, and asked them to stand on their benches. He felt that that punishment was not enough and asked them to stand on their desks. Swaminathan was among them and felt humiliated at that eminence. Then they were lectured. When it was over, they were asked to offer explanations one by one. One said that he had had an attack of headache and therefore could not come to the school. He was asked to bring a medical certificate. The second said that while he had been coming to the school on the previous day, someone had told him that there would be no school, and he had gone back home. The Head Master replied that if he was going to listen to every loafer who said there would be no school, he deserved to be flogged. Anyway, why did he not come to the school and verify? No answer. The punishment was pronounced: ten days' attendance cancelled, two rupees fine, and the whole day to be spent on the desk. The third said that he had had an attack of headache. The fourth said that he had had stomach-ache. The fifth said that his grandmother died suddenly just as he was starting for the school. The Head Master asked him if he could bring a letter from his father. No. He had no father. Then, who was his guardian? His grandmother. But the grandmother was dead, was she not? No. It was another grandmother. The Head Master asked how many grandmothers a person could have. No answer. Could he bring a letter from his neighbours? No, he could not. None of his neighbours could read or write, because he lived in the more illiterate parts of Ellaman Street. Then the Head Master offered to send a teacher to this illiterate locality to ascertain from the boy's neighbours if the death of the grandmother was a fact. A pause, some perspiration and then the answer that the neighbours could not possibly know anything about it, since the grandmother died in the village. The Head Master hit him on the knuckles with his cane, called him a street dog, and pronounced the punishment: fifteen days' suspension.

He was deaf to the question that the Head Master was putting to him. A rap on his body from the Head Master's cane brought him to himself.

'Why did you keep away yesterday?' asked the Head Master, looking up. Swaminathan's first impulse was to protest that he had never been absent. But the attendance register was there. 'No—no—I was stoned. I tried to come, but they took away my cap and burnt it. Many strong men held me down when I tried to come. . . . When a great man is sent to gaol. . . . I am surprised to see you a slave of the Englishmen. . . . Didn't they cut off— Dacca Muslin— Slaves of slaves. . . .' These were some of the disjointed explanations which streamed into his head, and, which even at that moment, he was discreet enough not to express. He had wanted to mention a headache, but he found to his distress that others beside him had had one. The Head

Master shouted, 'Won't you open your mouth?' He brought the cane sharply down on Swaminathan's right shoulder. Swaminathan kept staring at the Head Master with tearful eyes, massaging with his left hand the spot where the cane was laid. 'I will kill you if you keep on staring without answering my question,' cried the Head Master.

'I—I—couldn't come,' stammered Swaminathan.

'Is that so?' asked the Head Master, and turning to a boy said, 'Bring the peon.'

Swaminathan thought: 'What, is he going to ask the peon to thrash me? If he does any such thing, I will bite everybody dead.' The peon came. The Head Master said to him, 'Now say what you know about this rascal on the desk.'

The peon eyed Swaminathan with a sinister look, grunted, and demanded, 'Didn't I see you break the panes . . . ?'

'Of the ventilators in my room?' added the Head Master with zest.

Here there was no chance of escape. Swaminathan kept staring foolishly till he received another whack on the back. The Head Master demanded what the young brigand had to say about it. There was nothing more to it. He had unconsciously become defiant and did not care to deny the charge. When another whack came on his back, he ejaculated, 'Don't beat me, sir. It pains.' This was an invitation to the Head Master to bring down the cane four times again. He said, 'Keep standing here, on this desk, staring like an idiot, till I announce your dismissal.'

Every pore in Swaminathan's body burnt with the touch of the cane. He had a sudden flood of courage, the courage that comes of desperation. He restrained the tears that were threatening to rush out, jumped down, and, grasping his books, rushed out muttering, 'I don't care for your dirty school.' . . .

'Hallo, Swaminathan, what is the matter?'

'Nothing, sir. I have come on a little business.'

'All well at home?'

'Quite. Doctor, I have got to have a doctor's certificate immediately.'

'What is the matter with you?'

'I will tell you the truth, doctor. I have to play a match next week against the Young Men's Union. And I must have some practice. And yet every evening there is Drill Class, Scouting, some dirty period or other. If you could give me a certificate asking them to let me off at four-thirty, it would help the M. C. C. to win the match.'

'Well, I could do it. But is there anything wrong with you?'

Swaminathan took half a second to find an answer: 'Certainly, I am beginning to feel of late that I have delirium.'

'What did you say?' asked the doctor anxiously.

Swaminathan was pleased to find the doctor so much impressed, and repeated that he was having the most violent type of delirium.

'Boy, did you say delirium? What exactly do you mean by delirium?'

Swaminathan did not consider it the correct time for cross-examination. But he had to have the doctor's favour. He answered: 'I have got it. I can't say exactly. But isn't it some, some kind of stomach-ache?'

The doctor laughed till a great fit of coughing threatened to choke him. After that he looked Swaminathan under the eye, examined his tongue, tapped his chest, and declared him to be in the pink of health, and told him he would do well to stick to his drill if he wanted to get rid of delirium. Swaminathan again explained to him how important it was for him to have his evenings free. But the doctor said: 'It is all very well. But I should be prosecuted if I gave you any such certificate.'

The English Teacher (extracts)

R. K. Narayan

I was on the whole very pleased with my day—not many conflicts and worries, above all not too much self-criticism. I had done almost all the things I wanted to do, and as a result I felt heroic and satisfied. The urge had been upon me for some days past to take myself in hand. What was wrong with me? I couldn't say, some sort of a vague disaffection, a self-rebellion I might call it. The feeling again and again came upon me that as I was nearing thirty I should cease to live like a cow (perhaps a cow, with justice, might feel hurt at the comparison), eating, working in a manner of speaking, walking, talkina, etc.—all done to perfection, I was sure, but always leaving behind a sense of something missing.

I took stock of my daily life. I got up at eight every day, read for the fiftieth time Milton, Carlyle and Shakespeare, looked through compositions, swallowed a meal, dressed, and rushed out of the hostel just when the second bell sounded at college; four hours later I returned to my room; my duty in the interval had been admonishing, cajoling and browbeating a few hundred boys of Albert Mission College so that they might mug up Shakespeare and Milton and secure high marks and save me adverse remarks from my chiefs at the end of the year. For this pain the authorities kindly paid me a hundred rupees on the first of every month and dubbed me a lecturer. One ought, of course, to be thankful. But such repose was not in my nature, perhaps because I was a poet, and I was constantly nagged by the feeling that I was doing the wrong work. This was responsible for a perpetual self-criticism and all kinds of things aggravated it. For instance what my good chief Brown had said to us that day might be very reasonable, but it irritated and upset me.

We were summoned to his room at the end of the day. Under normal conditions, he would welcome us with a smile, crack a joke or two, talk of nothing in particular for a couple of minutes and then state the actual business. But today we found him dry and sullen. He motioned us to our seats and said, "Could you imagine a worse shock for me? I came across a student of the English Honours, who did not know till this day that 'honours' had to be spelt with a 'u'?" He finished with a sharp, grim laugh. We looked at each other and were at a loss to know what to reply. Our Assistant Professor, Gajapathy, scowled at us as if it were us who had induced the boy to drop the 'u'. Brown cleared his throat as a signal for further speech, and we watched his lips. He began a lecture on the importance of the English language, and the need for preserving its purity. Brown's thirty years in India had not been ill-spent, if they had opened the eyes of Indians to the need for speaking and writing correct English! The responsibility of the English department was indeed very great. At this point

Gajapathy threw us a further furious look. The chief went on for forty-five minutes; and feeling that it was time to leaven his sermon with a little humour, added: "It would be a serious enough blunder even from a mathematics honours man!"

When going out I was next to Gajapathy. He looked so heavily concerned that I felt like pricking him so that he might vanish like a bubble leaving no trace behind. But I checked myself. It would be unwise: he was my senior in office, and he might give me an hour of extra work every day, or compel me to teach the history of language, of which I knew nothing. I had to bear with him till we reached the hostel gate. He kept glancing at his own shoulder, swelling with importance. He muttered: "Disgraceful! I never knew our boys were so bad. . . . We cannot pretend that we come out of it with flying colours. . . ." I felt irritated and said, "Mr. Gajapathy, there are blacker sins in this world than a dropped vowel." He stopped on the road and looked up and down. He was aghast. I didn't care. I drove home the point: "Let us be fair. Ask Mr. Brown if he can say in any of the two hundred Indian languages: 'The cat chases the rat'. He has spent thirty years in India."

"It is all irrelevant," said Gajapathy.

"Why should he think the responsibility for learning is all on our side and none on his? Why does he magnify his own importance?"

"Good night," said Gajapathy and was off. I felt angry and insulted, and continued my discussion long after both Gajapathy and Brown were out of my reach. Later when I went for a walk I still continued the debate. But suddenly I saw illumination and checked myself. It showed a weak, uncontrolled mind, this incapacity to switch off. I now subjected myself to a remorseless self-analysis. Why had I become incapable of controlling my own thoughts? I brooded over it. Needless to say it took me nowhere. It left me more exhausted and miserable at the end of the day. I felt a great regret of having spent a fine evening in brooding and self-analysis, and then reached a startlingly simple solution. All this trouble was due to lack of exercise and irregular habits: so forthwith I resolved to be up very early next day, go out along the river on a long walk, run a few yards, bathe in the river and regulate my life thus. . . .

After dinner my friends in the neighbouring rooms in the hostel dropped in as usual for light talk. They were my colleagues. One was Rangappa who taught the boys philosophy, and the other Gopal of the mathematics section. Gopal was sharp as a knife-edge where mathematical matters were concerned, but, poor fellow, he was very dumb and stupid in other matters. As a matter of fact he paid little attention to anything else. We liked him because he was a genius, and in a vague manner we understood that he was doing brilliant things in mathematics. Some day he hoped to contribute a paper on his subject which was going to revolutionize human thought and conceptions. But God knew what it was all about. All that I cared for in him was that he was an agreeable friend, who never contradicted and who patiently listened for hours, though without showing any sign of understanding.

Tonight the talk was all about English spelling and the conference we had with Brown. I was incensed as usual, much to the amazement of Rangappa. "But my dear fellow, what do you think they pay you for unless it is for dotting the i's and crossing the t's?" Gopal, who had been listening without putting in a word of his own, suddenly became active.

"I don't follow you," he said.

"I said the English department existed solely for dotting the i's and crossing the t's."

"Oh!" he said, opening wide his eyes. "I never thought so. Why should you do it?" His precise literal brain refused to move where it had no concrete facts or figures to grip. Symbols, if they entered his brain at all, entered only as mathematical symbols.

Rangappa answered: "Look here, Gopal. You have come across the expression 'Raining cats and dogs'?"

"Yes."

"Have you actually seen cats and dogs falling down from the sky?"

"No, no. Why?"

Rangappa would have worried him a little longer, but the college clock struck ten and I said: "Friends, I must bid you good night." "Good night," Gopal repeated mechanically and rose to go. Not so the ever-questioning philosopher. "What has come over you?" he asked, without moving.

"I want to cultivate new habits. . . ."

"What's wrong with the present ones?" he asked and I blinked for an answer. It was a long story and could not stand narration. Rangappa did not even stir from his seat; the other stood ready to depart and waited patiently. "Answer me," Rangappa persisted.

"I want to be up very early to-morrow," I said.

"What time?"

"Some time before five."

"What for?"

"I want to see the sunrise, and get some exercise before I start work."

"Very good; wake me up too, I shall also go with you—" said Rangappa rising. I saw them off at the door. I had an alarm clock on which I could sometimes depend for giving the alarm at the set time. I had bought it years before at a junk store in Madras. It had a reddening face, and had been oiled and repaired a score of times. It showed the correct time but was eccentric with regard to its alarm arrangement. It let out a shattering amount of noise, and it sometimes went off by itself and butted into a conversation, or sometimes when I had locked the room and gone out, it started off and went on ringing till exhaustion overcame it. There was no way of stopping it, by pressing a button or a lever. I don't know if it had ever had such an arrangement. At first I did not know about its trouble, so that I suffered a great shock and did not know how to silence it, short of dashing it down. But one day I learnt by some sort of instinctive experiment that if I placed a heavy book like Taine's *History of English Literature* on its crest, it stopped shrieking.

I picked up the clock and sat on my bed looking at it. I believe I almost addressed it: "Much depends upon you." I set it at four-thirty and lay down.

At four-thirty it shrieked my sleep away. I switched on the light, picked up Taine hurriedly, and silenced it. I went over to Rangappa's room, stood at his window and called him a dozen times, but there was no answer. As I stood looking at his sleeping figure with considerable disgust and pity, he stirred and asked: "Who is there?"

"It is nearing five, you wanted to be called out—"

"Why?"

"You said you would come out."

"Not me—"

"It is about five—" I said.

"It looks to me like midnight; go back to bed, my dear fellow, don't hang about windows pestering people—" His voice was thick and the last words trailed off into sleep. . . .

Nature, nature, all our poets repeat till they are hoarse. There are subtle, invisible emanations in nature's surroundings: with them the deepest in us merges and harmonizes. I think it is the highest form of joy and peace we can ever comprehend. I decided to rush back to my table and write a poem on nature.

I was going to write of the cold water's touch on the skin, the cold air blowing on chest and face, the rumble of the river, cries of birds, magic of the morning light, all of which created an alchemy of inexplicable joy. I paused for a moment and wondered how this poem would be received in a class-room—the grim tolerance with which boys listen to poetry, the annotator's desperate effort to convey a meaning, and the teacher's doubly desperate effort to wrest a meaning out of the poet and the annotator, the essence of an experience lost in all this handling. . . .

I returned to my room before seven. I felt very well satisfied indeed with my performance. I told myself: "I am all right. I am quite sound if I can do this every day. I shall be able to write a hundred lines of poetry, read everything I want to read, in addition to class-work. . . ." This gave place to a distinct memory of half a dozen similar resolves in the past and the lapses. . . . I checked this defeatism! "Don't you see this is entirely different? I am different today. . . ."

"How?" asked a voice. I ignored the question and it added, "Why?"

"Shut up," I cried. "Don't ask questions." I myself was not clear as to the "Why?" except that my conscience perpetually nagged over arrears of work, books from libraries and friends lying in a heap on the table untouched, letters unanswered and accumulating, lines of poetry waiting for months to be put on paper, a picture of my wife meant to be framed and hung on the wall, but for months and months standing on the table leaning against the wall in its cardboard mount, covered with dust, bent by the weight of the books butting into it. . . .

This table assailed my sight as soon as I entered and I muttered, "Must set all this right," as I sat down on my chair. I called Singaram our servant. He had been a hostel servant for forty years and known all of us as undergraduates and now as teachers—an old man who affected great contempt for all of us, including our senior professors and principal. He spoke to us with habitual rudeness. Somehow he felt that because he had seen all of us as boys, our present stature and age and position were a make-believe, to which he would be no party. "Singaram," I called, and he answered from somewhere, "You will have to wait till I come. If you hurt your throat calling me, don't hold me responsible for it. . . ." In a few minutes he stood before me, a shrunken old fellow, with angry wrinkles on his face. "Now what is it this time? Has that sweeper not done her work properly? If she is up to her old tricks . . ."

"Tell the cook to bring my coffee. . . ."

"So late! Why should you dally over your coffee so long, when you ought to be reading at your table. . . ."

"I went for a bathe in the river, Singaram. I found it very fine. . . ." He was happy to hear it.

"I'm glad you are ceasing to be the sort who lounges before bathrooms, waiting for a hot bath. A river bath is the real thing for a real man. I am eighty years old, and have never had a day's sickness, and have never bathed in hot water."

"Nor in cold water, I think," I said as he went away to send me my coffee.

I made a space on the table by pushing aside all the books; took out a sheet of paper and wrote a poem entitled "Nature," about fifty lines of verse. I read and re-read it, and found it very satisfying. I felt I had discharged a duty assigned to me in some eternal scheme.

I had four hours of teaching to do that day. Lear for the Junior B.A. class, a composition period for the Senior Arts; detailed prose and poetry for other classes. Four periods of continuous work and I hadn't prepared even a page of lecture.

I went five minutes late to the class, and I could dawdle over the attendance for a quarter of an hour. I picked out the attendance register and called out the first name. "Here, sir—," "Present," and I marked. Two boys in the front bench got up and suggested, "Sir, take the attendance at the end of the period."

"Sit down please, can't be done. I can't encroach into the next hour's work. . . ."

A babble rose in the class, a section demanding that the attendance be taken immediately and another demanding postponement. I banged the table with my fist and shouted over the din: "Stop this, otherwise I will mark everyone absent."

"Attendance takes up most of our hours, sir."

"We can't help it. Your attendance is just as important as anything else. Stop all noise and answer your names; otherwise, I will mark all of you absent. . . ." At this the boys became quiet, because I out-shouted them. The lion-tamer's touch! In a sober moment perhaps I would reflect on the question of obedience. Born in different households, perhaps petted, pampered, and bullied, by parents, uncles, brothers—all persons known to them and responsible for their growth and welfare. Who was I that they should obey my command? What tie was there between me and them? Did I absorb their personalities as did the old masters and merge them in mine? I was merely a man who had mugged earlier than they the introduction and the notes in the Verity edition of Lear, and guided them through the mazes of Elizabethan English. I did not do it out of love for them or for Shakespeare but only out of love for myself. If they paid me the same one hundred rupees for stringing beads together or tearing up paper bits every day for a few hours, I would perhaps be doing it with equal fervour. But such reflections do not mar our peace when we occupy the class-room chair. So that I banged the table—shouted till they were silenced, and went through the attendance; all this tittle-tattle swallowed up half an hour.

I opened my Verity. I had made a pencil mark where I had stopped on the previous day: middle of the first scene in the third act.

I began in a general way: "You will see that I stopped last time where Lear faces the storm. This is a vital portion of this great tragedy. . . ." The words rang hollow in my ears. Some part of me was saying: "These poor boys are now all attention, cowed by your superior force. They are ready to listen to you and write down whatever you may say. What have you to give them in return?" I noticed that some boys were already sitting up alert, ready to note down the pearls dropping from my mouth. . . .

I felt like breaking out into a confession! "My dear fellows, don't trust me so much. I am merely trying to mark time because I couldn't come sufficiently prepared, because all the morning I have . . ." But I caught myself lecturing: "This is the very heart of the tragedy." . . .

I had to wait in the bathroom passage for some time, all the cubicles were engaped. Behind the doors, to the tune of falling water a couple of boys were humming popular film songs. I paced the passage with the towel round my neck. It was a semi-dark, damp place, with a glass tile giving it its sole lighting. "I shall soon be rid of this nuisance," I reflected, "when I have a home of my own. Hostel bathrooms are hell on earth. . . . [God said to his assistants, 'Take this man away to hell,' and they brought him down to the hostel bathroom passage, and God said, 'torture him,' and they opened the room and pushed him in. . . . No, no, at this moment the angels said the room is engaged.' . . . God waited as long as a god can wait and asked, 'Have you finished?' and they replied, 'Still engaged,' and in due course they could not see where their victim was, for grass had grown and covered him up completely while he waited outside the bathroom door. This promises to be a good poem. Must write it someday. . . ."] At this moment a door opened and someone came out dripping. It was a student of the second-year class. He asked agitatedly: "Sir, have I kept you waiting long?"

"Yes, my dear fellow, but how could you come out before finishing that masterpiece of a song?" The other held the door ostentatiously open and I passed in. . . .

"I must have a house," I told myself, "which faces south, for its breeze, keeps out the western sun, gets in the eastern, and admits the due measure of northern light that artists so highly value. The house must have a room for each one of us and for a guest or two. It must keep us all together and yet separate us when we would rather not see each other's faces. . . . We must have helpful people and good people near at hand, but obnoxious neighbours ten miles away. It must be within walking distance of college and yet so far out as to let me enjoy my domestic life free from professional intrusions."

I spent the entire evening scouring various parts of the town watching for "To Let" signs.

"The builder of this house must have been dead-drunk while doing the latter portion of the house. This is a house evidently intended for monkeys to live in. This house must have been designed by a tuberculosis expert so that his business may prosper for the next hundred years. This house is ideal for one whose greatest desire in life is to receive constant knocks on his head from door-posts. A house for a twisted pigmy." Thus, variously, I commented within myself as I inspected the vacant houses in the east, west and south of the town. . . .

Four days later my table and trunk and chair were loaded into a bullock cart, my old room was locked up and the key was handed to Singaram. My hostel friends stood on the veranda and cracked a joke or two. The hostel was a place where people constantly arrived and departed and it was not in anyone's nature there to view these matters pensively. Rangappa and the mathematics man stood on the veranda and said. "Well, good-bye, friend. Good luck. Don't forget us for the house-warming," and laughed. Singaram had been very busy the whole day packing up and loading my things. He had attended on me for ten years—sweeping my room, counselling me and running my errands. He walked behind the creaking cart warning the driver: "When you unload, remove the trunk first and the table last. If I hear that you have broken any leg, I will break your head, remember. . . ." I walked behind the cart. Singaram had come to the border of his domain—the hostel drive, and stopped. He salaamed me and said, "Don't forget our hostel, keep visiting us now and then." He hesitated for a moment and said: "Now permit this old man to go. . . ." It was his hint that the time had come for him to receive his reward. He nearly held out his hand for it. I took out my purse and put a rupee on his palm. He looked at me coldly and said: "Is that all the value you attach to the old man?" "Yes," I replied. "I should have given half that to anyone else. . . ."

"No, no, don't say so. Don't grudge an honest man his payment. I've been your servant for ten years. Do you know what Professor X gave me when he left this hostel?" "I don't want all that information," I said and added a nickel to the rupee. He said: "Don't grudge an old servant his due. You will perhaps not see me again: I will perhaps be dead; next year I'm retiring and going back to my village. You will never see me again. You will be very sorry when you hear that old Singaram is dead and that you wouldn't give the poor fellow eight annas more. . . ." I put in his hand an eight-anna coin. He bowed and said: "God will make you a big professor one day . . ." and walked away. I passed out of the hostel gate, following my caravan and goods. . . .

On the following Friday, I was pacing the little Malgudi railway station in great agitation. I had never known such suspense before. She was certain to arrive with a lot of luggage, and the little child. How was all this to be transferred from the train to the platform? And the child must not be hurt. I made a mental note, "Must shout as soon as the train stops: 'Be careful with the baby.'" This seemed to my fevered imagination the all-important thing to say on arrival, as otherwise I fancied the child's head was sure to be banged against the doorway. . . . And how many infants were damaged and destroyed by careless mothers in the process of coming out of trains! Why couldn't they maeke thse railway carriages of safer dimensions? It ought to be

PROVERBS

A thorn sticks into a great man and hundreds run to help; a poor man falls down a cliff and no one comes near.

In the absence of wind, a heap of cotton is as steady as a mountaintop.

Speak to please the world; eat to please yourself.

For the belly's sake we put on many a disguise.

Four *Vedas;* the fifth teaching is a cudgel.

All are naked under their loincloths.

If your own family point their fingers at you, outsiders will point their feet.

If you clap with but one hand, will there be a sound?

Put not your trust in rivers, in savage beasts, in horned cattle, in women, in princes.

Kings, women, and creepers lay hold of what is nearest them.

done in the interests of baby welfare in India. "Mind the baby and the door." And then the luggage! Susila was sure to bring with her a huge amount of luggage. She required four trunks for her sarees alone! Women never understood the importance of travelling light. Why should they? As long as there were men to bear all the anxieties and bother and see them through their travails! It would teach them a lesson to be left to shift for themselves. Then they would know the value of economy in these matters. I wrung my hands in despair. How was she going to get out with the child and all that luggage! The train stopped for just seven minutes. I would help her down first and then throw the things out, and if there were any boxes left over they would have to be lost with the train, that was all. No one could help it. I turned to the gnarled blue-uniformed man behind me. He was known as Number Five and I had known him for several years now. Whatever had to be done on the railway platform was done with his help. I had offered him three times his usual wages to help me to-day. I turned to him and asked: "Can you manage even if there is too much luggage?"

"Yes, master, no difficulty. The train stops for seven minutes." He seemed to have a grand notion of seven minutes; a miserable flash it seemed to me. "We unload whole waggons within that time."

"I will tell the pointsman to stop it at the outer signal, if necessary," he added. It was a very strength-giving statement to me. I felt relieved. But I think I lost my head once again. I believe, in this needless anxiety, I became slightly demented. Otherwise I would not have rushed at the stationmaster the moment I set eyes on him. I saw him come out of his room and move down the platform to gaze on a far off signal post. I ran behind him, panting: "Good morning, stationmaster!" He bestowed an official smile and moved off to the end of the platform and looked up. I felt I had a lot of doubts to clear on railway matters and asked inanely: "Looking at the signals?"

"Yes," he replied, and took his eyes down, and turned to go back to his room. I asked: "Can't they arrange to stop this train a little longer here?" "What for? Isn't there enough trouble as it is?" I laughed sympathetically and said: "I said so because it may not be possible for passengers to unload all their trunks."

"I should like to see a passenger who carries luggage that will take more than six minutes. I have been here thirty years."

I said: "My wife is arriving to-day with the infant. I thought she would require a lot of time in order to get down carefully. And then she is bound to have numerous boxes. These women, you know," I said laughing artificially, seeking his indulgence. He was a good man and laughed with me. "Well, sometimes it has happened that the train was held up for the convenience of a second-class passenger. Are your people travelling second?" "I can't say," I said. I knew well she wouldn't travel second, although I implored her in every letter to do so. She wrote rather diplomatically: "Yes, don't be anxious, I and the baby will travel down quite safely." I even wrote to my father-in-law, but that gentleman preserved a discreet silence on the matter. I knew by temperament he disliked the extravagance of travelling second, although he could afford it and in other ways had proved himself no miser. I felt furious at the thought of him and told the stationmaster: "Some people are born niggards . . . would put up with any trouble rather than . . ." But before I could finish my sentence a bell rang inside the station office and the stationmaster ran in, leaving me to face my travail and anguish alone. I turned and saw my porter standing away from me, borrowing a piece of tobacco from someone. "Here, Number Five, don't get lost." A small crowd was gathering unobtrusively on the platform. I feared he might get lost at the critical moment. A bell sounded. People moved about. We heard the distant puffing and whistling. The engine appeared around the bend.

A whirling blur of faces went past me as the train shot in and stopped. People were clambering up and down. Number Five followed me about, munching his tobacco casually, "Search on that side of the mail van." I hurried through the crowd, peering into the compartments. I saw my father-in-law struggling to get to the doorway. I ran up to his carriage. Through numerous people getting in and out, I saw her sitting serenely in her seat with the baby lying on her lap. "Only three minutes more!" I cried. "Come out!" My father-in-law got down. I and Number Five fought our way up, and in a moment I was beside my wife in the compartment.

"No time to be sitting down; give me the baby," I said. She merely smiled and said: "I will carry the baby down. You will get these boxes. That wicker box, bring it down yourself, it contains baby's bottle and milk vessels." She picked up the child and unconcernedly moved on. She hesitated for a second on the thick of the crowd and said: "Way please," and they made way for her. I cried: "Susila, mind the door and the baby." All the things I wanted to say on this occasion were muddled and gone out of mind. I looked at her apprehensively till she was safely down on the platform helped by her father. Number Five worked wonders within a split second. . . .

In the earlier years of our married life we often sat together with one or other of the books, in the single top-floor room in her father's house, and tried to read. The first half an hour would be wasted because of an irresponsible mood coming over her, which made her laugh at everything; even the most solemn poem would provoke her, especially such poems as were addressed by a lover. "My true love hath my heart and I have his." She would laugh till she became red in the face. "Why can't each keep his own or her own heart instead of this exchange?" She then put out her hand and searched all my pockets saying: "In case you should take away mine!"

"Hush, listen to the poem," I said, and she would listen to me with suppressed mirth and shake her head in disapproval. And then another line that amused her very much was "Oh, mistress mine, where are you roaming?" She would not allow me to progress a line beyond, saying: "I shall die of this poem someday. What is the matter with the woman loafing all over the place except where her husband is?"

However much she might understand or not understand, she derived a curious delight in turning over the pages of a book, and the great thing was that I should sit by her side and explain. While she read the Tamil classics and Sanskrit texts without my help, she liked English to be explained by me. If I showed the slightest hesitation, she would declare: "Perhaps you don't care to explain English unless you are paid a hundred rupees a month for it?" . . .

I always fancied that I was born for a poetic career and some day I hoped to take the world by storm with the publication. Some of the pieces were written in English and some in Tamil. (I hadn't yet made up my mind as to which language was to be enriched with my contributions to its literature, but the language was unimportant. The chief thing seemed to be the actual effort.) I turned over the pages looking at my previous writing. The last entry was several months ago, on nature. I felt satisfied with it but felt acute discomfort on realizing that I had hardly done anything more than that. Today I was going to make up for all lost time; I took out my pen, dipped it in ink, and sat hesitating. Everything was ready except a subject. What should I write about?

My wife had come in and was stealthily watching the pages over my shoulder. As I sat biting the end of my pen, she remarked from behind me: "Oh, the poetry book is out: why are you staring at a blank page?" Her interruption was always welcome. I put away my book, and said: "Sit down," dragging a stool nearer. "No, I'm going away. Write your poetry. I won't disturb you. You may forget what you wanted to write." "I have not even thought of what to write," I said. "Someday I want to fill all the pages of this book and then it will be published and read all over the world." At this she turned over the leaves of the notebook briskly and laughed: "There seem to be over a thousand pages, and you have hardly filled the first ten."

"The trouble is I have not enough subjects to write on," I confessed. She drew herself up and asked: "Let me see if you can write about me."

"A beautiful idea," I cried. "Let me see you." I sat up very attentively and looked at her keenly and fixedly like an artist or a photographer viewing his subject. I said: "Just move a little to your left please. Turn your head right. Look at me straight here. That's right. . . . Now I can write about you. Don't drop your lovely eyelashes so much. You make me forget my task. Ah, now, don't grin please. Very good, stay as you are and see how I write now, steady. . . ." I drew up the notebook, ran the fountain pen hurriedly over it and filled a whole page beginning:

> "She was a phantom of delight
> When first she gleamed upon my sight:
> A lovely apparition, sent
> To be a moment's ornament."

It went on for thirty lines ending:

> "And yet a spirit still, and bright
> With something of an angel-light."

I constantly paused to look at her while writing, and said: "Perfect. Thank you. Now listen."

"Oh, how fast you write!" she said admiringly.

"You will also find how well I've written. Now listen," I said, and read as if to my class, slowly and deliberately, pausing to explain now and then.

"I never knew you could write so well."

"It is a pity that you should have underrated me so long; but now you know better. Keep it up," I said. "And if possible don't look at the pages, say roughly between 150 and 200 in the Golden Treasury. Because someone called Wordsworth has written similar poems." This was an invitation for her to run in and fetch her copy of the Golden Treasury and turn over precisely the forbidden pages. She scoured every title and first line and at last pitched upon the original. She read it through, and said: "Aren't you ashamed to copy?"

"No," I replied. "Mine is entirely different. He had writtten about someone entirely different from my subject."

"I wouldn't do such a thing as copying."

"I should be ashamed to have your memory," I said. "You have had the copy of the Golden Treasury for years now, and yet you listened to my reading with gaping wonder! I wouldn't give you even two out of a hundred if you were my student." At this point our conversation was interrupted by my old clock. It burst in upon us all of a sudden. It purred and bleated and made so much noise that it threw us all into confusion. Susila picked it up and tried to stop it without success, till I snatched Taine and smothered it.

The Prevalence of Witches (extracts)

Aubrey Menen

I had come to Limbo because I had always wanted to possess a country of my own. I did not want a large country that would be bound to get me into trouble with other large countries, but one quite small, and preferably round. For me, a tent would be rather too small: the Federated States of Limbo were rather too big. They were six hundred and fifty miles of clumsy hills and jungle: not tangled jungle but the sort where the trees grow straight and the only confusion comes from clumps of bamboos that spread out at the top like shaving brushes. But I thought it would do. On the map it was as beautifully round as it was blank. For a thousand years the inhabitants had shot at everybody who came into it with arrows and their aim was usually adequate to their purpose of keeping people out; where the bowman failed to get home, the mosquitos did not. Once a year one Englishman visits Limbo, surrounded by clouds of insecticide through which can just be discovered the Union Jack. During this visit, Limbo is a part of the British Empire in India. When the Englishman has gone, the various Chiefs of Limbo, sighing with relief, take off their trousers and go hunting again with their bows and arrows, the mosquitos come cautiously out to bury their dead, and Limbo is safe for odd persons like me who are determined to live in a country of our own, even if it kills us.

When I first arrived at the central village I could tell by the smell of insecticide and the flag that had been run up on a rather bent flagstaff that the English king of the place had got there before us. His friends called him Catullus: the name had nothing to do with the Roman poet; it simply fitted Catullus' Roman face. I do not suppose that any Roman ever looked like those busts which they have left behind them, with the smooth segments of eggs instead of eyes, but Catullus did, most especially when he was doing his Civil Service job of being an itinerant king of the Federated States. When he was being your friend, it was different. The stone face remained, very obvious and bold about the nose and lips, but the expression changed. It was as though a school-boy had reached up and drawn two mischievous eyes on the blank egg-segments, and had been caught just before he could draw in the saucy moustaches that obviously went with them. When he was being your friend you could not understand how he could bear to be an official king.

I was conducted to my seat by a servant dressed in white and scarlet. He saluted and showed me a chair marked Miss Thelma Macey, on which I sat. I turned to the man sitting next to me and said, "I hope Miss Thelma Macey will not turn up at the last moment." He turned a pale grey face to me glittering with a pair of rather skittish American spectacles.

"You're the new Education Officer."

"Yes. You must be the American missionary." I had heard that there was one, from Virginia, and this man's accent fitted.

"I am."

"I was saying, I hope Miss Thelma Macey does not turn up now."

"I agree with you," he said. "She has been dead ten years."

"Oh! I'm sorry," I said rather foolishly.

"Not that there aren't quite a few people out there who wouldn't be in the least surprised if she did come back," said the missionary, nodding his head at the squatting Limbodians. "Dead witches do."

"Was Miss Macey a witch?"

"She said she was."

"Really? Tell me, Mr. . . . er . . . "

"Small is the name," he said, shaking hands with me. It was a diffident handshake, part of his whole nervous manner. But his expression was pleasant; he seemed willing to be friendly but almost certain that nobody would like him.

"Have you seen a witch yet?" he asked me.

"No. I should like to."

"Don't do anything in a hurry about witches. Things go wrong. Things get back at you."

"You take witches very seriously, Mr. Small?"

"One does, in Limbo. Limbo's witch-country." . . .

"Thelma Macey set herself a programme. She split up her life into three-year periods. Two years she'd spend working here, doing good and spreading the Gospel. Then she'd go to the States to raise money to build a church. The Mission paid her passage both ways, but that was all they would do. But Thelma had a way of making money out of everything. Not for herself, mind you, but for her church. She lived for that church. She used to get jobs as a stewardess or a nurse-companion on the boats that took her to and from the U.S.A., and save the passage money. Every cent she saved she entered in her account books and then put it away in the bank. When she got home she would start organizing bazaars and lecture tours and everything she could think of to raise money: and she was a woman with plenty of ideas in that direction. It all went down in her account books. It took a long time getting the money and she was a long time without her church. But she got so that her account books were almost as good a thing to her as an actual stone-and-mortar church. She loved figures, and she'd spend hours looking at her sums, as happy as a woman could be."

Small looked thoughtfully at the witch's gravestone for a while and then went on.

"One day she was adding up what she'd got and what she'd made by investing it, and it all totalled up to enough to begin the church. Not enough to finish it, but enough to begin. By that time the Limbodians had got around to liking her, and when she talked to them about her church they promised to build it for her. She drew them plans and pictures and she gave them an idea of where she wanted it built. Then she left for the U.S.A. on her last trip to raise cash. She worked as though she was inspired, and got the cash and a little to spare. She got a boat for Limbo once more, though she was so happy she felt she could have walked across the Atlantic Ocean on her two feet. When she got here she found that the Limbodians had prepared a surprise. They'd built her church for her. It wasn't all that an architect could have desired, maybe, but it was everything that Miss Macey wanted. It wasn't exactly where she had thought of it being built. . . .

"It didn't take her long to see what had happened. The Limbodians had cheated her: they had used her money to build a handsome shrine for their premier witch. That was the meaning of the gifts which she found each day on the platform, and the flowers which she had thought such a charming tribute to her church. She sat down and swore. She'd never sworn in her life, and she was not very good at it. She put every word she said in her diary, as a sort of penance. I've read it, and she repeats herself. But there's no mistaking her feelings.

"Then she went back home and took out her account books. She brooded over them for a long while, and when she closed them she knew just what she had to do. She made up her mind that the Limbodians should pay back every cent of the money. Then she would build another church. It was no good just rooting up this old stone. A witch was buried here and it would be witch's ground for evermore. She had to get a brand new church, and for that she wanted her money back on this one.

"There was one way to do that, and she took it without a moment's doubt. She pulled down the platform so that this stone would show plainly. She made it all neat and tidy and then called the Limbodians together. When she had got as many in the church as it could hold she talked to them. She didn't say a word about their trickery: she did not accuse them of anything. She said that it was about time that she told them the truth. She had had a long talk with the dead witch, who had thanked her for raising the money to build her a shrine. In return, the dead woman had passed on to Thelma all her powers of evil. In a word, Thelma Macey was setting up in business as a witch.

"She went about it with the same energy as she had brought to getting the money for the church. She had learned a good deal about it from her work in Limbo, and what she didn't know she invented. She threatened to curse the crops, and the Limbodians had to buy her off with tithes. She muttered spells whenever she heard of an impending wedding and could only be mollified by presents of hard cash. She took responsibility for every stomache-ache and cold in the nose in the village, and it all meant payment to her in cash or in kind. The kind she used to take once a week outside Limbo and sell in a local market. Whatever she earned went down in her account books.

"The Limbodians thought it was all right and proper and took it with good grace. Witches hand on their powers to their favourites, and Thelma Macey, especially whenever she thought of the money she had lost, had a look which anyone who had seen a witch would recognize as a first-class evil eye. So they paid up and considered themselves lucky to have the chance to do so. On the whole they thought her a fairly tolerant sort of witch: there were no epidemics and no man-eating tigers while she held sway, but only the usual run of small misfortunes.

"The misfortunes may have been small but there were plenty of them, and soon Thelma Macey had got all her money back. She checked it up in her account books one evening, drew a red line under the totals, and wrote the whole story in a letter back to her Church in the U.S.A. She was frank about what she'd done, although she didn't put it as plainly as I have. She said that she had gone through all the ceremonies that a witch is supposed to do and she said it had not been very easy. Once or twice she had had to drink strong liquor with witch-doctors, as custom demanded, and it had made her pretty sick. But now it was over. She enclosed a cheque for the money and asked permission to pull down the abomination of a church that she already had, and build a new one on a new site. When she finished telling of what she had done, she added that she felt she had laboured not unworthily in the vineyard of the Lord, though maybe at a peculiar job. She signed her name and felt satisfied.

"While she waited for the reply (and it took weeks) she did not go to the church and she gave up being a witch. Then the letter came. It was from the head of her Church. It did not say a word about her having been a witch. It did not mention the stone in the church. It just said that they had held a meeting and sought guidance. As she well knew, it was strictly against the fundamental principles of their Church to touch strong liquor. They were waging a bitter war against the demon of alcohol in the States and they felt that one weak member of their community would bring into discredit the whole glorious fight. They were sorry she had fallen by the wayside. In other words, she was fired. They thanked her for the money."

Small paused and took off his spectacles. He peered at the witch's stone for a little and then said,

"It broke her heart. As I said, she's been dead a good few years now. Dead," said the Reverend Small, "and, I sincerely trust, in heaven." . . .

Catullus explained with great enjoyment. "You see, the land belongs to the Chiefs, but the trees, being teak and worth a good deal of money, belong to the Administration. That's me. I often wonder what sort of meanly wicked men made these treaties for England with their quibbles and tricks. We got an uncomfortably large slice of our Empire not by being good soldiers but by being quick at languages. First we sent the missionaries to make grammars and translations of the Bible, then we sent the Civil Servants to use the grammars to write out treaties. The Americans got the Red Indians drunk on gin: we got our Indians fuddled with words. That is why there are so many lawyers in India, because for a century we quibbled away a piece of land here and quibbled away a piece of land there till the whole country collapsed about the Indians' ears in ruins and we ran among them, squeaking with delight, gobbling up the bits." . . .

"Look there," he said, pointing to the village street of round grass huts. "Somebody's built a tiny hut beside that big one. I wonder what it's for?" He trotted off down the earth road to find out.

The small hut was built exactly like the larger one: round walls of plaited bamboo, a tiny mud doorstep too small to put one's whole foot upon, and a round grass roof rising to a point. In all it was four feet high.

"It's a kennel. I'm sure it's a kennel. Or a chicken-run," Catullus said as he bent over it. "How charming, how sweet, how utterly ridiculous."

He bent down to peer into the small doorway. There was a giggle from inside and three small boys, quite naked, crawled out one after the other and, shrieking with laughter, fled down the road. Catullus straightened himself, delighted.

"It's a brothel," he said, with immense satisfaction. "Isn't that interesting? Imagine one of these little huts in every school playground in England and America, and you will get some measure of how remarkable these people are. 'Jones, where is Smith major,' " he said, imitating a schoolmaster. He changed his already high voice easily to the treble, " 'In the hut sir, with Brown minimus. Shall I call him, sir?' 'Good Lord, no, boy, I wouldn't think of such a thing.' These people have no sense of sin at all. They can't have, because evil is due, wholly and all the time, to witches, and it is plainly absurd to blame a man for being the victim of a witch. They go further: witches are busy people and do not concern themselves with trivial things we call vice. Death and disease, ruin and madness are the things they deal in. These and catastrophes like them are what the Limbodians call evil. Small sins, the sins that concern our schoolmasters and parents and divorce judges, our priests and Sunday journalists, do not measure up to the vast wickedness of witches. They are too small to be noticed. With us, our eyes fixed on little sins, we do not notice the big ones, so that those who commit them are not hung up by the heels and beaten within an inch of their life, but made statesmen, tycoons and archbishops. We look up and adore them while they rain disasters down upon our silly faces. What shall we do now?" he asked breathlessly. "I know, we shall go and see the prison." He cantered off down the road towards it, singing in a falsetto voice. Then he noticed that I was not too happy at his project, and he burst out with a flood of advice. "But you must always see prisons if you want to understand any country. I always make them the first thing I see. It is very intelligent to be interested in prisons. It tells you everything about a people at a glance."

"You mean the criminals are a sort of cross-section," I said, half running beside him to keep up with his trotting walk.

"But no, no, no," he said; "you don't go to see the criminals, you go to see the gaolers. Prisons are vicious places. Always study the vices of a people, not its virtues. Virtues are always the same wherever you go. . . . Origen might have thought he had invented a new virtue in castrating himself so that he would have no lustful thoughts, but Socrates was again before him with his much-advertised night with Alcibiades, and he made his point in a much less disgusting manner. But wickedness! . . . When have people stopped inventing new wickedness? Only once, you are about to say, about the time of the division of the Roman Empire, and you would be quite right, quite right. A good point, a very good point."

I said it was his point, not mine. I hadn't said a word.

"Well, whoever made it," Catullus sped on, "it was a good point, but it does not go far enough. The Romans had exhausted their pagan ingenuity and New Rome in Constantinople was pretty much as filthy with the same sort of filth as Old Rome.

Then along came St. Augustine and practically invented the Manichees, and in a couple of books gave the world a whole list of new wickedness which it spent a thousand years in stamping out. And, of course, no sooner had St. Augustine invented the Manichees than lots of people started being Manichees. I learned all that from Bay. Bay is a Manichee. Do you know Bay? You must. He comes to stay with me to-morrow. He is officially a Manichee. It says so on his diplomatic passport. He will tell you all about it. No, study vices, not virtues." . . .

When you go into any office of any functionary of the Indian Government you can tell the importance of the man who sits there by the size of his desk. It is carefully regulated in feet and inches: and if, as rarely happens, the functionary gets up off his seat, you can make quite certain by seeing whether he sits on a cushion. Only important people are allowed to have a cushion. . . .

Catullus spoke again.

"You took her to a tree and hung her up?"

"You cannot ask witches questions as you would ask your own wife," said the headman, and cast around in his head for some way of making it plain to these sensitive people. Already he could see that the man he was talking to was getting hurt, in spite of all his efforts.

"When you ask a witch," he said, " 'Is there any water left in the well?' or 'Do you find the weather very hot?' that is not an important question, because it's the sort of question you can ask any woman and you are asking the witch not as a witch but as a woman. So it does not matter how you ask her. But when you ask her an important question like, 'Did you cast a spell to make my son sick?' she will not answer unless you hang her upside down. When you come to the Durbar," he ended, in a sudden illumination, "you wear gold and all the rest of us do not wear gold. When we examine a witch, she is upside down and all the rest of us are the right way up."

"Then you did beat her?" The headman could not tell from Catullus' voice whether he thought that this would be a proper thing to do or whether it would be too harsh for him to understand. This was difficult: no doubt, in the end, he must say what happened exactly as it did happen. There were no two ways about that. No Limbodian told lies, as everyone knew, because there was always a witch or a magician who could talk to the dead and find out the truth in no time. But he did not want to hurt these people's feelings, and it would be gross ill-manners to do so, since they were listening so politely to him.

"Oh yes," he said, "we beat her and beat her and beat her and beat her." He watched for the smile of understanding from Catullus, but it did not seem to be coming. "We all of us beat her," he said, then, taking care to be accurate, "at least, two of us beat her at a time, while the others watched. . . ." He looked again for the friendly understanding, but it still was not there. Then, to make it sound more sensitive and dressed and like what these better-off people did, he added, "laughing and joking." . . .

"You were there on a visit, living in the house on the hill for just one night, and we did not want to wake you from your sleep. So we could not beat the witch, and we could not leave her to go on working her mischief. Have I already said that three men were sick? We could not have any more go down, not with you there. So what did we do?" He paused again. He scratched his ribs on the other side, not really for effect, but to show his satisfaction. Now it was he, the headman without any clothes, that was asking the questions, and all because he was telling a story. Indeed, how like children they were! "So what did we do?"

"Go on," said Catullus. "Tell me what you did. I remember that I did sleep in the bungalow above your village one night. Go on."

"We took her to the little lake that is at the bottom of the hill on which you were sleeping. We were very quiet. So was the witch because we had tied a cloth around her mouth. Then we waded into the water until it was up to our thighs. Two of the strongest and tallest of us took up the witch in our arms, and put her head beneath the water. We were careful to hold her upside down, as I have explained to you before. That is very necessary, even although this was not a regular and proper argument. After a while, we pulled out her head and asked her if she would take off the spells and make the men well. She made no sign, so we dipped her again. We dipped her several times, and then the strong men got tired and left her head under quite a while; they were quite out of breath with holding her, because she was a heavy witch. You see what I mean? She had become heavy because she had so much wickedness in her. Then she decided to die. When we pulled her up and asked her the usual question, she was all blue and swollen, like the pictures of devils. I thought that maybe she had exchanged faces with the devil underneath the water. Not because it meant anything special, but just because it would give us an unpleasant surprise.

"The two strong men threw her body on to the bank and said, 'That's the end of her.' As I said, they were young men, and they knew no better. The discussion had come to nothing, the witch had not taken off the spells, so we were all very angry and tired. We took her body to where we could bury it and be sure no other witch would dig it up without our seeing her." . . .

"I shall begin my defence with the first chapter of Genesis," said Bay. "I shall use it to prove that the idea of the wicked woman is fundamental to all morality. Eve was, of course, the prototype of all witches. In its original form the story must have said so very clearly, but unfortunately it has come down to us only in the vocabulary of what appears to me to be an old man with a remarkably libidinous mind. Then I shall go on to quote the Fathers of the Church, all of whom firmly believed in witches. I shall wind up with St. Thomas Aquinas, and in case the learned Judge should feel that my style was a little heavy, I shall crack a joke. I shall say that St. Thomas Aquinas, when he died, had his head cut off (as in fact he did), and reverent monks boiled it in water in order to preserve it. That," he said turning to me, "will lighten the trail a little, don't you think? It is very important not to be too solemn."

I said that I thought it depended on the Judge.

"The Judge," Bay continued, "will be a Church of England man, no doubt, and when I have reduced him to listening to me with respect by my quotations from the Fathers, I shall show my hand. I am not a Church of England man. I am a Manichee." . . .

"What do Manichees believe?" I asked him.

"That there is an equal amount of good and an equal amount of evil in the world," he answered, " and that the forces of one are as strong as the forces of the other."

"Couldn't you write the pamphlet yourself and put paid to the Bishop of wherever it is?"

"I could. But the answer will sound laboured and too long considered. A pamphlet should be hot off the press before the one it answers has had time to cool. The Bishop of Hippo's other name," he said, as a kindly after-thought to me, "was St. Augustine."

"The Judge's name," Catullus interrupted, "is Mr. Justice Chandra Bose and he is a Hindu."

"Better and better. We shall play upon his orthodoxy," said Bay. Then he stood up with excitement. "I have it! Tell me, Catullus, is there not a clause in the constitution of whatever it is that governs Limbo and all India that no law is valid if it interferes with a man's religious belief?"

Catullus thought for a moment. "There is no clause, but it is a principle which is never broken. As a Civil Servant I may do nothing contrary to a man's religion."

"Then you certainly can't hang him for believing in it," said Bay. "What we have to do is to prove beyond doubt that this man believes in witches, and that everything he did, even the murder that you say he committed, was done in accordance with that belief. If we can prove that, the most that he can get is a couple of years in gaol, and we can fight that through every court in the land even if he gets it." . . .

We all read ten-days-old newspapers that had been delivered by a runner and had been, of course, dropped in the river. The ducking had in a way improved the news: reports of war and threats of war, political stratagems and coups were inclined to disappear, after a legible start, into a grey blur, as though the Press correspondents, after getting well launched in their stories, had looked up and found themselves in Limbo and realized that this sort of disturbing thing would not do at all. . . .

The Judge got up himself. "I assure you, Mr. Leavis, you need not worry. I am not an orthodox Brahmin. In fact, I have given up Hinduism as an idle superstition. Oh yes, I gave it up long ago, on the occasion of my first visit to England." He looked round at us with bird-like eyes. "I am a life-subscriber to the Rationalist Press Association."

"Mr. Bose," said Bay, sitting heavily back upon his statue, "do you mean to tell me you have abandoned the metaphysical subtleties, the spiritual maturities, the scope, depth and insight of the Brahmin faith for a subscription to a crank society? What do you get in return for your sacrifice?"

"I get their Quarterly post-free and the Annual. The Annual comes once a year," the Judge added, to make himself clear. "Oh yes, I've given up all that Hindu nonsense years ago. Really, you can't expect a contemporary man like myself who's travelled and seen the world to believe in humbug like gods with twelve arms and reincarnation." He flung himself about vigorously to show that he was contemporary with everybody, even a boy of twenty-one.

Bay put his hands over his ears.

"Do not say such things, I beg of you, Mr. Bose," he said earnestly. "Have you ever thought of that dread moment when, wafted to the abode of the immortals in the Himalayan mountains, you are brought face to face with your Maker? Have you imagined that awful question, echoing from ten thousand icy precipices, 'What, Mr. Justice Bose, have you done for your God?' and your answer, 'I regularly subscribed to an irreligious book society.' Again comes the mighty voice, 'And what else, Mr. Justice Bose?' And you say, 'Once I said reincarnation was humbug.' And then your Maker stretches out one little finger of one hand of his twelve sky-embracing arms and flicks you back to the land of the living again to be reborn, Mr. Bose, reborn as a . . . as . . . a . . ."

"Printer's devil," said Catullus.

"Thank you, Catullus," Bay said; "yes, indeed, a printer's devil." He shook his head in sorrow. "Have you thought of that, Mr. Bose?"

The little Judge chuckled happily and said, "Well, it's something to be able to say that an old man like me could shock a lot of young men like you." He threw his arms about to show that he was not, of course, at all old, but really in the prime of life.

"We are not shocked, Mr. Bose," Catullus told him, in a kindly voice, "but only very distressed."

"May I ask why?"

"But perhaps," said Bay, ignoring his question, "if you do not believe in God, you at least believe in the Devil?"

"I do not believe in the Devil."

"Then you don't believe in witches?"

"I do not, Mr. Leavis, believe in witches." He looked at Catullus in an amused fashion and said, "And tell me sir, do you?"

"I believe," Catullus said in a depressed tone of voice, "that there is a man whom you may hang for murder before you leave Limbo, who, if you do hang him, will have as much right to put you and me on a homicide charge as I have to put him."

"Did he do it?" asked the Judge.

"If you mean did he hit somebody over the head with a stone so that the man died, that's for you to say when you hear the evidence; but I think I may say that he did. But whether you think he is a murderer or not, to put it shortly, depends on whether you, Mr. Bose, believe in the Devil. And that of course depends on whether you believe in God."

"Well, gentlemen," the little Judge said, kicking vigorously at the ground, "I do not believe in God." . . .

Mr. Small turned to Catullus. "Is that the unfortunate man, sir, who says a witch made him kill his wife's . . . er . . . paramour?"

The Judge answered the question. "It is, Mr. Small. And they were trying to convince me that it was the proper thing for me to do to believe in this witchery and flapdoodle. But they forget that I am a Judge, used to patiently delving for the truth. I am not accustomed to being asked to believe in fictions."

"On the contrary," said Catullus, a trifle sharply, since the Judge had taken a high tone, "every time you sit on the Bench you willingly acquiesce in the fiction that the King-Emperor can do no wrong, although you must know from your history books that the Kings of England have rarely done anything else." . . .

The Judge got up. He said nothing to Small. But he turned to Bay and Catullus and said in an impatient way, "Can't you get me something, somebody, some authority about this man and his witches that I can accept as evidence? Evidence according to the law. There must be somebody who knows about these things—an expert, an acknowledged expert." . . .

Mum had made Cuff go to church three times in the week and twice on Sundays. What with this, and the story that he had seen God, people began to say that Cuff was well on the way to being a saint. Mum was very proud, and this made Cuff happy. But he was very bored in church.

One day a dark man with a beard, calling himself the Swami-something, came and talked to members of the church about India. Afterwards they had a meeting and decided that they would have a mission station in some place that the Swami had particularly mentioned. They set about raising money, and Cuff, who discovered in it something that a young and growing saint could do with propriety besides going to church, raised more money than anybody.

Mum was happy and Cuff was happy and then Mickey got a job.

"Mickey," said the headman carefully, and picked out a stone from the group on the floor.

"Yes," said the missionary, "Martha's son. He got a job, and a very good job. But as for me, I could not get a job at all."

Martha had not let the opportunity for triumph slip past her. She had come to Mum's house and she had talked a great deal about Mickey's new job. Then she had asked when Cuff was going to earn his living. Mum said, "My Cuff is the stuff that saints are made of." She always said that when Cuff's name was mentioned. Usually people lowered their eyes respectfully when they heard her say it and agreed with her warmly, especially church people. But this time, Martha, inflated with her triumph, did not lower her eyes. She looked at Mum and said, "Oh yes, and how are you going to make that pay?" Mum had been wonderful in the way she had taken the insult. She stood still for a moment, very upright, and then she said, very quietly, "My son is going to be a missionary."

PROVERBS

How should one sleep who is overwhelmed with debt, who has a disagreeable wife, who is surrounded by enemies?

A stranger, if he is a rich man, is a relation; but a kinsman, if he is poor, is an outcast.

The speaker of unpleasant truths cannot find a listener.

If you pull out my feathers, I will pull out your hair.

Cleanliness in a crow; honesty in a gambler; mildness in a serpent; women satisfied with love; vigor in a eunuch; truth in a drunkard; friendship in a king; who ever heard of these things?

Cash comes to men in six ways. They are: begging for charity, flunkeyism at court, farmwork, the learned professions, usury, and trade.—PANCHATANTRA

Now profitable trade has seven branches: They are: false weights and balances, price-boosting, keeping a pawnshop, getting regular customers, a stock company, articles de luxe such as perfumes, and foreign trade.—PANCHATANTRA

Cuff had been so pleased at the way Mum had handled the situation that he had overlooked the fact that he did not in the least want to be a missionary. But once Mum had told Martha, he could not very well let her down. He went through his training in an agony of boredom. For some time the hope that perhaps he would see God again kept up his spirits. But he never did see God, not even on the day when he was made a minister and given Limbo as his cure of souls.

"That was twenty years ago," said Cuff Small, "and I've been a missionary ever since. I've decided to give it up twenty times in these twenty years, but I've never done so. I've gone to bed sick with loneliness and determined to pack up and go the very next morning. But when the morning comes I always stay. I dream of Mum in the night, and how sorry she'd be if I let her down. She died ten years ago, but it's still the same. I'm still lonely, I still dream, and I still stay." His voice failed him for a moment, but he quickly recovered. He got to his feet laughing, and said, "But I always am tempted to let people down. This evening, for an instance, I came here to help you," he said to the headman, "and instead I spend the time talking about myself."

The headman rose with Cuff.

"Help me?" he asked.

"Yes. But I've failed." He picked up the lamp and it shone on his face. He looked more weary and alone than I had ever seen him. "But failing's nothing new to me," he said.

"You say you have not helped me," said the headman quietly. "Perhaps I can help you."

We both stood and waited for him to continue.

He held up one of the stones that he had used to mark the characters of Cuff's story.

"Mum," he said, "Mum was a witch." . . .

Then Catullus spoke out of the darkness.

"What we need to convince the Judge is not an expert, it's a miracle," he said.

I had quite forgotten the Judge. I had forgotten that the man was to hang. I sank in my chair and was glad of the darkness.

Then Bay said suddenly, "Catullus! You're right! A miracle. It's the only thing a pig-headed lawyer could ever be got to believe. We have got to convince him that what the Limbodians believe is a real religion, a religion in the eyes of law."

Bay swept on in his enthusiasm.

"We can't dress the witches in copes and mitres. We haven't time to write them a holy book. But we can make them work a miracle. Like Lourdes, for instance. Healing the sick. The Judge may not believe in it, but with his reputation for scoffing at holy things in a country like India he dare not say so. He'd be accused of allowing his private beliefs to distort his judgment. He'd be forced to retire. Yes, that's just what we want—a miracle." He fell silent for a while. Then he said, "Of course, it will have to be faked." He was again silent for a full minute. Suddenly he threw his heels in the air. "Catullus!" he shouted. "How far is the nearest telegraph?"

"Fifty miles," said Catullus. "The telegraph is a wonderful invention, but perhaps the Judge has seen one and would scarcely rank it as miraculous enough."

"Can we send a runner to the telegraph-post with a message?" asked Bay.

"Certainly. Why?"

"The Swami-something of poor Cuff Small. I've suddenly remembered who he is. Wire to him to come immediately—all expenses paid." . . .

"Your Swami sounds the least bit bogus."

"He is the most delightful charlatan I have ever met," agreed Bay. "I doubt whether he is sufficiently adept at saying mystic formulae to make his soul fly out of his head, but he has certainly said them, and in the most sophisticated capitals in the world, in such a manner as to make a considerable amount of money fly into his pocket. He is," Bay said with enthusiasm, "in my opinion, the biggest quack since Cagliostro."

"What is his line?" asked Catullus.

"Mysticism: blue light beating around the initiate's head: visions and angels. He does it all very well."

"I am delighted. I hope he isn't one of these silent sages who write on slates."

"He wasn't the last time I met him. Not by a very long way. In any case, even if he had taken a vow of silence, he would not write on a slate. He has always moved in the most expensive society. He would be much more likely to refuse to conduct a conversation except through the medium of the radio-telegraph."

"I'm so glad," said Catullus. "I shall be able to hold long conversations with him, I have always wanted to hear a sage answer Charles Lamb's question 'Whether the higher order of seraphim ever sneer.' But tell me, Bay, why did you ask him?"

Bay rose from his chair and said:

"It's mystic fudge,
Wherein we'll catch the conscience of the Judge." . . .

"Oh really," said the Swami deprecatingly, "I owe it all to Mr. Aldous Huxley. You remember," the Swami said when we had settled ourselves in chairs, "just before the war, Mr. Huxley was publishing some books that dealt with the mystical side of things. Now, I am no judge of literature, but I understand from people who are that those books and others by the same author are so well done that of all the things written in our time they have the greatest chance of surviving. Well, when an author as great as that starts talking about something, the whole world listens to him: and some part of the world will want to follow him, too.

"I often wonder if great authors know what they're starting when they write a book. For instance, this business of mysticism. Mr. Huxley laid great stress, you may remember, on contemplation, and pointed out how if there was one thing that got in the way of the contemplator more than any other thing it was what he called distractions." . . .

"Twenty years in a tomb would not suit everybody."

"It suited St. Anthony," said Catullus. "When the anxious populace broke down the walls and dug him out, he stepped through the breach and, clearing the dust from his throat with a cup of water, went straight on to preach what I must say has always struck me as a rather ordinary sermon."

"And as for pillars—" I said, taking up my turn.

"Most people have a bad head for heights," the Swami interrupted crisply, "so that settled that. No, if I was to be of any use to these poor seekers after the truth I must think of something neat, compact and unobtrusive. One day, turning over this problem in my mind, I had occasion to make a telephone call. I was in a noisy hotel lounge and I made my way through the throng to a telephone booth. I went in, shut the door, and remarked thankfully on the peace that descended upon me. At that moment the idea was born. It was, if you like, a coincidence that I should have to telephone just when I was turning over my problem."

"Nonsense. It's Newton and the apple all over again. A million apples dropping in front of a million men but only one Newton to deduce a theory from it," said Bay.

"Thank you. As a matter of history, the actual notion of the box did not come to me all of a piece. It rather hung about in the back of my mind. The actual moment when I saw it plain and whole I remember very well. I was delivering a public lecture. My subject was the relationship of the disciple to the guru or teacher in the attainment of mystical knowledge, and I had taken for my theme the position of Yajnavalkya in the Brihadaranyaka Upanishad."

"Good Lord," I said, "did you get many of the public to come?"

"Oh yes," he said midlly; "I called my lecture Dial o if you cannot get your Connection. And while I was elaborating my simile, I saw it. A neat, comfortable telephone box, where the average man could close the door and be shut off from the world, and which would form an inconspicuous and even tasteful article of furniture in the contemporary home. They went very well. The original design did not include a telephone." . . .

The Swami was sitting on the far side of the bamboo mat, with myself between him and the witch-doctor. The Swami leaned across me and said something to the wizard, but could not make himself heard.

The witch-doctor put his hand to his ear, and leaned nearer to the Swami.

"What did you say?" he shouted above the noise.

"I said, I see you use music," the Swami shouted back. The witch-doctor nodded.

"Do you find it helps?" the Swami asked at the top of his voice.

"People like it," yelled the witch-doctor.

The Swami nodded in complete understanding. They both watched the performance for a while and then the witch-doctor leaned across me and said, "I don't use it when I'm by myself."

"No," bawled the Swami, "neither do I. As a matter of fact, I don't use it at all. But it's an idea."

The witch-doctor nodded in his turn. "Not too much of it, though. Makes it too much of an entertainment."

The Swami shouted "Quite. They'll be expecting dancing girls next."

The witch-doctor laughed heartily.

They both returned to watching the performance with expertly critical expressions.

A man ran out from a group towards us and sat down a few feet away, facing our hillock. He took off his turban, and the drummers struck up a new and insistently regular beat, He began to jerk his head from side to side with great violence, as though at each beat he had been hit.

"What's this?" the Swami asked the witch-doctor. And then, as the witch-doctor was about to speak, "No, don't tell me. Let me guess." He screwed up his eyes and studied the rocking man for a moment. "I know. Trance."

"That's right," said the witch-doctor.

"It looks painful. Do you have to do this?"

"Yes."

The Swami watched the man for a minute or two longer in silence. The man's head was jerking now so hard that one could feel a sympathetic pain travel down one's neck and spine.

"Have you ever tried a crystal ball?" the Swami asked, leaning across me.

"No," the witch-doctor said with interest. "How does it work?"

"You just look at it. It gets you in a trance in no time. Only you mustn't use it if you're tired. You'll just fall asleep. And if there's anybody else watching when you wake up you feel rather silly."

"I must try it," the witch-doctor said. . . .

The Swami saved us.

"Here am I," he said, "opening the secrets of my soul and my art to the world and you talk of it as though I were opening a new bridge. But never mind. Tell us in a sentence."

"Oh!" said Small. "A sentence? Well, how about 'Love your neighbour'?"

"Who were your neighbours in your home town?"

"Mr. and Mrs. Schultz and the Van Adamses. The Schultzes had a Miss Carcopino staying with them as a paying guest," the missionary said obediently.

"Then why didn't you stay at home and love them?"

"Well, I might have managed to love Miss Carcopino, but she was very temperamental. I don't think Mr. and Mrs. Schultz wanted to be loved, and if I'd loved the Van Adamses they would have said I only did it for their money. Altogether it would have been very difficult."

"Exactly," said the Swami, "you missionaries find it difficult to love your neighbours at home, so you settle on the somewhat eccentric belief that it will be easier to love a bunch of semi-nude savages." . . .

"I have my principles," said Catullus; "any man has. True, as a Civil Servant, I may not keep to them all the time." . . .

"My dear Catullus," said Bay, "whatever is wrong?"

"Wrong? Oh, nothing nothing at all." Then, folding the letter with great precision, and putting it back into its envelope:

"Winifred's flying out from England."

"Winifred?"

"My wife."

"Really? It must be five years since I met her. She dined with me, I remember. Charming woman. It was in my rooms at Oxford, and she found some books under the table. I remember she told me I was an untidy bachelor and I think I made a bad impression. But I explained that I'd left them there for Fenstone-Brown, the authority in the third passus of Piers Plowman. He always read his books under the table," he explained to me.

"Yes," I said, "Catullus told me. Why?"

"Privacy, largely. He preferred a table laid for breakfast, not formal dinners. Tablecloths were used for breakfast, whereas the modern fashion is to have the plain polished wood for dinner. The tablecloth cut him off more from the world, he used to say."

"What did my wife say?" Catullus asked him.

"Nothing, as I remember. But she was charming throughout dinner, and I think she accepted my explanation. But why is she coming out here in this heat?" asked Bay, fanning himself again. . . .

From the night of the witch's visit onwards the Swami's work went smoothly and undisturbed, and would have continued so if it had not been for the arrival of Winifred.

She was a short woman with a rather big head. There were no hard features on her face, and when she was young she might have been pretty; pretty, but definitely not beautiful. She was middle-aged now, but both her hair and her figure looked younger. Mostly, her appearance was unimportant: what one remembered of her was her voice. It was very low, so that when she said anything to you, either you did not hear what she said, or you leaned over towards her, strained your hearing, and cudgelled your wits to fill in the missing words: in short you gave her your undivided and intense attention; which was exactly what she wanted.

When you did manage to hear her voice you found it full of sympathy and kindliness, not of the motherly type, but of a less possessive sort. She spoke in the tones that might be used by a young girl with a fortune of a million pounds, perfect health and kind parents, talking of a successful love-affair to a devoted girl friend over lawn tea on a sunny Sunday afternoon.

It was in this voice that, coming up the verandah steps and greeting Catullus, she placidly said, "How nice to see you again, darling. I am a little late but I was delayed by a tiger."

The servants came forward with garlands of flowers and hung them round her neck, as it is the custom to do with all visiting wives of Officials. But wives (and it is a common complaint among travellers in India) are at a loss to know what to do with them. The garlands are too bulky to wear with grace, and yet it is impolite to take them off. The usual thing that is done is to wait until the donor is out of sight and then hurriedly to take the garland off and hang it in the most conspicuous place in the room. If the donor returns, one casts admiring glances at it every so often, as though one had taken it off only the better to see it. If the donor does not return, one puts it in the dustbin.

Winifred received her garlands with quiet little exclamations of thanks, looking kindly and long at each servant, giving the impression that she was memorizing the face of a man who had been so very kind to her as to give her flowers.

"Thank you. Thank you, indeed. And you, what beautiful jasmine! Thank you!"

she said to them severally, and then with so little change of voice that they all but missed the order, "Bring me some tea made with boiling water and some thin toast and I shall have it on a tray on the verandah."

Then Catullus said, "This is the new Education Officer," and she shook hands with me, speaking as she did so. I was not yet used to her intimate way of speaking, and she may have been saying "Oh yes, and a fine scoundrel you've picked for the post, too," for all I could tell. Judging rapidly from her expression, I said, "Yes, indeed!" She told me afterwards that what she had said, by way of a joke, was, "So you have an Education Officer. Well, we all of us stand in need of a little educating," and that see had been disconcerted by my reply. She had rather wondered if her husband had picked up with yet another friend like Bay.

Catullus said next, "And I think you've met Mr. Leavis," and Bay shook hands with her.

"Oh yes, Mr. Leavis asked me to a most charming dinner-party. These are very different surroundings to find you in, Mr. Leavis. So bizarre compared with your rooms in Oxford; or are they? And now, P. A., tell me all about what you have been doing."

Since Catullus answered her, we concluded that she called her husband by the name he is known by in his Service. Being a political agent, his equals refer to him as P. A., just as they would call me, as the Education Officer, E. O. It made Catullus sound very august to hear his wife speak of him in that fashion, saying 'P. A.' as one said 'The Duke' when talking of the Duke of Wellington in his lifetime. That, as I understood when I got to know Winifred better, was exactly her design. . . .

"So you're off, Mr. Leavis," said Winifred.

Bay, who was watching his luggage being loaded into the back of the truck, nodded.

"I've told the Swami to be ready with his bags, and you'll be able to pick him up at the hut," she went on. "I quite liked him the last time I met him. He was so reasonable when I explained that a proper doctor will be coming and that perhaps it would be better if he went back to the stage."

"He might not have been so reasonable if you'd told him it would take a year to get the doctor's post sanctioned and then six months to find a doctor who'll take it," Catullus said. All morning he had been in an uneasy gloom, broken only by exaggerated politeness to Bay in passing him things at the breakfast table.

"No, P. A.," Winifred said, taking his arm, "if we advertised all the secrets of Administration, nobody would be reasonable. You should know that, of all people, P. A."

Bay superintended the stowage of the Swami's telephone box, and when it was placed to his satisfaction came back to us on the verandah, his black hat in his hand.

"Well, now," he said, "if I can only find the driver, who seems to have disappeared into the servants' quarters, I think I can start."

"Oh, do hurry, Mr. Leavis," Winifred said with an arch smile.

"That has less than your usual subtlety," Bay said to her. "You must be careful. Don't let the country get you down."

"Oh, I didn't mean it like that. It was just a little joke. You see, the police are after you, Mr. Leavis, all the six policemen in Limbo. At least they would be, only the poor dears are busy elsewhere this morning. But I wouldn't rely on them being busy this afternoon."

"Winifred," said Catullus, "what have you been up to? I do wish, you know, you would not play with the Administration of Limbo as though it were your own private doll's house. One day you will get people into trouble."

"I've got people into trouble," she said contentedly. "Mr. Leavis, for one, if he doesn't fly, fly, fly from the hounds of the law. I've had a chat with that clever man, Mr. Justice Bose."

A servant came in with a small hamper.

"Oh, thank you," she said, taking it. She gave it to Bay. "I've put a few little things to eat in it for you, in case you can get nothing on the way."

"That's very kind of you," said Bay.

"And there's a file hidden in a loaf of bread in case the worst should happen," she added in a whisper.

"My dear, what is the conspiracy?" asked Catullus.

"Not mine. It's Mr. Leavis' conspiracy. I explained it all to Mr. Bose. About arranging the miracles to impress him and all that. So eccentric and charming, I thought it. But Mr. Bose isn't an Englishman, of course, and anything but eighteenth century. He seemed quite annoyed. He talked about defeating the ends of justice. I can never understand lawyers. Can you, Mr. Leavis? As I tried to explain to him, you weren't defeating the ends of justice at all."

"That was generous of you."

"Yes. I told him you were defeating its beginnings. He wants to swear out a warrant or something, but he doesn't quite know his position with regard to my husband. Anyway, he wanted to swear all right, only he didn't like to do so in the presence of a lady."

"Of course you told him that Bay's plot didn't work?" Catullus said anxiously. "I mean, it was a real miracle."

"Oh yes," nodded Winifred. "But I don't think I really impressed him. My faith had been shaken. You see, I had a talk with that witch-doctor with the nice manners. He's come down here for the eclipse of the moon tonight. Some devil-worship or other. But anyway, that's his business. What interested me was what he said when I told him how wonderful it was that the Swami had the gift of healing. He said, 'Yes. We did very well, didn't we? The boy was one of my students. I always thought he was stupid, but he showed great talents.'"

Bay put down the hamper and, pulling up his trousers to save the crease, sat on it. He put his hat on his head, then took it off again. He held it in his hands and looked at it as though it were a crown he was for ever renouncing. Then he said, "I see it all now."

"Then that makes two of us, Mr. Leavis," said Winifred sweetly.

"What about the man in gaol?" asked Catullus.

"He'll probably get ten years, Mr. Bose thinks. Or be locked up as a lunatic. Mr. Bose seems to want to do a lot of locking up."

Catullus was staring at his wife in distress. He transferred his gaze to Bay. Bay looked up at him, and then quickly back at his hat. Catullus' eyes wandered to me. Then he jerked his head up and began to look like a Roman statue again.

"Go and find the driver, will you?" he said to me.

I went into the servants' quarters very willingly, because the farewell party on the verandah was growing very strained. The driver was not there, and I looked round the compound. No one was to be seen. I shouted his name several times, but there was no answer.

"It's all right, he's out front, shooting at a hedgehog with his bow and arrow," said a voice behind me. It was Catullus. "He'll be through soon. Don't worry about the driver. I only sent you here to have a private word with you. We've got to do something quickly."

"Yes, of course. About Bay. Is it serious?"

"No, not about Bay. I shall fix all that. I can't do anything about the Judge, because I mustn't interfere in the Judiciary, but the Police are under my control. I'll give them all a holiday starting at noon today."

"You have to give a reason."

"I'll find something. I'll say it's to celebrate the birthday of Sir Robert Peel."

"Fine. Then you mean, do something about the man in gaol?"

"I've got that settled, too." He looked at me uncertainly, obviously not quite sure in his mind that he should tell me. The horn of the truck sounded to let us know that Bay was ready to go.

"The driver must have shot his hedgehog. Bay's going," said Catullus, with great rapidity. "Look. Go in the truck with him. Give any excuse so that Winifred won't be suspicious. Say you're looking for a site for a new school. Say anything, but tell Bay . . . " he paused, and the horn sounded again, "tell Bay I'm going to visit the man in gaol and slip him the key to his cell. I hope he's got the sense to use it in the night."

"Catullus, that's wonderful. But what will Winifred say if she finds out?"

"That's just what Bay or you or somebody must do something about. Get the woman away from here."

I was so surprised by his change of tone and the look of determination on his face that I could find nothing to say, just nodding my head. The horn clamoured for us, and I took Catullus by the arm and led him back to the verandah to say goodbye to Bay. . . .

" 'We only got the moon clear by the skin of our teeth,' the witch-doctor said to me, 'and if that doesn't prove she's a witch, what does. To say nothing of the tiger.' Oh, he was a very angry man," said Catullus with a happy grin.

He had come to my bungalow in a state of great excitement. A deputation of Limbodians had waited on him in the morning, all armed with bows and arrows and headed by the witch-doctor.

"They kept on testing their bows and arrows while the witch-doctor was talking, and one of them shot down a bird that was flying overhead, just casually, as a sort of underlying to what the witch-doctor was saying about Winifred. He had it all very neatly laid out. Item: the eclipse of the moon was almost disastrously long; item: she had caused a man to be wounded by a tiger; item: she had deliberately annoyed the tiger by unnecessarily shooting at it and missing, so that it had come back to the village that night and, ignoring the goat they had tied up for it, stolen away a baby;

item: she had matched her witchcraft with our local witch and stolen away the Swami. Then she had bound him by spells so that to save his life he had had to run away from Limbo; item: she had pulled to pieces a garland so as to dissipate the good magic of a kindly gift; item the last: she had used for domestic purposes a jar dedicated to holding food for the tiger-god, and clearly marked on the outside with tigers to show what it was used for. The witch-doctor said he could hold the Limbodians back just so far, but he couldn't say what they would do if provoked. When he said this one or two of the men began feeling the points of their arrows in an absent-minded way."

"What did you say?"

"As I explained later to Winifred behind closed shutters (I insisted that she hide herself) I had to take official cognizance of it. Once trouble like that starts, you don't know where it will end. Open rebellion, I shouldn't wonder," said Catullus with satisfaction.

"Is she going?"

"Yes. Today. She argued a little, but I said it was a question of my career. I couldn't have twenty years of service blotted by a Court of Inquiry, especially on the topic of my wife being a witch. That seemed to convince her." Catullus heaved a great sigh. Then he said, "It was a very dark night last night, wasn't it? You were out on the road. Was it very dark?"

"Very. Did you give the man the key?"

"Yes. He'd gone when they brought breakfast to him this morning. The warders reported it to me immediately, but I was having a bath. It was rather late by the time I got to the office and sent out a search party." He paused. "You saw Bay go?"

"Yes."

"Do you think he'll come back? I'm writing to him to thank him for this morning. Do you think he'll come back?"

"Well, yes, from what I overheard him saying as he went away."

"Tell me," said Catullus.

When they had said goodbye to me (I told Catullus) they went off together down the road. I heard the Swami say to Bay, "Well, we've made history in Limbo."

"Contemporary history," answered Bay in a dissatisfied voice. "Now what is needed is for us to give a past history to Limbo. I have been thinking it over. I have been making some notes. Of course, I shall need to do more research before they are complete. I must now tell you of the first and rather eccentric King of the Limbodians that I have invented. . . . "

He went on talking, but he was too far away for me to hear what he said.

CEYLON

ON CEYLONESE HUMOR

Since the Buddhism of Ceylon is sometimes called the pure form of that religion, it is useful to see how the humor of that nation reflects its religious orientation. Buddhist temples dot Ceylon's landscape and saffron-robed monks fill the streets. For more than two thousand years Ceylon has been a magnet for foreign Buddhists, Oriental as well as Western, who want to see the country where Hinayana Buddhism is practiced.

The Buddha taught that since unhappiness comes from unsatisfied desires, the way to eliminate grief is to eliminate desire. This can be achieved by following the eightfold path: right beliefs, right aims, right speech, right conduct, right livelihood, right effort, right thought, and right rapture. Sensual desires, worldly ambitions, hostile passions all provide obstacles to the achievement of the Buddhist ideals.

Having read this about Buddhism, one might expect the Ceylonese to demonstrate the serene detachment which their religion teaches. But no such relationship between theory and fact is actually demonstrable. Many Ceylonese are charming and witty and hospitable, many are intelligent and articulate and learned. But the country has a high rate of suicide, homicide, alcoholism, gambling, and mob violence. The traditional art and literature of Ceylon were controlled by the Buddhist clergy and are puritanical, but during the one period of secular rule by a fifth-century king the famous Sigiriya frescoes were painted—concentrating on bare-bosomed beauties whose major interest in life was clearly not spiritual.

The satiric spirit is very strong in modern Ceylon. English-language newspapers have in recent years run regular columns by satirists, the Sinhalese journals are full of invective (sometimes witty, sometimes merely malicious), and the men in the market and tavern like to indulge in entertaining insults and disparaging anecdotes about everyone from the prime minister down to servants in the neighborhood. Lin Yutang says that the Chinese gossip more than anyone else in the world, but he would have a hard time convincing a Ceylonese of that fact. Nor is the gossip of a kindly variety, as would befit the followers of the gentle Buddha.

Although the origins of Ceylonese culture were influenced by India, local variations through the centuries have stressed indigenous qualities. As far as humor and satire are concerned, those qualities are not really restrained. Ceylonese politicians are vituperative in their attacks on one another, the dominant quality in social gossip is malice, and there is a cruelty and a cynicism in the expressions of the common man and the Ceylonese intellectual that suggest that the ideals of Buddhist detachment and tolerance have not been completely achieved by the inhabitants of Ceylon.

FOLKTALES (JESTS OF ANDARE)

translated by Geeta Solomon

Andare was a legendary jester at the court of a legendary Ceylonese king. Many of the incidents traditionally associated with other famous jesters have in Ceylon been ascribed to Andare, who is so popular that Ceylonese children read about his pranks in their schoolbooks. Like many jesters, Andare is ingenious, brash, and often cruel.

The Story of the Three Oil Cakes / Andare, anxious to display his wit even at a tender age, decided to pull his father's leg one day. Showing a plate which had two oil cakes on it, he said that there were three cakes.

Andare's father, accustomed to his son's pranks, did not contradict; instead he asked Andare to prove it. "Why, that is simple," said Andare and started counting them one by one—"Here's one and here's two; don't one and two make three?"

"You are right, son, so now let us divide them among the three of us," said Andare's father and gave one cake to his wife, took one for himself and, giving the empty plate to Andare said, "There is your one."

•

Waiting for the Beard to Grow / One morning young Andare, deciding to play a trick on the village barber, paid a visit to the barber's house. On seeing Andare the barber asked him what the purpose of his visit was, to which Andare replied, "What else would I come to the barber except for a clean shave?"

Smarting under this retort, the barber politely ordered him to sit down and put an apron around his neck. He then applied some shaving soap to his face and went about his other business.

Andare, getting tired of sitting down for so long, called the barber and asked him what the delay was that he had to wait so long for a shave. The barber calmly replied, "I am waiting for your beard to grow before I could shave you."

•

Tit for Tat / Andare often bought hoppers with the two-pence that his mother would give him. Invariably the hopper-woman gave him only very small hoppers which he would take home without complaining. One day, on receiving some small hoppers, he asked her why she gave him only small ones. She replied, "Isn't it easier to carry them home when they are small?" Andare, determined to teach her a lesson, threw some money into the tray and walked off.

The woman having counted the money and finding it short, called back to Andare stating that he had underpaid her, to which he yelled back, "Isn't it easier to count less money?" and walked home triumphantly.

Climbing a Tree to Collect Pasture / Near Andare's house was a 'kitul' tree. Seeing the toddy tapper collecting toddy every morning Andare was tempted to taste a little of it. One day Andare got a sickle and climbed up the tree to collect some toddy.

On seeing the owner of the tree approaching, Andare stopped drinking and calmly started climbing down the tree.

The owner approached Andare and asked him what he was doing up the tree, to which he replied that he went up to cut some grass for his cow. The owner, surprised at this explanation, asked, "Where do you get grass on a tree?" Andare replied, "That is exactly why I am getting down."

•

Andare Fools His Wife and the Queen / One day the queen called Andare, the court jester, and told him that she would like to meet his wife. Andare deciding to play a joke replied, "I would be glad to bring her, Your Highness, but how would you converse with her? She is deaf." Nonetheless the queen wished to see her and promised that she would talk very loudly.

Andare went home and told his wife of the queen's wish to meet her but explained that unfortunately the queen was deaf and therefore she would have to yell at the top of her voice to be heard. She willingly agreed.

Andare presented his wife to the queen. The queen, assuming her to be deaf, asked at the top of her voice, "Why is it that I have not seen you for so long?" Andare's wife, thinking the queen was deaf, shouted that it was Andare's fault that he had not brought her to the palace. Thus both were screaming at the tops of their voices which brought all the palace attendants to the scene to see what the commotion was all about. Meanwhile Andare sat aside enjoying the results of his mischief.

•

Andare Jumps into the Well / Andare's wife, determined to make him pay for his mischief, once locked the door of their house and retired for the night without waiting for Andare when he failed to return home by nightfall.

Andare, having knocked on the door repeatedly and received no response, was not willing to spend the rest of the night out in the cold. So he changed his tactics and appealed to his wife very endearingly and yet his wife did not open the door for him. Feeling indignant about this treatment Andare resorted to a clever ruse. Screaming, "Okay, then I am going to jump into the well and kill myself," he rolled a big rock into the well. Having heard his threat and the loud splash in the water his wife came running out screaming, "Oh, Mother! Oh, Mother!" In the meantime Andare, who was hiding behind a bush, quietly slipped into the house and bolted the door.

•

How Andare Guarded the Coconut Plantation / Andare was made the watcher of a new coconut plantation belonging to the king. His Highness had ordered Andare to take good care of the young plants both day and night.

Taking care of them during day was no big problem to Andare who sat under a tree and watched them all through the day. When darkness fell Andare was faced with the problem of how to sit out all night too. Therefore every evening he uprooted all the tender plants and transported them to his home garden and watched them from a convenient place sitting inside his house. Next morning he would again take them back to the plantation and replant them and watch over them as usual. After a few days the young plants naturally started withering due to the constant uprooting and replanting.

The king, having noticed his plants were all dying, chided Andare for neglect and asked for an explanation. In bewilderment Andare replied, "Your Highness, not only did I have an eye on them during daytime, but I even took them home every evening and watched them throughout the night too."

•

Andare Becomes the Rooster / Andare, being the court jester, always had his way inside the palace as well as outside. The rest of the courtiers being envious of this one day conspired to make him look a fool and thus invited him to join them in the royal pool for swimming.

Andare was unaware of the fact that every one of them had an egg hidden under their loin cloths. Once they got into the water the chief minister exclaimed that he could go under water and come up with an egg in hand, and all the other men said they could do it too. Andare had nothing to say and the others believed that they could humiliate him. So they declared that the one who failed to come up with an egg would be the loser or the fool.

Andare dived in with the others and when all emerged with an egg in hand, he came up making a noise like a rooster, flipping his wings shaking away the water, crowing as loud as he could and exclaiming, "All of you are hens and I am the only cock-bird." The king's men were extremely embarrassed.

•

The Story of the Immovable Rock / In the paddy field of a rich farmer was an enormous rock which was a great hindrance to ploughing and thus a great loss in the total yield of paddy.

Neither the large sum of money spent nor the great number of people whom he had consulted had been successful in removing this cumbersome rock out of his field.

Andare, having heard of this problem, thought of a way of fooling the farmer. One day he approached the rich farmer and said, "I cannot understand why you spent so much time and money in trying to remove this rock. If you would entertain me as a guest in your house and treat me the way I like for a month, I would remove the rock without further trouble."

The farmer, delighted at the idea of getting rid of this problem, treated Andare just the way he wanted. Every noon and night he was entertained to a sumptuous meal with all the delicacies Andare asked for. At the end of the month Andare had a hearty breakfast and went to the vicinity of the rock. Many had heard of this great feat of strength and were there to witness it. Andare walked up to the rock with a cushion on his shoulder and asked the people gathered around to lift the rock on to his shoulder so that he could take it away from the field. Seeing the amazement on their faces Andare said, "If all of you together cannot put it on my shoulder how could I take it away?"

•

The Dish of Hot Curry / Andare was in the habit of boasting that there was no dish in this world that he was unable to eat, however hot. Tired of hearing this bragging the king decided to disprove it. One day he got the palace cook to make a curry of red hot peppers and invited Andare for a meal and served a big helping of it.

Andare started perspiring and turning red with tears streaming down his face for the curry was unbearably hot and yet he managed to eat it for fear of being ridiculed.

Seeing Andare's predicament the king asked him why he was crying. Andare replied, "Sire, when my mother was alive, knowing this was one of my favourite dishes, she used to make it almost daily. Now tasting it I cannot help but cry because it reminds me of my beloved mother who is dead."

•

His Majesty's Horse / One day the king, wishing to ride to the palace gardens, ordered his favourite horse to be brought. Unfortunately on this day the normally passive animal was so obstinate that he refused to take a single step forward. The more His Majesty's men tried to persuade him to step forward the more he kicked and kept moving backwards. All their efforts seemed in vain for the horse was determined not to move forward at all.

The king, seeing Andare watching this, asked him whether he had any idea of how he could make the horse take him to the gardens. Andare, exclaiming that all these men were just a bunch of horses, simply turned the horse completely around so that he had his hind legs in the direction of the gardens and the front facing the palace, and signalled the horse to move. This way he kept urging the horse backwards until he reached the gardens.

ANECDOTES

translated by John M. Senaveratna

Nothing Plus Nothing / Seven Andiyas—a tribe of fakirs—who happened to be in the same lodging, agreed to cook a pot of congee for their common use as breakfast for the day. Each one agreed to contribute a handful of rice. A pot of water was placed over the fire, and each of the Andiyas, thinking that the others would put in their quota of rice, went near the pot and pretended to put in a handful. However, when the contents of the pot were poured out, it was found to contain nothing but water.

•

No Hurry / A Badala is a gold- or silversmith or a man of that caste. A certain woman ordered, for the use of her little daughter, a pair of earrings to be worn on the day of her weaning. As the silversmith failed to deliver the earrings on the appointed day, she made him promise that he would have them ready by the day that the daughter's daughter would be weaned. When the silversmith's father heard of the promise his son had made, he gave him a thrashing for taking up such urgent work.

•

Calling Her Bluff / When the washerman had come during mealtime, several times the lady of the house had told him, "Dhoby, there is rice and there is curry, but I am sorry I am unable to give you to eat since there is no plaintain-leaf available." (In a respectable Sinhalese household, a low-caste man is given food not on a plate but on a plaintain leaf.) One day the dhoby put a plaintain leaf in his bundle of clothes and, when the lady made her usual excuse, he produced it, saying, "Here is one, Lady. I brought it with me." "Upon my word, dhoby," she said, "all these days I told you the truth, but today I was just joking."

•

Vanity / A friendly dog who had observed the dog owned by a certain Brahman to be very lean, asked the thin dog to come to his master's house where there was a great deal of food. The lean dog replied, "I am living in a Brahman's house, and when the Brahman gets angry he calls his wife a bitch, and thus she is my daughter and the Brahman my son-in-law. On this account I cannot leave the Brahman's house." The dog soon died of starvation because of his vanity.

•

The Chicken and the Eggs / There was man who had a murunga (drumstick) tree in his garden. One day when he saw the first blossoms on it, he began to think about the way in which the drumsticks they would produce should be tied into bundles. Then he thought about the profits he would get by selling them, the trade he would get with this money, the extensive commerce which eventually he would maintain with foreign countries, and the storehouses that would be built to store the foreign goods. And as the murunga tree seemed to obstruct the way to the storehouses, he cut it down.

•

Logic / A certain village chief used to give his barber a bag of rice every year for shaving him. One day, when the barber came to the house during the chief's absence, the chief's wife got her own head shaved in place of her husband's, and boasted of her wise act when her husband returned.

•

Touché / The parents, who had given away their daughter in marriage to a poor man on account of his high birth, went to see the daughter some time after the marriage. The daughter had nothing in the house to offer her parents to eat. So in her rage she placed an old frying-pan over the fire and pretended that she was stirring its contents. When the parents asked what she was doing, she replied, "I am trying to fry the honor you got for me."

•

Fools Abounding / Once there lived a village chief and his wife, whose only child was a daughter named Kaluhamy. The young woman died and shortly afterwards a thin beggar came to the door while the chief was away. The sorrowing mother asked the beggar how he had gotten so lean. "I've just returned from the other world," the beggar replied, meaning that he had been very ill recently and had barely escaped death. The foolish mother, taking his reply literally, asked if he had seen Kaluhamy there. The beggar took quick advantage of the occasion. "It is I who married her in the other world," he said. Kulahamy's mother then embraced him and gave him all the jewels and silk that were in the house to be taken to the other world for the use of Kulahamy. Soon after the beggar had gone away the chief returned home. When the wife told him what had happened he was furious. After rebuking his wife for her stupidity, he mounted his horse and rode off in the same direction as the beggar, hoping to catch him. The beggar, seeing him approaching, climbed up a tree. The chief, seeing him, tied the horse at the foot and began to climb after him. The beggar,

PROVERBS

Paddy and money are preventive remedies against abuse.

Better to act well than to speak sweetly.

What? Hot rice for beggars?

When the blacksmith finds a malleable iron, he leaps to bring his hammer down. (Point of the proverb: the more one yields, the harder he is beaten.)

You have a big book at home, but you can't remember anything.

Even priests who live in the same temple have arguments.

The ex-priest atoned for his previous celibacy by taking two wives.

A good bull yoked with a bad one will also become bad.

Though a cat be taken to Europe, it will still cry "Miaou, miaou."

The unthrashed child, like the unstirred congee, is useless.

What can the doctor do to a child born to misery?

The cobra will bite you, whether you call him Snake or Lord Snake.

however, jumped down from a branch, untied the horse, and rode off as fast as he could. The unfortunate chief, still up in the tree and seeing that nothing could be done, cried out, "Son-in-law! Tell Kaluhamy that the jewels and clothes are from her mother, but the horse is from me."

•

The Justice of the King of Kerilla / In Kerilla, while thieves were burgling a house, a wall collapsed and killed one of them. The remaining thieves complained to the king of Kerilla who, inquiring as to who was responsible for this loss of life, was told that it was presumably the house owner, who had no business living in so dilapidated a building. The house owner was sent for, but he protested that the blame was the mason's who was responsible for the construction. The mason laid the guilt on the plasterer, who had probably added too much water to his mortar-mixture. The plasterer, when he was sent for, admitted the excess of water, but attributed it to the fault of the water-pot, which had an unusually large mouth. The potter was then brought, but he offered a valid excuse; he admitted that the mouth of the pot was too large, but explained a certain beautiful lady had passed by while he was moulding the pot. Her beauty had distracted his attention and he had, while gazing at her, fashioned a mouth too large for the pot. The woman was then brought before the king, but she said that she had not intended to distract the potter. She had paid the village goldsmith to make some jewelry for her, and as the man had delayed in completing the work, she had gone out to remonstrate with him.

They brought up the goldmsith then—a lank, bony individual—and he had no excuse to give at all. The king thereupon ordered him to be killed on the spot in the usual way: that is, to be gored by the Royal Elephant. The man, however, demurred, not because he feared to die, but because the king would thus do himself irreparable damage. "How?" asked the king, whereupon the goldsmith replied, "Your Majesty can see for yourself what a scarecrow of a man I am—a skeleton, no more than skin and bone. The tusk of the elephant will pierce through me easily, but break when it strikes the rock behind me, and the Royal Tusker will be disfigured for all time."

"But how can I avoid it?" asked the king.

The goldsmith replied, "There lives next door to me, Your Majesty, a fat Moorman who can take my place without injury to the Royal Elephant, and I pray that he be substituted for me."

"An excellent suggestion," said the king. He thereupon had the fat Moorman summoned and gored to death in his presence. In this way the responsibility for the death of the burglar fixed on the fat Moorman, who was punished "according to the justice of the king of Kerilla."

•

Illusion and Reality / When the cook was asked how the jaggery for the Sinhalese king was prepared, he replied, "A white canopy above, a carpet on the floor, a screen of white cloth all around. The workers first bathe, then wear a clean white dress, and after tying a clean white cloth over their mouths to prevent their breath from contaminating the preparation, they sit to their work." But when the questioner went to see the jaggery makers at work, he saw only dirty jaggery-boys sprawling about, licking the pots and pans on the floor.

Pots and Sages / A man whose calf had put his head into a pot consulted Mahadenamutta (literally, "the great well-informed one") as to what to do to extricate the calf's head without any injury to it or to the pot. The sage mounted his elephant and rode in the direction of the man's house. In order to enter the garden he had to have a wall broken down and a house, to gain the inner compound where the calf was tethered. Then he ordered the calf's head to be cut off, and after breaking the pot, he took the head out and gave it to the owner of the calf, saying, "How on earth will you people get along when I am dead and gone?"

•

The Gold Frog / A certain woman inherited a gold frog from her ancestors. She wanted to melt this frog and make some ornaments out of the gold, but her distrust of goldsmiths—a thieving tribe—prevented her from doing so. She therefore apprenticed her son to a goldsmith and, after the young fellow had learned the art, she handed him the gold frog with instructions to melt it and make her the required ornament. What he did, however, was what even a professional goldsmith would not have dared to do. He hid a live frog behind the small furnace near which he worked and, when he blew into the fire, the frog hopped away. The son then shouted, "Mother, Mother, see the gold frog running away."

•

The Secret-Keepers / There were once three brothers who all spoke through the nose—a defect since birth. When a marriage proposal was made for the oldest, all three were invited to go to dinner at the house of the bride-to-be. Before they left, their mother sternly cautioned them against speaking when in the bride's house, lest their nasal defect be discovered. At the meal one of them began behaving like a glutton, whereupon the second pinched him. "This fellow is killing me," yelled the man in pain, whereupon the second yelled, "Shut up, you fool." The third then shouted, "I am the only one who remained silent as Mother directed." The proposed marriage was broken off.

•

The Pragmatist / A man who had taken *Sil* for the day—that is, had vowed to observe the Buddhist precepts, including the one ordaining "not to kill"—saw a deadly snake near his house. In order to follow the precept and yet have the snake

PROVERBS

Like the chastity of an ugly woman.

Eat coconuts while you have your teeth.

"It is not that I cannot dance, but the floor is not level," said the dancer.

The dog, even if it becomes a king, bites sandals.

When elephants fight, the cassia plants between them are ruined.

One's own fault is invisible, those of others apparent.

On a lucky day you can catch fish with twine, but on an unlucky day the fish will break even chains of iron.

Crow flesh at hand is better than peacock flesh afar off.

You can fence in a whole country, but you cannot fence the tongue.

Scratching begets more scratching, and gossip begets more gossiping.

One's habit is greater than one's nature.

destroyed, he yelled to another man near him, "There's the creature, here's the stick, I have taken *Sil.*"

•

An International Joke / A son who was in a distant country was observed by a friend to be writing a letter to his mother in very large characters. Asked why he used such big handwriting, he replied, "As my mother is deaf, I write in noisy characters."

•

Count Off / A ship manned by Sinhalese and Moorish sailors was in danger of sinking at sea, and the Sinhalese captain had to sacrifice some of the crew to save the vessel. The captain assembled the crew on deck, after first secretly instructing the Sinhalese sailors to take their positions so as to make a Moor occupy every ninth place. Then the captain loudly announced that every ninth man would have to go overboard, so all the Moors were sacrificed. When the last Moorman's turn came, he shouted, "This is a great Moorish slaughter," as he was flung out to sea.

SKETCHES

Pundits in Conclave

J. Vijayatunga (20th century)

J. Vijayatunga's Grass for My Feet, *from which the following sketch is taken, is a minor classic, an evocative picture of life in a Ceylonese village during the early years of this century. Since the 1920's Vijayatunga has published fiction, poetry, essays, and children's literature in Ceylon, India, and England; has edited magazines and worked for radio stations; and has lectured at American universities.*

It is stimulating to meet a man who is full of confidence. How much more stimulating to meet a whole community of men who are equally cock-sure! This is the case with the men of our village. There is so little room among us for the inferiority complex that the number of men—shouldn't they properly be called worms?—who have any misgivings about their own self-importance can be counted on the fingers of one hand. One outstanding example of this very small minority is a relative of ours. A most ignoble relative, whom we should have disowned but for the fact that blood is thicker than water and that he serves the community as a butt for their practical jokes. The only abnormality that is visible on him is that he has no hair on his face. There is a general timidity and weakness about him, but as these are by no means feminine traits they cannot be said to indicate unmasculine glands. Even if he has the secret desire for it there is no opportunity for him to indulge in any unconventional romancing, but I think that altogether he is a harmless man—he is unanimously accepted as such—who is altogether well satisfied with things as they are. And would have been always had not his meddling relatives put the temptation of desire in his way.

There is another man, no relative of ours, one of those crude country bumpkins living in the inaccessible 'hinterland' of the village, who is very much like our hopeless relation to all appearances. This man is married to a woman who we all are agreed has all the signs—from flat feet and meeting straight eyebrows and a long second toe—of the Unlucky. They have no children, by the grace of Providence. This man, he being himself innocent of any hirsute adornment on his face, was prevailed upon to join the conspiracy against our poor unsuspecting, harmless idiot of a relative: the conspiracy being that he should be told that his relatives being greatly concerned about his single state had arranged a marriage for him. He was not one to question too much, so that the manoeuvres of my uncles were of the simplest and most obvious. Early one moonlight night they brought the other fellow to our house, and he was dressed up like a woman (presumably after a bath) in clothes, lent at the persuasion of her male cousins, by my mother. Some of her cheaper jewellery such as ear-rings, necklaces and bangles was also lent to add verisimilitude to the transformation. This man has a falsetto voice, so that no simulating was necessary on that account. In the meantime, some of the gang were with the idiot, fussing about him and keeping up his enthusiasm. Finally, the rest, their preparations complete, led the blushing 'bride' along jungle paths lighted only by the moon to the cottage of the expectant swain. At last the two were brought face to face, and possibly 'the bride' simpered coyly enough to melt the heart of the most impervious idiot. With a few explanations and a brief ceremony, the 'bride' was handed over to the bridegroom, and with appropriate explanations of the propriety of the procedure, the rest of the assembly left. But once out of his sight, they hid themselves in the shrubbery and behind the trees that surrounded the cottage, all ready to enjoy the denouement.

The bridgroom, full of a tenderness he had never experienced before, began to comfort the 'bride', who was still shy, reticent and retiring, altogether too much reminiscent of the joyous hearth and home she had wrenched herself from to share her spouse's cottage. Nor was he insensible to the sacrifice. He took her by the hand, brought her out to the veranda of the cottage and began pointing out the compensations. 'There on that hill,' he said, pointing in the direction 'is my uncle's house. Tomorrow we shall visit him. Here in this direction is my other uncle's house. Tomorrow we shall visit him. There down in that valley is where my aunt lives. Tomorrow we shall visit her. There . . .

We shall never know 'where' or 'what' or 'why,' but as if the agreed length of time had elapsed, the supposed bride gave a scream and breaking away from his side rushed out into the darkness. Just at that moment a ghostly concert of jeering 'hoo-hoo' laughter arose, followed by a number of faces that appeared from out of the shadows. Obviously, like the momentary anguish of a shot animal before it dies, there must have been anguish in his breast and on his face, but the compensation of being an idiot is that you forget things soon enough. The practical jokers had their joke and the rest of the village its fun. I do not defend the heartlessness or the crudity of the humour, but I suppose that's the peasant everywhere. And when it comes to comparison with his civilized cousin in some of the latter's means of amusement I believe he stands his ground very well.

Well, then, there are these two idiots in the village—for we will include the country

PROVERBS

The fruit of the jak tree is more common than the yam; commoner still is the headache.

Woman is the way to prison.

He who listens to the advice of a woman is a fool.

Even the devil wants to be a hermit in old age.

What's the use of consulting the horoscope when the man is dead?

Seven thunderbolts are ordained for the matchmaker. (Both parties invoke curses upon his head when things go wrong, as they usually do, *after* the marriage.)

Even after going to Matara, have you learned only to scrape coconut? (Is that all the knowledge you have brought back from such a famous seat of learning?)

If broken by the mother-in-law it is an earthen vessel, if by the daughter-in-law it is a gold vessel.

bumpkin too because of that 'marriage' tie, though he is not one of our relations—and there is another simpleton, who really lives on the boundary between Urala and Yatalmatta and for all statistical purposes should belong there, but who insists on being incorporated into our social fabric. Cornelis Appu is his name. Appu is colloquial Singhalese, Cornelis is near Latin. As a hewer of wood and a carrier of loads he has no equal in our village, or in any of the villages around us. But once he has hewed the wood he has been given, or carried the load to its destination, it will be days before he can be moved to activity again. If laziness ever became a championship in Cornelis' lifetime, Urala would gladly accept a citizen of disputed domicile and would have one more trophy to boast about. But Cornelis' greatest claim to fame, and one that does not redound to his sociability, is that he is the champion rice-eater. Whereas a seer of rice when cooked is sufficient for four normal adults, Cornelis can easily polish off two seers of cooked rice, after which he will look around to see whether something more is forthcoming. The same Providence that created Cornelis had seen to it that he was set in the midst of a community of Buddhists, whose calendar is strewn with public alms-givings to the priests. On these occasions the broad shoulders and the brawny arms of Cornelis are put to ready use in the various tasks and errands, and after the Bhikkus have been fed, Cornelis eats enough to support a year's hibernation.

Well, I suppose we must include Cornelis too in our village census. That is being generous enough. When these three men have been accounted for, all the other male adults of our village are, as I said, cock-sure fellows. Each excels in something or other. One has the gift of making vegetables and grain grow to the envy of the rest of the village. With another the most ferocious bull is as docile as a tame squirrel. Another can boast of the number of wild bee-hives he has raided without ever being seriously stung. Another has shot so many wild boars. Another is the master of the most infallible Mantrams, or charms. Another is the most expert fish-catcher. Another had once driven a cart at dead of night through the Kottawa forest when a herd of wild elephants led by the bull elephant had charged at him and he survived to make his claim, solely because of his bravery. Yet another is the most skilled climber of coconut palms. Another can drink more arrack than any one of them and remain sober longer. Another is the luckiest gambler. Another a devil of a philanderer. And so on. Each excelling his fellows, but all equally 'know-alls'.

And the things they know! One of the most exciting evenings is when nearly a dozen of these know-alls meet without any prearranged plan at our house. First of all there will be Kande Mama, back from a visit to Galle the previous day. Seeing him enjoying his betel chew while making the front of the house a red-spattered battlefield of copious spitting, my Headman uncle, walking homewards, slightly tipsy on 'toddy', will stop on the road and start speaking. 'Ahuh bhovan, Hamu. Kohamadha sepa sanipa?' ('May you live long, Hamu. How is your health?') Then, making a quick decision, he walks in, sits down and is shortly competing with Kande Mama in trying to make, with the help of betel juice, a mosaic of the sandy front of the house. From towards the back of the house, as if silently emerging out of an ambush, appears my stone-mason uncle. He has crossed the stream at the back of the house. He is still holding up his Sarong, his hairy legs are wet, and the sand still clings to his feet. The next to follow is the model bachelor of the villge, an uncle of mine nearly fifty years old, who has been content to live with his two spinster sisters who promise to be our model spinsters. Uncle David strolls in, proud and slightly insolent towards the old fogies, and as he is not on speaking terms with Kande Mama, enters within, there to take some refreshment and later to oblige mother on some errand, for which he leaves by the back door, not caring to see those faces a second time. The company in the veranda is now honoured by the most wise looking man of the village, my Pissu Balu Muttha, or 'Rabid Dog Great-Uncle,' so called because he is one of Ceylon's best-known hydrophobia specialists. He used to be the Headman for the village until he retired and was succeeded by my present Headman uncle. With a stately white beard, which falls to his navel, his is an impressive figure. If he were the least bit 'mystical,' he could easily pass for an Oriental 'mystic,' so beloved by Europeans and Americans. His hydrophobia cure is a secret but admittedly very efficacious. His reputation has spread far and wide, and people come to fetch him from great distances. However late, however bad the case—according to report—he looks supremely confident. Sometimes after walking on foot the twelve miles to Galle he has to make a half-day's journey by train before he reaches his patient. But in most cases he manages to effect a cure, which after it is over entails among other things omitting pork from one's food for the rest of one's life. Naturally, then, he has the right of being the Pundit of the occasion, and even Kande Mama, the most assertive man of the village, defers to the verdict of Pissu Balu Muttha.

The topics range from seed-grain and possible drought to the Governor of the Island and to the war, warships, and even the Kaiser and the Germans. For some inexplicable reason there is from some quarter or other a spirited defence of the prowess of the 'Gerrmun' people. Time and again the topic veers homewards and there is a discussion of the Governor (whom they call Rajjuruvo), of the various Supreme Court Judges, their fabulous salaries—each 'know-all' adding an extra thousand rupees to each salary—of the excellence of the various well-known Advocates of the Bar (on the criminal side) which leads to the subject of the latest stabbing murder, and how 'I heard when I was in Galle, a man in the market-place reciting a ballad of this murder, and oh, wasn't it gruesome?' This evokes unanimous agreement that drink is the root of all evil. Which leads to a comparing of the best-known preachers among the Bhikkus. Which brings about a reminiscence of how such-and-such a Bhikku utterly routed in a public debate a Convert Clergyman. The various Buddhist evangelists in vogue next come in for review. This by its own circuitous route leads to the subject of the miracles of Pirith (Buddhist chanting) and what phenomena there were when the Yakkhas (devils) started a stampede in their final surrender to the powers of Pirith on such an occasion at such a place. At this point Astrology steps in. The various planets are passed in review, and there is complete agreement among all that the world is very sinful today, that this Kali Yuga (Kali's Cycle of Time) must see terrible catastrophes, and that some of the plagues, pestilences, and national disasters are the result of the wrath of Shiva at the increase among people of beef-eating. Gradually the topic comes still nearer home to food. Kande Mama boasts: 'I was in Galle yesterday. At my nephew the Advocate's place, you know. They have a grand house, servants and cutlery all in English style. You should see. Why, even their tea-trays are run on wheels.'

'Indeed!' exclaims my stone-mason uncle.

'Indeed, yes,' asserts Kande Mama with greater emphasis. 'And at dinner, do you know what I ate—a Bistake?' (Beef-steak). At this there is a surreptitious passing of tongue over lips among the audience, for the 'Bistake' being by report the White Man's favourite food has always had a fascination for them. 'And after the meal they gave me some red stuff to drink. I hesitated, but my nephew and his wife—you know he married the eldest daughter of the Kuccheri Muhandiram of Batala Oya: fifty thousand rupees in cash, that was the dowry, and fifty thousand in jewellery and land, yes, sir—well, my nephew and my niece, his wife, they said: "Mamandi (Uncle, Sir) it is only wine, drink it." Well, dash it, I drank it off then. He-he-hee . . . '

A noticeable pause and then the bachelor uncle takes up the cue. 'I was in Baddegama a month ago, visiting the Village Tribunal President, and they gave me to eat at tea a Red Keju fruit.' (Cheese is meant here.)

Whereupon my Headman uncle: 'There is no gainsaying, these here White People, they really eat strength-giving food. Not like our Bathala (sweet potatoes) and Kos.'

Pissu Balu Muttha: 'Yes, that is right.'

And so the conversation see-saws. Immense is the range of their topics, but by some utilitarian instinct they break up only after they have all agreed to meet on the morrow for a communal fish-catching.

The lamps are lighted, the roads are dark and deserted, the thrice-replenished tray of betel leaf and areca-nut is once again bare, the incessant swish of saliva spat out projectilewise has been an intermittent accompaniment of the talk, and mother, rather bored, makes some casual comment as she refills the betel tray, thinking the meanwhile that a fresh layer of sand will have to be strewn on the front yard the following morning to cover up the traces of the evening's session. . . .

Finally it was decided that we bid good-bye to Urala and go to Galle, which is a town, a seaport, a railway station, and had all that a town should have—a lunatic asylum, a jail, a home for incurables, a hospital, barracks, brothels, missionaries, churches, schools and colleges falling pell-mell one over another so many they were, and hotels and shops. A house was rented at Galle, and after consultation with the astrologer a day was fixed on which to leave Urala.

PROVERBS

Seeing Money's power, Respectability went slinking to hide itself in the thicket.

It is said that six months after the death of the mother-in-law a tear came into the eye of the daughter-in-law.

Will my troubles never cease, will my sorrows never end, will my mother-in-law never die?

It is not enough that all the nine planets are auspicious if the tenth is still unfavorable. (By the "tenth planet" here is meant one's wife.)

Pride goes before destruction.

It is good to be a Headman, even in hell.

Even if the "Disava" is friendly, when the "dasava" is unlucky no rank can be obtained.
(Pun: Disava was a high official; dasava is the period during which a person is under the influence of one of the planets.)

Jak-fruit becomes bitter the day rice is seen.

Better to be born a slave than the youngest in a family.

Tempus Definitely Fugits

Tarzie Vittachi (20th century)

Tarzie Vittachi is a prominent Ceylonese journalist and former editor of the Ceylon Observer. *For several years he wrote a popular satiric column under the nom de plume Flybynight. In a country where satiric writers abound, Vittachi has long been recognized as a particularly entertaining social commentator and courageous critic of public figures and institutions.*

Loch Lomond Estate
Talawakelle

My dear Pamela,

Your p. c. from Margate was recd. last week. Ta very much for your kind wishes and enquiries about our future plans.

Well, my dear, after 30 years in Ceylon Hugh and I are returning Home. This time not on furlough but for Good! Things are not what they used to be. Conditions here are deteriorating very rapidly. The C. H. & F. C. were beaten this year by 18 points by the native boys. The Colombo Cricket Club has decided not to play in First Class competitions because it is not good for morale to get licked by an innings. Even Hockey has become a bore—the Ladies Hockey Club is given a regular drubbing by these local stenographers' clubs, my dear.

So you can imagine what a dreadful state of affairs we have reached! Even the Swimming Club is not what it used to be when you were here 20 years ago. During the war we allowed British Officers to use the pool but now—my good heavens, everyone, but everyone seems to be a member. Pimply druggists; agents, anaemic counter jumpers, subaccountants at the Bank, clerks sent out here by the Commonwealth Relations Office—only the cooks on P & O ships seem to be excluded!

The Colombo Club has now opened its doors to native business types. My dear, you should just see them tucking their napkins in their waists and sucking their soup in an arc, with the spoon inches away from their mouths! Disgusting!

The Ridgeways Golf Club is now the happy hunting ground of the diplomatic crowd. The local boys are also allowed in now so there is a great to do about fraternization. The Embassy types all try desperately to sell their "way of life" and to show how adaptable they are to the local officials and business wallahs, and the local boys make up to the diplomatic wives. Revolting, my dear. Positively sickening.

Only the Queen's Club (Prince's to you) is holding the fort. But after the fall of Singapore and the evacuation of Trincomalee how long can the Queen's hold out?

In spite of all this, Hugh and I would have stuck it out longer, but the labour problem is becoming intolerable. The other day—would you believe it?—the Immigration wallahs wrote to Hugh refusing to extend our Cook Appoo's T.R.P. They had the cheek to suggest that Sinnassamy could not be considered essential or indispensable. When Hugh interviewed the Commissioner for Immigration and pointed out that without Sinnassamy we'd be simply lost, the Commissioner laughed rudely in Hugh's face. Hugh pleaded that Sinnassamy should be regarded as a foreign Expert because no local cook could possibly turn out such marvellous stews and steaks and curry on Sundays. The Commissioner had the brass to retort that while it was quite possible that our cook Appoo was irreplaceable, we were not and that if we insisted on a T.R.P. for Sinnassamy, we might be asked to surrender ours! Can you imagine that sort of thing happening in your time? My dear, the man would have been horse-whipped.

You recall in your letter the parties H. F. used to give at Queen's House. Those days are definitely over. Do you know that we have not been asked even once to Queen's House since they had a native Governor-General? Such manners, my dear Pamela! Why, the other day the papers reported that a Cabinet Minister actually asked His Excellency why he had been invited to Queen's House if no patties and cool drinks were being served! Such a scream! ! ! Patties and cool drinks, my dear, can you imagine? And, it seems, the poor man had to ask the butler to run out to the Pagoda or some such place to fetch a parcel of curry puffs and a case of Lanka lime! ! ! !

My No. 1 House boy who is a sixty-third cousin of the Butler, says that his cousin was mortified about such awful goings on and is thinking of joining a union!

Their unions have to be seen to be believed. They now have an All-Ceylon Snake Charmers Union, a Quasi-Temporary-Non-Pensionable Clerks Union and a Senior School Certificate Examination (Failed) Candidates Union!

Such changes, my dear Pam! People you wouldn't dream of having at your table have crashed into Society. You remember how wonderfully smart and chic the August races were in your time when Morley was Secretary of the Turf Club. You should have seen the performance of the present day fillies in all their ghastly finery. Society's Queen now-a-days is a Mrs. Ooh la la Jutehessian, who actually wore long gloves with her saree—and in a tropical Summer! The pretender to the fashion crown, a Mrs. Jones or Smith or some such common name, turned up in a jacket and cloth and barefooted my dear—would you believe it? Even our nanny would die before she would be seen in such clothes at a do like that. I'm told that these two "fashion plates" have even got themselves into the limelight at Ascot and Wimbledon! Good heavens, can't the Lord Chamberlain pass a law against them, or something?

Even Horton Place where you used to live has become a slum. Goodness gracious the place is absolutely crawling with Fine Arts students clad in national costumes and Americans in mango-pattern sports shirts. Can you conceive of that happening to Belgrave Square? Enough to break your heart, isn't it?

The Diplomatic Corps has practically stormed Colombo. You couldn't spit out your cherry seed without hitting three diplomats. The bloated plutocrats of America and the bloated proletarians of Russia insist on the best addresses and we poor benighted Britons have to take refuge in Havelock Town or Surbiton.

The ladies' social service activities which we used to control in the old days have passed on to the American Ladies' League. They are what they themselves call Big League. They rush around town distributing pop corn and pessaries with such earnestness that we can't begin to compete.

There is nothing I can think of to bring you as a souvenir of Ceylon. I thought of an antique Dutch chest. But they've all been removed to Hoboken, N.J. or Poughkeepsie, Pa.

With love,
Yours affly,
Bertha Buff-Orpington

Let's Build Another Sigiriya? . . . Let's Not!

Tarzie Vittachi

How many Englishmen, or for a matter of that, how many Londoners have ever been to the Tower of London? Very few I am prepared to wager.

It is the same with the Eiffel Tower. Parisians may pass by the Tower every day of their lives, often making up their minds that on their next vacation they will view Paris from the top of the Tower like the tourists. But when the next vacation comes round there is always something else that seems to claim priority. So the Parisian decides—eh bien! The Tower will always be there, will it not? It will not walk away on its spatulate legs, will it? And he goes to his grave without ever having looked at Paris from the top of the Eiffel Tower.

The same holds for the Empire State Building. When the Flybynight Family was on top of the Eiffel Tower once we heard two American tourists exchanging the following piece of marvellous dialogue:

"Is this thing taller than the Empire State Building?"

"Dunno! Never been up the goddam Empire State myself. Have you?"

"Naw. Funny thing that. Huh!"

It is precisely the same with your Uncle and the ancient monuments of Ceylon. Having been intensely preoccupied with the modern views of Ceylon, the ancient ruins have somehow contrived to escape the Flybynight attention. Thousands of visitors have come panting to Ceylon and charged up the Sigiriya Rock motivated solely by the high-powered patriotic sales-talk I have done about old Kasyapa, the Fresco Kid. But not until a month or two ago did I get a chance to see for myself the rugged magnificence of Sigiriya.

Unfortunately, after the tremendously elevating impact of that first impression of that architectural miracle, a thought entered my head and kept buzzing around under its iridescent dome all the way up the rock and back to the rest-house, making it impossible for me to see Sigiriya whole and see it steadily. It was really a ghastly thought but a nagging and persistent one. The kind of thought that sneaks in like a worm i' the bud and refuses to leave.

The thought was this: Suppose the Government of Ceylon circa 1958 tried to build Sigiriya, what would happen? Isn't that a marvellous idea? Let's see now. How would they set about it?

The first step, of course, is to select a suitable rock. Considerations of suitability, effectiveness and accessibility of the site have to give place to the theory of relativity in the selection process. In other words the real point at issue would be to discover who among the politicians in power can find a rock owned by a relative who needs quick and big money most.

When the rock has been finally acquired the next stage of the operation is to deal with the petitions that will be sent in by those whose land was not selected, accusing the G.A., the Land Commissioner's Department and the Valuation Department of bribery, corruption and nepotism on an unprecedented scale. When these petitions become too vociferous the Government will "consider" appointing a Commission of

Enquiry into the whole affair. It will take one year for the Commission to be appointed, two more for the Commission to enquire, one more for the report to be written, one more for the report to be published, and then it will never see the light again. But everybody, having had his say, is happy.

The Public Works Department now gets the green light on the project. The Designs Office will get down to the job but they may have someone in the office who is a bit of an amateur culture-fiend who has done six months painting under Mudaliyar Amarasekera or has designed a saree border for the Prime Minister's wife and must therefore be humoured. He makes suggestions, he designs motifs, he insists on having a Kandyan octagonal roof covering the entire rock. The Engineers will no doubt protest that this would be a bit too much, speaking structurally, and the entire P.W.D. will split down the middle on this matter. The "octagonal" partisans will be accused of obscurantism. The Engineers will be accused of aping Western Culture and of being Enemies of the People.

At this stage the question of Frescoes comes up. A section of opinion led by the Ceylon-America Society suggests that the whole thing must be properly modernized. They want the best Pin-Up Girl pictures pasted on the Rock. The verdict is heavily in favour of buying the original Marilyn Monroe Calendar for the purpose. The Junior Chamber of Commerce prefers a set of Esquire Girls or the Playgirls from Playboy Magazine.

But the Minister of Cultural Affairs is horrified. He wants the Sigiriya Pin-Up Girls to be Ceylonized. The English Language newspapers demand that the contract for painting the frescoes should be given to the '43 group. The Sinhalese Language newspapers say Ha, ha, a national undertaking like this must not be given to Westernized painters who wear trousers but to the Kong Koat Korps at the Heywood Art School. This last proposal is accepted by the Cabinet. And now the real trouble arises.

The chaste ladies of the more voluble section of the Sinhalese Institute of Culture, who are suffering from ingrowing virtuousness because they have never been chased, step into the breach. They demand shrilly that if the Government must have frescoes painted they must be properly clad unlike those forward creatures of Kasyapa's times who had themselves painted in their bras.

They kick up such a shine that the Government capitulates completely. The Cabinet decides to put the fresco ladies in high-necked blouses and Kandyan sarees.

The Press now takes it up. The Ceylon Observer will hold a mammoth competition asking for designs and suggestions for the new national project. The competition is won by a reader who makes the most practical and stupendously original suggestion.

PROVERBS

The truthful man finds no room even in the tavern.

Be upright to the upright, be kind to the kind, and dishonest to the deceitful.

When the teacher urinates standing, the pupils do the same running.

The pain is the same even when you stab with a golden weapon.

You must be foolish to be wise.

Why take a ladder to the gallows when you can go there easily by the help of a woman?

Dear Sir:

Sigiriya, the new national monument under discussion should symbolise National Unity. The entire superstructure should seem to be precariously placed but is steadied by a solid foundation of national goodwill. To promote goodwill between the two racial groups in the island a 100 foot long and 25 foot wide Jaffna cigar should be placed in the lion's mouth.

Yours etc.,
P. B. Publico.

There will be no question about it now—Mr. Publico's suggestion will be passed by the Cabinet, approved by the Government Group and accepted with wide acclaim by the General Public.

But there is a catch. A clerk in the Treasury is not so sure that he can permit the Government and the People to make this colossal blunder. He finds a ruling under which all such projects must be sent to the Treasury Economy Committee for approval. The Economy Committee sits only once in three months and they sat only last week. Sigiriya must wait at least six months before Treasury approval can be obtained.

It comes up before the Committee six months later. In the meantime letters have appeared in the Press, asking what is happening and if not, why not, or if so, when.

Mr. F. Justitia (247, Ipecacuana Junction, Kesbawa) has insisted that the Government must "move in the matter immediately or else . . ." Or else, presumably, Mr. Justitia himself will consider moving in the matter.

Mr. O. T. O. Mores ("Sea View," Katukelle Road, Kandy) has been asking constantly whether the apathy of the Government is due to the fact that some P.W.D. overseer or Treasury official has not received his cut. Mr. Disgusted has pointed out that what the Cabinet has already approved the Treasury cannot disapprove.

But the Committee which lives in a Power Vacuum feels different. They decide that the Cabinet has only approved the project in principle. The principle, says the Committee generously, may be fine but they are not so sure of the Principal, the dough. On the strength of this glorious pun the Committee passes the buck to the Planning Secretariat.

The Planning Secretariat cannot decide priorities. They put it up to the Our Glorious Heritage Committee of the National Planning Council whose members have been co-opted en bloc to serve on the high powered Atomic Energy Committee of the N.P.C.

Four months later it comes up before the appropriate Committee. But this Committee has no time to tackle future projects right now. The Budget is about to be presented and they are busy 24 hours of the day preparing excuses for their failure to do anything at all during the previous year. They are trying to fill in the Explanation blanks with apposite words like "flood," "drought," "unfortunately," "circumstances beyond our control," "drop in the world market prices," "strikes," "Enemies of the People" and so on. . . .

The Sigiriya Project eventually comes up before the Committee after the Budget. They bat it back and forth between them but cannot make up their minds. Those members of the committee who had read a couple of Teach-Yourself-Economics books feel that such a project as Sigiriya would be labelled Unproductive by the best economists. They point out that the Marginal Utility of the Sigiriya Rock Project compares very unfavourably with the Marginal Utility of an Earth Dam. They argue that in putting up a structure on a rock the Diminishing Returns set in very early. Moreover, they say, the country's finances being what they are, and the money supply not being exactly what it should be, the liquidity preference of the people must be considered. . . .

The other faction in the Committee points out that it would be politically unsound to drop the Sigiriya project. They argue with considerable cogency, that although its Marginal Utility must be lousy, the Sigiriya project has plenty of Political Utility.

The Government decides to settle the dispute by importing 23 foreign experts. They produce 22 reports—one is only a Lonesome Rider—all of them bristling with erudition and all of them contradictory. What now? Obviously invite Mrs. Joan Robinson from Cambridge to give us her opinion. She comes to Ceylon, sets up a studio and begins drawing graphs. Three months later she is ready. She invites the Planning Council to come up sometime and see her Demand Curves. They take one look at them and decide that It Can't be Done. . . .

Such, my Lords and Ladies, are the ways of modern government. Everything decided scientifically—no hit or miss methods as in old Kasyapa's times. After all Kasyapa, blundering along in his unscientific way, took 17 years to build Sigiriya. Quite. But Kasyapa built Sigiriya in 17 years. You modern scientific types have taken precisely 17 years, 8 months, 3 weeks and 4 days to decide that It Can't Be Done.

BIBLIOGRAPHY

China

Bynner, Witter (trans.): *The Jade Mountain: Chinese Poems 618–906*. New York, Doubleday & Co., 1964
Chen Cheng-chi (ed.): *Six Hundred Chinese Proverbs*. Taipei, Far East Book Co., n.d.
Chinese Fables and Anecdotes. Peking, Foreign Languages Press, 1964
Clark, Barrett H. (ed.): *Great Short Stories of the World*. New York, Robert M. McBride, 1925
Giles, Herbert A. (trans.): *Gems of Chinese Literature*. New York, Dover Publications, 1965
Golden Lotus (*Chin P'ing Mei*). New York, Capricorn Books, 1960
Ho Yi: *Yeh-Hsuan's Fables*. Peking, Foreign Languages Press, 1961
Hsia, C. T.: *The Classic Chinese Novel*. New York, Columbia University Press, 1968
Hsu, Francis: *Americans and Chinese*. London, Cresset Press, 1965
Hsu Kai-yu (ed.): *Twentieth Century Chinese Poetry*. New York, Doubleday & Co., 1963
Kao, George (ed.): *Chinese Wit and Humor*. New York, Coward-McCann, 1946
Lau Shaw: *Rickshaw Boy*. Trans. by Evan King. New York, Reynal & Hitchcock, 1945
Legge, James (trans.): *The Sayings of Confucius*. Leigh-on-Sea, England, F. Lewis, 1946
Li Ju-chen: *Flowers in the Mirror*. Trans. by Lin Tai-yi. Berkeley and Los Angeles, University of California Press, 1965
Lin Yutang: *Wisdom of China and India*. New York, Random House, 1942
Liu, James J. Y.: *The Art of Chinese Poetry*. Chicago, University of Chicago Press, 1965
Liu T'ieh-yun: *The Travels of Lao Ts'an*. Trans. by Harold Shadick. Ithaca, N. Y., Cornell University Press, 1941
Lusin (Chou Shu-jen): *Ah Q and Others*. Trans. by Wang Chi-chen. New York, Columbia University Press, 1941
Payne, Robert (ed.): *The White Pony: An Anthology of Chinese Poetry*. New York, Mentor Books, 1960
Rexroth, Kenneth (trans.): *mors One Hundred Poems from the Chinese*. New York, New Directions, 1956
Saturday Afternoon at the Mill and Other One-Act Plays. Peking, Foreign Languages Press, 1957

Scott, A. C. (ed.): *Traditional Chinese Plays*. Madison, University of Wisconsin Press, 1967

Shih Nai-an: *All Men Are Brothers*. Trans. by Pearl Buck. New York, Grove Press, 1957

Third Sister Liu. Trans. by Yang Hsien-yi and Gladys Yang. Peking, Foreign Languages Press, 1962

Tsao Hsueh-chin: *Dream of the Red Chamber*. Trans. by Wang Chi-chen. Doubleday & Co., 1958

Waley, Arthur (trans.): *A Hundred and Seventy Chinese Poems*. London, Constable, 1962

Waley, Arthur: *The Life and Times of Po Chü-i*. London, George Allen & Unwin, 1949

———: *The Poetry and Career of Li Po*. New York, Macmillan Co., 1950

———: *Translations from the Chinese*. New York, Alfred A. Knopf, 1941

Women's Representative, The: Three One-Act Plays. Peking, Foreign Languages Press, 1956

Wu Ching-tzu: *The Scholars*. Trans. by Yang Hsien-yi and Gladys Yang. Peking, Foreign Languages Press, 1964.

Yuan Shui-p'ai: *Soy Sauce and Prawns*. Trans. by Sidney Shapiro. Peking, Foreign Languages Press, 1963

Japan

Akutagawa, Ryunosuke: *Kappa*. Trans. by Seiichi Shiojiri. Tokyo, Hokuseido Press, 1949

———: *Rashomon*. Trans. by T. Kojima. New York, Liveright Publishing Corp., 1952

Aston, W. G.: *History of Japanese Literature*. London, Heinemann, 1908

Blyth, R. H.: *Edo Satirical Verse Anthologies*. Tokyo, Hokuseido Press, 1961

———: *Japanese Humour*. Tokyo, Japan Travel Bureau, 1957

———: *Japanese Life and Character in Senryu*. Tokyo, Hokuseido Press, 1960

——— (ed. and trans.): *Oriental Humour*. Tokyo, Hokuseido Press, 1959

——— (ed. and trans.): *Senryu: Japanese Satirical Verses*. Tokyo, Hokuseido Press, 1949

Chamberlain, Basil H.: *Things Japanese*. Tokyo, J. J. Thompson, 1939

Hibbett, Howard: *The Floating World in Japanese Fiction*. New York, Oxford University Press, 1959

Ihara Saikaku: *The Life of an Amorous Man*. Trans. by Kengi Hamada. Rutland, Vt., and Tokyo, Charles E. Tuttle Co., 1964

———: *The Life of an Amorous Woman and Other Writings*. Trans. by Ivan Morris. New York, New Directions, 1963

———: *This Scheming World*. Trans. by Masanori Takatsuka and David C. Stubbs. Rutland, Vt., and Tokyo, Charles E. Tuttle Co., 1965

Ikeda, Hiroko: *A Type and Motif Index of Japanese Folk Literature*. Ann Arbor, University of Michigan Press, 1955

Jippensha Ikku: *Shank's Mare* (*Hizakurige*). Trans. by Thomas Satchell. Rutland, Vt., and Tokyo, Charles E. Tuttle Co., 1968

Kaneko, Norbert: *Old Japanese Humor*. Tokyo, Tokyo News Service, 1959

Keene, Donald: *Japanese Literature: An Introduction for Western Readers*. New York, Grove Press, 1955

Natsume, Soseki: *Botchan*. Trans. by Umeji Sasaki. Rutland, Vt., and Tokyo, Charles E. Tuttle Co., 1968

———: *I Am a Cat*. Trans. by Katsue Shibata and Motonari Kai. Tokyo, Kenkyusha, 1961

Nozaka, Akiyuki: *The Pornographers*. Trans. by Michael Gallagher. New York, Alfred A. Knopf, 1968

Okada, Rokuo: *Japanese Proverbs and Proverbial Phrases*. Tokyo, Japan Travel Bureau, 1955

Rexroth, Kenneth (trans.): *One Hundred Poems from the Japanese*. New York, New Directions, 1964

Sakanishi, Shio (trans.): *The Ink-Smeared Lady and Other Kyogen*. Rutland, Vt., and Tokyo, Charles E. Tuttle Co., 1960

Ueda, Makoto: *Literary and Art Theories in Japan*. Cleveland, Western Reserve University Press, 1967

India

Ayyar, A. S. P.: *Indian After-Dinner Stories*, vols. I, II, and III. Madras, Teachers' Publishing House, 1948, 1949

———: *Tenali Rama*. Madras, Orient Publishing Co., 1957

Chandra, G. S. Sharat: *Bharata Natyam Dancer*. Calcutta, Writers Workshop, 1968

Dandin: *The Ten Princes*. Trans. by Arthur W. Ryder. Chicago, University of Chicago Press, 1960

Knowles, J. H.: *Folk-Tales of Kashmir*. London, Kegan Paul, Trench, Trubner & Co., 1893

Lal, P. (ed.): *Great Sanskrit Plays*. New York, New Directions, 1964

Lin Yutang: *The Wisdom of India*. Bombay, Jaico Publishing Co., 1955

Menen, Aubrey: *Dead Man in the Silver Market*. New York, Charles Scribner's Sons, 1953

———: *The Prevalence of Witches*. London, Chatto & Windus, 1948

Narayan, R. K.: *The English Teacher*. Mysore, Indian Thought Publications, 1955

———: *The Financial Expert*. East Lansing, Michigan State University Press, 1953

———: *Grateful to Life and Death*. East Lansing, Michigan State University Press, 1953

———: *The Guide*. New York, Viking Press, 1958

———: *The Man-Eater of Malgudi*. New York, Viking Press, 1961

———: *The Printer of Malgudi*. East Lansing, Michigan State University Press, 1957

———: *Swami and Friends*. Mysore, Indian Thought Publications, 1956

———: *The Vendor of Sweets*. New York, Viking Press, 1967

——: *Waiting for the Mahatma.* East Lansing, Michigan State University Press, 1955

Russell, Ralph, and Islam, Khurshidul: *Three Mughal Poets: Mir, Sauda, Mir Hasan.* Cambridge, Mass., Harvard University Press, 1968

Ryder, Arthur W. (trans.): *The Panchatantra.* Chicago, University of Chicago Press, 1964

——— (trans): *Shakuntala and Other Works* [by Kalidasa]. New York, E. P. Dutton & Co., 1920

Senaveratna, John M.: *Wiles and Ways of Women.* Colombo, Ceylon, privately printed, 1955

Sethi, N. K.: *Hindu Proverbs.* Mount Vernon, N.Y., Peter Pauper Press, 1962

Thompson, Stith, and Balys, Jonas: *Oral Tales of India.* Bloomington, Indiana University Press, 1958

Van Buitenen, J. A. B.: *Tales of Ancient India.* New York, Bantam Books, 1961

Wortham, B. H. (trans.): *Sukasaptati.* London, Luzac & Co., 1911

Ceylon

Godakumbura, C. E.: *Sinhalese Literature.* Colombo, Colombo Apothecaries' Co., 1955

Saratchandra, E. R.: *Folk Plays of Ceylon.* Colombo, Lake House, 1953

——: *The Sinhalese Novel.* Colombo, M. D. Gunasena & Co., 1950

Senaveratna, John M.: *Dictionary of Proverbs of the Sinhalese.* Colombo, Times of Ceylon Co., 1936

Vijayatunga, J.: *Grass for My Feet.* London, Edward Arnold & Co., 1935

Vittachi, Tarzie: "Let's Build Another Sigiriya? . . . Let's Not!" *Ceylon Observer Pictorial,* Colombo, Lake House, 1958

——: "Tempus Definitely Fugits." *Ceylon Observer Pictorial,* Colombo, Lake House, 1959

INDEX TO AUTHORS, TITLES, AND TRANSLATORS

Authors' names appear in small capitals, titles of selections in italics, and translators' names in ordinary roman type. Each title is followed by a brief indication of its category (joke, poem, novel, etc.) and country of origin, using the following abbreviations: Ch. (Chinese), J. (Japanese), In. (Indian), and Cey. (Ceylonese).

The "weathermark" identifies this book as having been planned, designed, and produced at the Tokyo offices of John Weatherhill, Inc. Book design and typography by Meredith Weatherby. Composed, printed, and bound by Samhwa Printing Co., Seoul. The main text is set in 10-point Monotype Times New Roman, with display type in Universe Medium.